Handbook of Secondary Fungal Metabolites

VOLUME III

Handbook of Secondary Fungal Metabolites

VOLUME III

RICHARD J. COLE
Albany, Georgia

BRUCE B. JARVIS
Department of Chemistry and Biochemistry
University of Maryland
College Park, Maryland

MILBRA A. SCHWEIKERT
National Peanut Research Laboratory
Dawson, Georgia

ACADEMIC PRESS

An imprint of Elsevier Science

Amsterdam Boston London New York Oxford Paris
San Diego San Francisco Singapore Sydney Tokyo

Cover images: Photography by Dr. Bruce Horn and design by Brian E. Cole. The cover is a collage of various fungi, some presented in pure culture and others in their natural forms, i.e. mushrooms, which are the easily recognizable fruiting structures of some fungi, superimposed on these fungi are the chemical structures of some representative secondary fungal metabolites.

Academic Press Rapid Manuscript Reproduction

This book is printed on acid-free paper. ∞

Academic Press
An imprint of Elsevier Science
525 B Street, Suite 1900, San Diego, California 92101-4495, USA
http://www.academicpress.com

Academic Press
84 Theobald's Road, London WC1X 8RR, UK
http://www.academicpress.com

Library of Congress Catalog Card Number: 2003103019

International Standard Book Number: 0-12-179460-1 (Set)
International Standard Book Number: 0-12-179461-X (Volume 1)
International Standard Book Number: 0-12-179462-8 (Volume 2)
International Standard Book Number: 0-12-179463-6 (Volume 3)

PRINTED IN THE UNITED STATES OF AMERICA
03 04 05 06 07 8 7 6 5 4 3 2 1

Contents

Preface

The "Handbook of Secondary Fungal Metabolites" is presented in three volumes and is comprehensive to the extent that all major groups of secondary fungal metabolites are included. The format is similar to that presented in the "Handbook of Toxic Fungal Metabolites" with the major exception that actual spectra are not included; however, spectral data are included where available. Also included in these volumes are the methods used by the authors to isolate and purify metabolites. Another major difference is that the appropriate references are presented with each metabolite, negating the need to turn to the end of each group to find the appropriate references. Each volume contains four indexes: secondary metabolite index, molecular formula index, molecular weight index, and fungal/plant source index. In a few instances, plant sources are included when the metabolites are closely related to fungal metabolites or the source of precursors may be fungal; i.e., the baccharins, which are found in extracts from *Baccharis megapotamica*. These metabolites are closely related to the macrocyclic trichothecenes found in extracts of fungi such as *Myrothecium* spp. and *Stachybotrys* spp. Also, metabolites from the fungal symbiont of lichens are sometimes presented. To aid in the interpretation of NMR data, the numbering system presented in the literature is included for the major representative fungal metabolite and, at times, for several related metabolites. Fungal sources are given as reported in the original references. It is recognized that the taxonomy in several cases has been revised, perhaps more than once. It is beyond the scope of these volumes to deal with what is "currently accepted taxonomy" because this is a dynamic science that, in many cases, is as yet undefined.

The "Handbook" has been divided into sections, and the placement of metabolites is based on chemical relationships. One section of each volume contains a miscellaneous section to accommodate metabolites difficult to place into one of the sections. The miscellaneous section of Volume III contains some metabolites related to those that appear in Volumes I and II. This occurred when related metabolites were discovered after Volumes I and II were completed.

It is hoped that this compilation of data on secondary fungal metabolites will aid investigators in the identification of known or related fungal metabolites. Because fungal metabolites represent a wide diversity of chemical species, these volumes will be useful to scientists interested in correlations of structural features with various spectral and biological characteristics. The known biological activity of metabolites is presented, which may aid in future studies related to the identification of new uses for fungal metabolites.

Richard J. Cole
Bruce B. Jarvis
Milbra A. Schweikert

Acknowledgments

The authors thank the following investigators for their assistance in producing the "Handbook of Secondary Fungal Metabolites." Their contributions made this compilation of data on fungal metabolites possible.

Wayne L. Bryden
University of Queensland
Gotton, Queensland 4343
Australia

Brian E. Cole
Images, Inc.
Snellville, Georgia

Horace G. Cutler
Department of Pharmacology
Mercer University
Atlanta, Georgia

Jens C. Frisvad
Department of Biotechnology
Technical University of Denmark
DK-2800 Lyngby
Denmark

Bruce Horn
USDA-ARS
National Panut Research Laboratory
Dawson, Georgia

William Norred
Toxicology and Mycotoxin Research Unit
USDA-ARS
Athens, Georgia

James K. Porter
Toxicology and Mycotoxin Research Unit
USDA-ARS
Athens, Georgia

Ronald T. Riley
Toxicology and Mycotoxin Research Unit
USDA-ARS
Athens, Georgia

Victor S. Sobolev
USDA-ARS
National Peanut Research Laboratory
Dawson, Georgia

1

Atranones

- Atranone A
- Atranone B
- Atranone C
- Atranone D
- Atranone E
- Atranone F
- Atranone G

Common/Systematic Name

Atranone A

Molecular Formula/Molecular Weight

$C_{24}H_{32}O_6$; MW = 416.21989

General Characteristics

Crystals; mp., 179-184°C; $[\alpha]_D^{20}$ +29° (c= 0.86 in $CHCl_3$).

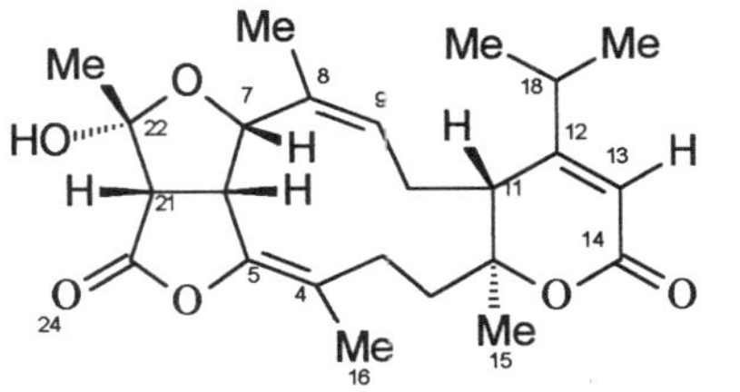

Fungal Source

Stachybotrys chartarum (*S. atra*) S-11.

Isolation/Purification

After four weeks of growth, a rice culture of *Stachybotrys atra* (*S. chartarum*, S-11) was extracted with methanol-chloroform and, following solvent removal, the crude extract triturated with hexane to give 11.5g of a black gum. The majority of the extract was chromatographed over PEI silica, eluting with increasing proportions of methylene chloride in hexane, then increasing amounts of methanol in methylene chloride to give four fractions. Fraction 2 (eluted with 100% methylene chloride) was applied to a 2mm Chromatotron plate and eluted with ethyl acetate-hexane-methanol (40:60:5, v/v/v) to give atranone B. A later fraction from the plate was found to contain a 2:1 mixture of atranones A and C. These were resolved by semipreparative HPLC using the following conditions: reversed phase C_{18} column (Phenomenex, 10 x 250mm); solvent methanol-water (isocratic; 2:5, v/v); flow 3.5ml/min; detection UV 250nm; retention time for atranone A and C was 35.8 and 40.9 min, respectively.

Spectral Data

UV:

λ_{max}^{MeOH} 224nm (ε = 10,500).

IR:

($CHCl_3$) 3684, 3598, 3036, 1789, 1706, 1522, 1424, and 1212cm^{-1}.

^{1}H NMR:

(benzene-d_6) 0.71(3H, d, *J*=6.7Hz, H-19); 0.77(3H, d, *J*=6.8Hz, H-20); 0.80(3H, s, H-15) 1.27(1H, ddd, *J*=2.7, 12.5, and 14.0Hz, H-2B); 1.40(3H, s, H-23), 1.46(1H, m, H-10B) 1.48(3H, br s, H-17); 1.54(1H, m, H-3B); 1.67(3H, d, *J*=1.5Hz, H-16); 1.81(1H, m, H-3A); 1.82(1H, m, H-10A); 1.98(1H, dt, *J*=5.2 and 4.0Hz, H-2A); 2.08 (1H, qq, *J*=6.7 and 6.8Hz, H-18); 2.47(1H, br dd, *J*=2.5 and 7.9Hz, H-11); 2.67(1H, d, *J*=11.1Hz, H-21); 2.91(1H, ddq, *J*=1.5, 4.1 and 11.1Hz, H-6); 5.16(1H, d, *J*=4.1Hz, H-7); 5.23(1H, br dd, *J*=4.1and 12.0Hz, H-9); and 5.82ppm (1H, d, *J*=2.5Hz, H-13).

^{13}C NMR:

(benzene-d_6) 84.7, C-1; 39.2, C-2; 26.8, C-3; 111.4, C-4; 145.7, C-5; 47.8, C-6; 80.7, C-7; 134.3, C-8; 128.9, C-9; 23.4, C-10; 44.0, C-11; 166.8, C-12; 114.7, C-13; 163.5, C-14; 20.8, C-15; 14.9, C-16; 17.6, C-17; 29.5, C-18; 21.8, C-19; 22.8, C-20; 57.5, C-21; 105.1, C-22; 25.6, C-23; and 170.3ppm C-24.

References

B. B. Jarvis, Y.-W. Lee, S. N. Yatawara, and C. S. Cömezoglu; Trichothecenes Produced by *Stachybotrys atra* from Eastern Europe; Appl. Environ. Microbiol., Vol. 51, pp. 915-918(1986).

S. F. Hinkley, J. Jiang, E. P. Mazzola, and B. B. Jarvis; Atranones: Novel Diterpenoids from the Toxigenic Mold *Stachybotrys atra*; Tetrahedron Lett., Vol. 40, pp. 2725-2728(1999).

S. F. Hinkley, E, P. Mazzola, J. C. Fettinger, Y.-F. Lam, and B. B. Jarvis; Atranones A-G: A Unique Series of Metabolites from the Toxigenic Mold *Stachybotrys atra*; Phytochemistry, Vol. 55, pp. 663-673 (2000).

Common/Systematic Name

Atranone B

Molecular Formula/Molecular Weight

$C_{25}H_{34}O_7$; MW = 446.23045

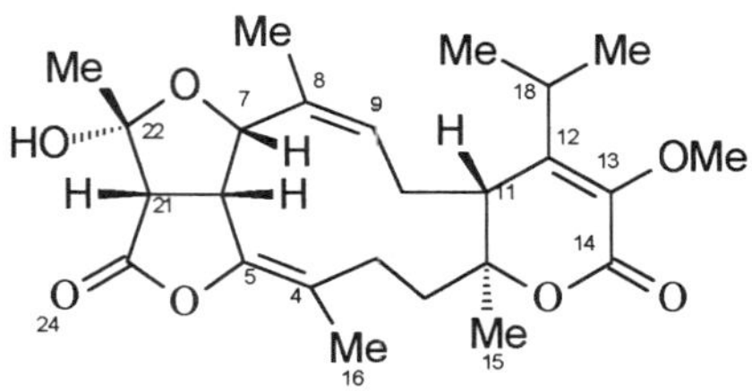

General Characteristics

Crystals; mp., 213-218°C; $[\alpha]_D^{20}$ +25° (*c*=1.50 in $CHCl_3$).

Fungal Source

Stachybotrys chartarum (*S. atra*) S-11.

Isolation/Purification

After four weeks of growth, a rice culture of *Stachybotrys atra* (*S. chartarum*, S-11) was extracted with methanol-chloroform and, following solvent removal, the crude extract triturated with hexane to give 11.5g of a black gum. The majority of the extract was chromatographed over PEI silica, eluting with increasing proportions of methylene chloride in hexane, then increasing amounts of methanol in methylene chloride to give four fractions. Fraction 2 (eluted with 100% methylene chloride) was applied to a 2mm Chromatotron plate and eluted with ethyl acetate-hexane-methanol (40:60:5, v/v/v) to give atranone B. A later fraction from the plate was found to contain a 2:1 mixture of atranones A and C. These were resolved by semipreparative HPLC using the following conditions: reversed phase C_{18} column (Phenomenex, 10 x 250mm); solvent methanol-water (isocratic; 2:5, v/v); flow 3.5ml/min; detection UV 250nm; retention time for atranone A and C was 35.8 and 40.9 min, respectively.

Spectral Data

UV:

λ_{max}^{MeOH} 231nm (ε = 10,800).

IR:

($CHCl_3$) 3684, 3599, 3018, 1790, 1704, 1522, 1424, 1212 and 1136cm^{-1}.

^{1}H NMR:

(benzene-d_6) 0.86(3H, s, H-15); 1.10(3H, d, J=7.0Hz, H-20); 1.22(3H, d, J=6.9Hz,

H-19); 1.22(1H, m, H-2B); 1.33(3H, s, H-23); 1.44(1H, m, H-10B); 1.46(3H, br s, H-17); 1.50(1H, br dt, *J*=2.3 and 14Hz, H-3B); 1.64(3H, br s, H-16); 1.75(1H, dt, *J*=5.0 and 14.5Hz, H-3A); 1.82(1H, m, H-10A); 1.94(1H, dt, 5.0 and 14.5Hz, H-2A); 2.19(1H, qq, *J*=6.9 and 7.0Hz, H-18); 2.58(1H, br d, *J*=8.1Hz, H-11); 2.64(1H, d, *J*=11.2Hz, H-21); 2.90(1H, ddq, *J*=2.0, 4.0, and 11.2Hz, H-6); 3.63(3H, s, OMe); 5.14(1H, d, *J*=4.0Hz, H-7); and 5.73ppm (1H, br dd, *J*=4.1 and 12.0Hz, H-9).

^{13}C NMR:

(benzene-d_6) 84.0, C-1; 39.2, C-2; 26.5, C-3; 111.3, C-4; 145.7, C-5; 47.8, C-6; 80.9, C-7; 134.3, C-8; 128.9, C-9; 24.4, C-10; 43.4, C-11; 143.6, C-12; 142.5, C-13; 160.1, C-14; 20.5, C-15; 14.8, C-16; 17.6, C-17; 29.1, C-18; 20.1, C-19; 20.4, C-20; 57.4, C-21; 105.0, C-22; 25.6, C-23; 170.1, C-24; and 58.9ppm, OMe.

References

B. B. Jarvis, Y.-W. Lee, S. N. Yatawara, and C. S. Cömezoglu; Trichothecenes Produced by *Stachybotrys atra* from Eastern Europe; Appl. Environ. Microbiol., Vol. 51, pp. 915-918(1986).

S. F. Hinkley, J. Jiang, E. P. Mazzola, and B. B. Jarvis; Atranones: Novel Diterpenoids from the Toxigenic Mold *Stachybotrys atra*; Tetrahedron Lett., Vol. 40, pp. 2725-2728(1999).

S. F. Hinkley, E, P. Mazzola, J. C. Fettinger, Y.-F. Lam, and B. B. Jarvis; Atranones A-G: A Unique Series of Metabolites from the Toxigenic Mold *Stachybotrys atra*; Phytochemistry, Vol. 55, pp. 663-673 (2000).

Common/Systematic Name

Atranone C

Molecular Formula/Molecular Weight

$C_{24}H_{32}O_6$; MW = 416.21989

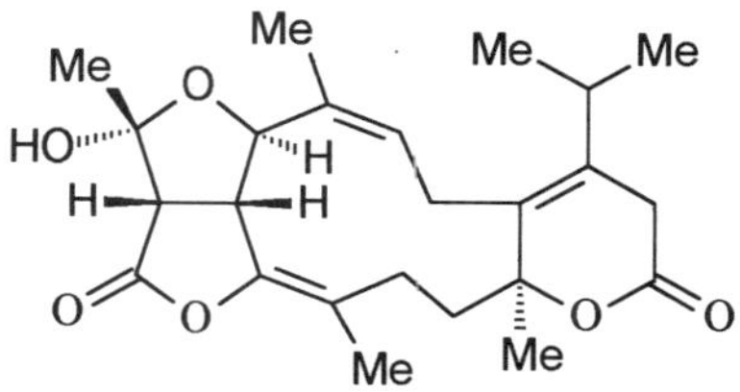

General Characteristics

Crystals; mp., 204-208°C; $[\alpha]_D^{20}$ + 74° (*c*= 0.44 in $CHCl_3$).

Fungal Source

Stachybotrys chartarum (*S. atra*) S-11.

Isolation/Purification

After four weeks of growth, a rice culture of *Stachybotrys atra* (*S. chartarum*, S-11) was extracted with methanol-chloroform and, following solvent removal, the crude extract triturated with hexane to give 11.5g of a black gum. The majority of the extract was chromatographed over PEI silica, eluting with increasing proportions of methylene chloride in hexane, then increasing amounts of methanol in methylene chloride to give four fractions. Fraction 2 (eluted with 100% methylene chloride) was applied to a 2 mm Chromatotron plate and eluted with ethyl acetate-hexane-methanol (40:60:5, v/v/v) to give atranone B. A later fraction from the plate was found to contain a 2:1 mixture of atranones A and C. These were resolved by semipreparative HPLC using the following conditions: reversed phase C_{18} column (Phenomenex, 10 x 250mm); solvent methanol-water (isocratic; 2:5, v/v); flow 3.5ml/min; detection UV 250nm; retention time for atranone A and C was 35.8 and 40.9 min, respectively.

Spectral Data

UV:

λ_{max}^{MeOH} End absorption only.

IR:

($CHCl_3$) 3607, 2970, 2935, 1791, 1716, 1521, 1475, 1386, 1297 and 1136cm^{-1}.

^{1}H NMR:

(benzene-d_6) 0.52(3H, d, *J*=6.6Hz, H-19); 0.68(3H, d, *J*=6.8Hz, H-20); 0.92(3H, s,H-15); 1.38(3H, s, H-23); 1.39(1H, m, H-2B); 1.53(3H, br s, H-17); 1.61(1H, dt, *J*=

2.7 and 13.3Hz, H-3B); 1.63(3H, br s, H-16); 1.95(1H, m, H-3A); 1.98(1H, dt, J=4.8 and 14.3Hz, H-2A); 2.38(1H, m, H-10B); 2.51(1H, br d, J=20.6Hz, H-13B); 2.53(1H, m, H-18); 2.56(1H, dd, J=12.0 and 14.8Hz, H-10A); 2.61(1H, d, J=11.4Hz, H-21); 2.87(1H, d, J=20.6Hz, H-13A); 2.92(1H, br ddq, J=2, 4.6, and 11.4Hz, H-6); 5.18(1H, d, J=4.6Hz, H-7); and 5.40ppm (1H, dd, J=6.3 and 12.0Hz, H-9).

^{13}C NMR:

(benzene-d_6) 86.6, C-1; 39.1, C-2; 27.2, C-3; 111.3, C-4; 145.4, C-5; 47.8, C-6; 80.9, C-7; 133.3, C-8; 128.9, C-9; 25.6, C-10; 129.5, C-11; 135.5, C-12, 29.3, C-13; 168.9, C-14; 28.2, C-15; 14.7, C-16; 17.8, C-17; 29.7, C-18; 19.6, C-19; 20.0, C-20; 57.4, C-21; 105.1, C-22; 25.6, C-23; and 170.4ppm C-24.

References

B. B. Jarvis, Y.-W. Lee, S. N. Yatawara, and C. S. Cömezoglu; Trichothecenes Produced by *Stachybotrys atra* from Eastern Europe; Appl. Environ. Microbiol., Vol. 51, pp. 915-918(1986).

S. F. Hinkley, J. Jiang, E. P. Mazzola, and B. B. Jarvis; Atranones: Novel Diterpenoids from the Toxigenic Mold *Stachybotrys atra*; Tetrahedron Lett., Vol. 40, pp. 2725-2728(1999).

S. F. Hinkley, E, P. Mazzola, J. C. Fettinger, Y.-F. Lam, and B. B. Jarvis; Atranones A-G: A Unique Series of Metabolites from the Toxigenic Mold *Stachybotrys atra*; Phytochemistry, Vol. 55, pp. 663-673 (2000).

Common/Systematic Name

Atranone D

Molecular Formula/Molecular Weight

$C_{24}H_{34}O_4$; MW = 386.24571

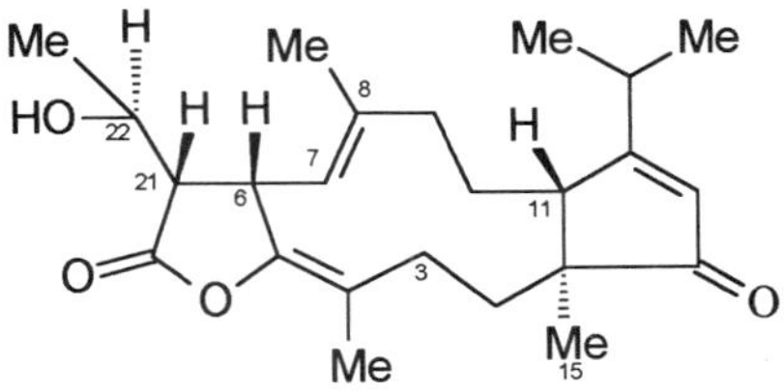

General Characteristics

Clear film; $[\alpha]_D^{20}$ + 21° (c=0.70 in $CHCl_3$).

Fungal Source

Stachybotrys chartarum (*S. atra*) S-11.

Isolation/Purification

After four weeks of growth, a rice culture of *Stachybotrys atra* (*S. chartarum*, S-11) was extracted with methanol-chloroform and, following solvent removal, the crude extract triturated with hexane to give a black gum. The majority of the extract was chromatographed over PEI silica, elution with increasing proportions of methylene chloride in hexane, then increasing amounts of methanol in methylene chloride to give four fractions. Fraction 1 (eluted with hexane to 80% methylene chloride-hexane) was applied to a 2mm Chromatotron plate (eluting with 10% ethyl acetate in methylene chloride) to yield atranones D and E.

Spectral Data

UV:

λ_{max}^{MeOH} 231nm (ε= 14,800).

IR:

($CHCl_3$) 3684, 3607, 3015, 2971, 2935, 1780, 1693, 1522, 1424, and 1213cm^{-1}.

^{1}H NMR:

($CDCl_3$) 1.01(3H, br s, H-15); 1.14(3H, d, *J*=6.9Hz, H-20); 1.16(3H, d, *J*=6.7Hz, H-19); 1.27(1H, m, H-2B); 1.30(1H, m, H-3B); 1.32(3H, d, *J*=6.4Hz, H-23); 1.69(1H, m, H-10B); 1.72(3H, br s, H-17); 1.80(3H, s, H-16); 1.84(1H, m, H-3A); 2.22(1H, dddd, *J*=3.0, 5.9, 12.4, and 12.4Hz, H-9B); 2.24(1H, m, H-10A); 2.31(1H, m, H-2A); 2.42(1H, m, H-9A); 2.62(1H, qq, *J*=6.7 and 6.9Hz, H-18); 2.70(1H, dq, *J*=1.0 and 12.2Hz, H-11); 3.03(1H, dd, *J*=5.2 and 11.5Hz, H-21), 4.07(1H, dq, *J* =5.2 and 6.4Hz,

H-22); 4.15(1H, br dd, J=10.4 and 11.5Hz, H-6); 5.51(1H, br d, J=10.4Hz, H-7); and 5.83ppm (1H, d, J=1.0 Hz, H-13).

^{13}C NMR:

($CDCl_3$) 52.0, C-1; 35.7, C-2; 27.0, C-3; 114.5, C-4; 144.9, C-5; 38.1, C-6; 126.7, C-7; 137.3, C-8; 36.3, C-9; 24.0, C-10; 43.7, C-11; 188.0, C-12; 124.3, C-13; 212.0, C-14; 24.0, C-15; 15.8, C-16; 16.6, C-17; 29.1, C-18; 21.2, C-19; 22.1, C-20; 50.5, C-21; 66.8, C-22; 20.9, C-23; and 175.3ppm C-24.

References

S. F. Hinkley, J. Jiang, E. P. Mazzola, and B. B. Jarvis; Atranones: Novel Diterpenoids from the Toxigenic Mold *Stachybotrys atra*; Tetrahedron Lett., Vol. 40, pp. 2725-2728(1999).

S. F. Hinkley, E, P. Mazzola, J. C. Fettinger, Y.-F. Lam, and B. B. Jarvis; Atranones A-G: A Unique Series of Metabolites from the Toxigenic Mold *Stachybotrys atra*; Phytochemistry, Vol. 55, pp. 663-673 (2000).

Common/ Systematic Name

Atranone E

Molecular Formula/Molecular Weight

$C_{24}H_{34}O_4$; MW = 386.24571

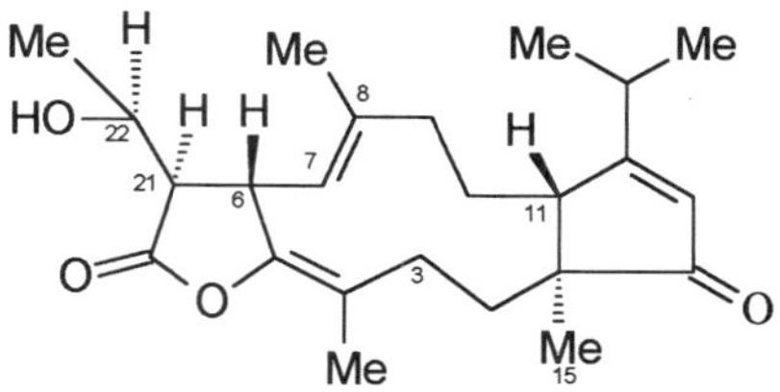

General Characteristics

Clear film; $[\alpha]_D^{20}$ – 16° (*c*=0.75 in $CHCl_3$).

Fungal Source

Stachybotrys chartarum (*S. atra*) S-11.

Isolation/Purification

After four weeks of growth, a rice culture of *Stachybotrys atra* (*S. chartarum*, S-11) was extracted with methanol-chloroform and, following solvent removal, the crude extract triturated with hexane to give a black gum. The majority of the extract was chromatographed over PEI silica, eluting with increasing proportions of methylene chloride in hexane, then increasing amounts of methanol in methylene chloride to give four fractions. Fraction 1 (eluted with hexane to 80% methylene chloride-hexane) was applied to a 2mm Chromatotron plate (eluting with 10% ethyl acetate in methylene chloride) to yield atranones D and E.

Spectral Data

UV:

λ_{max}^{MeOH} 226nm (ε= 12,600).

IR:

($CHCl_3$) 3688, 3608, 3518, 2970, 2937, 2874, 1773, 1692, 1606, 1459, 1386, 1374, 1277, 1133, and 1068cm^{-1}.

^{1}H NMR:

($CDCl_3$) 1.10(3H, s, H-15); 1.14(3H, d, *J*=6.8Hz, H-20); 1.16(3H, d, *J*=6.7Hz, H-19); 1.21(1H, m, H-3B); 1.30(3H, d, *J*=6.4Hz, H-23); 1.35(1H, m, H-2B); 1.69(1H, m, H-10B); 1.71(3H, d, *J*=2Hz, H-17); 1.80(3H, s, H-16); 1.99(1H, ddd, *J*=2.1, 12.2, and12.8Hz, H-3A); 2.23(1H, m, H-9B); 2.24(1H, ddd, *J*=4.5, 12.9, and 13.1Hz, H-10A); 2.34(1H , ddd, *J*=5.5, 12.8, and 13.4Hz, H-2A); 2.40(1H, m, H-9A); 2.50(1H, dd, *J*=6.3 and 8.9Hz, H-21); 2.62(1H, qq, *J*=6.7 and 6.8Hz, H-18); 2.70(1H, br d, *J*=12.9Hz, H-11); 3.82(1H, br dd, *J*=8.9 and 9.5Hz, H-6); 4.00(1H, dq, *J*=6.3 and 6.4Hz, H-22); 5.44(1H, d, *J*= 9.5Hz, H-7); and 5.82ppm (1H, br s, H-13).

^{13}C NMR:

($CDCl_3$) 52.0, C-1; 35.8, C-2; 27.0, C-3; 115.6, C-4; 143.6, C-5; 39.6, C-6; 129.6, C-7; 135.0, C-8; 36.4, C-9; 23.9, C-10; 43.6, C-11; 188.0, C-12; 124.2, C-13; 212.0, C-14; 24.2, C-15; 15.5, C-16; 17.0, C-17; 29.1, C-18; 21.2, C-19; 22.1, C-20; 52.9, C-21; 67.5, C-22; 20.8, C-23; and 175.3ppm C-24.

References

S. F. Hinkley, J. Jiang, E. P. Mazzola, and B. B. Jarvis; Atranones: Novel Diterpenoids from the Toxigenic Mold *Stachybotrys atra*; Tetrahedron Lett., Vol. 40, pp. 2725-2728(1999).

S. F. Hinkley, E, P. Mazzola, J. C. Fettinger, Y.-F. Lam, and B. B. Jarvis; Atranones A-G: A Unique Series of Metabolites from the Toxigenic Mold *Stachybotrys atra*; Phytochemistry, Vol. 55, pp. 663-673 (2000).

Common/Systematic Name

Atranone F

Molecular Formula/Molecular Weight

$C_{24}H_{32}O_7$; MW = 432.21480

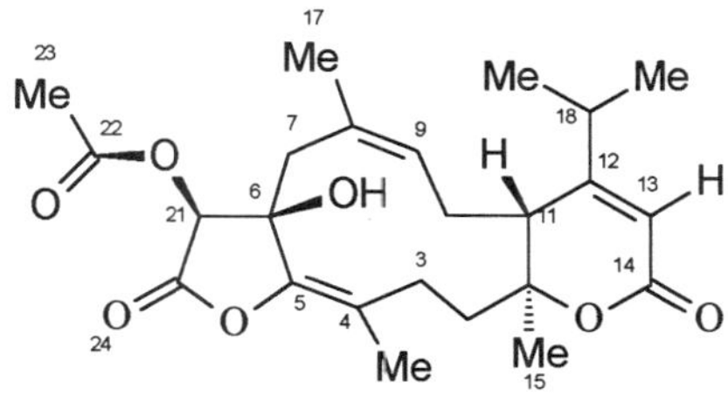

General Characteristics

Pale yellow film; $[\alpha]_D^{20}$ + 24° (*c*=0.70 in $CHCl_3$).

Fungal Source

Stachybotrys chartarum (*S. atra*) S-11.

Isolation/Purification

After four weeks of growth, a rice culture of *Stachybotrys atra* (*S. chartarum*, S-11) was extracted with methanol-chloroform and, following solvent removal, the crude extract triturated with hexane to give a black gum. The majority of the extract was chromatographed over PEI silica, eluting with increasing proportions of methylene chloride in hexane, then increasing amounts of methanol in methylene chloride to give four fractions. Fraction 3 (eluted with 1-20% methanol-methylene chloride) was loaded onto a 2mm Chromatotron plate and eluted with ethyl acetate-hexane-methanol (gradient from 1:9:0, v/v/v to 70:30:1, v/v/v) to give atranones F and G.

Spectral Data

UV:

λ_{max}^{MeOH} 237nm (ε = 4,170).

IR:

($CHCl_3$) 3369(br), 2969, 2934, 1807, 1743, 1712, 1691, 1382, 1230, 1196, 1030, and 991cm^{-1}.

^{1}H NMR:

($CDCl_3$) 1.06(3H, d, *J*=7.0Hz, H-20); 1.18(3H, d, *J*=6.6Hz, H-19); 1.31(3H, s, H-15); 1.75(3H, s, H-16); 1.77(3H, br s, H-17); 1.87(1H, m, H-10B); 2.00(1H, m, H-2B); 2.02(3H, s, H-23); 2.14(1H, m, H-3B); 2.34(1H, m, H-3A); 2.62(1H, qq, *J*=6.6 and 6.7Hz, H-18); 2.71(1H, AB, *J*=18.1Hz, H-21B); 2.74(1H, m, H-10A); 3.24(1H, dd, *J*=11.0 and 11.4Hz, H-2A); 3.27(1H, dd, *J*=2.2 and 9.2 Hz, H-11); 3.43(1H, AB, *J*=18.1Hz, H-21A); 5.79(1H, s, H-13); 5.83(1H, br t, *J*=8.4Hz, H-9); and 6.08ppm (1H, d, *J*=1Hz, H-7).

^{13}C NMR:

($CDCl_3$) 86.4, C-1; 37.4, C-2; 23.6, C-3; 117.0, C-4; 149.5, C-5; 76.5, C-6; 75.2, C-7; 132.6, C-8; 134.0, C-9; 25.7, C-10; 43.9, C-11; 169.1, C-12; 112.6, C-13; 165.0, C-14; 21.8, C-15; 16.9, C-16; 18.9, C-17; 31.0, C-18; 20.6, C-19; 23.7, C-20; 41.0, C-21; 169.7, C-22; 20.7, C-23; and 170.9ppm C-24.

References

S. F. Hinkley, J. Jiang, E. P. Mazzola, and B. B. Jarvis; Atranones: Novel Diterpenoids from the Toxigenic Mold *Stachybotrys atra*; Tetrahedron Lett., Vol. 40, pp. 2725-2728(1999).

S. F. Hinkley, E, P. Mazzola, J. C. Fettinger, Y.-F. Lam, and B. B. Jarvis; Atranones A-G: A Unique Series of Metabolites from the Toxigenic Mold *Stachybotrys atra*; Phytochemistry, Vol. 55, pp. 663-673 (2000).

Common/Systematic Name

Atranone G

Molecular Formula/Molecular Weight

$C_{25}H_{34}O_8$; MW = 462.22537

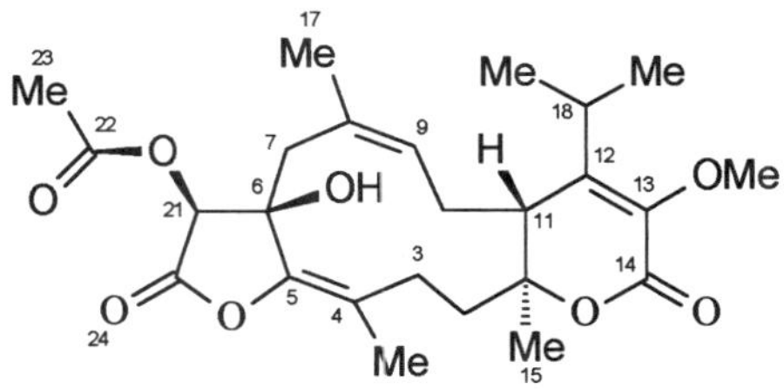

General Characteristics

Pale yellow film; $[\alpha]_D^{20}$ + 28° (*c*=0.20 in $CHCl_3$).

Fungal Source

Stachybotrys chartarum (*S. atra*) S-11.

Isolation/Purification

After four weeks of growth, a rice culture of *Stachybotrys atra* (*S. chartarum*, S-11) was extracted with methanol-chloroform and, following solvent removal, the crude extract triturated with hexane to give a black gum. The majority of the extract was chromatographed over PEI silica, eluting with increasing proportions of methylene chloride in hexane, then increasing amounts of methanol in methylene chloride to give four fractions. Fraction 3 (eluted with 1-20% methanol-methylene chloride) was loaded onto a 2mm Chromatotron plate and eluted with ethyl acetate-hexane-methanol (gradient from 1:9:0, v/v/v to 70:30:1, v/v/v) to give atranones F and G.

Spectral Data

UV:

λ_{max}^{MeOH} 237nm (ε= 4,170).

IR:

($CHCl_3$) 3390, 2963, 2930, 1808, 1743, 1718, 1374, 1260, 1233, 1092, and 1023cm^{-1}.

^1H NMR:

($CDCl_3$) 1.21(3H, d, *J*=6.9Hz, H-19); 1.31(3H, d, *J*=6.9Hz, H-20); 1.36(3H, s, H-15); 1.73(3H, s, H-16); 1.76(3H, br s, H-17); 1.87(1H, dd, *J*=8.0 and 15.5Hz, H-10B); 1.97(1H, m, H-2B); 2.01(3H, s, H-23); 2.10(1H, dd, *J*=5.1 and 11.8Hz, H-3B); 2.24(1H, ddd, *J*=8.3, 11.8 and 14.0Hz, H-3A); 2.49(1H, br qq, *J*=6.9 and 6.9Hz, H-18) 2.70(1H, m, H-10A); 2.74(1H, AB, J=18.0Hz, H-21B); 3.22(1H, dd,

J=12.7 and 13.3Hz, H-2A); 3.26(1H, br d, *J*=9.0Hz, H-11); 3.45(1H, AB, *J*=18.0Hz, H-21A) 3.67(3H, s, OMe); 5.80(1H, dd, *J*=8.0 and 8.1Hz, H-9) and 6.05ppm (1H, s, H-7).

^{13}C NMR:

(CDCl$_3$) 85.7, C-1; 37.2, C-2; 23.5, C-3; 116.5, C-4; 149.7, C-5; 76.1, C-6; 75.4, C-7; 132.6, C-8; 134.3, C-9; 26.1, C-10; 44.5, C-11; 147.1, C-12; 141.0, C-13; 161.1, C-14; 21.3, C-15; 16.5, C-16; 20.6, C-17; 30.3, C-18; 20.3, C-19; 20.8, C-20; 40.9, C-21; 169.7, C-22; 20.6, C-23; 171.0, C-24; and 59.4ppm OMe.

References

S. F. Hinkley, J. Jiang, E. P. Mazzola, and B. B. Jarvis; Atranones: Novel Diterpenoids from the Toxigenic Mold *Stachybotrys atra*; Tetrahedron Lett., Vol. 40, pp. 2725-2728(1999).

S. F. Hinkley, E, P. Mazzola, J. C. Fettinger, Y.-F. Lam, and B. B. Jarvis; Atranones A-G: A Unique Series of Metabolites from the Toxigenic Mold *Stachybotrys atra*; Phytochemistry, Vol. 55, pp. 663-673 (2000).

2

Austalides

Austalide A
Austalide B
Austalide C
Austalide D
Austalide E
Austalide F
Austalide G
Austalide H
Austalide I
Austalide J
Austalide K
Austalide L

Common/Systematic Name

Austalide A

Molecular Formula/Molecular Weight

$C_{28}H_{36}O_9$; MW = 516.23593

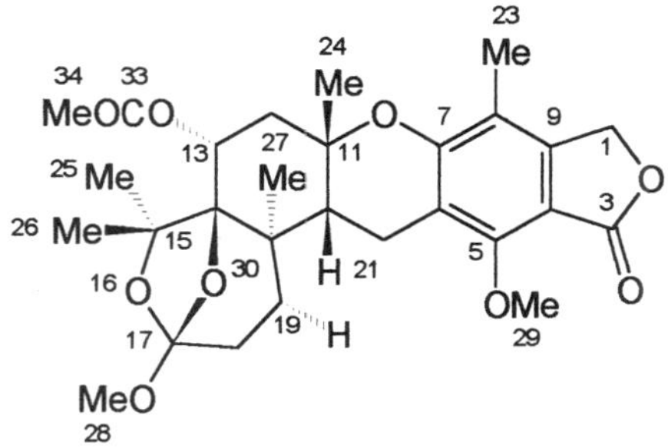

General Characteristics

Crystals from chloroform-methanol; mp., 212-214°C; $[\alpha]_D^{24}$ -84.4° (c=1.00, in $CHCl_3$).

Isolation/Purification

Aspergillus ustus was grown in bulk on wet, sterilized, whole yellow maize kernels for 21 days at 25°C. Cultures were dried at 45°C for 24 hours and milled to a fine meal. The resulting material was acutely toxic to day-old ducklings. The dried, milled, moldy maize was extracted with chloroform-methanol (1:1, v/v) for 48 hours. The solvent was removed under reduced pressure and the resulting, toxic extract was partitioned between aqueous methanol (90%) and *n*-hexane. The methanol solution was evaporated and the residual material partitioned between chloroform and water, yielding toxic material in the organic layer. This material was fractionated on a formamide impregnated cellulose powder column which was eluted with solvent of increased polarity from *n*-hexane, *n*-hexane-benzene, benzene, to benzene-ethyl acetate (1:1, v/v). Fractions (100ml) were collected and combined on the basis of their chromatographic behavior on thin-layer chromatography affording five fractions (A-E). Each of these fractions was partitioned between chloroform and water to remove any traces of formamide. All five fractions were acutely toxic to day-old ducklings. Fraction A was highly lipidic in nature and was dissolved in aqueous methanol (90%) and repeatedly extracted with *n*-hexane. The resulting polar material was subjected to column chromatography on silica gel 60H with chloroform as eluant, to give, in order of elution, austocystin A, austalide A, and 7-chloro-2-(3-furyl)-1,3,8-trimethoxyxanthone.

Fungal Source

Aspergillus ustus (isolate MRC 1163).

Biological Activity

Reported to be toxic to ducklings.

Spectral Data

UV:
λ_{max}^{MeOH} 222(ϵ= 35,400) and 267nm (17,140).

IR:
(KBr) 1740cm^{-1}.

^{1}H NMR:
($CDCl_3$) 0.970(3H, s, H-27); 1.213(3H, s, Me); 1.318(3H, s, Me); 1.569(3H, s, Me); 1.822-1.946(4H, m, H-18 and H-19); 2.030(3H, s, H-23); 2.530(1H, dd, *J*=16.1 and 2.2Hz, H-12); 2.136(1H, dd, *J*=16.1, and 4.4Hz, H-12); 2.398(1H, d, *J*=8.2Hz, H-21), 5.067(1H, dd, *J*=4.4 and 2.2Hz, H-13); 2.827(1H, dd, *J*= 18.7 and 8.2Hz, H_b-22); 2.930 (1H, d, *J*=18.7Hz, Ha-22); 3.417 (3H, s, H-28); 4.087 (3H, s, H-29); and 5.070ppm (2H, s, H-1).

^{13}C NMR:
10.365, q, C-23; 17.92, t, C-22; 17.95, q, C-27; 21.01, q; 27.39, q; 28.45, q; 25.81, q; 30.28, t; 30.56, t; 35.86, d, C-21; 40.35, s, C-20; 38.00, t, C-12; 48.69, q, C-28; 61.78, q, C-29; 68.04, t, C-1; 70.84, d, C-13; 75.48, s, C-11; 84.41, s; 85.33, s; 107.27, s; 113.79, s; 115.57, s; 119.24, s; 145.53, s; 155.23, s; 157.79, s; and 169.13ppm,s, C-3.

Mass Data:
HREIMS: 516.236*m/e*; found: C, 55.05; H, 5.85%; $C_{28}H_{36}O_9$•$CHCl_3$ requires 516.236; C, 54.77; H, 5.86%.

References

R. M. Horak, P. S. Steyn, P. H. Van Rooyen, R. Vleggaar, and C. J. Rabie; Structures of the Austalides A-E, Five Novel Toxic Metabolites from *Aspergillus ustus*; J. C. S. Chem. Comm., pp. 1265-1267(1981).

R. M. Horak, P. S. Steyn, and R. Vleggaar; Metabolites of *Aspergillus ustus*. Part 1. Application of the Heteronuclear Selective Population Inversion (SPI) N.M.R. Technique to the Structure Elucidation of the Austalides A-F, Novel Ortho Ester Meroterpenoids; J. Chem. Soc. Perkin Trans. I, pp. 345-356(1985).

Common/Systematic Name

Austalide B

Molecular Formula/Molecular Weight

$C_{26}H_{34}O_8$, MW = 474.22537

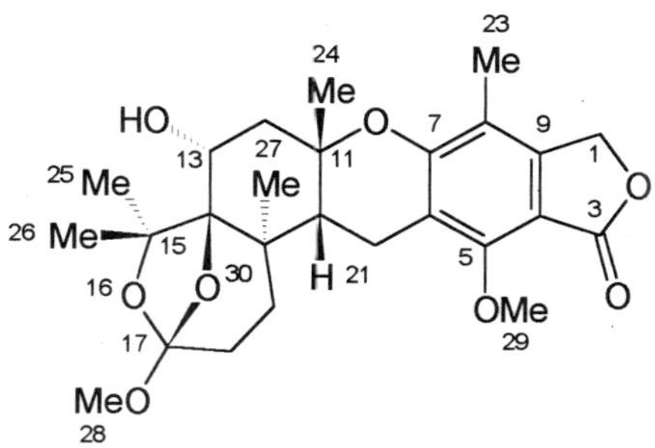

General Characteristics

Crystals from benzene-*n*-hexane; mp., 243-245°C; $[\alpha]_D^{24}$ -46.2° (*c*=1.00, in $CHCl_3$).

Isolation/Purification

Aspergillus ustus was grown in bulk on wet, sterilized, whole yellow maize kernels for 21 days at 25°C. Cultures were dried at 45°C for 24 hours and milled to a fine meal. The resulting material was acutely toxic to day-old ducklings. The dried, milled, moldy maize was extracted with chloroform-methanol (1:1, v/v) for 48 hours. The solvent was removed under reduced pressure and the resulting, toxic extract was partitioned between aqueous methanol (90%) and *n*-hexane. The methanol solution was evaporated and the residual material partitioned between chloroform and water, yielding toxic material in the organic layer. This material was fractionated on a formamide impregnated cellulose powder column which was eluted with solvent of increased polarity from *n*-hexane, *n*-hexane-benzene, benzene, to benzene-ethyl acetate (1:1, v/v). Fractions (100ml) were collected and combined on the basis of their chromatographic behavior on thin-layer chromatography affording five fractions (A-E). Each of these fractions was partitioned between chloroform and water to remove any traces of formamide. All five fractions were acutely toxic to day-old ducklings. Fraction B was purified by silica gel column chromatography with chloroform as eluant to give, in order of elution, 4,6-*O,O*-bisdemethylaustocystin A, 4-*O*-demethylaustocystin A, 6-*O*-demethylaustocystin A, 8-deoxy-6-*O*-methylversicolorin A, and a mixture. The mixture was subjected to column chromatography on silica gel with *n*-hexane-ethyl acetate (1:1, v/v) as eluant to give austocystin H, austalide A, austalide B, and austalide C.

Fungal Source

Aspergillus ustus (isolate MRC 1163).

Biological Activity

Reported to be toxic to ducklings.

Spectral Data

UV:

λ_{max}^{MeOH} 223(ϵ= 28,700) and 269nm (16,800).

IR:

(KBr) 1740cm^{-1}.

^{1}H NMR:

($CDCl_3$) 0.969(3 H, s, H-27); 1.249(3H, s, Me); 1.462(3H, s, Me); 1.631(3H, s, Me); 1.689-1.935(4H, m, H-18 and -19); 2.022(3H, s, H-23); 2.322(2H, d, *J*=3.3Hz, H-12); 2.379(1H, d, *J*=7.7Hz, H-21); 2.491(1H, d, *J*=8.5, OH-13); 2.85(1H, dd, *J*=18.7 and 7.7Hz, H_b-22); 2.925(1H, d, *J*=18.7Hz, H_a-22); 3.397(3H, s, H-28); 4.098(1H, dd, *J*= 8.5 and 3.3Hz, H-13); 4.122(3H, s, H-29); and 5.104ppm (2H, s, H-1).

^{13}C NMR:

($CDCl_3$) 10.65, q, C-23; 18.53, t, C-22; 19.23, q, C-27; 26.18, q; 27.14, q; 28.84, q; 30.4, t; 31.54, t; 36.68, d, C-21; 39.74, s, C-20; 41.32, t, C-12; 48.75, q, C-28; 62.01, q, C-29; 68.15, t, C-1; 69.91, d, C-13; 78.29, s, C-11; 84.85, s; 86.35, s; 108.22, s; 114.26, s; 116.57, s; 118.95; 145.64, s; 155.43, s; 157.13, s; and 169.07ppm, s, C-3.

Mass Data:

LREIMS: 474*m/e*; found: C, 65.65; H, 7.2%; $C_{26}H_{34}O_8$ requires 474; C, 65.81; H, 7.22%.

References

R. M. Horak, P. S. Steyn, P. H. Van Rooyen, R. Vleggaar, and C. J. Rabie; Structures of the Austalides A-E, Five Novel Toxic Metabolites from *Aspergillus ustus*; J. C. S. Chem. Comm., pp. 1265-1267(1981).

R. M. Horak, P. S. Steyn, and R. Vleggaar; Metabolites of *Aspergillus ustus*. Part 1. Application of the Heteronuclear Selective Population Inversion (SPI) N.M.R. Technique to the Structure Elucidation of the Austalides A-F, Novel Ortho Ester Meroterpenoids; J. Chem. Soc. Perkin Trans. I, pp. 345-356(1985).

Common/Systematic Name

Austalide C

Molecular Formula/Molecular Weight

$C_{30}H_{38}O_{11}$; MW = 574.24141

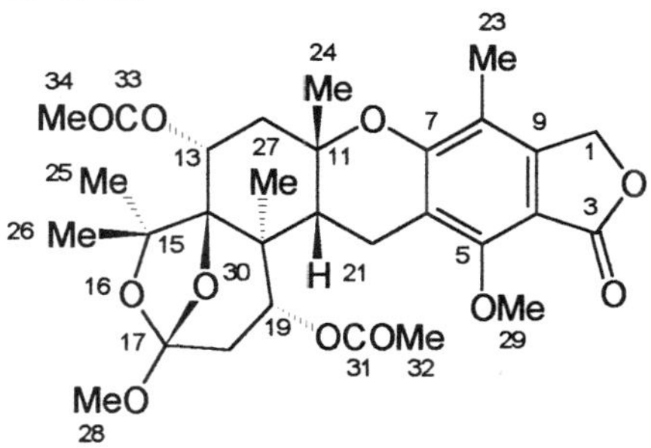

General Characteristics

A white amorphous solid; $[\alpha]_D^{24}$ -99.0° (c=1.00, in $CHCl_3$).

Isolation/Purification

See austalide B.

Fungal Source

Aspergillus ustus (isolate MRC 1163).

Biological Activity

Reported to be toxic to ducklings.

Spectral Data

UV:

λ_{max}^{MeOH} 221(ϵ= 26,900) and 265nm (13,800).

IR:

(KBr) 1740cm^{-1}.

^{1}H NMR:

($CDCl_3$) 1.023(3H, s, H-27); 1.232(3H, s, Me); 1.348(3H, s, Me); 1.705(3H, s, Me); 1.951(1H, d, J=15.0Hz, H_b-18); 1.966(3H, s, H-34); 2.034(3H, s, Me); 2.043(3H, s, H-32); 2.147(1H, dd, J=16.0 and 4.2Hz, H_b-13); 2.202(1H, d, J=8.5 Hz, H-21); 2.302(1H, dd, J=15.0 and 6.1Hz, H_a-18); 2.600(1H, dd, J=16.0 and 2.1Hz, H-12); 2.979(1H, dd, J=19.0 and 8.5Hz, H_b-22), 3.266(1H, d, J=19.0Hz, H_a-22); 3.41(3H, s, H-28); 4.142(3H, s, H-29); 5.077(2H, s, H-1); 5.147(1H, dd, J=4.2 and 2.1Hz, H-13); and 5.506ppm (1H, d, J=6.1Hz, H-19).

^{13}C NMR:

($CDCl_3$) 10.38, q, C-23; 12.94, q, C-27; 19.35, t, C-22; 21.02, q, C-34; 21.06, q; 25.44, q; 27.63, q; 29.37, q; 37.12, t; 37.61, d, C-21; 37.8, t; 45.50, s, C-20; 48.79, q, C-28; 62.04, q, C-29; 68.05, t, C-1; 70.72, d; 70.95 d; 75.47, s, C-11; 85.25, s; 85.33, s; 107.76, s; 113.67, s; 115.34, s; 117.83, s, C-17; 145.61, s; 155.50, s; 157.36, s; 169.04, s; 169.22, s, C-33; and 170.06ppm, s, C-31.

Mass Data:

HREIMS: 574.242*m/e*; found: C, 62.45; H, 6.5%; $C_{30}H_{38}O_{11}$ requires 574.241; C, 62.7; H, 6.6%.

References

R. M. Horak, P. S. Steyn, P. H. Van Rooyen, R. Vleggaar, and C. J. Rabie; Structures of the Austalides A-E, Five Novel Toxic Metabolites from *Aspergillus ustus*; J. C. S. Chem. Comm., pp.1265-1267(1981).

R. M. Horak, P. S. Steyn, and R. Vleggaar; Metabolites of *Aspergillus ustus*. Part 1. Application of the Heteronuclear Selective Population Inversion (SPI) N.M.R. Technique to the Structure Elucidation of the Austalides A-F, Novel Ortho Ester Meroterpenoids; J. Chem. Soc. Perkin Trans. I, pp. 345- 356 (1985).

Common/Systematic Name

Austalide D

Molecular Formula/Molecular Weight

$C_{28}H_{36}O_{10}$; MW = 532.23085

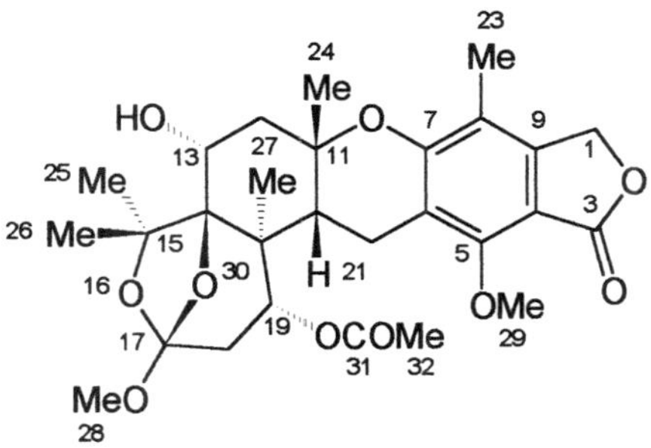

General Characteristics

Crystals from acetone; mp., 259-261°C; $[\alpha]_D^{24}$ -73.4° (*c*=1.00, in $CHCl_3$).

Isolation/Purification

Aspergillus ustus was grown in bulk on wet, sterilized, whole yellow maize kernels for 21 days at 25°C. Cultures were dried at 45°C for 24 hours and milled to a fine meal. The resulting material was acutely toxic to day-old ducklings. The dried, milled, moldy maize was extracted with chloroform-methanol (1:1, v/v) for 48 hours. The solvent was removed under reduced pressure and the resulting, toxic extract was partitioned between aqueous methanol (90%) and *n*-hexane. The methanol solution was evaporated and the residual material partitioned between chloroform and water, yielding toxic material in the organic layer. This material was fractionated on a formamide impregnated cellulose powder column which was eluted with solvent of increased polarity from *n*-hexane, *n*-hexane-benzene, benzene, to benzene-ethyl acetate (1:1, v/v). Fractions (100ml) were collected and combined on the basis of their chromatographic behavior on thin-layer chromatography affording five fractions (A-E). Each of these fractions was partitioned between chloroform and water to remove any traces of formamide. All five fractions were acutely toxic to day-old ducklings. Fraction C was purified by silica gel column chromatography; elution with *n*-hexane-ethyl acetate (3:2, v/v) gave,in order of elution, 8-deoxy-6-*O*-methylversicolorin A, austocystins A, B, and H, and austalides D and E.

Fungal Source

Aspergillus ustus (isolate MRC 1163).

Biological Activity

Reported to be toxic to ducklings.

Spectral Data

UV:

λ_{max}^{MeOH} 222(ϵ= 32,700) and 268nm (17,700).

IR:

(KBr) 1745cm^{-1}.

^{1}H NMR:

($CDCl_3$) 0.964(3H, s, H-27); 1.258(3H, s, Me); 1.488(3H, s, Me); 1.771(3H, s, Me); 2.274(1H, dd, *J*=15.0 and 6.1Hz, H-18); 1.935(1H, d, *J*=15.0Hz, H-18); 2.019(3H, s, H-23); 2.399(1H, dd, *J*=15.8 and 2.2Hz, H-12); 2.320(1H, dd, *J*=15.8 and 4.2Hz, H-12); 2.176(1H, d, *J*=8.5Hz, H-21), 4.184(1H, m, *J*= 4.2 and 2.2Hz, H-13); 2.630(1H, d, *J*=8.0Hz, OH-13); 2.975 (1H, dd, *J*=18.9 and 8.5Hz, H_b-22); 3.229(1H, d, *J*= 18.9 Hz, H_a-22); 3.378(3H, s, H-28); 4.119(3H, s, H-29); 2.041(3H, s, H-32 and 5.087ppm (2H, s, H-1).

^{13}C NMR:

10.61, q, C-23; 19.73, t, C-22; 14.07, q, C-27; 21.13, q; 27.35, q; 29.65, q; 25.73, q; 37.34, t; 38.49, d, C-21; 44.98, s, C-20; 40.84, t, C-12; 48.17, q, C-28; 62.16, q, C-29; 68.10, t, C-1; 69.92, d, C-13; 78.23, s, C-11; 86.10, s, C-14; 85.69, s, C-15; 71.07, d, C-19; 108.63, s; 114.10, s; 116.26, s; 117.47, s; 145.76, s; 155.61, s; 156.58, s; 170.27, s; and 168.93ppm, s, C-3.

Mass Data:

LREIMS: 532*m/e*; found: C, 63.15; H, 6.8%; $C_{28}H_{36}O_{10}$ requires 532; C, 63.14; H, 6.1%.

References

R. M. Horak, P. S. Steyn, P. H. Van Rooyen, R. Vleggaar, and C. J. Rabie; Structures of the Austalides A-E, Five Novel Toxic Metabolites from *Aspergillus ustus*; J. C. S. Chem. Comm., pp. 1265-1267(1981).

R. M. Horak, P. S. Steyn, and R. Vleggaar; Metabolites of *Aspergillus ustus*. Part 1. Application of the Heteronuclear Selective Population Inversion (SPI) N.M.R. Technique to the Structure Elucidation of the Austalides A-F, Novel Ortho Ester Meroterpenoids; J. Chem. Soc. Perkin Trans. I, pp. 345-356(1985).

Common/Systematic Name

Austalide E

Molecular Formula/Molecular Weight

$C_{28}H_{36}O_{10}$; MW = 532.23085

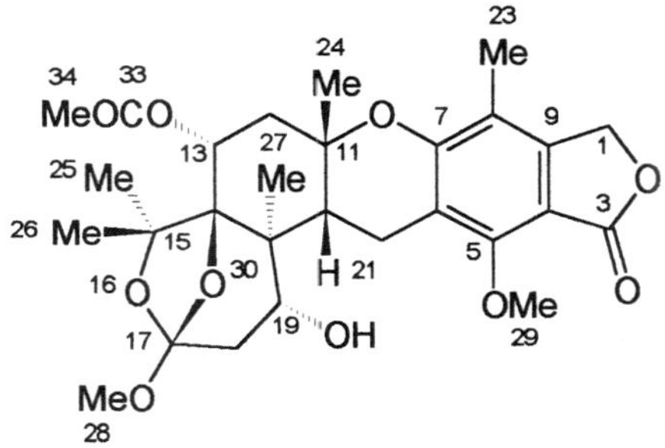

General Characteristics

Crystals from acetone; mp., 262-264°C; $[\alpha]_D^{24}$ -73.4° (c=1.00, in $CHCl_3$).

Isolation/Purification

See austalide D.

Fungal Source

Aspergillus ustus (isolate MRC 1163).

Biological Activity

Reported to be toxic to ducklings.

Spectral Data

UV:

λ_{max}^{MeOH} 222(ε= 34,600) and 266nm (19,600).

IR:

(KBr) 1745cm^{-1}.

^{1}H NMR:

($CDCl_3$) 1.162(3H, s, H-27); 1.200(3H, s, Me); 1.357(3H, s, Me); 1.690(3H, s, Me); 1.976(3H, s, H-34), 2.043(1H, d, J=14.6Hz, 18-H_b), 2.058(3H, s, Me); 2.108(1H, d, J= 9.1Hz, H-21); 2.142 (1H, dd, J=16.0 and 3.5, H_b-12), 2.355(1H, dd, J=14.6 and 5.0Hz, H-18); 2.558(1H, br d, J=16.0Hz, H_a-12); 2.873(1H, dd, J=18.8 and 9.1Hz, H_b-22); 3.009(1H, d, J=18.8Hz, Ha-22); 3.410(3H, s, H-28), 4.020(1H, m, H-19); 4.105(3H, s, H-29); 5.092(2H, s, H-1); and 5.115ppm (1H, m, H-13).

^{13}C NMR:

(CDCl$_3$) 10.38, q, C-23; 13.34, q, C-27; 19.10, t, C-22; 21.09, q, C-34; 25.89, q; 27.63, q; 29.20, q; 37.61, t; 37.75, d, C-21; 39.03, t, C-18; 46.29, s, C-20; 49.17, q, C-28; 62.00, q, C-29; 68.08, t, C-1; 70.76, d, C-19; 70.82, d, C-13; 75.53 s, C-11; 85.78, s; 86.03, s;.107.33, s; 113.66, s; 115.10, s; 118.76, s, C-17; 145.63, s; 155.33, s; 157.57, s; 169.13, s; and 169.36, s, C-33.

Mass Data:

LREIMS: 532*m/e*; found: C, 63.05; H, 6.85%; $C_{28}H_{36}O_{10}$ requires 532; C, 63.14; H, 6.18%.

References

R. M. Horak, P. S. Steyn, P. H. Van Rooyen, R. Vleggaar, and C. J. Rabie; Structures of the Austalides A-E, Five Novel Toxic Metabolites from *Aspergillus ustus*; J. C. S. Chem. Comm., pp. 1265-1267(1981).

R. M. Horak, P. S. Steyn, and R. Vleggaar; Metabolites of *Aspergillus ustus*. Part 1. Application of the Heteronuclear Selective Population Inversion (SPI) N.M.R. Technique to the Structure Elucidation of the Austalides A-F, Novel Ortho Ester Meroterpenoids; J. Chem. Soc. Perkin Trans. I, pp. 345-356(1985).

Common/Systematic Name

Austalide F

Molecular Formula/Molecular Weight

$C_{26}H_{34}O_9$; MW = 490.22028

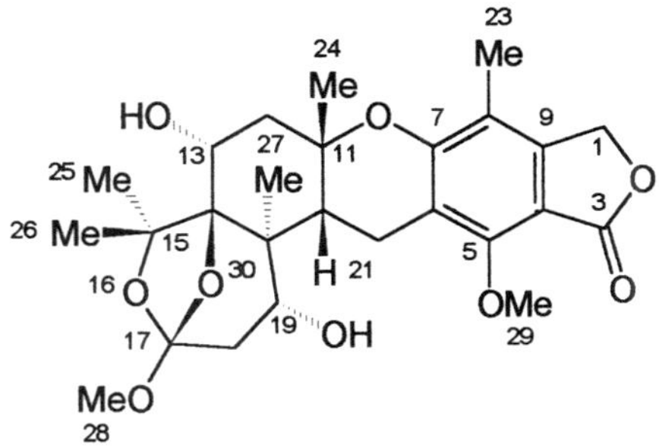

General Characteristics

Crystals from acetone; mp., 261-263°C; $[\alpha]_D^{24}$ -57.7° (*c*=1.00, in $CHCl_3$).

Isolation/Purification

Aspergillus ustus was grown in bulk on wet, sterilized, whole yellow maize kernels for 21 days at 25°C. Cultures were dried at 45°C for 24 hours and milled to a fine meal. The resulting material was acutely toxic to day-old ducklings. The dried, milled, moldy maize was extracted with chloroform-methanol (1:1, v/v) for 48 hours. The solvent was removed under reduced pressure and the resulting, toxic extract was partitioned between aqueous methanol (90%) and *n*-hexane. The methanol solution was evaporated and the residual material partitioned between chloroform and water, yielding toxic material in the organic layer. This material was fractionated on a formamide impregnated cellulose powder column which was eluted with solvent of increased polarity from *n*-hexane, *n*-hexane-benzene, benzene, to benzene-ethyl acetate (1:1, v/v). Fractions were collected and combined on the basis of their chromatographic behavior on thin-layer chromatography affording five fractions (A-E). Each of these fractions was partitioned between chloroform and water to remove any traces of formamide. All five fractions were acutely toxic to day-old ducklings. Fraction C was purified by silica gel column chromatography; elution with *n*-hexane-ethyl acetate (3:2, v/v) gave,in order of elution, 8-deoxy-6-*O*-methylversicolorin A, austocystins A, B, and H, and austalides D and E. Subsequent elution of the column with *n*-hexane-ethyl acetate (3:7, v/v) gave austalide F.

Fungal Source

Aspergillus ustus (isolate MRC 1163).

Biological Activity

Reported to be toxic to ducklings.

Spectral Data

UV:

λ_{max}^{MeOH} 220(ϵ= 30,900) and 264nm (16,800).

IR:

(KBr) 1740cm^{-1}.

^{1}H NMR:

($CDCl_3$) 1.144(3H, s, H-27); 1.240(3H, s, Me); 1.491(3H, s, Me); 1.764(3H, s, Me); 2.034(3H, s, Me); 2.067-2.096(2H, m, H-18); 2.313-2422(3H, m); 2.710(1H, d, *J*=8.7Hz, OH); 2.895(1H, dd, *J*=18.8 and 8.3Hz, H_b-22); 2.988(1H, d, *J*=18.8 Hz, H_b-22); 3.051(1H, d, *J*=10.1Hz, OH); 3.393(3H, s, H-28); 3.922(1H, m, H-19); 4.126(3H, s, H-29); 4.131(1H, m, H-13); and 5.110ppm (2H, s, H-1).

^{13}C NMR:

($CDCl_3$) 10.54, q, C-23; 14.32, q, C-27; 19.47, t, C-22; 26.02, q; 27.23, q; 29.36, q; 38.14, t, C-18; 39.06, d, C-21; 40.78, t, C-12; 45.60, s, C-20; 49.09, q, C-28; 62.05, q, C-29; 68.07, t, C-1; 69.72, d, C-13; 71.11, d, C-19; 78.31, s, C-11; 86.12, s; 86.93, s; 108.16, s; 114.08, s; 116.02, s; 118.40, s, C-17; 145.72, s; 155.35, s; 156.71, s; and 168.96ppm s, C-3.

Mass Data:

LREIMS: 490*m/e*; found: C, 63.65; H, 6.9%; $C_{26}H_{34}O_9$ requires 490; C, 63.66; H, 6.99%.

References

R. M. Horak, P. S. Steyn, P. H. Van Rooyen, R. Vleggaar, and C. J. Rabie; Structures of the Austalides A-E, Five Novel Toxic Metabolites from *Aspergillus ustus*; J. C. S. Chem. Comm., pp. 1265-1267(1981).

R. M. Horak, P. S. Steyn, and R. Vleggaar; Metabolites of *Aspergillus ustus*. Part 1. Application of the Heteronuclear Selective Population Inversion (SPI) N.M.R. Technique to the Structure Elucidation of the Austalides A-F, Novel Ortho Ester Meroterpenoids; J. Chem. Soc. Perkin Trans. I, pp. 345-356(1985).

Common/Systematic Name
Austalide G

Molecular Formula/Molecular Weight
$C_{28}H_{38}O_9$; MW = 518.25158

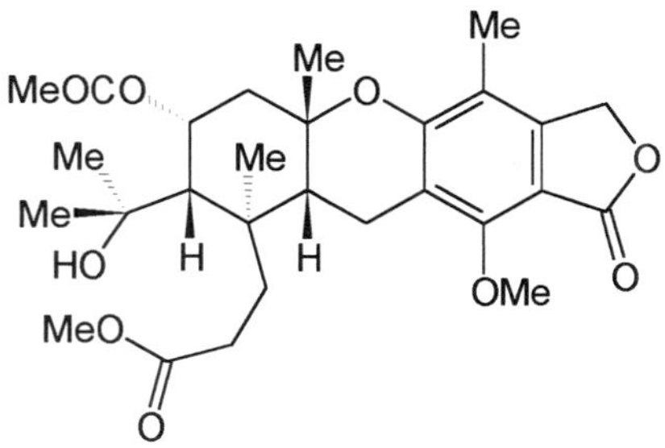

General Characteristics
Isolated as a colorless glass; $[\alpha]_D^{24}$ -100.2° (*c*=1.00, in $CHCl_3$).

Isolation/Purification
Aspergillus ustus was grown in bulk on wet, sterilized, whole yellow maize kernels for 21 days at 25°C. Cultures were dried at 45°C for 24 hours and milled to a fine meal. The resulting material was acutely toxic to day-old ducklings. The dried, milled, moldy maize was extracted with chloroform-methanol (1:1, v/v) for 48 hours. The solvent was removed under reduced pressure and the resulting, toxic extract was partitioned between aqueous methanol (90%) and *n*-hexane. The methanol solution was evaporated and the residual material partitioned between chloroform and water, yielding toxic material in the organic layer. This material was fractionated on a formamide impregnated cellulose powder column which was eluted with solvent of increased polarity from *n*-hexane, *n*-hexane-benzene, benzene, to benzene-ethyl acetate (1:1, v/v). Fractions (100ml) were collected and combined on the basis of their chromatographic behavior on thin-layer chromatography affording five fractions (A-E). Each of these fractions was partitioned between chloroform and water to remove any traces of formamide. All five fractions were acutely toxic to day-old ducklings. Fraction C was purified by silica gel column chromatography; elution with *n*-hexane-ethyl acetate (3:2, v/v) gave,in order of elution, 8-deoxy-6-*O*-methylversicolorin A, austocystins A, B, and H, and austalides D and E. Subsequent elution of the column with *n*-hexane-ethyl acetate (3:7, v/v) gave austalides F, G, and I.

Fungal Source
Aspergillus ustus (isolate MRC 1163).

Biological Activity
Reported to be toxic to ducklings.

Spectral Data

UV:

λ_{max}^{MeOH} 2213(ϵ=26,500) and 267nm (14,100).

IR:

(KBr) 1720-1770cm^{-1}.

^{1}H NMR:

($CDCl_3$) 1.022(3H, s, H-27); 1.171(3H, s, Me); 1.380(3H, s, Me); 1.593(1H, s br, OH); 1.626(1H, d, *J*=8.2Hz, H-21), 1.697(1H, d, *J*=2.2Hz, H-14), 1.767(1H, dd, *J*=16.0 and 4.2Hz, H_b-12), 1.823(1H, ddd, *J*=15.0, 11.5 and 60Hz, H_b-19); 1.967(3H, s, Me); 1.968(3H, s, Me); 2.029(3H, s, Me); 2.250(1H, ddd, *J*=15.3, 11.2, and 6.0Hz, H_b-18); 2.417(1H, ddd, *J*=15.0, 11.2, and 3.6 Hz, H_a-19); 2.538(1H, ddd, *J*=15.3, 11.5, and 3.6 Hz H_a-18); 2.718 (1H, dd, *J*=18.6 and 8.2Hz, H_b-22); 2.624(1H, dd, *J*=16.0 and 2.3Hz, H-12); 3.004(1H, d, *J*=18.6Hz, H_a-22); 3.673(3H, s, H-28); 4.111(3H, s, H-29); 5.088(2H, s, H-1); and 5.391ppm (1H, ddd, *J*=4.2, 2.3, and 2.2Hz, H-13).

^{13}C NMR:

($CDCl_3$) 10.53, q, C-23; 17.24 t, C-22; 20.66, q, C-27; 21.54, q, C-34; 27.81, q; 29.21, t, C-19; 29.80, q; 34.26, q; 34.50, t, C-18; 41.01, d, C-21; 41.30, s, C-20; 42.01, t, C-12; 51.67, d, C-14; 51.67, q, C-28; 62.04, q, C-29; 68.15, t, C-1; 75.15, s; 71.03, d, C-13; 75.56, s; 107.38, s; 113.79, s; 115.36, s; 145.58, s; 155.46, s; 158.10, s; 169.27, s; 170.29, s; and 174.47ppm, s, C-17.

Mass Data:

HREIMS: 518.251*m/e* $(M)^+$, $C_{28}H_{38}O_9$ requires 518.252.

References

R. M. Horak, P. S. Steyn, P. H. Van Rooyen, R. Vleggaar, and C. J. Rabie; Structures of the Austalides A-E, Five Novel Toxic Metabolites from *Aspergillus ustus*; J. C. S. Chem. Comm., pp. 1265-1267(1981).

R. M. Horak, P. S. Steyn, and R. Vleggaar; Metabolites of *Aspergillus ustus*. Part 1. Application of the Heteronuclear Selective Population Inversion (SPI) N.M.R. Technique to the Structure Elucidation of the Austalides A-F, Novel Ortho Ester Meroterpenoids; J. Chem. Soc. Perkin Trans. I, pp. 345-356(1985).

R. M. Horak, P. S. Steyn, and R. Vleggaar; Metabolites of *Aspergillus ustus*. Part 3. Structure Elucidation of Austalides G-L; J. Chem. Soc. Perkin Trans. I, pp. 363-367(1985).

Common/Systematic Name

Austalide H

Molecular Formula/Molecular Weight

$C_{26}H_{36}O_8$; MW = 476.24102

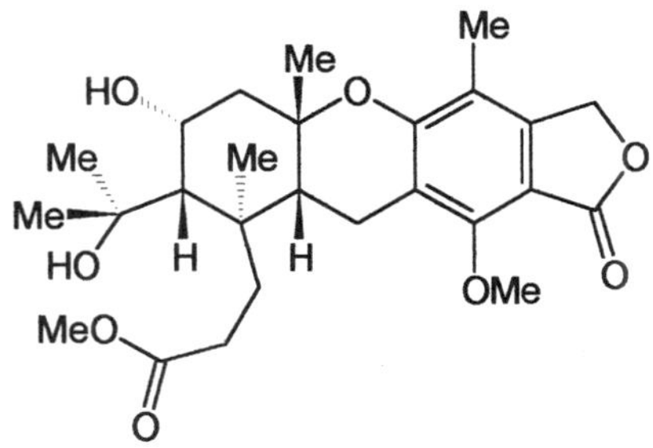

General Characteristics

Isolated as a colorless glass; $[\alpha]_D^{24}$ -19.5° (*c*=1.00, in $CHCl_3$).

Isolation/Purification

Aspergillus ustus was grown in bulk on wet, sterilized, whole yellow maize kernels for 21 days at 25°C. Cultures were dried at 45°C for 24 hours and milled to a fine meal. The resulting material was acutely toxic to day-old ducklings. The dried, milled, moldy maize was extracted with chloroform-methanol (1:1, v/v) for 48 hours. The solvent was removed under reduced pressure and the resulting, toxic extract was partitioned between aqueous methanol (90%) and *n*-hexane. The methanol solution was evaporated and the residual material partitioned between chloroform and water, yielding toxic material in the organic layer. This material was fractionated on a formamide impregnated cellulose powder column which was eluted with solvent of increased polarity from *n*-hexane, *n*-hexane-benzene, benzene, to benzene-ethyl acetate (1:1, v/v). Fractions (100ml) were collected and combined on the basis of their chromatographic behavior on thin-layer chromatography affording five fractions (A-E). Each of these fractions was partitioned between chloroform and water to remove any traces of formamide. All five fractions were acutely toxic to day-old ducklings. Fraction D was purified by silica-gel column chromatography with chloroform-methanol (98:2, v/v) as eluant to give, in order of elution, 8-deoxy-6-*O*-methylversicolorin A, austocystin D, and a mixture. This mixture was subjected to column chromatography on silica gel 60H with *n*-hexane-ethyl acetate (1:1, v/v) as eluant to afford austalide F, G, and H.

Fungal Source

Aspergillus ustus (isolate MRC 1163).

Biological Activity

Reported to be toxic to ducklings.

Spectral Data

UV:
λ_{max}^{MeOH} 221(ϵ=20,400) and 267nm (9,600).

IR:
(KBr) 1740cm^{-1}.

^{1}H NMR:
($CDCl_3$) 0.962(3, s, H-27); 1.244(3H, s, Me); 1.322(1H, d, J=2.5Hz, H-14); 1.431(3H, s, Me); 1.437(3H, s, Me); 1.655(1H, d, J=7.9 Hz, H-21); 1.799(1H, dd, J=15.3 and 3.7Hz, H_b-12); 1.885-1.998(1H, m); 2.022(3H, s, H-23); 2.187-2.273(2H, m); 2291-2.389(1H m); 2.504(1H, dd, J=15.3 and 3.1Hz H_a-12); 2.771(1H, dd, J=18.7 and 7.9Hz, H_b-22); 3.071(1H, J=18.7Hz, H_a-22); 3.683(3H, s, H-28); 4.128(3H, s, H-29); 4.629(1H, m, H-13); and 5.100ppm (2h, s, H-1).

^{13}C NMR:
($CDCl_3$) 10.76, q, C-23; 18.49, t, C-22; 21.48, q, C-27; 27.44, q; 29.62, t; 31.67, q; 33.49, q; 35.00, t; 40.41, d, C-21; 40.96, s, C-20; 43.99, t, C-12; 49.43, d, C-14; 51.82, q, C-28; 62.17, q, C-29; 68.15, t, C-1; 69.96, d, C-13; 75.61, s; 78.60, s; 108.51, s; 114.09, s; 116.00, s; 145.75, s; 155.51, s; 156.50, s; 160.0, s, C-3; and 173.87ppm s, C-17.

Mass Data:
HREIMS: 476.240*m/e* $(M)^+$, $C_{26}H_{36}O_8$ requires 476.241.

References

R. M. Horak, P. S. Steyn, P. H. Van Rooyen, R. Vleggaar, and C. J. Rabie; Structures of the Austalides A-E, Five Novel Toxic Metabolites from *Aspergillus ustus*; J. C. S. Chem. Comm., pp. 1265-1267(1981).

R. M. Horak, P. S. Steyn, and R. Vleggaar; Metabolites of *Aspergillus ustus*. Part 1. Application of the Heteronuclear Selective Population Inversion (SPI) N.M.R. technique to the Structure elucidation of the Austalides A-F, Novel Ortho Ester Meroterpenoids; J. Chem. Soc. Perkin Trans. I, pp. 345-356(1985).

R. M. Horak, P. S. Steyn, and R. Vleggaar; Metabolites of *Aspergillus ustus*. Part 3. Structure Elucidation of Austalides G-L; J. Chem. Soc. Perkin Trans. I, pp. 363-367(1985).

Common/Systematic Name
Austalide I

Molecular Formula/Molecular Weight
$C_{27}H_{34}O_8$; MW = 486.22537

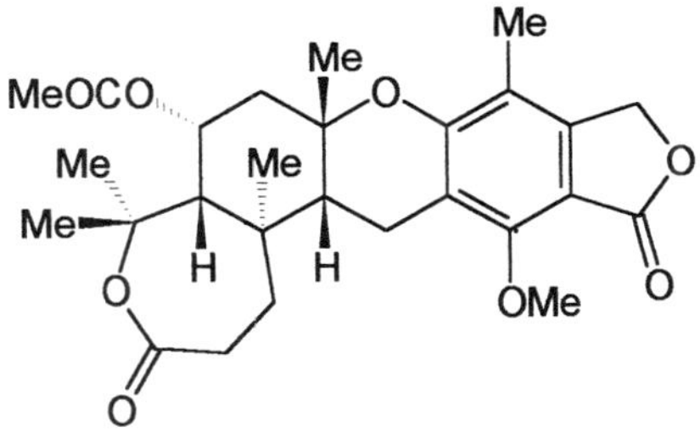

General Characteristics
Crystals; mp., 236-238°C; $[\alpha]_D^{24}$ -132.6° (*c*=1.00, in $CHCl_3$).

Isolation/Purification
Aspergillus ustus was grown in bulk on wet, sterilized, whole yellow maize kernels for 21 days at 25°C. Cultures were dried at 45°C for 24 hours and milled to a fine meal. The resulting material was acutely toxic to day-old ducklings. The dried, milled, moldy maize was extracted with chloroform-methanol (1:1, v/v) for 48 hours. The solvent was removed under reduced pressure and the resulting, toxic extract was partitioned between aqueous methanol (90%) and *n*-hexane. The methanol solution was evaporated and the residual material partitioned between chloroform and water, yielding toxic material in the organic layer. This material was fractionated on a formamide impregnated cellulose powder column which was eluted with solvent of increased polarity from *n*-hexane, *n*-hexane-benzene, benzene, to benzene-ethyl acetate (1:1, v/v). Fractions (100ml) were collected and combined on the basis of their chromatographic behavior on thin-layer chromatography affording five fractions (A-E). Each of these fractions was partitioned between chloroform and water to remove any traces of formamide. All five fractions were acutely toxic to day-old ducklings. Fraction D was purified by silica-gel column chromatography with chloroform-methanol (98:2, v/v) as eluant to give, in order of elution, 8-deoxy-6-*O*-methylversicolorin A, austocystin D, and a mixture. This mixture was subjected to column chromatography on silica gel 60H with *n*-hexane-ethyl acetate (1:1, v/v) as eluant to afford austalide F, G, and H. Subsequent elution of the column with *n*-hexane-ethyl acetate (3:7, v/v) gave austalides F, G, I, and J.

Fungal Source
Aspergillus ustus (isolate MRC 1163).

Biological Activity
Reported to be toxic to ducklings.

Spectral Data

UV:

λ_{max}^{MeOH} 221(ϵ=35,600) and 266nm (17,000).

IR:

(KBr) 1720-1750cm^{-1}.

^{1}H NMR:

($CDCl_3$) 1.065(3H, s, H-27); 1.205(3H, s, Me); 1.486(3H, s, Me); 1.501(3H, s, Me); 1.571(1H, d, *J*=8.1Hz, H-21); 1.829(1H, m); 1.862(1H, d, *J*=3.9 Hz, H-14); 1.989(3H, s, Me); 2.005(3H, s, Me); 2.085-2.135(1H, m); 2.677-2.726(2H, m); 2.783-2.848(2H, m); 2.844(1H, dd, *J*=18.8 and 8.1Hz, Hb-22); 3.079(1H, d, *J*=18.8Hz, H-22); 4.127(3H, s, H-29); 5.103(2H, s, H-1); and 5.407ppm (1H, m, H-13).

^{13}C NMR:

($CDCl_3$) 10.23, q, C-23; 15.84, q, C-27; 18.10, t, C-22; 21.23, q, C-34; 26.48, q; 27.43, q; 31.24, t, C-19; 33.89, q; 36.59, t, C-18; 40.86, s, C-20; 41.63, t, C-12; 45.94, d, C-21; 55.35, d, C-14; 61.86, q, C-29; 67.99, t, C-1; 69.92, d, C-13; 74.96, s, C-11; 85.12, s, C-15; 107.30, s; 113.74, s; 114.82, s; 145.56, s; 155.14, s; 157.58, s; 168.97, s; 169.76, s; and 174.40ppm s, C-17.

Mass Data:

HREIMS: 486.225*m/e* (M)$^+$, $C_{27}H_{34}O_8$ requires 486.225; found: C, 66.4%; H, 6.8 requires C, 66.65%; H, 7.04.

References

R. M. Horak, P. S. Steyn, P. H. Van Rooyen, R. Vleggaar, and C. J. Rabie; Structures of the Austalides A-E, Five Novel Toxic Metabolites from *Aspergillus ustus*; J. C. S. Chem. Comm., pp. 1265-1267(1981).

R. M. Horak, P. S. Steyn, and R. Vleggaar; Metabolites of *Aspergillus ustus*. Part 1. Application of the Heteronuclear Selective Population Inversion (SPI) N.M.R. Technique to the Structure Elucidation of the Austalides A-F, Novel Ortho Ester Meroterpenoids; J. Chem. Soc. Perkin Trans. I, pp. 345-356(1985).

R. M. Horak, P. S. Steyn, and R. Vleggaar; Metabolites of *Aspergillus ustus*. Part 3. Structure Elucidation of Austalides G-L; J. Chem. Soc. Perkin Trans. I, pp. 363-367(1985).

Common/Systematic Name
Austalide J

Molecular Formula/Molecular Weight
$C_{25}H_{32}O_7$; MW = 444.21480

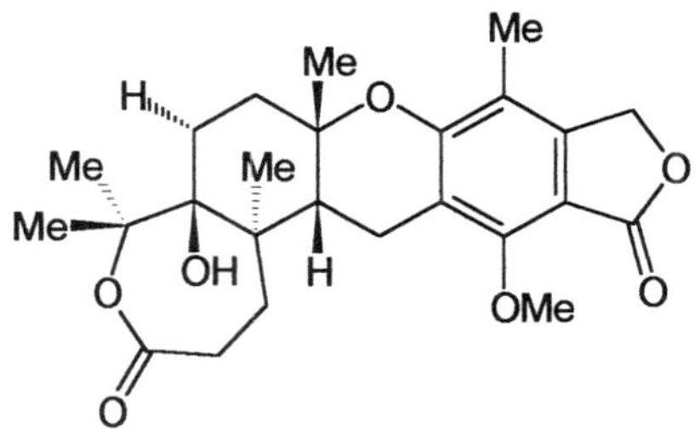

General Characteristics
Crystals from methanol; mp., 284-286°C; $[\alpha]_D^{24}$ -42.1° (*c*=1.00, in $CHCl_3$).

Isolation/Purification
Aspergillus ustus was grown in bulk on wet, sterilized, whole yellow maize kernels for 21 days at 25°C. Cultures were dried at 45°C for 24 hours and milled to a fine meal. The resulting material was acutely toxic to day-old ducklings. The dried, milled, moldy maize was extracted with chloroform-methanol (1:1, v/v) for 48 hours. The solvent was removed under reduced pressure and the resulting, toxic extract was partitioned between aqueous methanol (90%) and *n*-hexane. The methanol solution was evaporated and the residual material partitioned between chloroform and water, yielding toxic material in the organic layer. This material was fractionated on a formamide impregnated cellulose powder column which was eluted with solvent of increased polarity from *n*-hexane, *n*-hexane-benzene, benzene, to benzene-ethyl acetate (1:1, v/v). Fractions (100ml) were collected and combined on the basis of their chromatographic behavior on thin-layer chromatography affording five fractions (A-E). Each of these fractions was partitioned between chloroform and water to remove any traces of formamide. All five fractions were acutely toxic to day-old ducklings. Fraction D was purified by silica-gel column chromatography with chloroform-methanol (98:2, v/v) as eluant to give, in order of elution, 8-deoxy-6-*O*-methylversicolorin A, austocystin D, and a mixture. This mixture was subjected to column chromatography on silica gel 60H with *n*-hexane-ethyl acetate (1:1, v/v) as eluant to afford austalide F, G, and H. Subsequent elution of the column with *n*-hexane-ethyl acetate (3:7, v/v) gave austalides F, G, I, and J.

Fungal Source
Aspergillus ustus (isolate MRC 1163).

Biological Activity
Reported to be toxic to ducklings.

Spectral Data

UV:

λ_{max}^{MeOH} 221(ϵ=31,900) and 267nm (16,200).

IR:

(KBr) 1720, 1750, and 1760cm^{-1}.

^{1}H NMR:

($CDCl_3$) 0.852(3H, s, H-27); 1.190(3H, s, Me); 1.365(3H, s, Me); 1.385(3H, s, Me); 1.719-1.748(1H, m); 1.826-1.900(1H, m); 1.925-1.965(2H, m); 2.020 3H, s, H-23); 2.035-2.176(2H, m); 2.417-2.517(2H, m); 2.620-2.683(1H, m); 2.799(1H, dd, *J*=18.6 and 8.0Hz, Hb-22); 2.909(1H, d, *J*=18.6 Hz, Ha- 22), 4.091(3H, s, H-29); and 5.090ppm (2H, s, H-1).

^{13}C NMR:

($CDCl_3$) 10.57, q, C23; 17.94, t, C-22; 20.75, q, C-27; 25.22, t; 26.90, q; 27.14, t; 29.13, t, C-19; 29.13, q; 30.12, q; 32.98, t; 37.43, d, C-21; 39.73, s, C-20; 61.93, q, C-29; 68.18, t, C-1; 75.85, s, C-11; 79.58, s, C-15; 91.33, s, C-14; 107.38, s; 114.38, s; 115.26, s; 145.63, s; 155.18, s; 158.22, s; 169.27, s; and 173.38ppm s, C-17.

Mass Data:

HREIMS: 444.214*m/e* $(M)^+$, $C_{25}H_{32}O_7$ requires 444.213; found: C, 67.75%; H, 7.35; requires C, 67.55%; H, 7.26.

References

R. M. Horak, P. S. Steyn, P. H. Van Rooyen, R. Vleggaar, and C. J. Rabie; Structures of the Austalides A-E, Five Novel Toxic Metabolites from *Aspergillus ustus*; J. C. S. Chem. Comm., pp. 1265-1267(1981).

R. M. Horak, P. S. Steyn, and R. Vleggaar; Metabolites of *Aspergillus ustus*. Part 1. Application of the Heteronuclear Selective Population Inversion (SPI) N.M.R. Technique to the Structure Elucidation of the Austalides A-F, Novel Ortho Ester Meroterpenoids; J. Chem. Soc. Perkin Trans. I, pp. 345-356(1985).

R. M. Horak, P. S. Steyn, and R. Vleggaar; Metabolites of *Aspergillus ustus*. Part 3. Structure Elucidation of Austalides G-L; J. Chem. Soc. Perkin Trans. I, pp. 363-367(1985).

Common/Systematic Name

Austalide K

Molecular Formula/Molecular Weight

$C_{25}H_{32}O_5$; MW = 412.22497

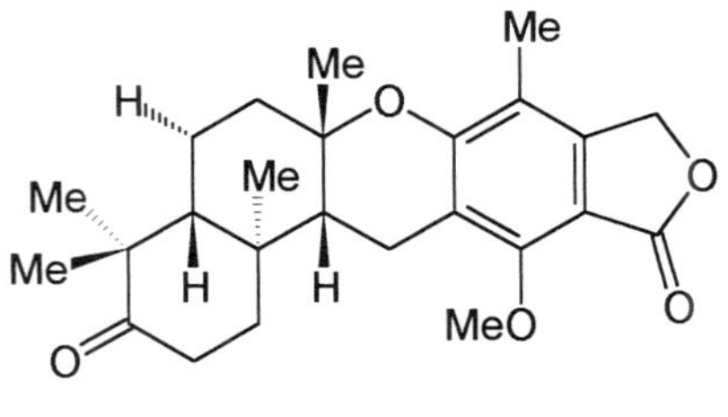

General Characteristics

Isolated as a white glass; $[\alpha]_D^{24}$ -75.9° (c=1.00, in $CHCl_3$).

Isolation/Purification

Aspergillus ustus was cultured on malt extract medium at 25°C in static culture. After 14 days the cultures were filtered and the mycelium macerated with acetone in a Waring blender. The acetone mixture was filtered, evaporated, and the resulting brown gum was partitioned between aqueous methanol (90%) and *n*-hexane. Evaporation of the methanol solution gave a residue which was partitioned between chloroform and water. The organic layer was concentrated and percolated through an aluminum oxide column with chloroform-methanol (95:5, v/v). The combined eluants were evaporated to give a light-yellow gum. This material was subjected to column chromatography on silica gel with *n*-hexane-ethyl acetate (1:1, v/v) as eluant. Fractions were evaluated by TLC (*n*-hexane-ethyl acetate, 1:1, v/v) and appropriate fractions combined to give three fractions: R_f 0.48, 0.31, and 0.13. The latter fraction crystallized from *n*-hexane-acetone to give austalide J. The material with R_f 0.48 was purified on a silica gel column. Elution with chloroform-methanol (99:1, v/v) gave austalide A and austalide K.

Fungal Source

Aspergillus ustus (isolate MRC 1163).

Biological Activity

Reported to be toxic to ducklings.

Spectral Data

UV:

λ_{max}^{MeOH} 222(ϵ=18,900) and 267nm (11,000).

IR:
(KBr) 1700 and 1745cm^{-1}.

^{1}H NMR:
(CDCl$_3$) 0.697(3H, s, H-27); 0.999(3H, s, Me); 1.090(3H, s, Me); 1.165(3H, s, Me); 1.458-1.518(4H, m, H$_b$-13, H-14, H$_b$-19, and H-21); 1.615(1H, ddd, *J*=13.9, 13.9, and 4.2Hz, H-12); 1.785(1H, dddd, *J*=13.9, 13.9, 13.9, and 3.0Hz, H-13); 2.018(3H, s, H-23); 2.072(1H, ddd, *J*=13.3, 6.9, and 3.8Hz, H- 19); 2.260(1H, ddd *J*=13.9, 3.0, and 3.0Hz, H-12); 2.365(1H, ddd, *J*=16.1, 6.5, and 3.8Hz, H$_b$-18); 2.485(1H, ddd, *J*=16.1, 11.6, and 6.9Hz, H-18); 2.790(1H, dd, *J*=18.5 and 8.0 Hz, H$_b$-22); 2.910(1H, d, *J*=18.5 Hz, H-22); 4.078(3H, s, H-29); and 5.087ppm (2H, s, H-1).

^{13}C NMR:
(CDCl$_3$) 10.51, q, C-23; 14.07, q, C-27; 18.15, t, C-22; 21.53, q; 26.97; 26.61, q; 29.54, t; 33.91, t, C- 18; 37.49, s, C-20; 38.24, t; 39.60, t, C-19; 46.95, d, C-21; 47.09, s, C-15; 54.07, d, C-14; 61.75, q, C-29; 68.07, t, C- 1; 76.20, s, C-11; 107.18, s; 114.29, s; 115.14, s; 145.38, s; 155.23, s; 158.45, s; 169.17, s, C-3; and 216.23ppm s, C-17.

Mass Data:
HREIMS: 412.224*m/e* (M)$^+$, $C_{25}H_{32}O_5$ requires 412.225; found: C, 72.6%; H, 7.9; requires C, 72.79%; H, 7.82.

References

R. M. Horak, P. S. Steyn, P. H. Van Rooyen, R. Vleggaar, and C. J. Rabie; Structures of the Austalides A-E, Five Novel Toxic Metabolites from *Aspergillus ustus*; J. C. S. Chem. Comm., pp. 1265-1267(1981).

R. M. Horak, P. S. Steyn, and R. Vleggaar; Metabolites of *Aspergillus ustus*. Part 1. Application of the Heteronuclear Selective Population Inversion (SPI) N.M.R. Technique to the Structure Elucidation of the Austalides A-F, Novel Ortho Ester Meroterpenoids; J. Chem. Soc. Perkin Trans. I, pp. 345-356(1985).

R. M. Horak, P. S. Steyn, and R. Vleggaar; Metabolites of *Aspergillus ustus*. Part 3. Structure Elucidation of Austalides G-L; J. Chem. Soc. Perkin Trans. I, pp. 363-367(1985).

Common/Systematic Name

Austalide L

Molecular Formula/Molecular Weight

$C_{25}H_{32}O_6$; MW = 428.21989

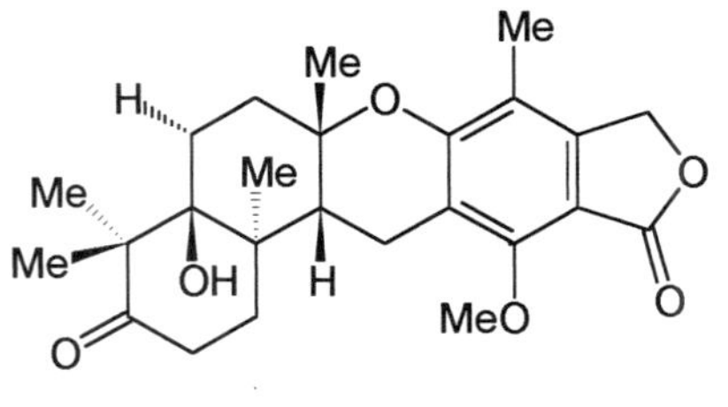

General Characteristics

Crystals; mp., 207-208°C; $[\alpha]_D^{24}$ -71.0° (*c*=1.00, in $CHCl_3$).

Isolation/Purification

Aspergillus ustus was cultured on malt extract medium at 25°C in static culture. After 14 days the cultures were filtered and the mycelium macerated with acetone in a Waring blender. The acetone mixture was filtered, evaporated, and the resulting brown gum was partitioned between aqueous methanol (90%) and *n*-hexane. Evaporation of the methanol solution gave a residue which was partitioned between chloroform and water. The organic layer was concentrated and percolated through an aluminum oxide column with chloroform-methanol (95:5, v/v). The combined eluants were evaporated to give a light-yellow gum. This material was subjected to column chromatography on silica gel with *n*-hexane-ethyl acetate (1:1, v/v) as eluant. Fractions were evaluated by TLC (*n*-hexane-ethyl acetate, 1:1, v/v) and appropriate fractions combined to give three fractions: R_f 0.48, 0.31, and 0.13. The material associated with R_f 0.31 was purified on a silica gel column eluted with chloroform-methanol (99:1, v/v) to give purified austalides D and L.

Fungal Source

Aspergillus ustus (isolate MRC 1163).

Biological Activity

Reported to be toxic to ducklings.

Spectral Data

UV:

λ_{max}^{MeOH} 223(ϵ=31,200) and 269nm (16,600).

IR:

(KBr) 1700 and 1745cm^{-1}.

^{1}H NMR:

(CDCl$_3$) 0.780(3H, s, H-27); 1.092(3H, s, Me); 1.128(3H, s, Me); 1.167(3H, s, Me); 1.467(1H, ddd, *J*=13.4, 4.0, and 4.0 Hz, H_b-12); 1.751(1H, ddd, *J*=12.9, 8.0 and 4.0Hz, H_b-19); 1.979-2.038(2H, m, H_b-13 and H-19); 2.015(3H, s, H-23); 2.075(1H, ddd, *J*=13.4, 13.4, and 4.0Hz, H_a-13); 2.155(1H, ddd, *J*=13.4, 13.4, and 4.0Hz, H-12); 2.254(1H, dd, *J*=7.0 and 1.9Hz, H-21); 2.463(1H, ddd, *J*=15.6, 8.0, and 8.0Hz, H_b-18); 2.549(1H, ddd, *J*=15.6, 8.0, and 4.0Hz, H_a-18); 2.740-2.831(2H, m, H-22); 4.061(3H, s, H-29); and 5.078ppm (2H, s, H-1).

^{13}C NMR:

(CDCl$_3$) 10.61, q, C-23; 18.04, t, C-22; 18.28, q, C-27; 21.64, q; 23.59, q; 24.19, t; 26.81, q; 33.16, t, C-19; 33.39, t; 33.79, t, C-18; 40.73, d, C-21; 41.23, s, C-20; 52.62, s, C-15; 61.83, q, C-29; 68.18, t, C-1; 76.14, s, C-11; 79.53, s, C-14; 107.23, s; 114.40, s; 115.84, s; 145.41, s; 155.29, s; 158.59, s; 169.35, s, C-3 and 216.40ppm, s, C-17.

Mass Data:

HREIMS: 428.219*m/e* $(M)^+$, $C_{25}H_{32}O_6$ requires 428.220; found: C, 69.8%; H, 7.4; requires C, 70.07%; H, 7.53.

References

R. M. Horak, P. S. Steyn, P. H. Van Rooyen, R. Vleggaar, and C. J. Rabie; Structures of the Austalides A-E, Five Novel Toxic Metabolites from *Aspergillus ustus*; J. C. S. Chem. Comm., pp. 1265-1267(1981).

R. M. Horak, P. S. Steyn, and R. Vleggaar; Metabolites of *Aspergillus ustus*. Part 1. Application of the Heteronuclear Selective Population Inversion (SPI) N.M.R. Technique to the Structure Elucidation of the Austalides A-F, Novel Ortho Ester Meroterpenoids; J. Chem. Soc. Perkin Trans. I, pp. 345-356(1985).

R. M. Horak, P. S. Steyn, and R. Vleggaar; Metabolites of *Aspergillus ustus*. Part 3. Structure Elucidation of Austalides G-L; J. Chem. Soc. Perkin Trans. I, pp. 363-367(1985).

3

Altertoxins

Altertoxin I
Altertoxin II
Altertoxin III

Common/Systematic Name

Altertoxin I; Dihydroalterperylenol

Molecular Formula/Molecular Weight

$C_{20}H_{16}O_6$; MW = 352.09469

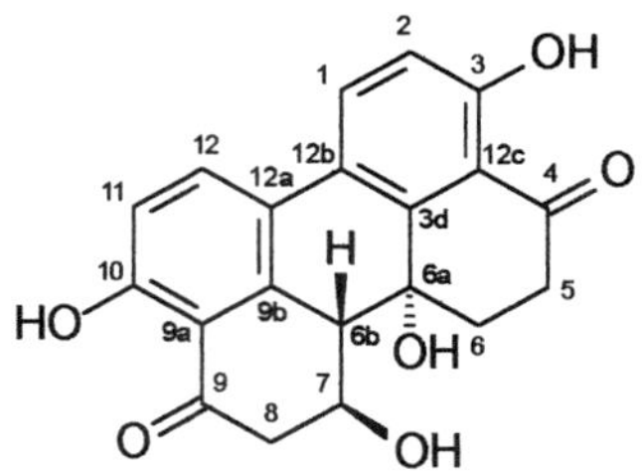

General Characteristics

Crystals from chloroform:hexane; m.p., > 180°C (dec.); $[\alpha]_D$ + 484° (*c*=0.002, in $CHCl_3$); bright yellow fluorescence under UV light.

Fungal Source

Alternaria tenuis (strain 42, deposited with the Division of Microbiology, Food and Drug Administration, Washington D.C.), *A. tenuis*, and *A. mali*.

Isolation/Purification

Moldy rice was broken up with a spatula, blended with 1L $CHCl_3$ and filtered. The filter cake was re-blended with $CHCl_3$ and filtered. The combined filtrates were concentrated using a rotary evaporator. The concentrated extracts were added to a silica gel column (E. Merck silica gel 60, 0.06 - 0.2mm) and eluted with 3L CH_2Cl_2 to obtain altertoxin III, then 3L $CHCl_3$ for altertoxin II, and finally with 3L $CHCl_3$-MeOH (98:2) to obtain altertoxin I. Crystallization from $CHCl_3$:hexane yielded purified altertoxins.

Biological Activity

The ID_{50} of altertoxin I to HeLa cells was 20μg/ml; toxicity to *Bacillus mycoides* was 250μg/disc on agar plates. In mice dosed IP (DMSO carrier), an LD_{50} was between 100-200mg/kg; at 200mg/kg, an LD_{100} was observed.

Spectral Data

UV:

λ_{max}^{MeOH} 215(ε=25,500), 256(34,600), 285(16,300), 296sh (13,300), and 356nm (6,000).

IR:

(KBr) 3450, 1641, 1598, 1489, 1465, 1368, 1337, 1234, 1170, 1062, 951, and 829cm^{1}.

CD:

+391, -351, +313($\Delta\epsilon$ +19.7, -8.8, +7.3) (c=2 x 10^{-4} in $CHCl_3$).

^{1}H NMR:

($CDCl_3$) H-1, 7.87*(d, J=8.8Hz); H-2, 7.01(d, J=8.8Hz); H-5eq, 2.65(dt, J=15.0Hz); H-5ax, 3.17(m); H-6ax, 2.43(dt, J=13.0, 3.0Hz); H-6eq, 3.17(m); H-6b, 3.09(d, J=9.0Hz); H-7, 4.78(ddd, J=12.0, 9.0, 5.0Hz); H-8ax, 2.94(dd, J=16.0, 12.0Hz); H-8eq, 3.07(dd, J=16.0, 5.0Hz); H-11, 6.92(d, J=8.8Hz); H-12, 7.82*(d, J=8.8Hz); H-3-OH, 12.7; and H-10-OH, 12.4ppm.

* Assignments may be interchanged.

^{13}C NMR:

($CDCl_3$) C-1, 132.7(d); C-2, 119.5(d); C-3, 162.3*; C-3a, 116.9*; C-4, 205; C-5, 34.0*(t); C-6, 34.5*(t); C-6a, 69.2; C-6b, 51.9(d); C-7, 66.1(d); C-8, 47.7(t); C-9, 202; C-9a, 117.4*; C-9b, 139.1; C-10, 162.0*; C-11, 117.5(d); C-12, 132.4(d); C-12a, 124.1; C-12b, 122.7; and C-12c, 135.5ppm.

* Assignments may be interchanged.

Mass Spectrum:

HREIMS: 352.0948(M+, calcd for $C_{20}H_{16}O_6$, 352.0946), 334(M^+ - H_2O), 316(M^+ - $2H_2O$), 314(M^+ - $2H_2O$ - 2H), 291(M^+ -H_2O - C_2H_3O), 290(M^+ - $C_2H_6O_2$), and 275m/e (M^+ -$2H_2O$ - C_2HO).

References

R. J. Cole and R. H. Cox; Handbook of Toxic Fungal Metabolites; Academic Press, New York, p. 635 (1981).

M. E. Stack, E. P. Mazzola, S. W. Page, and A. E. Pohland; Mutagenic Perylenequinone Metabolites of *Alternaria alternata*: Altertoxins I, II, and III; J. Nat. Prod., Vol. 49, pp. 866-871(1986).

Common/Systematic Name

Altertoxin II

Molecular Formula/Molecular Weight

$C_{20}H_{14}O_6$; MW = 350.07904

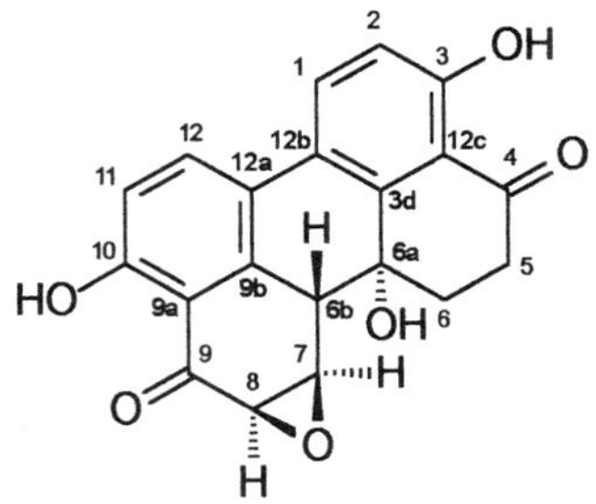

General Characteristics

Crystals from chloroform:hexane; m.p., 245-250°C (dec.); $[\alpha]_D$ + 636° (*c*=0.001, in $CHCl_3$); bright yellow fluorescence under UV light.

Fungal Source

Alternaria tenuis (strain 42, deposited with the Division of Microbiology, Food and Drug Administration, Washington D.C.), *A. tenuis*, and *A. mali*.

Biological Activity

The ID_{50} of altertoxin II to HeLa cells was 0.5µg/ml; inhibition of *Bacillus mycoides* was observed at 250µg/disc on agar plates. In mice dosed IP (DMSO carrier), an LD_{50} was between 100-200mg/kg; at 200mg/kg, an LD_{100} was observed.

Isolation/Purification

Moldy rice was broken up with a spatula, blended with 1L $CHCl_3$ and filtered. The filter cake was re-blended with $CHCl_3$ and filtered. The combined filtrates were concentrated using a rotary evaporator. The concentrated extracts were added to a silica gel column (E. Merck silica gel 60, 0.06 - 0.2mm) and eluted with 3L CH_2Cl_2 to obtain altertoxin III, then 3L $CHCl_3$ for altertoxin II, and finally with 3L $CHCl_3$-MeOH (98:2) to obtain altertoxin I. Crystallization from $CHCl_3$:hexane yielded purified altertoxins.

Biological Activity

The ID_{50} of altertoxin I to HeLa cells was 20µg/ml; toxicity to *Bacillus mycoides* was 250µg/disc on agar plates. In mice dosed IP (DMSO carrier), an LD_{50} was between 100-200mg/kg; at 200mg/kg, an LD_{100} was observed.

Spectral Data

UV:
λ_{max}^{MeOH} 215(ε=27,700), 258(31,700), 286sh (17,000), 297sh (13,500), and 358nm (5,300).

IR:
(KBr) 3462, 1643, 1598, 1485, 1384, 1342, 1321, 1296sh, 1223, 1184, 1138, 1103, 1095, 1061, 1041, 952, 833, and 774cm^{1}.

CD:
395, 327(Δε +21.0, 8.8) (*c*=2 x 10^{-4} in $CHCl_3$).

^{1}H NMR:
($CDCl_3$) H-1, 7.91*(d, *J*=8.8Hz); H-2, 7.12**(d, *J*=8.8Hz); H-5_{eq}, 2.83(ddd, *J*=17.0, 3.0, 2.0Hz); H-5_{ax}, 3.26(ddd, *J*=17, 14, 4Hz); H-6_{ax}, 2.41(dt, *J*=14.0, 3.0Hz); H-6_{eq}, 2.89(ddd, *J*=14, 4, 2.0Hz); H-6b, 3.55(d, *J*=0.5Hz); H-7, 4.23(d, *J*=3.0Hz); H-8_{ax}, 3.71(dd, *J*=3.0, 0.5Hz); H-11, 7.07**(d, *J*=8.8Hz); H-12, 7.86*(d, *J*=8.8Hz); H-3-OH, 12.7; and H-10-OH, 12.1ppm.

*, **, *** Assignments may be interchanged.

^{13}C NMR:
($CDCl_3$) C-1, 133.0(d); C-2, 119.9(d); C-3, 163.3*; C-3a, 113.5*; C-4, 204.1; C-5, 32.1***(t); C-6, 33.3***(t); C-6a, 68.3; C-6b, 45.1(d); C-7, 55.7(d); C-8, 52.8(t); C-9, 196.6; C-9a, 114.6**; C-9b, 138.8; C-10, 162.6*; C-11, 118.0(d); C-12, 132.6(d); C-12a, 124.0; C-12b, 122.4; and C-12c, 133.5ppm.

*, ** Assignments may be interchanged.

Mass Spectrum:
HREIMS: 350.0784(M^+, calcd for $C_{20}H_{14}O_6$, 350.0790), 332(M^+ - H_2O), 321(M^+ - CHO), 305(M^+ - CHO_2), and 291*m/e* (M^+ -2CHO_2 - H).

References

R. J. Cole and R. H. Cox; Handbook of Toxic Fungal Metabolites; Academic Press, New York, pp. 635 (1981).

M. E. Stack, E. P. Mazzola, S. W. Page, and A. E. Pohland; Mutagenic Perylenequinone Metabolites of *Alternaria alternata*: Altertoxins I, II, and III; J. Nat. Prod., Vol. 49, pp. 866-871(1986).

Common/Systematic Name

Altertoxin III

Molecular Formula/Molecular Weight

$C_{20}H_{12}O_6$; MW = 348.06339

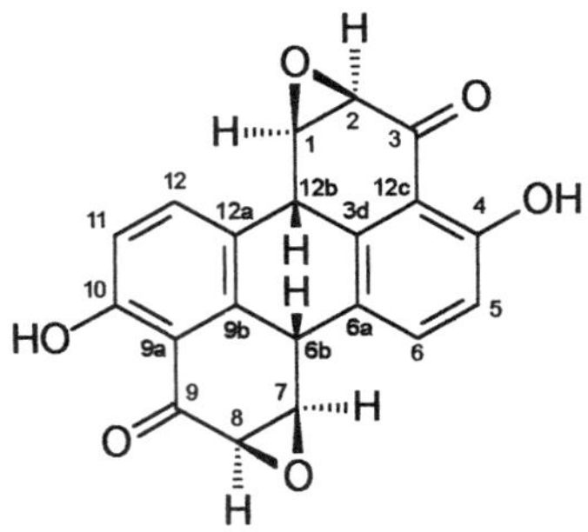

General Characteristics

Crystals from chloroform:hexane; m.p., 175-230°C (subl.); $[\alpha]_D$ + 845° (c=4 x 10^{-4}, in $CHCl_3$).

Fungal Source

Alternaria tenuis (strain 42, deposited with the Division of Microbiology, Food and Drug Administration, Washington D.C.).

Isolation/Purification

Moldy rice was broken up with a spatula, blended with 1L $CHCl_3$ and filtered. The filter cake was re-blended with $CHCl_3$ and filtered. The combined filtrates were concentrated using a rotary evaporator. The concentrated extracts were added to a silica gel column (E. Merck silica gel 60, 0.06 - 0.2mm) and eluted with 3L CH_2Cl_2 to obtain altertoxin III, then 3L $CHCl_3$ for altertoxin II, and finally with 3L $CHCl_3$-MeOH (98:2) to obtain altertoxin I. Crystallization from $CHCl_3$:hexane yielded purified altertoxins.

Biological Activity

The ID_{50} of altertoxin I to HeLa cells was 20μg/ml; toxicity to *Bacillus mycoides* was 250μg/disc on agar plates. In mice dosed IP (DMSO carrier), an LD_{50} was between 100-200mg/kg; at 200mg/kg, an LD_{100} was observed.

Spectral Data

UV:

λ_{max}^{MeOH} 210(ϵ=19,500), 265(14,500), and 352nm (5,200).

IR:

(KBr) 3452, 1650, 1620, 1420, 1473, 1440, 1382, 1372, 1249, 1234, 1198, 1045,

1003, 806, 746, and 715cm^{1}.

CD:
344nm (Δϵ +39.2) (c=2 x 10^{-5} in $CHCl_3$).

^{1}H NMR:
($CDCl_3$) H-1, 4.60(d, J=3.4Hz); H-2, 3.86(dd, J=3.4, 1.0Hz); H-5_{eq}, 6.90(d, J=8.6Hz); H-6, 7.60(d, J=8.6Hz); H-6b, 4.20(br s); H-7, 4.60(d, J=3.4Hz); H-8_{ax}, 3.86(dd, J=3.4, 1.0Hz); H-11, 6.90(d, J=8.6Hz); H-12, 7.60(d, J=8.6Hz); H-12b, 4.2(br s); H-3-OH, 11.5; and H-10-OH, 11.5ppm.

^{13}C NMR:
($CDCl_3$) C-1, 56.0(d); C-2, 53.6(d); C-3, 196.8; C-3a, 112.3; C-4, 159.6; C-5, 114.5(d); C-6, 132.1(dt); C-6a, 128.8; C-6b, 37.5(d); C-7, 56.0(d); C-8, 53.6(d); C-9, 196.8; C-9a, 112.3; C-9b, 143.0; C-10, 159.6; C-11, 114.5(d); C-12, 132.1(d); C-12a, 128.8; C-12b, 37.5; and C-12c, 143.0ppm.

Mass Spectrum:
HREIMS: 348.0633(M^+, calcd for $C_{20}H_{12}O_6$, 348.0634), 346(M^+ - 2H), 331(M^+ - OH), 329(M^+ - $2H_2O$ - H), 319(M^+ CHO), 314(M^+ - 2OH), 291(M^+ - CHO – CO), 263, and 250m/e.

Reference

M. E. Stack, E. P. Mazzola, S. W. Page, and A. E. Pohland; Mutagenic Perylenequinone Metabolites of *Alternaria alternata*: Altertoxins I, II, and III; J. Nat. Prod., Vol. 49, pp. 866-871(1986).

4

Cercophorins

- Cercophorin A
- Cercophorin B
- Cercophorin C

Common/Systematic Name

Cercophorin A

Molecular Formula/Molecular Weight

$C_{20}H_{16}O_9$; MW = 400.07943

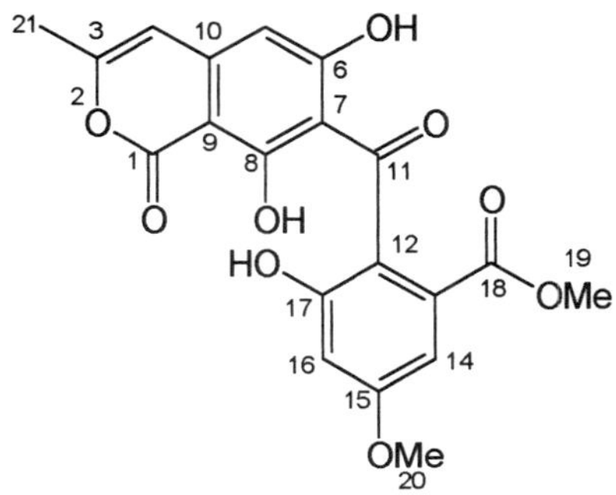

General Characteristics

White solid; mp., 208-210°C.

Fungal Source

Cercophora areolata (JS-166 = UAMH 7495) isolated from porcupine dung.

Isolation/Purification

The filtered broth was extracted with ethyl acetate and the organic phase was dried ($MgSO_4$) and concentrated to yield a dark red oil. The extract was subjected to silica gel column chromatography with a step gradient from 0 to 40% (v/v) MeOH in $CHCl_3$, and 8mL fractions were collected. Similar fractions (as determined by TLC) were pooled and bioassayed. Active fractions were further purified by Sephadex LH_{20} column chromatography eluting with hexane-toluene-MeOH (3:1:1, v/v/v), followed by reversed-phase semipreparative HPLC using a gradient from 20 to 70% MeOH in 0.01M NH_4OAc over 20 min and then 70-100% MeOH in 0.01M NH_4OAc over 2 min. HPLC fractions were concentrated *in vacuo* to afford 4-acetyl-8-hydroxy-6-methoxy-5-ethylisocoumarin, cercophorin B, and cercophorin C. The dried mycelial material was extracted with ethyl acetate, followed by filtration and concentration of the solvent to yield a dark red solid. This extract was processed by silica gel and Sephadex LH_{20} column chromatography as described above and then by preparative HPLC using a gradient from 70 to 100% MeOH in H_2O over 45 min to afford decarboxycitrinone, cercophorin A, and roridin E.

Biological Activity

Cercophorins A-C inhibited the growth of the early successional coprophilous fungi *Sordaria fimicola* (NRRL 6459) and *Ascobolus furfuraceus* (NRRL 6460) at 200µg/disk in centerpoint inoculation disk assays. Decarboxycitrinone caused a 100% reduction in radial growth against both fungi, while 4-acetyl-8-hydroxy-6-methoxy-5-methylisocou-

marin and cercophorins A, B, and C caused 46, 34, 10, and 51% growth reduction against S. *fimicola*, respectively. Roridin E caused a 100% reduction in growth of S. *fimicola* and *A. furfuraceus* and an inhibition zone of 29mm against *Candida albicans* (ATCC 14053) at the same concentration. In standard disk assays, cercophorin A was the most potent of these metabolites against *Bacillus subtilis* (ATCC 6051) and *Staphylococcus aureus* (ATCC 29213), affording zones of inhibition of 26 and 16mm, respectively, at 200μg/disk. Cercophorins A, B, and C showed only limited cytotoxicity in the NCI tumor cell line bioassay panel, displaying average GI_{50} values of 9.4, 26.2, and 20.8μg/mL, respectively.

Spectral Data

UV:

λ_{max}^{MeOH} 253 (ϵ=8,400), 318 (6,900), and 348nm (4,900).

IR:

(KBr) 3586, 2950, 2830 1671, and 1241cm^{-1}.

^{1}H NMR:

($CDCl_3$) 6.15(1H, s, H-4); 6.34(1H, s, H-5); 12.52(1H, s, OH-6); 12.17(1H, s, OH-8); 7.00(1H, d, *J*=2.3Hz, H-14); 6.60(1H, d, *J*=2.3Hz, H-16); 7.42(1H, br s, OH-17); 3.57(3H, s, OMe); 3.85(3H, s, OMe); and 2.23ppm (3H, s, CH_3-21).

^{13}C NMR:

($CDCl_3$) 166.6, C-1; 157.0, C-3; 104.4, C-4; 103.4, C-5; 168.5, C-6; 110.5, C-7; 165.1, C-8; 98.1, C-9; 143.3, C-10; 199.1, C-11; 120.8, C-12; 132.6, C-13; 108.7, C-14; 162.1, C-15; 105.5, C-16; 156.7, C-17; 166.4, C-18; 52.3, C-19; 55.7, C-20; and 19.6ppm, C-21.

Mass Spectrum:

FABMS (thioglycerol): 401($[M + H]^+$, 20), 369(15), 341(30), 219(100), and 209*m/e* (86); EIMS: 400(M^+, 2), 351(18), 341(100), 219(36), and 209*m/e* (64); HRFABMS: 401.0867*m/e* $(M + H)^+$, calcd for $(C_{20}H_{16}O_9 + H)^+$ 401.0873.

HPLC Data

Retention time, 26.5min (84:16, v/v; MeOH-H_2O).

Reference

A. C. Whyte, J. B. Gloer, J. A. Scott and D. Malloch; Cercophorins A-C: Novel Antifungal and Cytotoxic Metabolites from the Coprophilous Fungus *Cercophora areolata*; J. Nat. Prod., Vol. 59, pp. 765-769(1996).

Common/Systematic Name

Cercophorin B

Molecular Formula/Molecular Weight

$C_{20}H_{16}O_{10}$; MW = 416.07435

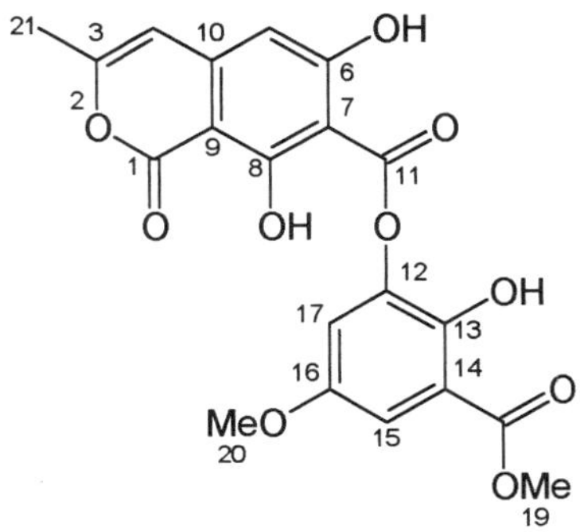

General Characteristics

Yellow solid; mp., 99-101°C.

Fungal Source

Cercophora areolata (JS-166 = UAMH 7495) isolated from porcupine dung.

Isolation/Purification

The filtered broth was extracted with ethyl acetate and the organic phase was dried ($MgSO_4$) and concentrated to yield a dark red oil. The extract was subjected to silica gel column chromatography with a step gradient from 0 to 40% (v/v) MeOH in $CHCl_3$, and 8ml fractions were collected. Similar fractions (as determined by TLC) were pooled and bioassayed. Active fractions were further purified by Sephadex LH_{20} column chromatography eluting with hexane-toluene-MeOH (3:1:1, v/v/v), followed by reversed-phase semipreparative HPLC using a gradient from 20 to 70% MeOH in 0.01M NH_4OAc over 20 min and then 70-100% MeOH in 0.01M NH_4OAc over 2 min. HPLC fractions were concentrated *in vacuo* to afford 4-acetyl-8-hydroxy-6-methoxy-5-methylisocoumarin, cercophorin B, and cercophorin C. The dried mycelial material was extracted with ethyl acetate, followed by filtration and concentration of the solvent to yield a dark red solid. This extract was processed by silica gel and Sephadex LH_{20} column chromatography as described above and then by preparative HPLC using a gradient from 70 to 100% MeOH in H_2O over 45 min to afford decarboxycitrinone, cercophorin A, and roridin E.

Biological Activity

Cercophorins A-C inhibited the growth of the early successional coprophilous fungi *Sordaria fimicola* (NRRL 6459) and *Ascobolus furfuraceus* (NRRL 6460) at 200μg/disk in centerpoint inoculation disk assays. Decarboxycitrinone caused a 100% reduction in radial growth against both fungi, while 4-acetyl-8-hydroxy-6-methoxy-5-methylisocou-

marin and cercophorins A, B, and C caused 46, 34, 10, and 51% growth reduction against S. *fimicola,* respectively. Roridin E caused a 100% reduction in growth of S. *fimicola* and *A. furfuraceus* and an inhibition zone of 29mm against *Candida albicans* (ATCC 14053) at the same concentration. In standard disk assays, cercophorin A was the most potent of these metabolites against *Bacillus subtilis* (ATCC 6051) and *Staphylococcus aureus* (ATCC 29213), affording zones of inhibition of 26 and 16mm, respectively, at 200µg/disk. Cercophorins A, B, and C showed only limited cytotoxicity in the NCI tumor cell line bioassay panel, displaying average GI_{50} values of 9.4, 26.2, and 20.8µg/mL, respectively.

Spectral Data

UV:

λ_{max}^{MeOH} 252(ϵ=9,400) and 333nm (6,500).

IR:

(KBr) 2987, 2855 1720sh, 1688, and 1619cm^{-1}.

^{1}H NMR:

($CDCl_3$) 6.26(1H, s, H-4); 6.17(1H, s, H-5); 11.73(1H, br s, OH-6); 11.60(1H, s, OH-8); 10.38(1H, s, OH-13); 7.30(1H, d, *J*=2.9Hz, H-15); 7.11(1H, d, *J*=2.9Hz, H-17); 3.98(3H, s, OMe-19); 3.81(3H, s, OMe-20); and 2.21ppm (3H, s, CH_3-21).

^{13}C NMR:

($CDCl_3$) 166.6*, C-1; 156.7, C-3; 104.9, C-4; 101.7, C-5; 162.3, C-6; 112.1, C-7; 161.1, C-8; 101.6, C-9; 141.3, C-10; 165.1*, C-11; 143.0, C-12; 148.8, C-13; 114.8, C-14; 111.1, C-15; 152.8, C-16; 117.1, C-17; 170.4, C-18; 53.3, C-19; 56.3, C-20; and 19.3ppm, C-21.

* Assignments may be reversed.

Mass Spectrum:

FABMS (glycerol): 439([M + Na]$^+$, 75), 417([M + H]$^+$, 28), 399(60), 299(74), 219(68), and 172*m/e* (100); EIMS: 416(M$^+$, 2), 372(29), 340(29), 267(13), and 236*m/e* (10); HRFABMS: 439.0660*m/e* (M + Na)$^+$, calcd for ($C_{20}H_{16}O_{10}$ + Na)$^+$ 416.0743.

HPLC Data

Retention time, 26.7min (MeOH).

Reference

A. C. Whyte, J. B. Gloer, J. A. Scott and D. Malloch; Cercophorins A-C: Novel Antifungal and Cytotoxic Metabolites from the Coprophilous Fungus *Cercophora areolata*; J. Nat. Prod., Vol. 59, pp. 765-769(1996).

Common/Systematic Name
Cercophorin C

Molecular Formula/Molecular Weight
$C_{20}H_{16}O_{10}$; MW = 416.07435

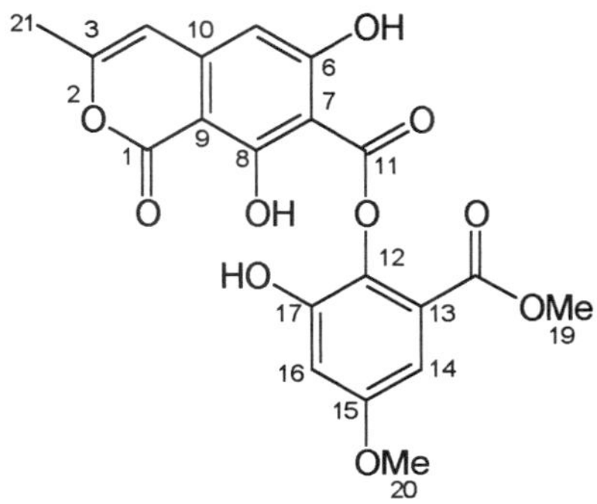

General Characteristics
Yellow solid; mp., 102-105°C.

Fungal Source
Cercophora areolata (JS-166 = UAMH 7495) isolated from porcupine dung.

Isolation/Purification
The filtered broth was extracted with ethyl acetate and the organic phase was dried ($MgSO_4$) and concentrated to yield a dark red oil. The extract was subjected to silica gel column chromatography with a step gradient from 0 to 40% (v/v) MeOH in $CHCl_3$, and 8ml fractions were collected. Similar fractions (as determined by TLC) were pooled and bioassayed. Active fractions were further purified by Sephadex LH_{20} column chromatography eluting with hexane-toluene-MeOH (3:1:1, v/v/v), followed by reversed-phase semipreparative HPLC using a gradient from 20 to 70% MeOH in 0.01M NH_4OAc over 20 min and then 70-100% MeOH in 0.01M NH_4OAc over 2 min. HPLC fractions were concentrated *in vacuo* to afford 4-acetyl-8-hydroxy-6-methoxy-5-ethylisocoumarin, cercophorin B, and cercophorin C. The dried mycelial material was extracted with ethyl acetate, followed by filtration and concentration of the solvent to yield a dark red solid. This extract was processed by silica gel and Sephadex LH_{20} column chromatography as described above and then by preparative HPLC using a gradient from 70 to 100% MeOH in H_2O over 45 min to afford decarboxycitrinone, cercophorin A, and roridin E.

Biological Activity
Cercophorins A-C inhibited the growth of the early successional coprophilous fungi *Sordaria fimicola* (NRRL 6459) and *Ascobolus furfuraceus* (NRRL 6460) at 200μg/disk in centerpoint inoculation disk assays. Decarboxycitrinone caused a 100% reduction in radial growth against both fungi, while 4-acetyl-8-hydroxy-6-methoxy-5-methylisocou-

marin and cercophorins A, B, and C caused 46, 34, 10, and 51% growth reduction against S. *fimicola,* respectively. Roridin E caused a 100% reduction in growth of S. *fimicola* and *A. furfuraceus* and an inhibition zone of 29mm against *Candida albicans* (ATCC 14053) at the same concentration. In standard disk assays, cercophorin A was the most potent of these metabolites against *Bacillus subtilis* (ATCC 6051) and *Staphylococcus aureus* (ATCC 29213), affording zones of inhibition of 26 and 16mm, respectively, at 200µg/disk. Cercophorins A, B, and C showed only limited cytotoxicity in the NCI tumor cell line bioassay panel, displaying average GI_{50} values of 9.4, 26.2, and 20.8µg/mL, respectively.

Spectral Data

UV:

λ_{max}^{MeOH} 247(ε=9,100) and 327nm (4,200).

IR:

(KBr) 2950, 1726, 1689, 1620, 1354, and 1197cm^{-1}.

^{1}H NMR:

($CDCl_3$) 6.40(1H, s, H-4); 6.17(1H, s, H-5); 11.70(1H, br s, OH-8); 6.98(1H, d, *J*=3.0Hz, H-14); 6.82(1H, d, *J*=3.0Hz, H-16); 3.71(3H, s, OMe-19); 3.84(3H, s, OMe-20); and 2.21ppm (3H, s, CH_3-21).

^{13}C NMR:

($CDCl_3$) 166.5*, C-1; 157.0, C-3; 105.0, C-4; 101.3, C-5; 163.4, C-6; 111.1, C-7; 161.5, C-8; 101.5, C-9; 141.7, C-10; 165.7*, C-11; 135.0, C-12; 126.4, C-13; 107.7, C-14; 158.7, C-15; 108.1, C-16; 152.4, C-17; 165.9, C-18; 52.7, C-19; 56.1, C-20; and 19.3ppm, C-21.

* Assignments may be reversed.

Mass Spectrum:

FABMS (glycerol): 439($[M + Na]^+$, 12), 417($[M + H]^+$, 3), 399(21), 379(12), 355(36), 219(39), and 116*m/e* (100); EIMS: 372($[M^+ - CO_2]$, 100), 340(91), 312(24), 297(14), and 269*m/e* (14); HRFABMS: 439.0661*m/e* $(M + Na)^+$, calcd for $(C_{20}H_{16}O_{10} + Na)^+$ 416.0743.

HPLC Data

Retention time, 24.9min (MeOH).

Reference

A. C. Whyte, J. B. Gloer, J. A. Scott and D. Malloch; Cercophorins A-C: Novel Antifungal and Cytotoxic Metabolites from the Coprophilous Fungus *Cercophora areolata*; J. Nat. Prod., Vol. 59, pp. 765-769(1996).

5

Fiscalins

Fiscalin A
Fiscalin B
Fiscalin C

Common/Systematic Name

Fiscalin A

Molecular Formula/Molecular Weight

$C_{26}H_{27}N_5O_4$; MW = 473.20630

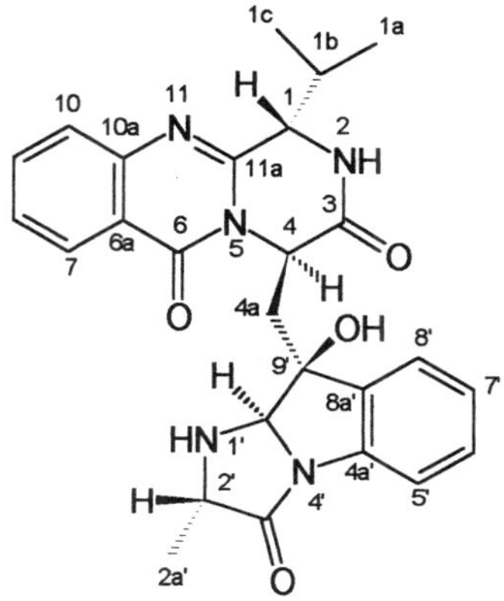

General Characteristics

Fiscalin A was recrystallized from dichloromethane-methanol (1:1, v/v) to provide colorless orthorhombic crystals; mp., 242~243°C; $[\alpha]_D$ -169° (*c*=0.5, in MeOH).

Isolation/Purification

The fermentation was carried out at 26°C with shaking at 220rpm. Fiscalin production and cell growth peaked after 6 days. The majority of fiscalins was associated with the cell mass. Harvested cells were extracted with ethyl acetate to yield a brown residue. After redissolving in a mixture of methanol and dichloromethane (1:1, v/v), the sample was subjected to flash silica gel column chromatography with stepwise elution using chloroform, chloroform-methanol (1:1, v/v), and methanol. Bioactive eluents were collected from the chloroform-methanol fraction, and dried *in vacuo* to yield a white powder. After rinsing with methanol, the white solids were redissolved in a mixture of dichloromethane-methanol (1:9, v/v) and then subjected to semi-preparative HPLC using a YMC reverse phase column (C_{18}) and isocratic elution with 86% methanol and 14% water at 1ml/minute. Eluents were collected to yield fiscalin A, B, and C.

Fungal Source

Neosartorya fischeri isolated from a plant rhizosphere collected near the We Fung Chi Cascade region of Taiwan. Anamorph stage is *Aspergillus fischerianus.*

Biological Activity

Inhibited the binding of radiolabeled substance P ligand to the human neurokinin (NK-1) receptor, with *Ki* value of 57μM.

Spectral Data

UV:
λ_{max}^{MeOH} 226, 278, and 306nm.

CD:
λ_{max} 228(-62.1) and 307nm (-9.5$\Delta\epsilon$).

IR:
(KBr) 3378-3279(NH) and 1689cm^{-1} (amide).

^1H NMR:
($CDCl_3$ + CD_3OD or DMSO-d_6) 4.41(1H, H-1); 8.43(1H, NH); 5.31(1H, H-4); 7.99(1H, H-7); 7.26(1H, H-8); 7.55(1H, H-9); 7.43(1H, H-10); 0.94(3H, H-1a); 2.85(1H, H-1b); 0.68(3H, H-1c); 2.51, 2.68(2h, H-4a); 3.14(1H, NH-1'); 3.47(1H, H-2'); 0.82(3H, H-2a'); 7.17(1H, H-5'); 6.88(1H, H-6'); 7.07(1H, H-7'); 7.14(1H, H-8'); and 4.93ppm (1H, H-9a').

^{13}C NMR:
($CDCl_3$) 60.4, C1; 172.4, C-3; 54.4, C-4; 163.9, C-6; 122.2, C-6a; 128.4, C-7; 129.1, C-8; 136.8, C-9; 129.2, C-10; 149.4, C-10a; 152.2, C-11a; 20.0, C-1a; 31.2, C-1b; 16.5, C-1c; 40.1, C-4a; 62.9, C-2'; 18.0, C-2a'; 177.0, C-3'; 139.1, C-4a'; 117.3, C-3'; 127.5, C-6'; 132.2, C-7'; 126.4, C-8'; 139.2, C-8a'; 76.3, C-9'; and 84.4ppm C-9a'.

Mass Spectrum:
HREIMS: 473.2032*m/e*; calculated, 473.2063.

Reference

S-M. Wong, L. L. Musza, G. C. Kydd, R. Kullnig, A. M. Gillum, and R. Cooper; Fiscalins: New Substance P Inhibitors Produced by The Fungus *Neosartorya fischeri,* Taxonomy, Fermentation, Structures, and Biological Properties; The Journal of Antibiotics, Vol. 46, pp. 545-553(1993).

Common/Systematic Name
Fiscalin B

Molecular Formula/Molecular Weight
$C_{23}H_{22}N_4O_2$; MW = 386.17428

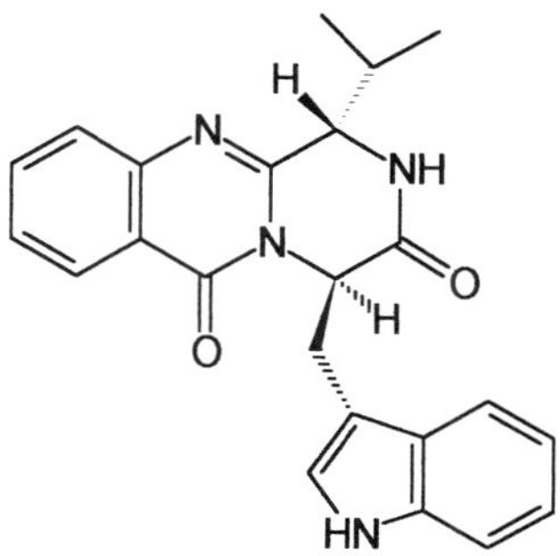

General Characteristics
Fiscalin B was obtained as a white amorphous solid.

Isolation/Purification
See fiscalin A.

Fungal Source
Neosartorya fischeri isolated from a plant rhizosphere collected near the We Fung Chi Cascade region of Taiwan. Anamorph stage is *Aspergillus fischerianus.*

Biological Activity
Inhibited the binding of radiolabeled substance P ligand to the human neurokinin (NK-1) receptor, with *Ki* value of 157μM.

Spectral Data

UV:
UV suggested the presence of quinazolone and indole chromophores.

CD:
λ_{max} 228(-62.1) and 307nm (-9.5Δϵ).

^{1}H NMR:
($CDCl_3$) 2.70(1H, H-1); 5.97(1H, NH); 5.63(1H, H-4); 8.33(1H, H-7); 7.49(1H, H-8); 7.74(1H, H-9); 7.53(1H, H-10); 0.61(3H, H-1a); 2.60(1H, H-1b); 0.62(3H, H-1c); 3.69, 3.59(2h, H-4a); 8.21(1H, H-4'); 7.38(1H, H-5'); 6.88(1H, H-6'); 7.08(1H, H-7'); 7.25(1H, H-8'); and 6.57ppm (1H, H-9a').

^{13}C NMR:

($CDCl_3$) 58.4, C1; 170.2, C-3; 57.1, C-4; 161.6, C-6; 120.7, C-6a; 127.4, C-7; 127.7, C-8; 135.3, C-9; 127.7, C-10; 147.7, C-10a; 151.0, C-11a; 19.0, C-1a; 29.8, C-1b; 14.9, C-1c; 27.6, C-4a; 127.8, C-4a'; 119.2, C-3'; 120.5, C-6'; 123.1, C-7'; 111.6, C-8'; 136.6, C-8a'; 109.7, C-9'; and 124.2ppm C-9a'.

Mass Spectrum:

387*m/e* $(M + H)^+$ and HREIMS of 386.1743*m/e* suggesting a molecular formula of $C_{23}H_{22}N_4O_2$, with two major fragments 257.1158 ($C_{14}H_{15}N_3O_2$) and 130.0649*m/e* (C_9H_8N).

Reference

S-M. Wong, L. L. Musza, G. C. Kydd, R. Kullnig, A. M. Gillum, and R. Cooper; Fiscalins: New Substance P Inhibitors Produced by The Fungus *Neosartorya fischeri*, Taxonomy, Fermentation, Structures, and Biological Properties; The Journal of Antibiotics, Vol. 46, pp. 545-553(1993).

Common/Systematic Name

Fiscalin C

Molecular Formula/Molecular Weight

$C_{27}H_{29}N_5O_4$; MW = 487.22195

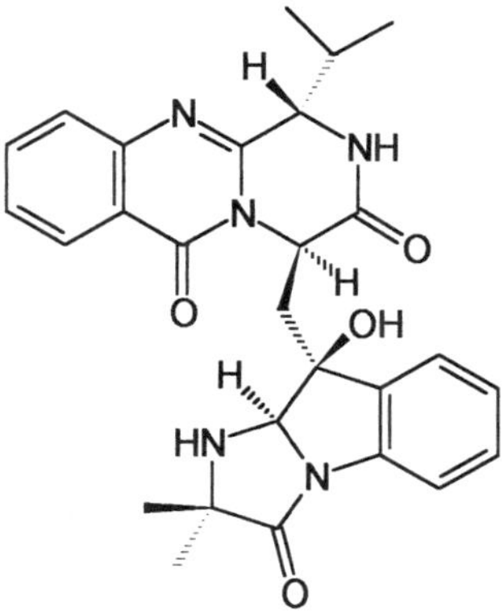

General Characteristics

Fiscalin C was obtained as a white amorphous solid.

Isolation/Purification

See fiscalin A.

Fungal Source

Neosartorya fischeri isolated from a plant rhizosphere collected near the We Fung Chi Cascade region of Taiwan. Anamorph stage is *Aspergillus fischerianus.*

Biological Activity

Inhibited the binding of radiolabeled substance P ligand to the human neurokinin (NK-1) receptor, with *Ki* value of 68μM.

Spectral Data

UV:

UV suggested the presence of quinazolone and indole chromophores.

CD:

λ_{max} 228(-44.6) and 307nm (-5.0Δε).

^{1}H NMR:
(CDCl$_3$) 4.56(1H, H-1); 6.12(1H, NH); 5.82(1H, H-4); 8.30(1H, H-7); 7.51(1H, H-8); 7.79(1H, H-9); 7.68(1H, H-10); 0.95(3H, H-1a); 3.16(1H, H-1b); 1.18(3H, H-1c); 2.47, 2.69(2H, H-4a); 1.39(3H, H-3a'); 1.49(1H, H-4'); 7.51(1H, H-5'); 7.09(1H, H-6'); 7.32(1H, H-7'); 7.32(1H, H-8'); and 5.25ppm (1H, H-9a').

^{13}C NMR:
(CDCl$_3$) 48.6, C-1; 170.8, C-3; 51.8, C-4; 161.3, C-6; 120.9, C-6a; 127.7, C-7; 128.0, C-8; 135.5, C-9; 128.1, C-10; 147.5, C-10a; 149.8, C-11a; 19.8, C-1a; 29.0, C-1b; 15.6, C-1c; 40.0, C-4a; 65.4, C-2'; 25.4, C-2a'; 26.4, C-2b'; 175.9, C-3'; 138.0, C-4a'; 116.3, C-5'; 125.8, C-6'; 130.8, C-7'; 124.7, C-8'; 138.5, C-8a'; 74.5, C-9'; and 78.9ppm C-9a'.

Mass Spectrum:
HREIMS: 488.2318*m/e* $(M + H)^+$.

Reference

S-M. Wong, L. L. Musza, G. C. Kydd, R. Kullnig, A. M. Gillum, and R. Cooper; Fiscalins: New Substance P Inhibitors Produced by The Fungus *Neosartorya fischeri*, Taxonomy, Fermentation, Structures, and Biological Properties; The Journal of Antibiotics, Vol. 46, pp. 545-553(1993).

6

Palmarumycins

Palmarumycin CP_1
Palmarumycin CP_2
Palmarumycin CP_3
Palmarumycin CP_4
Palmarumycin C_1
Palmarumycin C_2
Palmarumycin C_3
Palmarumycin C_4
Palmarumycin C_5
Palmarumycin C_6
Palmarumycin C_7
Palmarumycin C_8
Palmarumycin C_{10}
Palmarumycin C_{11}
Palmarumycin C_{12}
Palmarumycin C_{13}
Palmarumycin C_{14}
Palmarumycin C_{15}
Palmarumycin C_{16}

Common/Systematic Name

Palmarumycin CP_1
5-Hydroxyspiro[naphthalene-1(4*H*),2'-naphtho[1,8-*de*][1,3]dioxin]-4-one

Molecular Formula/Molecular Weight

$C_{20}H_{12}O_4$; MW = 316.07356

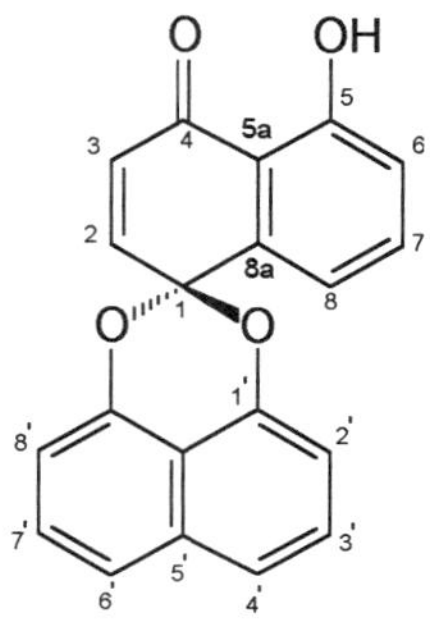

General Characteristics

Light yellow crystals from methylene chloride-petroleum ether; mp., 170°C (dec.); optically inactive.

Isolation/Purification

The palmarumycins were extracted with chloroform and CP_1 and CP_3 were isolated in pure form using preparative thin-layer chromatography [silica gel on aluminum foil (Merck)].

Fungal Source

Coniothyrium palmarum (internal strain number 2014), an endophytic fungus isolated from *Lamium purpureum*.

Biological Activity

Palmarumycin CP_1 showed no biological activity against the test fungus *Cladosporium cucumerinum*.

Spectral Data

UV:

$\lambda_{max}^{Methylene\ chloride}$ 232(log ϵ = 4,633), 288(3,961), 296(3,966), 330(3,785), and 362nm (3,731).

IR:

(KBr) 3456(OH), 3057, 1662(C=O), 1611, 1455, 1410, 1379, 1340, 1268(Ar-O), 1236, 1112, 1075, 942, and 744cm^{-1}.

^{1}H NMR:

(CDCl$_3$) 12.16(1OH, s); 7.66[1H, pseudo-t (dd), $J_{6,7}$=8.2Hz, $J_{7,8}$=7.9Hz, H-7]; 7.58(2H, d, $J_{3',4',(5',6')}$=8.3Hz, 4'-H and 5'H); 7.47[2H, pseudo-t (dd), $J_{3',4',(5',6')}$= 8.4Hz, $J_{2',3'(6',7')}$=7.5Hz, H-3' and H-6']; 7.46(1H, dd, $J_{6,8}$=1Hz, H-8); 7.14(1H, dd, $J_{6,7}$=8.4Hz, $J_{6,8}$=1Hz, H-6); 7.02(1H, d, $J_{2,3}$=10.4Hz, H-2); 6.98(2H, d, $J_{2',3'(6',7')}$=7.5Hz, H2' and H-7'); and 6.36ppm (1H, d, $J_{2,3}$=10.6Hz, H-3).

^{13}C NMR:

(CDCl$_3$) 188.8(C-4, s); 161.9(C-5, s); 147.2(C-1', C-8', s); 139.7(C-2, d); 138.8(C-8a, s); 136.6(C-7, d); 134.1(C-4a', s); 129.7(C-3, d); 127.6(C-3', C-6', d); 121.4(C-4', C-5', d); 119.7(C-8, d); 119.4(C-6, d); 113.9(C-4a, s); 113.0(C-8a', s); 109.9(C-2', C-7', d); and 93.0ppm (C-1, s).

Mass Data:

316(M$^+$, 100%), 288(24, M$^+$ - CO), 287(31, M$^+$ - CO), 209(27), 169(40), and 167*m/e* (32); HREIMS: obsd 316.0736*m/e*; calcd for $C_{20}H_{12}O_4$, 316.0736; anal C =75.5, H=3.68; calcd C=75.94, H=3.82.

Reference

K. Krohn, A. Michel, U. Florke, H.-J. Aust, S. Draeger, and B. Schulz; Palmarumycins CP$_1$ - CP$_4$ from *Coniothyrium palmarum*: Isolation, Structure Elucidation, and Biological Activity; Liebigs Ann. Chem., pp. 1093-1097(1994).

Common/Systematic Name

Palmarumycin CP_2

5-Hydroxy-2,3-dihydrospiro[naphthalene-1(4*H*),2'-naphtho[1,8-*de*][1,3]dioxin]-4-one

Molecular Formula/Molecular Weight

$C_{20}H_{14}O_4$; MW = 318.08921

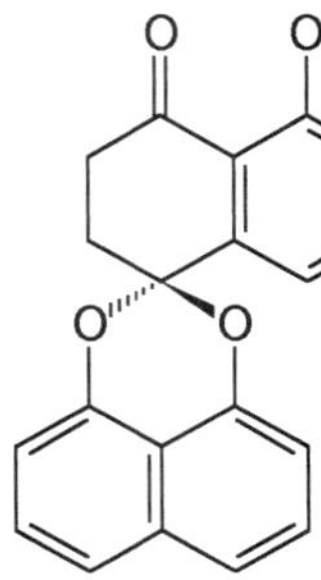

General Characteristics

Crystals; mp., 170°C (dec.); optically inactive.

Isolation/Purification

The palmarumycins were extracted with ethyl acetate and CP_2 was isolated in pure form using repeated column chromatography on silica gel using toluene as eluant.

Fungal Source

Coniothyrium palmarum (internal strain number 2014), an endophytic fungus isolated from *Lamium purpureum*.

Biological Activity

Palmarumycin CP_1 showed no biological activity against the test fungus *Cladosporium cucumerinum*. However, it showed weak activity against *Ustilago violacea* and *Eurotium repens*.

Spectral Data

UV:

$\lambda_{max}^{Methylene\ chloride}$ 285(log ϵ = 3.81), 297(4.12), 300(4.11), 315(3.98), and 329nm (3.99).

IR:

(KBr) 3438(OH), 3056, 1640(C=O), 1609, 1586, 1412, 1381, 1348, 1331, 1237, 1117, 1107, 1074, 920, 885, 819, 804, 795, 758, and 743cm^{-1}.

^{1}H NMR:

(CDCl$_3$) 12.43(1OH, s, H-7); 7.62[1H, pseudo-t (dd), $J_{6,7}$= 8.2Hz, $J=_{7,8}$ 7.9Hz, H-7]; 7.54(2H, dd, $J_{3',4',(5',6')}$= 8.3Hz, $J_{2',4'(5',7')}$= 0.6Hz, H-4' and H-5'); 7.46[2H, pseudo-t (dd), $J_{2',3'(6',7')}$=7.3Hz, $J_{3',4'(5',6')}$= 8.3Hz, H-3' and H-6']; 7.45 (1H, dd, $J_{7,8}$= 7.6Hz, $J_{6,8}$= 1.0Hz, H-8); 7.10 (1H, dd, $J_{6,7}$= 8.3Hz, $J_{6,8}$=1.0Hz, H-6); 6.97(2H, dd, $J_{2',3'(6',7')}$=7.3Hz, $J_{2',4'(5',7')}$= 0.6Hz, H-2' and H-7'); 2.85(2H, t, $J_{2,3}$= 6.5Hz, H-3); and 2.49ppm (2H, t, $J_{2,3}$=6.5Hz, H-2).

^{13}C NMR:

(CDCl$_3$) 203.3(C-4, s); 162.5(C-5, s); 147.5(C-1', C-8', s); 140.9(C-8a, s); 137.2(C-7, d); 134.3(C-4a', s); 127.6(C-3', C-6', d); 120.9(C-4', C-5', d); 119.6(C-8, d); 116.7(C-6, d); 115.5(C-4a, s); 109.5(C-2', d); 113.4(C-8a', s); 98.4(C-1, s); 34.1(C-3, t) and 29.5ppm (C-2, t).

Mass Data:

EIMS: 318(M$^+$, 100%), 301(M$^+$ - OH, 44), 159(36), and 132*m/e* (26); HREIMS: obsd 318.089*m/e*; calcd for $C_{20}H_{14}O_4$, 318.0892; anal C= 75.21, H= 4.23; calcd C=75.46, H=4.43.

Reference

K. Krohn, A. Michel, U. Florke, H.-J. Aust, S. Draeger, and B. Schulz; Palmarumycins CP$_1$ - CP$_4$ from *Coniothyrium palmarum*: Isolation, Structure Elucidation, and Biological Activity; Liebigs Ann. Chem., pp. 1093-1097(1994).

Common/Systematic Name

Palmarumycin CP_3

2*S**,4a*S**,8*S**,8a*S**-2,3,8,8a-Tetrahydrospiro[2,8-epoxynaphthalene-1(4*H*),2'-naphtho[1,8-*de*][1,3]dioxin]-4,5(4a*H*)-dione

Molecular Formula/Molecular Weight

$C_{20}H_{14}O_5$; MW = 334.08412

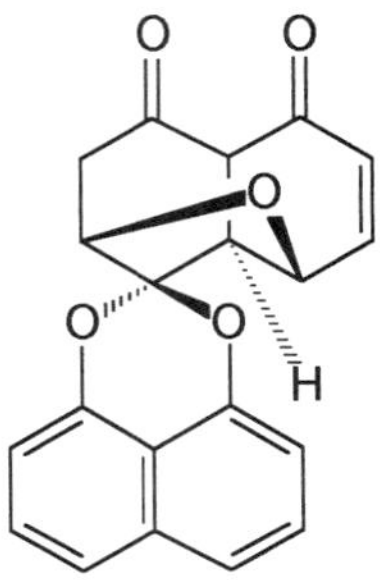

General Characteristics

Colorless prisms from methylene chloride-petroleum ether; mp., 190°C (dec.); $[\alpha]_D^{20}$ = - 108.8° (*c*=1.0, in $CDCl_3$).

Isolation/Purification

The palmarumycins were extracted 3 times with ethyl acetate. The combined extracts were dried ($MgSO_4$), filtered, and concentrated under reduced pressure. The crude extract was subjected to preparative liquid chromatography four successive times using ethyl acetate-methylene chloride (1:1, v/v); diethyl ether-methylene chloride (5:15, v/v); diethyl ether-methylene chloride (1:10, v/v); and diethyl ether-methylene chloride (2:98, v/v).

Fungal Source

Coniothyrium palmarum (internal strain number 2014), an endophytic fungus isolated from *Lamium purpureum*.

Biological Activity

Palmarumycin CP_3 showed biological activity against a variety of bacteria and fungi.

Spectral Data

UV:

$\lambda_{max}^{Chloroform}$ 290(log ϵ=4.06), 299(4.34), 307(4.27), 313(4.29), 3.27(4.22), and 381nm (4.06).

IR:

(KBr) 3079, 2982, 2955, 2901, 1728(C=O), 1688(C=O), 1607, 1584, 1414, 1381, 1275(Ar-O), 1252, 1230, 1169, 1153, 1124, 1055, 928, 833, and 770cm^{-1}.

^{1}H NMR:

($CDCl_3$) 7.57(1H, d, $J_{5',6'}$=8.3Hz, H-5'); 7.56(1H, d, $J_{3',4'}$=8.3Hz, H-4'); 7.47[1H, pseudo-t (dd), $J_{2',3'}$=7.6Hz, $J_{3',4''}$=8.3Hz, H-3']; 7.45[1H, pseudo-t (dd), $J_{5',6'}$=8.3Hz, $J_{6',7''}$=7.8Hz, H-6']; 7.07(1H, dd, $J_{2',3'}$=7.5Hz, $J_{2',4'}$=0.6Hz, H-2'; 6.99(1H, dd, $J_{6,7}$=10.1Hz, $J_{7,8}$=5.1Hz, H-7); 6.95(1H, dd, $J_{6',7}$=10.1Hz, $J_{7,8}$=5.1Hz, H-7); 6.14(1H, *d*, $J_{6,7}$=10.1Hz, H-6); 4.97[1H, pseudo-t (dd), $J_{7,8}$=4.8Hz, $J_{8,8a}$=4.8Hz, H-8]; 4.55(1H, m, H-2); 3.65(1H, d $J_{4a,8a}$=5.4Hz, H-4a); 3.18[1H, pseudo-t (dd), $J_{4a,8a}$=4.2Hz, $J_{8,8a}$=4.9Hz, $J_{2,8a}$=1.4Hz, H-8a]; 3.04[1H, d, (AB)dd, $J_{3ax,3eq}$=18.7Hz, $J_{2,3eq}$=2.4Hz, $J_{3eq,4a}$=0.7Hz, H-3eq]; and 2.84ppm [1H, d (AB)dd, $J_{3ax,3eq}$=18.7Hz, $J_{2,3ax}$=2.9Hz, $J_{3ax,4a}$=1.1Hz, H-3ax]

^{13}C NMR:

($CDCl_3$) C-4, 200(s); C-5, 189.9(s); C-8', 146.7(s); C-1', 146.5(s); C-7, 143.1(d); C-4a', 134.5(s); C-6, 1131.4(d); C-3', 127.7(d); C-6', 127.5(d); C-5', 122.0(d); C-4', 121.5(d); C-8a', 113.9(s); C-2', 110.1(d); C-7', 109.5(d); C-1, 105.6(s); C-2, 76.3(d); C-8, 70.1(d); C-4a, 58.1(d); C-3, 45.6(t); and C-8a, 42.4ppm (d).

Mass Data:

334(M^+, 100%), 305(8), 263(31), 235(30), 218(18), 212(15), 199(15), 171(14), 115(39), 114(24), 91(18), and 65*m/e* (24); anal, C=72.05, H=4.31; calcd C=71.85, H=4.22.

Reference

K. Krohn, A. Michel, U. Flörke, H.-J. Aust, S. Draeger, and B. Schulz; Palmarumycins C_1-C_{16} from *Coniothyrium* sp.: Isolation, Structure Elucidation, and Biological Activity; Liebigs Ann. Chem., pp. 1099-1108(1994).

Common/Systematic Name

Palmarumycin CP_4

(8*R**,8a*S**)-4,8-Dihydroxy-6,7,8,8a-tetrahydrospiro[naphthalene-1(5*H*),2'-naphtho[1,8-*de*][1,3]dioxin]-5-one

Molecular Formula/Molecular Weight

$C_{20}H_{16}O_5$; MW = 336.09977

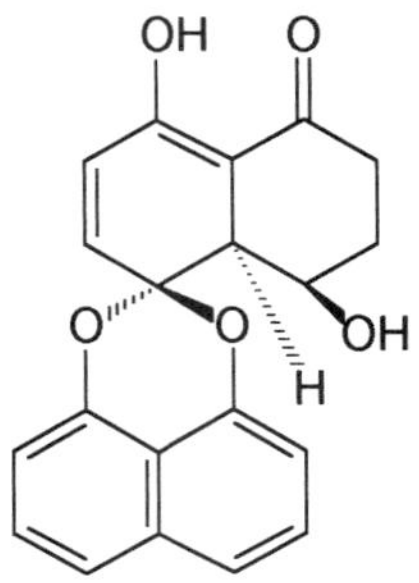

General Characteristics

Colorless prisms from methylene chloride; mp., 186°C (dec.); mp., 193°C (diethyl ether); $[\alpha]_D^{20} = +495°$ (c=0.2, in CH_2Cl_2) .

Isolation/Purification

The palmarumycins were extracted 3 times with ethyl acetate. The combined extracts were dried ($MgSO_4$), filtered, and concentrated under reduced pressure. The crude extract was subjected to preparative liquid chromatography four successive times using ethyl acetate-methylene chloride (1:1, v/v); diethyl ether-methylene chloride (5:15, v/v); diethyl ether-methylene chloride (1:1, v/v); and diethyl ether-methylene chloride (2:98, v/v). The polar fractions of the chromatography were further separated by PLC (Chromatotron, 2mm, CH_2Cl_2-CH_3OH; 99:1, v/v) to afford pure palmarumycin CP_4.

Fungal Source

Coniothyrium palmarum (internal strain number 2014), an endophytic fungus isolated from *Lamium purpureum*.

Biological Activity

Palmarumycin CP_3 showed biological activity against a variety of bacteria and fungi.

Spectral Data

UV:

$\lambda_{max}^{Chloroform}$ 283(log ϵ=3.62), 295(4.03), 301(4.07), 304(4.07), 314(4.10), and 328nm (4.08).

IR:

(KBr) 3551(OH), 3063, 2932, 2905, 1638, 1611, 1580, 1412, 1375, 1323, 1252, 1252, 1213, 1103, 1082, 1065, 1036, 959, 930, 919, 826, and 762cm^{-1}.

^{1}H NMR:

($CDCl_3$) 15.5(1H, s, OH); 7.55(1H, dd, $J_{5',6'}$=8.2Hz, $J_{5',7'}$=0.6Hz, H-5'); 7.54(1H, d, $J_{3',4'}$=8.2Hz, H-4'); 7.48(1H, t(dd), $J_{2',3'}$=7.4Hz, $J_{3',4'}$=8.3Hz, H-3'); 7.4[1H, pseudo-t (dd), $J_{5',6''}$=8.2Hz, $J_{6',7'}$=7.7Hz, H-6']; 7.04(1H, dd, $J_{2',3'}$=8.2Hz, $J_{2',4''}$=0.6Hz, H-2']; 6.91(1H, d, $J_{6',7'}$=7.5Hz, H-7'); 6.44(1H, d, $J_{2,3}$=10.3Hz, H-2); 6.13(1H, d, $J_{2,3}$=10.3Hz, H-3); 4.86[1H, pseudo-t (dd), $J_{7ax,8}$=2.3Hz, $J_{8,OH}$=2.3Hz, H- 8]; 3.77(2H, d, $J_{8AX,8a}$=2.3Hz, H-8a); 3.4(1H, s, OH); 2.98(1H, ddd, $J_{6ax,\,6eq}$=19.1Hz, $J_{6AX,7AX}$=12.4Hz, $J_{6AX,6eq}$=6.8Hz, H-6ax); 2.41(1H, dd, $J_{6ax,\,6eq}$=19.1Hz, $J_{6eq,7ax}$=5.5Hz, H-6eq); 2.25(1H, m, H-7eq); and 1.82ppm (1H, m, H-7ax).

^{13}C NMR:

($CDCl_3$) C-4, 181.3(s); C-5, 188.4(s); C-8', 146.5(s); C-1', 145.9(s); C-2, 137.3(d); C-4a', 134.2(s); C-3, 130.6(d); C-3', 127.7(d); C-6', 127.4(d); C-5', 121.3(d); C-4', 121.7(d); C-8a', 113.6(s); C-2', 110.1(d); C-7', 110.1(d); C-1, 99.3(s); C-8, 63.4(d); C-8a, 46.0(d); C-6, 27.6(d); and C-7, 27.1ppm (t).

Mass Data:

336(M^+, 100%), 318(94, M+ - H_2O), 289(15, 318 - CHO), 279(76, 318 - C_3H_3), 160(24), 159(76, 1,8-dihydroxynaphthalene-H), 144(19), 131(50), and 115*m/e*; HREIMS: $C_{20}H_{16}O_5$, obsd 336.0997*m/e*; calcd, 336.0998; anal, C, 71.26, H, 4.61; calcd, C, 71.42, H, 4.79.

Reference

K. Krohn, A. Michel, U. Flörke, H.-J. Aust, S. Draeger, and B. Schulz; Palmarumycins C_1-C_{16} from *Coniothyrium* sp.: Isolation, Structure Elucidation, and Biological Activity; Liebigs Ann. Chem., pp. 1099-1108(1994).

Common/Systematic Name

Palmarumycin C_1

3-Chloro-5-hydroxyspiro[naphthalene-1(4*H*),2'-naphtho[1,8-de][1,3]dioxin]-4-one

Molecular Formula/Molecular Weight

$C_{20}H_{11}ClO_4$; MW = 350.03459

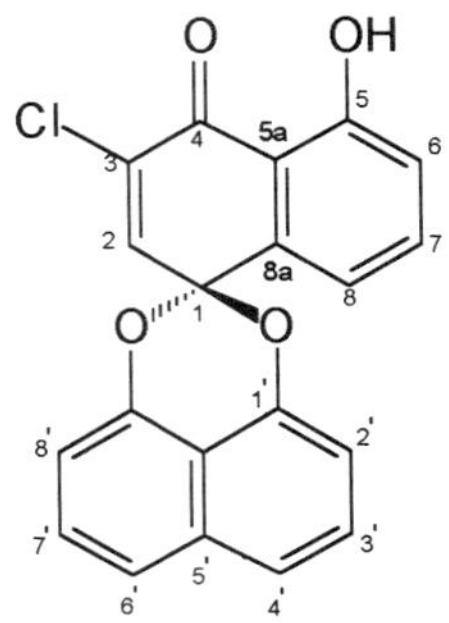

General Characteristics

Slightly yellow needles; mp., 280°C (dec.).

Isolation/Purification

Liquid fungal cultures were shaken for 14-22 days in 2L Fernbach flasks at 25°C and 125 rpm. The 50L of culture material was filtered and extracted three times with ethyl acetate. The combined extracts were dried (Na_2SO_4), filtered, and concentrated at reduced pressure to afford 331g of crude extract. The residue was treated with methanol and filtered. The precipitate was extracted with ethyl acetate to afford 2.0g of dissoluble material that was investigated later (palmarumycins C_4 and C_9). The filtrate from the methanol treatment was further separated by column chromatography using petroleum ether-methylene chloride (1:1, v/v) as eluant. The first fraction was further separated by thin-layer chromatography to afford palmarumycin C_1 and palmarumycin C_2.

Fungal Source

An unidentified *Coniothyrium* sp. (internal strain number 812) isolated from soil from a forest on West Borneo.

Spectral Data

UV:

$\lambda_{max}^{Chloroform}$ 285(log ϵ=3.52), 296(3.96), 301(4.05), 314(3.81), and 329nm (3.71).

IR:

(KBr) 3438(OH), 3202, 3067, 1734, 1718, 1580, 1704, 1653(C=O), 1628, 1611, 1458, 1412, 1381, 1271(Ar-O), 1231, 1167, 1070, 939, 903, 845, 826, 802, and 756cm^{-1}.

^{1}H NMR:

(CDCl$_3$) 11.84(1H, s, OH); 7.67[1H, pseudo-t (dd), $J_{6,7}$=8.4Hz, $J_{7,8}$=7.9Hz, H- 7]; 7.59(2H, d, $J_{3',4'(5',6')}$=8.3Hz, H-4', H-5'); 7.47[2H, pseudo-t (dd), $J_{2',3'(6',7')}$=7.6Hz, $J_{3',4'(5',6')}$=8.3Hz, H-3', H-6']; 7.45(1H, dd, $J_{7,8}$=7.9Hz, $J_{6,8}$=1.0Hz, H-8); 7.16(1H, (dd), $J_{6,7}$=8.4Hz, $J_{6,8}$=1.0Hz, H-6); 7.16(2H, s, H-2); and 6.98ppm (2H, d, $J_{2',3'(6',7')}$=7.6Hz, H-2', H-7').

^{13}C NMR:

(CDCl$_3$) C-4, 181.7(s); C-5, 161.9(s); C-8', 146.5(s); C-1', 146.5(s); C-8a, 137.8(s); C-7, 137.1(d); C-2, 135.5(d); C-4a', 113.0(s); C-3, 133.2(d); C-3', 127.5(d); C- 6', 127.5(d); C-4a, 113.0(s); C-8a', 112.4(s); C-2', 109.9(d); C-7', 109.9(d); and C- 1, 93.3ppm (s).

Mass Spectrum:

LREIMS: 352(M$^+$, 35%), 350(100), 315(32, M+ - Cl), 287(20), 259(13), 116(29), 96(42), 71(29), and 56*m/e* (53); HREIMS: $C_{20}H_{11}ClO_4$, obsd 350.0345*m/e*, calcd 350.0346.

Reference

K. Krohn, A.Michel, U. Flörke, H.-J. Aust, S. Draeger, and B. Schulz; Palmarumycins C_1-C_{16} from *Coniothyrium* sp.: Isolation, Structure Elucidation, and Biological Activity; Liebigs Ann. Chem., pp. 1099-1108(1994).

Common/Systematic Name

Palmarumycin C_2
(2*S**,3*R**)-5-Hydroxyspiro[2,3-epoxynaphthalene-1(2*H*),2'-naphtho[1,8-*de*][1,3]dioxin]-4(3*H*)-one

Molecular Formula/Molecular Weight

$C_{20}H_{12}O_5$; MW = 332.0647

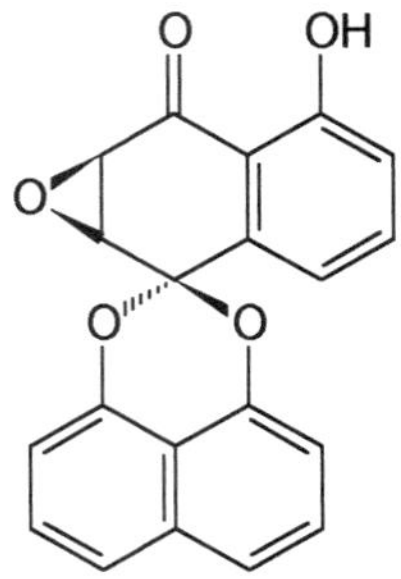

General Characteristics

Crystallized in long yellow needles; mp., 228°C (dec.); $[\alpha]_D^{20}$ = - 341°. Positive reaction with 2,4-dinitrophenylhydrazine and bromocresol green.

Isolation/Purification

Liquid fungal cultures were shaken for 14-22 days in 2L Fernbach flasks at 25°C and 125 rpm. The 50L of culture material was filtered and extracted three times with ethyl acetate. The combined extracts were dried (Na_2SO_4), filtered, and concentrated at reduced pressure to afford 331g of crude extract. The residue was treated with methanol and filtered. The precipitate was extracted with ethyl acetate to afford 2.0g of dissoluble material that was investigated later (palmarumycins C_4 and C_9). The filtrate from the methanol treatment was further separated by column chromatography using petroleum ether-methylene chloride (1:1, v/v) as eluant. The first fraction was further separated by thin-layer chromatography to afford palmarumycin C_1 and palmarumycin C_2.

Fungal Source

An unidentified *Coniothyrium* sp. (internal strain number 812) isolated from soil from a forest on West Borneo.

Spectral Data

UV:

$\lambda_{max}^{Chloroform}$ 295(log ϵ=4.11), 300(4.13), 314(4.08), and 328nm (4.10).

IR:

(KBr) 3432(OH), 3052, 1651(C=O), 1611, 1355, 1410, 1381, 1333, 1269(Ar-O), 1240, 1179, 1115, 1105, 1065, 1016, 970, 918, 874, 818, 506, 758, 752, 739, and 506cm^{-1}.

^{1}H NMR:

($CDCl_3$) 11.26(1H, s, OH); 7.64[1H, pseudo-t (dd), $J_{6,7}$=8.2Hz, $J_{7,8}$=7.9Hz, H- 7]; 7.59(1H, dd, $J_{3',4}$=8.3Hz, $J_{2',4}$=0.7Hz, H-4'); 7.56(1H, d, $J_{5',6}$=8.3Hz, H-5'); 7.52[1H, pseudo-t (dd), $J_{2',3}$=7.5Hz, $J_{3',4}$=8.3Hz, H-3']; 7.45[1H, pseudo-t (dd), $J_{5',6}$=8.3Hz, $J_{6',7}$=7.4Hz, H-6']; 7.45(1H, dd, $J_{7,8}$=7.9Hz, $J_{6,8}$=1.0Hz, H-8); 7.16(1H, (dd), $J_{6,7}$=8.4Hz, $J_{6,8}$=1.0Hz, H-6); 7.44(1H, dd, $J_{7',8}$=7.9Hz, $J_{6',8}$=1.0Hz, H- 8); 7.18(1H, dd, $J_{2',3}$=7.4Hz, $J_{2',4}$=0.7Hz,H-2'); 7.13(1H, dd, $J_{6,7}$=8.4Hz, $J_{6,8}$=1.0Hz, H-6); 6.92(1H, dd, $J_{6',7}$=7.4Hz, $J_{5',7}$=0.6Hz, H-7'); 4.08(1H, d, $J_{2,3}$=4.0Hz, H-3); and 3.68ppm (2H, d, $J_{2,3}$=4.0Hz, H-2).

^{13}C NMR:

($CDCl_3$) C-4, 196.5(s); C-5, 161.9(s); C-8', 146.9(s); C-1', 146.7(s); C-8a, 136.9(s); C-7, 137.7(d); C-2, C-3, 53.2(d); C-4a', 134.2(s); C-3', 127.8(d); C-6', 127.6(d); C-4a, 112.2(s); C-8a', 112.8(s); C-2', 109.3(d); C-7', 109.3(d); C-1, 96.0(s); C-4', 121.4(d); C-5', 121.3(d); C-6, 120.1(d); and C-8, 119.1ppm (d).

Mass Data:

LREIMS: 332(M$^+$, 100%), 287(20), 246(19), 232(50), 204(30), 176(20), 173(33), 159(22), 154(20), 145(20), 130(20), and 43*m/e* (55); HREIMS: $C_{20}H_{12}O_5$, obsd 332.0660*m/e*; calcd 332.0685; calcd, C=72.29, H=3.64; found C=72.16, H=3.59.

Reference

K. Krohn, A. Michel, U. Flörke, H.-J. Aust, S. Draeger, and B. Schulz; Palmarumycins C_1-C_{16} from *Coniothyrium* sp.: Isolation, Structure Elucidation, and Biological Activity; Liebigs Ann. Chem., pp. 1099-1108(1994).

Common/Systematic Name

Palmarumycin C_3

(2*S**,3*R**)-5,8-Dihydroxyspiro[2,3-epoxynaphthalene-1(2*H*),2'-naphtho[1,8-*de*][1,3]dioxin]-4(3*H*)-one

Molecular Formula/Molecular Weight

$C_{20}H_{12}O_6$; MW = 348.06339

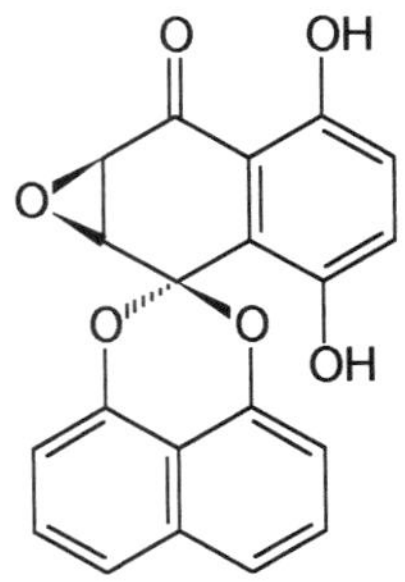

General Characteristics

Crystallized as greenish needles; mp., 220°C; $[\alpha]_D^{20}$ = -300°.

Isolation/Purification

Liquid fungal cultures were shaken for 14-22 days in 2L Fernbach flasks at 25°C and 125 rpm. The 50L of culture material was filtered and extracted three times with ethyl acetate. The combined extracts were dried (Na_2SO_4), filtered, and concentrated at reduced pressure to afford 331g of crude extract. The residue was treated with methanol and filtered. The precipitate was extracted with ethyl acetate to afford 2.0g of dissoluble material that was investigated later (palmarumycins C_4 and C_9). The filtrate from the methanol treatment was further separated by column chromatography using petroleum ether-methylene chloride (1:l, v/v) as eluant. The first fraction was further separated by thin-layer chromatography to afford palmarumycin C_1 and palmarumycin C_2. Column chromatography was continued with a gradient of methylene chloride-methanol (0-10%). The second fraction was further purified by column chromatography with petroleum ether-methylene chloride (1:1, v/v) as eluant to afford additional palmarumycin C_2 and palmarumycin C_3.

Fungal Source

An unidentified *Coniothyrium* sp. (internal strain number 812) isolated from soil from a forest on West Borneo.

Spectral Data

UV:

$\lambda_{max}^{Chloroform}$ 296(log ε=4.14), 299(4.14), 312(4.01), 327(3.91), and 380nm (3.91).

IR:

(KBr) 3499(OH), 3060, 1651(C=O), 1613, 1595, 1476, 1410, 1375, 1335, 1264(Ar-O), 1237, 1223, 1175, 1098, 1067, 1026, 954, 893, 876, 818, 797, 764, and 754cm^{-1}

^{1}H NMR:

($CDCl_3$) 11.48(1H, s, OH); 7.67(1H, d, $J_{3',4'}$=8.4Hz, H-4'); 7.61(1H, d, $J_{5',6'}$=8.2Hz, H-5'); 7.54[1H, pseudo-t (dd), $J_{2',3'}$=7.7Hz, $J_{3',4'}$=8.3Hz, H-3']; 7.49[1H, pseudo-t (dd), $J_{5',6'}$=8.2Hz, $J_{6',7'}$=7.7Hz, H-6']; 7.35(1H, s, OH); 7.29(1H, d, $J_{6,7}$=9.2Hz, H-7); 7.25(1H, d, $J_{2',3'}$=7.5Hz, H-2'); 7.11(1H, d, $J_{6,7}$=9.3Hz, H-6); 7.03(1H, d, $J_{6',7'}$=7.6Hz, H-7'); 4.03(1H, d, $J_{2,3}$=4.0Hz, H-3); and 3.63ppm (1H, d, $J_{2,3}$=4.0Hz, H-2).

^{13}C NMR:

($CDCl_3$) C-4, 195.5(s); C-5, 157.0(s); C-8, 149.1(s); C-8', 146.3(s); C-1', 144.9(s); C-4a', 134.0(s); C-7, 129.6(d); C-6', 127.8(d); C-3', 127.5(d); C-4', 122.7(d); C-6, 122.3,(d); C-5', 121.6(d); C-8a, 115.9(s); C-8a', 115.9(s); C-4a, 111.0(s); C-2', 111.0(d); C-7', 110.2(d); C-1, 98.8(s); C-2, 53.0 (d); and C-3, 52.5ppm (d).

Mass Data:

LREIMS: 348(M^{+}, 100%), 303(11), 189(9), 171(9), 125(11), 111(17), 97(22), 85(20), 83(22), 71(27), and 57m/e (35); calcd, C=68.97, H=3.47; found C=68.75, H=3.43.

Reference

K. Krohn, A. Michel, U. Flörke, H.-J. Aust, S. Draeger, and B. Schulz; Palmarumycins C_1-C_{16} from *Coniothyrium* sp.: Isolation, Structure Elucidation, and Biological Activity; Liebigs Ann. Chem., pp. 1099-1108(1994).

Common/Systematic Name

Palmarumycin C_4

(4a*RS*,8a*RS*)3-Chlorospiro[4a,8a-epoxynaphthalene-1(4*H*),2'-naphtho[1,8-*de*][1,3]dioxin]-4,5,8-trione

Molecular Formula/Molecular Weight

$C_{20}H_9ClO_6$; MW = 380.00877

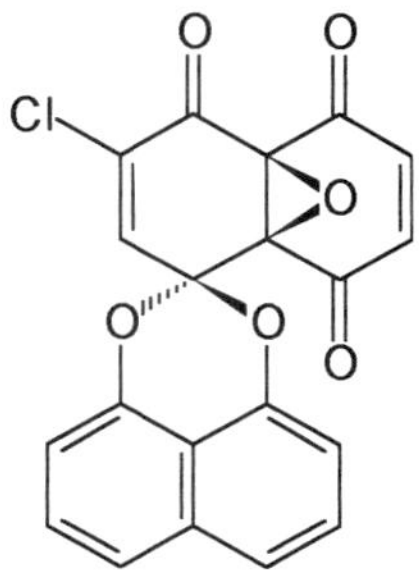

General Characteristics

An orange amorphous material; $[\alpha]_D^{20}$ -285° (*c*=1.0, in CH_2Cl_2).

Isolation/Purification

Liquid fungal cultures were shaken for 14-22 days in 2L Fernbach flasks at 25°C and 125 rpm. The 50L of culture material was filtered and extracted three times with ethyl acetate. The combined extracts were dried (Na_2SO_4), filtered, and concentrated at reduced pressure to afford 331 g of crude extract. The residue was treated with methanol and filtered. The precipitate was extracted with ethyl acetate to afford 2.0g of dissoluble material that was investigated later (palmarumycins C_4 and C_9). The filtrate from the methanol treatment was further separated by column chromatography using petroleum ether-methylene chloride (1:l, v/v) as eluant. The first fraction was further separated by thin-layer chromatography to afford palmarumycin C_1 and palmarumycin C_2.

Fungal Source

An unidentified *Coniothyrium* sp. (internal strain number 812) isolated from soil from a forest on West Borneo.

Spectral Data

UV:

$\lambda_{max}^{Chloroform}$ 285(log ϵ=3.52), 296(3.96), 301(4.05), 314(3.81), and 329nm (3.71).

IR:

(KBr) 3438(OH), 3202, 3067, 1734, 1718, 1580, 1704, 1653(C=O), 1628, 1611, 1458, 1412, 1381, 1271(Ar-O), 1231, 1167, 1070, 939, 903, 845, 826, 802, and $756 cm^{-1}$.

^{1}H NMR:

($CDCl_3$) 7.62(1H, d, $J_{3',4'}$=8.3Hz, H-4'); 7.60(1H, d, $J_{5',6'}$=8.2Hz, H-5'); 7.52[1H, pseudo-t (dd), $J_{2',3'}$=7.6Hz, $J_{3',4'}$=8.2Hz, H-3']; 7.45[1H, pseudo-t (dd), $J_{5',6'}$=8.2Hz, $J_{6',7'}$=7.6Hz, H-6']; 7.12(1H, dd, $J_{2',3'}$=7.5Hz, $J_{2',4'}$=0.5Hz, H-2'); 6.91(1H, d, $J_{6',7'}$=7.6Hz, H-7'); 6.75(s, H-2); 6.72(1H, d, $J_{6,7}$=10.8Hz, H-7); and 6.71ppm (1H, d, $J_{6,7}$=10.8Hz, H-6).

^{13}C NMR:

($CDCl_3$) C-4, 178.6(s); C-5, 183.3(s); C-8, 184.4(s); C-8', 184.5(s); C-1', 145.0(s); C-4a', 134.5(s); C-7, C-6, 136.8(d); C-6', 127.8(d); C-3', 128.0(d); C-4', 122.2 (d); C-5', 122.2 (d); C-8a, 55.3(s); C-8a', 112.6(s); C-4a, 62.1(s); C-2', 110.1(d); C-7', 109.8(d); C-1, 95.2(s); C-2, 133.6(d); and C-3, 132.2ppm (s).

Mass Spectrum:

LREIMS: 382(36), 380(M^+, 100), 352(M^+ - CO, 5), 317(4), 289(10), 230(12), 195(42), and 114*m/e* (28); HREIMS: $C_{20}H_9ClO_6$, found 380.0087*m/e*; calcd, 380.0088.

Reference

K. Krohn, A. Michel, U. Flörke, H.-J. Aust, S. Draeger, and B. Schulz; Palmarumycins C_1-C_{16} from *Coniothyrium* sp.: Isolation, Structure Elucidation, and Biological Activity; Liebigs Ann. Chem., pp. 1099-1108(1994).

Common/Systematic Name

Palmarumycin C_5

(4*R**)-3,4-Dihydro-4-methoxyspiro[2,3-epoxynaphthalene-1,(2*H*)2'-naphtho[1,8-*de*][1,3]dioxin]-5,8-dione

Molecular Formula/Molecular Weight

$C_{21}H_{16}O_5$; MW = 348.09977

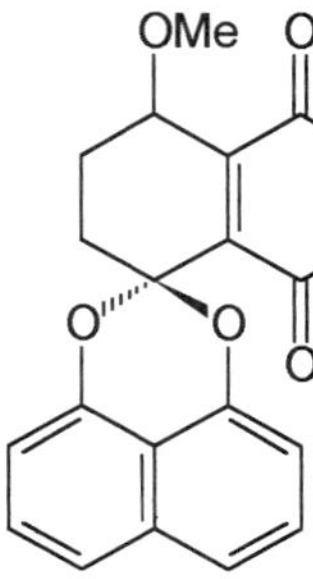

General Characteristics

The compound slowly decomposed on exposure to air.

Isolation/Purification

Liquid fungal cultures were shaken for 14-22 days in 2L Fernbach flasks at 25°C and 125 rpm. The 50L of culture material was filtered and extracted three times with ethyl acetate. The combined extracts were dried (Na_2SO_4), filtered, and concentrated at reduced pressure to afford 331g of crude extract. The residue was treated with methanol and filtered. The precipitate was extracted with ethyl acetate to afford 2.0g of dissoluble material that was investigated later (palmarumycins C_4 and C_9). The filtrate from the methanol treatment was further separated by column chromatography using petroleum ether-methylene chloride (1:l, v/v) as eluant. The first fraction was further separated by thin-layer chromatography to afford palmarumycin C_1 and palmarumycin C_2. Column chromatography was continued with a gradient of methylene chloride-methanol (0-10%). The second fraction was further purified by column chromatography with petroleum ether-methylene chloride (1:1, v/v) as eluant to afford additional palmarumycin C_2 and palmarumycin C_3. The third fraction was subjected to low-pressure column chromatography with methylene chloride as eluant to afford additional palmarumycin C_3 and palmarumycin C_5.

Fungal Source

An unidentified *Coniothyrium* sp. (internal strain number 812) isolated from soil from a forest on West Borneo.

Spectral Data

UV:

$\lambda_{max}^{Chloroform}$ 286(log ε=3.35), 299(4.02), 313(4.20), 317(4.16), and 329nm (4.04).

IR:

(KBr) 3050, 2930, 1665(C=O), 1608, 1583, 1414, 1381, 1354, 1333, 1271(Ar-O), 1237, 1183, 1119, 1084, 1047, 1034, 959, 926, 851, 818, and 750cm^{-1}

^{1}H NMR:

($CDCl_3$) 7.50(1H, dd, $J_{3',4'}$=8.5Hz, $J_{2',4'}$=0.8Hz, H-4'); 7.49(1H, dd, $J_{5',6'}$=8.3Hz, $J_{5',7'}$=0.8Hz, H-5'); 7.42[1H, pseudo-t (dd), $J_{2',3'}$=7.4Hz, $J_{3',4'}$=8.3Hz, H-3']; 7.41[1H, pseudo-t (dd), $J_{5',6'}$=8.4Hz, $J_{6',7'}$=7.4Hz, H-6']; 6.79(1H, d, $J_{6,7}$=10.2Hz, H- 7); 6.89(1H, dd, $J_{2',3'}$=7.3Hz, $J_{2',4'}$=0.9Hz, H-2'); 6.86(1H, d, $J_{6,7}$=10.3Hz, H-6); 6.87(1H, dd, $J_{6',7'}$=7.4Hz, $J_{5',7'}$=0.8Hz, H-7'); 4.44[1H, pseudo-t (dd), $J_{3eq,4}$=3.0Hz, $J_{3ax,4}$=3.0Hz, H-4]; 3.47(3H, s, OCH_3, H-9); 2.22(2H, m, H-2ax, H-2eq); 2.04(1H, dq, $J_{3eq,3ax}$= 14.6Hz, $J_{3eq,4eq}$=3.0Hz, H-3eq]; and 1.87ppm (1H, dddd, $J_{3eq,3ax}$=14.6Hz, $J_{2ax,3ax}$=11.3Hz, $J_{2eq,3ax}$=5.9Hz, $J_{3ax,4}$=3.0Hz, H-3ax).

^{13}C NMR:

($CDCl_3$) C-4, 68.4(d); C-5, C-8, 186.5(s); C-8', 147.6(s); C-1', 146.3(s); C-4a', 134.2(s); C-7, 137.8(d); C-6', 127.2(d); C-3', 127.4(d); C-4', 120.7(d); C-6, 135.3(d); C-5', 120.4(d); C-8a, 142.3(s); C-8a', 112.9(s); C-4a, 138.6(s); C-2', 109.2(d); C-7', 109.18(d); C-1, 98.7(s); C-2, 22.4(t); C-9, 58.3(q); and C-3, 26.6ppm (t).

Mass Spectrum:

LREIMS: 350(10%), 349(14), 348(M^+, 56), 318(18), 317(24), 316(M^+ - CH_3OH, 100), 299(10), 287(19), 271(10), 159(11), 131(14), 115(16), 114(14), 71(15), 57(13), and 43*m/e* (16); HREIMS: $C_{21}H_{16}O_5$, found 348.0997*m/e*, calcd 348.0998.

Reference

K. Krohn, A. Michel, U. Flörke, H.-J. Aust, S. Draeger, and B. Schulz; Palmarumycins C_1-C_{16} from *Coniothyrium* sp.: Isolation, Structure Elucidation, and Biological Activity; Liebigs Ann. Chem., pp. 1099-1108(1994).

Common/Systematic Name

Palmarumycin C_6

4,7-Dihydroxyspiro[1*H*-inden-1, 2'-naphtho[1,8-*de*][1,3]dioxin]-3(2*H*)-one

Molecular Formula/Molecular Weight

$C_{19}H_{12}O_5$; MW = 320.06847

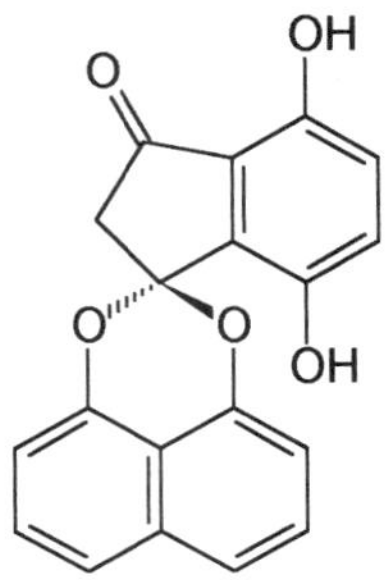

General Characteristics

Obtained as a microcrystalline powder that slowly turned dark upon contact with air; mp., 191-192°C (dec.).

Isolation/Purification

Liquid fungal cultures were shaken for 14-22 days in 2L Fernbach flasks at 25°C and 125 rpm. The 50L of culture material was filtered and extracted three times with ethyl acetate. The combined extracts were dried (Na_2SO_4), filtered, and concentrated at reduced pressure to afford 331g of crude extract. The residue was treated with methanol and filtered. The precipitate was extracted with ethyl acetate to afford 2.0g of soluble material that was investigated later (palmarumycins C_4 and C_9). The filtrate from the methanol treatment was further separated by column chromatography using petroleum ether-methylene chloride (1:1, v/v) as eluant. The fourth fraction from the column chromatography contained the majority of the secondary metabolites. Column chromatography was repeated with this fraction using a gradient of methylene chloride-methanol (0-10%) to afford six new fractions. From the first fraction an additional 20 mg of palmarumycin C_3 was isolated. From the second fraction 22mg of palmarumycin C_6 was crystallized (petroleum ether). From fraction four and five liquid chromatography (Chromatotron, 99.5% methylene chloride-0.5% methanol) an additional 15mg of palmarumycin C_6 and 30mg of the mixture of palmarumycin C_7 and C_8 could be isolated. Repeated liquid chromatography of fraction five (Chromatotron, 99.5% methylene chloride-0.5% methanol) afforded an additional 920mg of a mixture of diastereomeric diepoxides (palmarumycin C_9), 66mg of palmarumycin C_{10}, 30mg of palmarumycin C_{11}, and 198mg of palmarumycin C_{12}. An additional 246mg of palmarumycin C_{12} was isolated by repeated fractional crystallization from fraction six.

Fungal Source

An unidentified *Coniothyrium* sp. (internal strain number 812) isolated from soil from a forest on West Borneo.

Spectral Data

UV:

$\lambda_{max}^{Chloroform}$ 286(log ϵ=3.47), 296(3.76), 300(3.74), 314(3.55), 346(3.52), and 329nm (3.57).

IR:

(KBr) 3468(OH), 3376(OH), 3064, 2926, 1638(C=O), 1609, 1584, 1561, 1509, 1476, 1412, 1377, 1264(Ar-O), 1235, 1181, 1092, 1021, 938, 909, 874, 820, 793, 762, and 681cm^{-1}.

^{1}H NMR:

(DMSO-d_6) 9.83(1H, OH); 9.56(1H, OH); 7.61(2H, d, $J_{3',4'(5',6')}$=8.1Hz, H-4', H- 5'); 7.50[2H, pseudo-t (dd), $J_{2',3'(6',7')}$=7.6Hz, $J_{3',4'(5',6')}$=8.2Hz, H-3', H-6']; 7.14(1H, d, $J_{5,6}$=8.8Hz, H-6); 7.00(2H, d, $J_{2',3'(6',7')}$=7.5Hz, $J_{2',4}$=0.9Hz, H-2', H-7'); 6.96(1H, d, $J_{5,6}$=8.8Hz, H-5); and 2.76ppm (2H, s, H-2).

^{13}C NMR:

(DMSO-d_6) C-4, 148.1(s); C-5, 120.4(d); C-8', C-1', 148.26(s); C-4a', 134.0(s); C- 7, 147.5(s); C-6', C-3', 127.6(d); C-4', C-5', 120.8(d); C-6, 125.7(d); C-3, 196.9(s); C-8a', 113.5(s); C-3a, 123.1(s); C-2', C-7', 109.6(d); C-1, 103.5(s); C-2, 49.1(t); and C-7a, 131.8ppm (s).

Mass Spectrum:

LREIMS: 320(M$^+$, 100%), 303(M+ - OH, 55), 160(10), and 115*m/e* (11); LRCIMS: (NH_3, positive ion) 338(M$^+$ + NH_4, 55%), 321(M$^+$ + H, 100), 320(M$^+$, 22), 236(21), and 161*m/e* (30); HREIMS: $C_{19}H_{12}O_5$, found 320.0684*m/e*, calcd 320.0685.

Reference

K. Krohn, A. Michel, U. Flörke, H.-J. Aust, S. Draeger, and B. Schulz; Palmarumycins C_1- C_{16} from *Coniothyrium* sp.: Isolation, Structure Elucidation, and Biological Activity; Liebigs Ann. Chem., pp. 1099-1108(1994).

Common/Systematic Name

Palmarumycin C_7

(4*aRS*,8a*RS*)-3-Chloro-5-hydroxyspiro[4a,8a-epoxynaphthalene-1(4*H*),2'-naphtho[1,8-*de*][1,3]-dioxin]-4,8(5*H*)-dione

Molecular Formula/Molecular Weight

$C_{20}H_{11}ClO_6$; MW = 382.02442

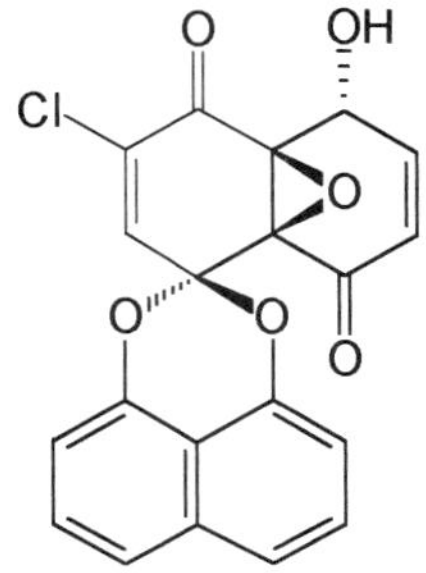

General Characteristics

Obtained as the major component of a mixture with palmarumycin C_8.

Isolation/Purification

Liquid fungal cultures were shaken for 14-22 days in 2L Fernbach flasks at 25°C and 125 rpm. The 50L of culture material was filtered and extracted three times with ethyl acetate. The combined extracts were dried (Na_2SO_4), filtered, and concentrated at reduced pressure to afford 331g of crude extract. The residue was treated with methanol and filtered. The precipitate was extracted with ethyl acetate to afford 2.0g of dissoluble material that was investigated later (palmarumycins C_4 and C_9). The filtrate from the methanol treatment was further separated by column chromatography using petroleum ether/methylene chloride (1:1, v/v) as eluant. The fourth fraction from the column chromatography contained the majority of the secondary metabolites. Column chromatography was repeated with this fraction using a gradient of methylene chloride-methanol (0-10%) to afford six new fractions. From the first fraction an additional 20mg of palmarumycin C_3 was isolated. From the second fraction 22mg of palmarumycin C_6 crystallized (petroleum ether). From fractions four and five liquid chromatography (Chromatotron, 99.5% methylene chloride- 0.5% methanol) an additional 15mg of palmarumycin C_6 and 30mg of the mixture of palmarumycin C_7 and C_8 could be isolated. Repeated liquid chromatography of fraction five (Chromatotron, 99.5% methylene chloride- 0.5% methanol) afforded an additional 920mg of a mixture of diastereomeric diepoxides (palmarumycin C_9), 66mg of palmarumycin C_{10}, 30mg of palmarumycin C_{11}, and 198mg of palmarumycin C_{12}. An additional 246mg of palmarumycin C_{12} was isolated by repeated fractional crystallization from fraction six.

Fungal Source

An unidentified *Coniothyrium sp.*(internal strain number 812) isolated from soil from a forest on West Borneo.

Biological Activity

Exhibited biological activity against a variety of bacteria and fungi, as well as biological activity against growth of garden cress.

Spectral Data

^{1}H NMR:

($CDCl_3$) 7.58(2H, m, H-4', H-5'); 7.50[1H, pseudo-t (dd), $J_{2',3'}$=7.5Hz, $J_{3',4'}$=8.2Hz, H-3']; 7.45[1H, pseudo-t (dd), $J_{6',7'}$=7.5Hz, $J_{5',6'}$=8.2Hz, H-6']; 7.11(1H, d, $J_{2',3'}$=7.5Hz, H-2'); 6.95(1H, d, $J_{6',7'}$=7.5Hz, H-7'); 6.85(1H, s, H-2); 6.78(1H, d, $J_{6,7}$=10.6Hz, $J_{5,6}$= 5.1Hz, H-6); 6.16(1H, d, $J_{6,7}$= 10.6Hz, $J_{5,7}$= 0.9Hz, H-7); and 5.32ppm (1H, m, H-5).

^{13}C NMR:

($CDCl_3$) C-8, 184.8(s); C-4, 184.3(s); C-8', 145.1(s); C-1', 144.4(s); C-6, 140.8(d); C-2, 135.9(d); C-4a', 134.1(s); C-3, 131.3(s); C-3', 127.9(d); C-7, 127.6(d); C-6', 127.5(d); C-4', 121.7(d); C-5', 121.6(d); C-4a', 112.3(s); C-2', 110.4(d); C- 7', 109.5(d); C-1, 95.0 (s); C-4a, 63.2(s); C-5, 61.1(d); and C-8a, 60.4ppm (s).

Reference

K. Krohn, A. Michel, U. Flörke, H.-J. Aust, S. Draeger, and B. Schulz; Palmarumycins C_1-C_{16} from *Coniothyrium* sp.: Isolation, Structure Elucidation, and Biological Activity; Liebigs Ann.Chem., pp. 1099-1108(1994).

Common/Systematic Name

Palmarumycin C_8

(4a*RS*,8a*RS*)-3-Chloro-6,7-dihydro-5-hydroxyspiro[4a,8a-epoxynaphthalene-1(4*H*),2'-naphtho[1,8-*de*][1,3]-dioxin]-4,8(5*H*)-dione

Molecular Formula/Molecular Weight

$C_{20}H_{13}ClO_6$; MW = 384.04007

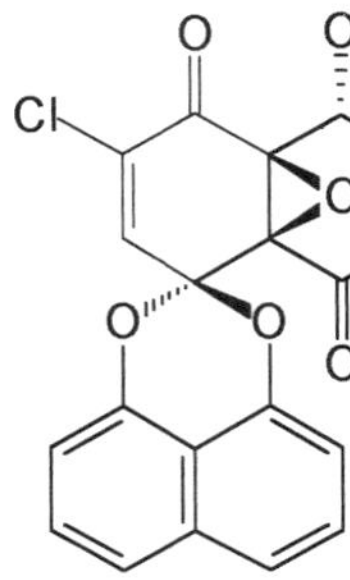

General Characteristics

Obtained as the minor component of a mixture with palmarumycin C_7.

Isolation/Purification

Liquid fungal cultures were shaken for 14-22 days in 2L Fernbach flasks at 25°C and 125 rpm. The 50L of culture material was filtered and extracted three times with ethyl acetate. The combined extracts were dried (Na_2SO_4), filtered, and concentrated at reduced pressure to afford 331g of crude extract. The residue was treated with methanol and filtered. The precipitate was extracted with ethyl acetate to afford 2.0g of dissoluble material that was investigated later (palmarumycins C_4 and C_9). The filtrate from the methanol treatment was further separated by column chromatography using petroleum ether-methylene chloride (1:1, v/v) as eluant. The fourth fraction from the column chromatography contained the majority of the secondary metabolites. Column chromatography was repeated with this fraction using a gradient of methylene chloride-methanol (0-10%) to afford six new fractions. From the first fraction an additional 20mg of palmarumycin C_3 was isolated. From liquid chromatography of the second fraction 22mg of palmarumycin C_6 crystallized (petroleum ether). From liquid chromatography of fractions four and five (Chromatotron, 99.5% methylene chloride-0.5% methanol) an additional 15mg of palmarumycin C_6 and 30mg of the mixture of palmarumycin C_7 and C_8 were isolated. Repeated liquid chromatography of fraction five (Chromatotron, 99.5% methylene chloride-0.5% methanol) afforded an additional 920mg of a mixture of diastereomeric diepoxides (palmarumycin C_9), 66mg of palmarumycin C_{10}, 30mg of palmarumycin C_{11}, and 198mg of palmarumycin C_{12}. An additional 246mg of palmarumycin C_{12} was isolated by repeated fractional crystallization from fraction six.

Fungal Source

An unidentified *Coniothyrium* sp. (internal strain number 812) isolated from soil from a forest on West Borneo.

Biological Activity

Exhibited biological activity against a variety of bacteria and fungi, as well as biological activity against growth of garden cress.

Spectral Data

^{1}H NMR:

($CDCl_3$) 7.58 0(2H, m, H-4', H-5'); 7.50 [1H, pseudo-t(dd), $J_{2',3'}$=7.5Hz, $J_{3',4'}$= 8.2Hz, H-3']; 7.43 [1H, pseudo-t(dd), $J_{6',7'}$=7.5Hz, $J_{5',6'}$=8.3Hz, H-6']; 7.11(1H, d, $J_{2',3'}$ =7.5Hz, H-2'); 6.93(1H, d, $J_{6',7'}$=7.6Hz, H-7'); 6.78(1H, s, H-2); 5.12(1H, s, H-5); 2.81(1H, ddd, $J_{7ax,7eq}$=18.6Hz, $J_{6ax,7ax}$=11.4Hz, $J_{6eq,7ax}$=3.6Hz, H-7ax); 2.51(1H, td, $J_{7ax,7eq}$=18.6Hz, $J_{6ax,7eq(6eq,7eq)}$=3.6Hz, H-7eq); and 2.09ppm (2H, m, H-6ax, H-6eq).

^{13}C NMR:

($CDCl_3$) C-8, 194.4(s); C-4, 185.3(s); C-8', 145.1(s); C-1', 144.5(s); C-6, 23.3(t); C-2, 135.4(d); C-4a', 134.1(s); C-3, 131.4(s); C-3', 127.6(d); C-7, 32.7(t); C-6', 127.4(d); C-4', 121.6(d); C-5', 121.55(d); C-8a', 112.4(s); C-2', 110.4(d); C- 7', 109.5(d); C-1, 95.5(s); C-4a, 62.9(s); C-5, 61.4(d); and C-8a, 61.3ppm (s).

Reference

K. Krohn, A. Michel, U. Flörke, H.-J. Aust, S. Draeger, and B. Schulz; Palmarumycins C_1-C_{16} from *Coniothyrium* sp.: Isolation, Structure Elucidation, and Biological Activity; Liebigs Ann. Chem., pp. 1099-1108(1994).

Common/Systematic Name

Palmarumycin C_{10}

(2*S**,3*S**,4*R**,4a*R**,8a*S*)-3,4-Dihydro-4-hydroxyspiro[2,3:4a,8a-diepoxynaphthalene-1,(2*H*) 2'-naphtho[1,8-*de*][1,3]-dioxin]-5,8-dione

Molecular Formula/Molecular Weight

$C_{20}H_{12}O_7$; MW = 364.05830

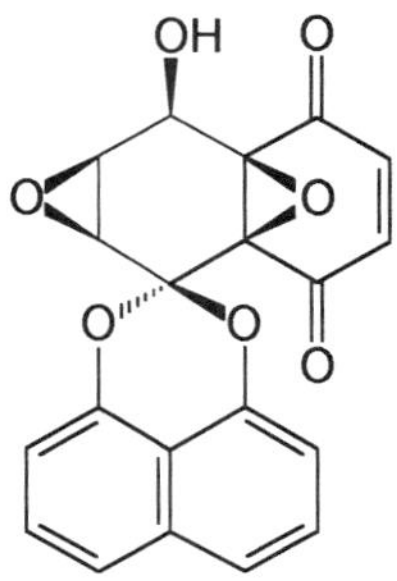

General Characteristics

A yellow solid; mp., 236°C (dec.); $[\alpha]_D^{20}$ =-48.2°.

Isolation/Purification

Liquid fungal cultures were shaken for 14-22 days in 2L Fernbach flasks at 25°C and 125 rpm. The 50L of culture material was filtered and extracted three times with ethyl acetate. The combined extracts were dried (Na_2SO_4), filtered, and concentrated at reduced pressure to afford 331g of crude extract. The residue was treated with methanol and filtered. The precipitate was extracted with ethyl acetate to afford 2.0g of dissoluble material that was investigated later (palmarumycins C_4 and C_9). The filtrate from the methanol treatment was further separated by column chromatography using petroleum ether-methylene chloride (1:1, v/v) as eluant. The fourth fraction from the column chromatography contained the majority of the secondary metabolites. Column chromatography was repeated with this fraction using a gradient of methylene chloride-methanol (0-10%) to afford six new fractions. From the first fraction an additional 20mg of palmarumycin C_3 was isolated; from the second fraction 22mg of palmarumycin C_6 crystallized (petroleum ether).Liquid chromatography (Chromatotron, 99.5% methylene chloride-0.5% methanol) of fractions four and five produced an additional 15mg of palmarumycin C_6 and 30mg of the mixture of palmarumycin C_7 and C_8. Repeated liquid chromatography of fraction five (Chromatotron, 99.5% methylene chloride-0.5% methanol) afforded an additional 920mg of a mixture of diastereomeric diepoxides (palmarumycin C_9), 66mg of palmarumycin C_{10}, 30mg of palmarumycin C_{11}, and 198mg of palmarumycin C_{12}. An additional 246mg of palmarumycin C_{12} was isolated by repeated fractional crystallization from fraction six.

Fungal Source

An unidentified *Coniothyrium* sp. (internal strain number 812) isolated from soil from a forest on West Borneo.

Biological Activity

Exhibited biological activity against a variety of bacteria and fungi, as well as biological activity against growth of garden cress.

Spectral Data

UV:

$\lambda_{max}^{EtOH / 10\% Methylene Chloride}$ 293(log ϵ =4.19), 299(4.31), 307(4.22), 313(4.24), and 327nm (4.16).

IR:

(KBr) 3480(OH), 1692(C=O), 1609, 1414, 1381, 1275(Ar-O), 1111, 1042, 951, 818, and 754cm^{-1}.

^{1}H NMR:

(DMSO-d_6) 7.66(1H, dd, $J_{3',4'}$=8.3Hz, H-4'); 7.65(1H, d, $J_{5',6'}$=8.3Hz, H-5'); 7.53(2H, m, $J_{5',6'}$=8.3Hz, H-3', H-4'); 7.13(1H, d, $J_{2',3'}$=7.5Hz, H-2'); 7.03(1H, d, $J_{6',7'}$= 7.5Hz, H-7'); [1H, pseudo-t(dd), $J_{5',6'}$=8.2Hz,$J_{6',7'}$=7.6Hz, H-6']; 6.77(1H, d, $J_{6,7}$= 10.7Hz, H-6); 6.66(1H, d, $J_{6,7}$=10.7Hz, H-7); 5.02(1H, d, $J_{3,4}$=3.0Hz, H-4); 3.46(1H, d, $J_{2,3}$ =4.1Hz, H-2); and 3.40ppm (1H, d,[pseudo-t(dd), $J_{2,3(3,4)}$=3.6Hz, H-3).

^{13}C NMR:

(DMSO-d_6) C-8, 190.1(s); C-5, 187.3(s); C-8', 145.2(s); C-1', 144.9(s); C-7, 136.4(d); C-6, 135.7, (d); C-4a', 133.8(s); C-3', 127.9(d); C-6', 127.8(d); C-4', C-5', 121.0(d); C-8a', 111.50(s); C-2', 109.2(d); C-7', 109.0(d); C-1, 94.5(s); C-4a, 65.4(s); C- 8a, 63.5(s); C-4, 59.4(d); C-2, 53.2(d); and C-3, 55.2ppm (d).

Mass Data:

LREIMS: 366(M$^+$+ 2H, 22%), 365(M$^+$+ H, 100), 364(M$^+$, 86), 211(6), 171(8), 159(8), 115(14), and 114m/e (18); HREIMS: $C_{20}H_{12}O_7$ calcd. 364.058303; found 364.058305; calcd. C=65.92, H=3.32; found C=65.85, H=3.40.

Reference

K. Krohn, A. Michel, U. Flörke, H.-J. Aust, S. Draeger, and B. Schulz; Palmarumycins C_1-C_{16} from *Coniothyrium* sp.: Isolation, Structure Elucidation, and Biological Activity; Liebigs Ann. Chem., pp. 1099-1108(1994).

Common/Systematic Name

Palmarumycin C_{11}

(2*S**,3*R**,4*S**)-3,4-Dihydrospiro[2,3-epoxynaphthalene-1,(2*H*) 2'-naphtho[1,8-*de*][1,3]-dioxin]-4,5-diol

Molecular Formula/Molecular Weight

$C_{20}H_{14}O_5$; MW = 334.08412

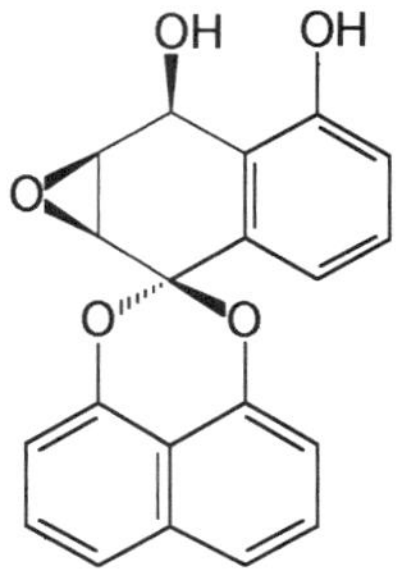

General Characteristics

Crystallized as colorless needles; mp., 207-208°C; $[\alpha]_D^{20} = -153°$.

Isolation/Purification

Liquid fungal cultures were shaken for 14-22 days in 2L Fernbach flasks at 25°C and 125 rpm. The 50L of culture material was filtered and extracted three times with ethyl acetate. The combined extracts were dried (Na_2SO_4), filtered, and concentrated at reduced pressure to afford 331g of crude extract. The residue was treated with methanol and filtered. The precipitate was extracted with ethyl acetate to afford 2.0g of dissoluble material that was investigated later (palmarumycins C_4 and C_9). The filtrate from the methanol treatment was further separated by column chromatography using petroleum ether-methylene chloride (1:l, v/v) as eluant. The fourth fraction from the column chromatography contained the majority of the secondary metabolites. Column chromatography was repeated with this fraction using a gradient of methylene chloride-methanol (0-10%) to afford six new fractions. From the first fraction an additional 20mg of palmarumycin C_3 was isolated. From the second fraction 22mg of palmarumycin C_6 crystallized (petroleum ether). Liquid chromatography (Chromatotron, 99.5% methylene chloride-0.5% methanol) of fractions four and five provided an additional 15mg of palmarumycin C_6 and 30mg of the mixture of palmarumycin C_7 and C_8. Repeated liquid chromatography of fraction five (Chromatotron, 99.5% methylene chloride-0.5% methanol) afforded an additional 920 mg of a mixture of diastereomeric diepoxides (palmarumycin C_9), 66mg of palmarumycin C_{10}, 30mg of palmarumycin C_{11}, and 198mg of palmarumycin C_{12}. An additional 246mg of palmarumycin C_{12} was isolated by repeated fractional crystallization from fraction six.

Fungal Source

An unidentified *Coniothyrium* sp. (internal strain number 812) isolated from soil from a forest on West Borneo.

Biological Activity

Exhibited biological activity against a variety of bacteria and fungi, as well as biological activity against growth of garden cress.

Spectral Data

UV:

$\lambda_{max}^{Methylene\ Chloride}$ 293(log ε=4.05), 296(4.09), 300(4.10), 314(3.83), and 327nm (3.62).

IR:

(KBr) 3540(OH), 3070(OH), 3000, 2900, 1619, 1590, 1467, 1412, 1381, 1327, 1232, 1180, 1130, 1111, 1072, 1028, 968, 872, 822, and 798cm^{-1}.

^{1}H NMR:

($CDCl_3$) 8.28(1H, s, OH); 7.57(1H, dd, $J_{3',4'}$=8.1Hz, $J_{2',4'}$=0.9Hz, H-4'); 7.55(1H, d, $J_{5',6'}$= 8.1Hz, H-5'); 7.51[1H, pseudo-t(dd), $J_{2',3'}$=7.4Hz, $J_{3',4'}$=8.3Hz, H-3']; 7.44[1H, pseudo-t(dd), $J_{5',6'}$=8.2Hz, $J_{6',7'}$=7.6Hz, H-6']; 7.37(1H, d, [pseudo-t(dd), $J_{7,8'}$=7.9Hz, $J_{6,7}$=7.5Hz, H-7); 7.14(1H, dd, $J_{2',3'}$=7.3Hz, $J_{2',4'}$=0.9Hz, H-2'); 7.04(1H, dd, $J_{6,7}$=7.0Hz, $J_{6,8}$=2.4Hz, H-6); 6.92(1H, d, $J_{6',7'}$=7.4Hz, H-7'); 3.74(1H, dd, $J_{2,3}$=4.4Hz, $J_{3,4}$=2.7Hz, H-3); 3.ppm(1H, d, $J_{2,3}$=4.Hz, H-2); 7.41(1H, dd, $J_{7,8}$=8.0Hz, $J_{6,8}$=2.3Hz); 5.44(1H, dd, $J_{4,OH}$=11.3Hz, $J_{3,4}$=2.7Hz, H-4); and 3.15ppm (1H, d, $J_{4,OH}$=11.3Hz, OH).

^{13}C NMR:

($CDCl_3$) C-4, 66.7(d); C-5, 156.5(s); C-8, 119.3(d); C-8', 147.3(s); C-1', 147.2(s); C-4a', 134.1(s); C-7, 130.6(d); C-6', 127.4(d); C-3', 127.7(d); C-4', 121.3(d); C-6, 118.9(d); C-5', 120.96(d); C-8a, 132.0(s); C-4a, 118.5(s); C-2', 109.9(d); C-7', 109.0(d); C-1, 96.7(s); C-2, 54.1(d); and C-3, 52.8ppm (d).

Mass Data:

LREIMS: 335(M^+ + H, 27%), 334(M^+, 8), 285(17), 209(70), 169(100), and 152*m/e* (72); HREIMS: $C_{20}H_{14}O_5$ calcd. 334.0841; found 334.0841*m/e*; calcd. C= 71.85, H, 4.22; found C, 71.57, H, 4.07.

Reference

K. Krohn, A. Michel, U. Flörke, H.-J. Aust, S. Draeger, and B. Schulz; Palmarumycins C_1-C_{16} from *Coniothyrium* sp.: Isolation, Structure Elucidation, and Biological Activity; Liebigs Ann. Chem., pp. 1099-1108(1994).

Common/Systematic Name

Palmarumycin C_{12}

(2*S**,3*S**,4*S**)-3,4-Dihydrospiro[2,3:4a,8a-epoxynaphthalene-1,(2*H*) 2'-naphtho[1,8-*de*][1,3]-dioxin]-4,5,8-triol

Molecular Formula/Molecular Weight

$C_{20}H_{14}O_6$; MW = 350.07904

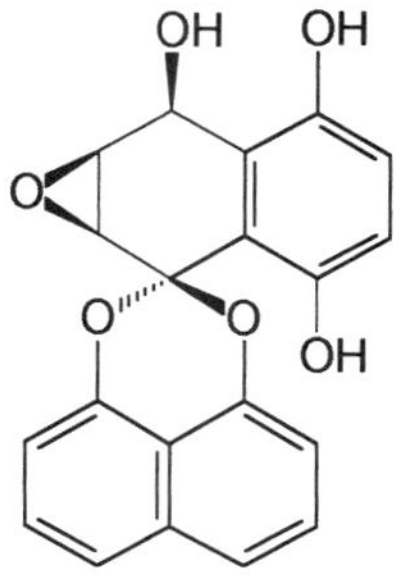

General Characteristics

Colorless prisms with poor solubility in methylene chloride; mp., 207-208°C (dec.); $[\alpha]_D^{20}$ = -179.6°.

Isolation/Purification

Liquid fungal cultures were shaken for 14-22 days in 2L Fernbach flasks at 25°C and 125 rpm. The 50L of culture material was filtered and extracted three times with ethyl acetate. The combined extracts were dried (Na_2SO_4), filtered, and concentrated at reduced pressure to afford 331g of crude extract. The residue was treated with methanol and filtered. The precipitate was extracted with ethyl acetate to afford 2.0g of dissoluble material that was investigated later (palmarumycins C_4 and C_9). The filtrate from the methanol treatment was further separated by column chromatography using petroleum ether-methylene chloride (1:l, v/v) as eluant. The fourth fraction from the column chromatography contained the majority of the secondary metabolites. Column chromatography was repeated with this fraction using a gradient of methylene chloride-methanol (0-10%) to afford six new fractions. From the first fraction an additional 20mg of palmarumycin C_3 was isolated. Palmarumycin C_6 crystallized (petroleum ether) from the second fraction. Liquid chromatography (Chromatotron, 99.5% methylene chloride-0.5% methanol) of fractions four and five provided an additional 15mg of palmarumycin C_6 and 30mg of the mixture of palmarumycin C_7 and C_8. Repeated liquid chromatography of fraction five (Chromatotron, 99.5% methylene chloride-0.5% methanol) afforded an additional 920mg of a mixture of diastereomeric diepoxides (palmarumycin C_9), 66mg of palmarumycin C_{10}, 30mg of palmarumycin C_{11}, and 198mg of palmarumycin C_{12}. An additional 246mg of palmarumycin C_{12} was isolated by repeated fractional crystallization from fraction six.

Fungal Source

An unidentified *Coniothyrium* sp. (internal strain number 812) isolated from soil from a forest on West Borneo.

Biological Activity

Exhibited biological activity against a variety of bacteria and fungi, as well as biological activity against growth of garden cress.

Spectral Data

UV:

$\lambda_{max}^{10\%\ Methylene\ Chloride}$ 288(log ε=3.64), 292(3.97), 299(4.10), 302(4.10), 313(3.99), and 327nm (3.46).

IR:

(KBr) 3476(OH), 1609, 1586, 1474, 1445, 1377, 1304, 1265(Ar-O), 1190, 1183, 1069, 1061, 1049, 1030, 947, 909, 870, 835, 820, 793, 760, and 739cm^{-1}.

^{1}H NMR:

($CDCl_3/CD_3OD$) 7.54(1H, d, $J_{3',4'}$=8.4Hz, H-4'); 7.49(1H, d, $J_{5',6'}$=8.4Hz, H-5'); 7.43[1H, pseudo-t(dd), $J_{2',3'}$=7.5Hz, $J_{3',4'}$=8.4Hz, H-3']; 7.39[1H, pseudo-t(dd), $J_{5',6'}$=8.4Hz, $J_{6',7'}$=7.5Hz, H-6']; 7.08(1H, d, $J_{2',3'}$=7.5Hz, H-2'); 6.92(1H, d, $J_{6',7'}$ =7.5Hz, H-7'); 6.87(1H, d, $J_{6,7}$=8.9Hz, H-7); 6.82(1H, d, $J_{6,7}$=8.9Hz, H-6); 5.29 (1H, d, $J_{3,4}$=2.3Hz, H-4); 3.67(1H, d, $J_{2,3}$=4.4Hz, H-2); and 3.57ppm (1H, dd, $J_{2,3}$=4.3Hz, $J_{3,4}$=2.7Hz, H-3).

^{13}C NMR:

($CDCl_3/CD_3OD$) C-8, 149.6(s); C-5, 149.3(s); C-8', 147.0(s); C-1', 145.7(s); C-4a', 134.0(s); C-3', 127.5(d); C-6', 127.4(d); C-4', 122.4 (d); C5', 121.2(d); C-4a, 120.0(s); C-7, 119.9(d); C-6, 118.9(d); C-8a, 115.4(s); C-8a', 113.0(s); C-2', 110.6(d); C-7', 109.8(d); C-1, 99.4(s); C-4, 65.5(d); C-2, 51.5(d); and C-3, 54.0ppm (d).

Mass Data:

LREIMS: 351(M^+ + H, 59%), 350(M^+, 90), 332(M^+ - H_2O, 100), 316(21), 304(332 - CO, 34), 303(332 - CHO, 34), 287(20), 275(16), 159(41), 131(23), 115(36), and 114*m/e* (33); HREIMS: $C_{20}H_{14}O_6$ calcd. 350.0790; found 350.0790*m/e*.

Reference

K. Krohn, A. Michel, U. Flörke, H.-J. Aust, S. Draeger, and B. Schulz; Palmarumycins C_1-C_{16} from *Coniothyrium* sp.: Isolation, Structure Elucidation, and Biological Activity; Liebigs Ann. Chem., pp. 1099-1108(1994).

Common/Systematic Name

Palmarumycin C_{13}; Diepoxide η
(2*S**,3*S**,4*R**,4a*R**,5*R**,8a*S**)-3,4-Dihydro-4,5-dihydroxyspiro[2,3:4a,8a-diepoxynaphthalene-1(2*H*),2'-naphtho[1,8-*de*][1,3]-dioxin]-8(5*H*)-one

Molecular Formula/Molecular Weight

$C_{20}H_{16}O_7$; MW = 366.07395

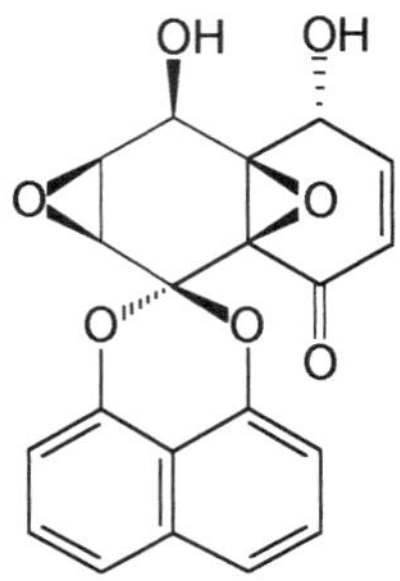

General Characteristics

Isolated as a 1:1 mixture with palmarumycin C_{14}.

Isolation/Purification

Liquid fungal cultures were shaken for 14-22 days in 2L Fernbach flasks at 25°C and 125 rpm. The 50L of culture material was filtered and extracted three times with ethyl acetate. The combined extracts were dried (Na_2SO_4), filtered, and concentrated at reduced pressure to afford 331g of crude extract. The residue was treated with methanol and filtered. The precipitate was extracted with ethyl acetate to afford 2.0g of dissoluble material that was investigated later (palmarumycins C_4 and C_9). The filtrate from the methanol treatment was further separated by column chromatography using petroleum ether-methylene chloride (1:l, v/v) as eluant. The fifth fraction from the column chromatography was first subjected to column chromatography and then twice to liquid chromatography (Chromatotron, 2mm silica gel, 93% methylene chloride-7% methanol) to afford palmarumycins C_{13} and C_{14} as a 1:1 mixture, along with palmarumycins C_{15}, and C_{16}.

Fungal Source

An unidentified *Coniothyrium* sp. (internal strain number 812) isolated from soil from a forest on West Borneo.

Biological Activity

Exhibited biological activity against a variety of bacteria, fungi and biological activity against growth of garden cress.

Spectral Data

^{1}H NMR:

(CD$_3$OD) 7.57(2H, m, $J_{3',4'(5',6')}$=8.4Hz, H-4', H-5'); 7.50[1H, pseudo-t(dd), $J_{2',3'}$=7.4Hz, $J_{3',4'}$=8.4Hz, H-3']; 7.46[1H, pseudo-t(dd), $J_{5',6'}$=8.4Hz, $J_{6',7'}$=7.5Hz, H-6']; 7.04(1H, dd, $J_{2',3'}$=7.4Hz, $J_{2',4'}$=1.0Hz,H-2'); 6.94(1H, dd, $J_{6',7'}$=7.5Hz, $J_{5',7'}$=0.6Hz, H-7'); 5.91(1H, dd, $J_{6,7}$=10.6Hz, $J_{5,7}$=0.9Hz, H-7); 6.74(1H, dd, $J_{6,7}$=10.6Hz, $J_{5,6}$=4.9Hz, H-6); 5.11(1H, m, H-4); 4.82(1H, dd, $J_{5,6}$=4.9Hz, $J_{5,7}$= 0.9Hz, H-5); and 3.45ppm (2H, m, H-2, H-3).

^{13}C NMR:

(CD$_3$OD) C-8, 190.1(s); C-5, 62.8(d); C-8', 147.5(s); C-1', 145.2(s); C-4a', 136.0(s); C-3', 129.0(d); C-6', 128.8(d); C-4', 122.2(d); C-5', 122.1(d); C-4a, 72.3(s); C- 7, 127.4(d); C-6, 145.1(d); C-8a, 65.4(s); C-8a', 113.7(s); C-2', 110.5(d); C-7', 110.0(d); C-1, 96.8(s); C-4, 62.5(d); C-2, 54.9(d); and C-3, 57.0ppm (d).

Reference

K. Krohn, A. Michel, U. Flörke, H.-J. Aust, S. Draeger, and B. Schulz; Palmarumycins C_1-C_{16} from *Coniothyrium* sp.: Isolation, Structure Elucidation, and Biological Activity; Liebigs Ann. Chem., pp. 1099-1108(1994).

Common/Systematic Name

Palmarumycin C_{14}; Diepoxine ζ
(2*S**,3*S**,4*R**,4a*R**,5*R**,8a*S**)-3,4,6,7-Tetrahydro-4,5-dihydroxyspiro[2,3:4a,8a-diepoxynaphthalene-1(2*H*), 2'-naphtho[1,8-*de*][1,3]-dioxin]-8(5*H*)-one

Molecular Formula/Molecular Weight

$C_{20}H_{16}O_7$; MW = 368.08960

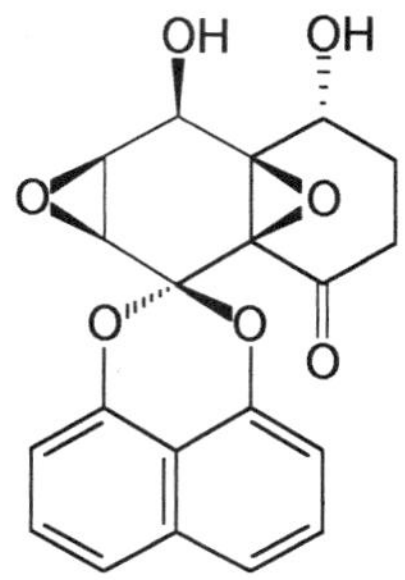

General Characteristics

Isolated as a 1:1 mixture with palmarumycin C_{13}.

Isolation/Purification

Liquid fungal cultures were shaken for 14-22 days in 2L Fernbach flasks at 25°C and 125 rpm. The 50L of culture material was filtered and extracted three times with ethyl acetate. The combined extracts were dried (Na_2SO_4), filtered, and concentrated at reduced pressure to afford 331g of crude extract. The residue was treated with methanol and filtered. The precipitate was extracted with ethyl acetate to afford 2.0g of dissoluble material that was investigated later (palmarumycins C_4 and C_9). The filtrate from the methanol treatment was further separated by column chromatography using petroleum ether-methylene chloride (1:1, v/v) as eluant. The fifth fraction from the column chromatography was first subjected to column chromatography and then twice to liquid chromatography (Chromatotron, 2 mm silica gel, 93% methylene chloride-7% methanol) to afford palmarumycins C_{13} and C_{14} as a 1:1 mixture, along with palmarumycins C_{15}, and C_{16}.

Fungal Source

An unidentified *Coniothyrium* sp. (internal strain number 812) isolated from soil from a forest on West Borneo.

Biological Activity

Exhibited biological activity against a variety of bacteria and fungi, as well as biological activity against growth of garden cress.

Spectral Data

^{1}H NMR:

(CD_3OD) 7.56(2H, m, $J_{3',4'(5',6')}$=8.4Hz, H-4', H-5'); 7.49[1H, pseudo-t(dd), $J_{2',3'}$=7.5Hz, $J_{3',4'}$=8.4Hz, H-3']; 7.45 [1H, pseudo-t(dd), $J_{5',6'}$=8.4Hz, $J_{6',7'}$=7.5Hz, H-6']; 7.03(1H, dd, $J_{2',3'}$=7.5Hz, $J_{2',4'}$=1.0Hz, H-2'); 6.95(1H, dd, $J_{6',7'}$=7.5Hz, $J_{5',7'}$=0.6Hz, H-7'); 4.87(1H, dd, $J_{3,4}$=2.5Hz, H-4); 4.71(1H, t, $J_{5,6ax(5,6eq)}$=3.0Hz, H-5); 3.45(2H, m, H-2, H-3); 2.57(1H, ddd, $J_{7ax,7eq}$=18.1Hz, $J_{6ax,7ax}$=12.4Hz, $J_{7eq,7ax}$=6.5Hz, H-7ax); 2.32(1H, ddd, $J_{7ax,7eq}$=18.1Hz, $J_{6ax,7eq}$=5.6Hz, $J6_{eq,7eq}$=2.4Hz, H-7eq); 2.04(1H, dddd, $J6_{ax,6eq}$=14.2Hz, $J_{6ax,7ax}$=12.4Hz, $J_{6ax,7eq}$=5.6Hz, $J_{5,6ax}$=3.0Hz, H-6ax); and 1.83ppm (1H, dddd, $J_{6ax,6eq}$=14.2Hz, $J_{6eq,7ax}$=6.5Hz, $J_{5,6eq}$=3.0Hz, $J_{6eq,7eq}$=2.4Hz, H-6eq).

^{13}C NMR:

(CD_3OD) C-8, 200.2(s); C-8', 147.5(s); C-1', 147.2(s); C-4a', 136.0(s); C-3', 129.0(d); C-6', 128.8(d); C-4', 122.2,(d); C-5', 122.1(d); C-4a, 71.3(s); C-7, 33.9(t); C-6, 25.7(t); C-8a, 64.1(s); C-8a', 113.7(s); C-2', 110.5(d); C-7', 110.0(d); C-1, 96.8(s); C-4, 63.2(d); C-2, 55.0(d); C-5, 64.1(d); and C-3, 56.9ppm (d).

Reference

K. Krohn, A. Michel, U. Flörke, H.-J. Aust, S. Draeger, and B. Schulz; Palmarumycins C_1-C_{16} from *Coniothyrium* sp.: Isolation, Structure Elucidation, and Biological Activity; Liebigs Ann. Chem., pp. 1099-1108(1994).

Common/Systematic Name

Palmarumycin C_{15}

(2*S**,3*S**,4*R**,4a*R**,5*R**,8*RS*,8a*S**)-3,4,5,8-Tetrahydrospiro[2,3:4a,8a-diepoxynaphthalene-1(2*H*),2'-naphtho[1,8-*de*][1,3]-dioxin]-4,5,8-triol

Molecular Formula/Molecular Weight

$C_{20}H_{16}O_7$; MW = 367.08178

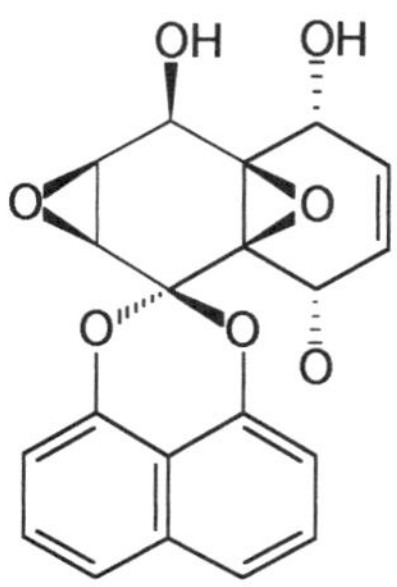

General Characteristics

Isolated as a white powder; mp., 150°C (dec.); $[\alpha]_D^{20}$ = -18.1°.

Isolation/Purification

Liquid fungal cultures were shaken for 14-22 days in 2L Fernbach flasks at 25°C and 125 rpm. The 50L of culture material was filtered and extracted three times with ethyl acetate. The combined extracts were dried (Na_2SO_4), filtered, and concentrated at reduced pressure to afford 331g of crude extract. The residue was treated with methanol and filtered. The precipitate was extracted with ethyl acetate to afford 2.0g of dissoluble material that was investigated later (palmarumycins C_4 and C_9). The filtrate from the methanol treatment was further separated by column chromatography using petroleum ether-methylene chloride (1:l, v/v) as eluant. The fifth fraction from the column chromatography was first subjected to column chromatography and then twice to liquid chromatography (Chromatotron, 2mm silica gel, 93% methylene chloride-7% methanol) to afford palmarumycins C_{13} and C_{14} as a 1:1 mixture, along with palmarumycins C_{15}, and C_{16}.

Fungal Source

An unidentified *Coniothyrium* sp. (internal strain number 812) isolated from soil from a forest on West Borneo.

Biological Activity

Exhibited biological activity against a variety of bacteria and fungi, as well as biological activity against growth of garden cress.

Spectral Data

UV:

$\lambda_{max}^{Methylene\ Chloride}$ 287(log ε = 3.79), 297(4.07), 312(3.71), and 327nm (3.44).

IR:

(KBr) 3426(OH), 2361, 1611, 1414, 1381, 1273(Ar-O), 1136, 1088, 1047, 1032, 941, 822, and 758cm^{-1}.

^{1}H NMR:

($CDCl_3$/CD_3OD) 7.51(1H, d, $J_{3',4'}$=8.2Hz, H-4'); 7.50(1H, d, $J_{5',6'}$=8.3Hz, H-5'); 7.42(2H, m, H-3', H-6'); 7.11(1H, d, $J_{2',3'}$=7.3Hz, H-2'); 6.96(1H, d, $J_{6',7'}$=7.4Hz, H-7'); 5.75(1H, ddd, $J_{6,7}$=10.5Hz, $J_{5,6}$=4.5Hz, $J_{6,8}$=1.7Hz, H-6); 5.60(1H, dd, $J_{6,7}$=10.5Hz, $J_{7,8}$=2.60Hz, H-7); 5.18(1H, s, H-8); 4.93(1H, d, $J_{3,4}$=2.8Hz, H-4); 4.61(1H, d, $J_{4,5}$=4.5Hz, H-5); 3.48(1H, d, $J_{2,3}$=4.3Hz, H-2); and 3.42ppm(1H, dd, $J_{2,3}$=4.3Hz, $J_{3,4}$=2.8Hz, H-3).

^{13}C NMR:

($CDCl_3$/CD_3OD) C-8, 63.0(d); C-5, 61.0(d); C-8', 145.8(s); C-1', 145.1(s); C-4a', 134.0(s); C-3', 127.7(d); C-6', 127.3(d); C-4', 121.5(d); C-5', 121.3(d); C-4a, 68.3(s); C-7, 126.9(d); C-6, 125.6(d); C-8a, 66.2(s); C-8a', 112.7(s); C-2', 110.3(d); C-7', 109.4(d); C-1, 96.6(s); C-4, 61.4(d); C-2, 53.2(d); and C-3, 55.8ppm (d).

Mass Data:

LREIMS: 368(M$^+$, 100%), 160(21), 125(26), 111(38), 97(51), 82(48), 71(55), and 57*m/e* (68); HREIMS: $C_{20}H_{16}O_7$ calcd. 368.0896; found 368.089*m/e*; calcd. C,65.22, H, 4.42; found C, 65.14, H, 4.42.

Reference

K. Krohn, A. Michel, U. Flörke, H.-J. Aust, S. Draeger, and B. Schulz; Palmarumycins C_1-C_{16} from *Coniothyrium* sp.: Isolation, Structure Elucidation, and Biological Activity; Liebigs Ann. Chem., pp. 1099-1108(1994).

Common/Systematic Name

Palmarumycin C_{16}

(2*S**,3*S**,4*R**,4a*R**,5*R**,8*RS*,8a*S**)-3,4,5,6,7,8-Hexahydrospiro[2,3:4a,8a-diepoxynaphthalene-1(2*H*),2'-naphtho[1,8-*de*][1,3]-dioxin]-4,5,8-triol

Molecular Formula/Molecular Weight

$C_{20}H_{18}O_7$; MW = 369.09743

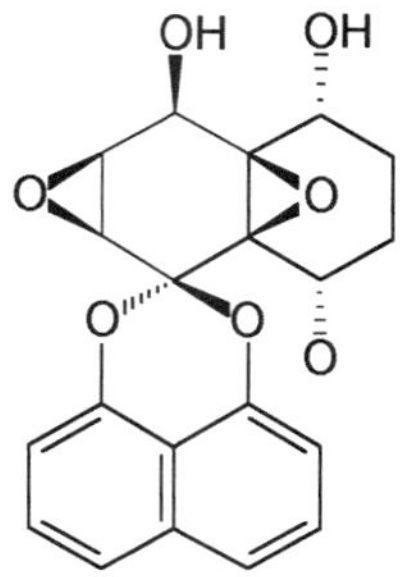

General Characteristics

Crystals; mp., 187-188°C (dec.); $[\alpha]_D^{20}$ = -43.3°.

Isolation/Purification

Liquid fungal cultures were shaken for 14-22 days in 2L Fernbach flasks at 25°C and 125 rpm. The 50L of culture material was filtered and extracted three times with ethyl acetate. The combined extracts were dried (Na_2SO_4), filtered, and concentrated at reduced pressure to afford 331g of crude extract. The residue was treated with methanol and filtered. The precipitate was extracted with ethyl acetate to afford 2.0g of dissoluble material that was investigated later (palmarumycins C_4 and C_9). The filtrate from the methanol treatment was further separated by column chromatography using petroleum ether-methylene chloride (1:1, v/v) as eluant. The fifth fraction from the column chromatography was first subjected to column chromatography and then twice to liquid chromatography (Chromatotron, 2mm silica gel, 93% methylene chloride-7% methanol) to afford palmarumycins C_{13} and C_{14} as a 1:1 mixture, along with palmarumycins C_{15} and C_{16}.

Fungal Source

An unidentified *Coniothyrium* sp. (internal strain number 812) isolated from soil from a forest on West Borneo.

Biological Activity

Exhibited biological activity against a variety of bacteria and fungi, as well as biological activity against growth of garden cress.

Spectral Data

UV:

$\lambda_{max}^{Methylene\ Chloride}$ 287 (log ε=3.60), 298 (3.81), 307 (3.66), 313 (3.68), and 327nm (3.60).

IR:

(KBr) 3426(OH), 2938, 2361, 1611, 1412, 1381, 1273(Ar-O), 1090, 1047, 1034, 1005, 965, 939, 820, and 758cm^{-1}.

^{1}H NMR:

(CD_3OD) 7.59(1H, dd, $J_{3',4'}$=8.5Hz, $J_{2',4'}$=1.1Hz, H-4'); 7.58(1H, d, $J_{5',6'}$=8.5Hz, H-5'); 7.52 [1H, pseudo-t(dd), $J_{2',3'}$=7.4Hz, $J_{2',4'}$=8.5Hz, H-3']; 7.49[1H, pseudo-t(dd), $J_{5',6'}$=8.5Hz, $J_{6',7'}$=7.5Hz, H-6']; 7.14(1H, dd, $J_{2',3'}$=7.3Hz, $J_{2',4'}$=1.0Hz, H-2'); 7.04(1H, dd, $J_{6',7'}$=7.5Hz, $J_{5',7'}$=0.7Hz, H-7'); 4.82(1H, d, $J_{3,4}$=2.8Hz, H-4); 4.68(1H, m, H-8); 4.47(1H, m, H-5); 3.45(1H, d, $J_{2,3}$=4.3Hz, H-2); 3.41(1H, dd, $J_{2,3}$=4.3Hz, $J_{3,4}$=2.8Hz, H-3); 1.94(2H, m, J=11.4Hz, H-6eq, H-7eq); and 1.48ppm (2H, m, J=11.4Hz, H-6ax, H-7ax).

^{13}C NMR:

($CDCl_3/CD_3OD$) C-8, 63.4(d); C-5, 64.3(d); C-8', 147.9(s); C-1', 147.6(s); C-4a', 135.9(s); C-3', 129.1(d); C-6', 128.9(d); C-4', C-5', 122.4(d); C-4a, 69.3(s); C-7, 26.0(t); C-6, 24.0(t); C-8a, 68.0(s); C-8a', 114.3(s); C-2', 111.4(d); C-7', 110.5(d); C-1, 98.4(s); C-4, 63.2(d); C-2, 54.0(d); and C-3, 57.2ppm (d).

Mass Data:

LREIMS: 370(M^+, 100%), 352(11), 213(16), 172(20), 160(72), 159(20), 139(31), 121(27), 116(26), 99(38), 86(60), and 56*m/e* (37); HREIMS: $C_{20}H_{18}O_7$ calcd. 370.1052; found 370.1052*m/e*; calcd. C, 64.86, H, 4.90; found C, 64.31, H, 4.76.

Reference

K. Krohn, A. Michel, U. Flörke, H.-J. Aust, S. Draeger, and B. Schulz; Palmarumycins C_1-C_{16} from *Coniothyrium* sp.: Isolation, Structure Elucidation, and Biological Activity; Liebigs Ann. Chem., pp. 1099-1108(1994).

7

Phomosines

Phomosine A
Phomosine B
Phomosine C

Common/Systematic Name

Phomosine A

Molecular Formula/Molecular Weight

$C_{18}H_{18}O_7$; MW = 346.10525

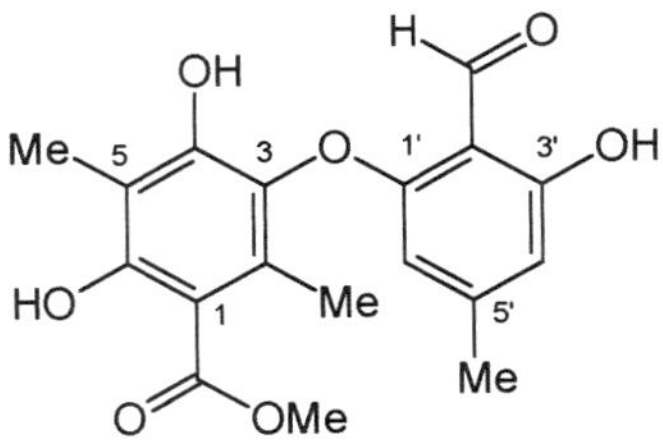

General Characteristics

Long, pale yellow needles from dichloromethane-petroleum ether; mp., 203-204°C.

Isolation/Purification

Culture medium from *Phomopsis* sp. was homogenized with a Waring blender, diluted with water and then extracted four times with ethyl acetate. The organic extracts were dried (Na_2SO_4), filtered, and evaporated *in vacuo*. The main compounds were detected in the residue on TLC at R_f values: phomosine A: R_f=0.71; phomosine B: R_f=0.53; phomosine C: R_f=0.48, 5% methanol-methylene chloride detected by UV irradiation at 254nm. Column chromatography on silica gel (methylene chloride-20% ethyl ether) gave four fractions. The second fraction gave material that was further purified by crystallization from dichloromethane-petroleum ether to afford phomosine A. The third fraction was further separated by Chromatotron chromatography (methylene chloride-petroleum ether; 1:1, v/v) into four fractions. The second fraction was purified by thin-layer chromatography (5% methanol-methylene chloride) and crystallization from dichloromethane-petroleum ether to afford additional phomosine A. From the fourth fraction, phomosine B and phomosine C were isolated by the same procedure.

Fungal Source

Phomopsis sp.

Biological Activity

All three metabolites showed moderate fungicidal and antibacterial activity against four fungal and two bacterial (one Gram-positive and one Gram-negative) test organisms.

Spectral Data

UV:

$\lambda_{max}^{Methylene\ Chloride}$ 232(log ϵ = 5.23) and 269nm (4.52).

IR:

(KBr) 3320(OH), 2955(CH_3), 1653(CO), 1637(CO), 1607, 1582, 1437, 1331, 1302, 1211, 1200, 1096, and 808cm^{-1}.

^{1}H NMR:

($CDCl_3$) 2.10(3H, s, H-3a); 2.16(3H, s, H-5'a); 2.28(3H, s, H-2a); 3.92(3 H, s, H-1b); 5.80(1H, s, H-6'); 6.36(1H, s, H-4'); 8.92(1H, OH); 10.43(1H, s, H-2'a); 11.87(1H, s, OH); and 11.92ppm (1H, s, OH).

^{13}C NMR:

($CDCl_3$) 8.4, C-5a, (q); 15.3, C-2a (q); 22.5, C-5'a (q); 52.3, C-lb (q); 104.3, C-6' (q); 104.9, C-l (s); 109.2, C-2' (s); 111.2, C-5 (s); 111.6, C-4' (d); 131.6, 133.0, C-2, C-3 (2s); 150.9 , C-5' (s); 153.8, C-4 (s); 161.0, C-3' (s); 161.1, C-6 (s); 164.1, C-1' (s); 172.9, C-1a (s); and 194.3ppm C-2a (s).

Mass Data:

346(M^+, 100%), 314(98), 286(54), 258(26), 165(32), and 151*m/e* (53); HREIMS: ($C_{18}H_{18}O_7$): 346.1050; calcd. 346.1052; found C=62.29, H=5.44; calcd. C=62.41, H=5.24.

Reference

K. Krohn, A. Michel, E. Römer, U. Flörke, H.-J. Aust, S. Draeger, B. Schulz, and V. Wray; Biologically Active Metabolites from Fungi 6; Phomosines A-C, Three New Biaryl Ethers from *Phomopsis* sp.; Natural Product Letters, Vol. 6, pp. 309-314(1995).

Common/Systematic Name
Phomosine B

Molecular Formula/Molecular Weight
$C_{19}H_{22}O_7$; MW = 362.13655

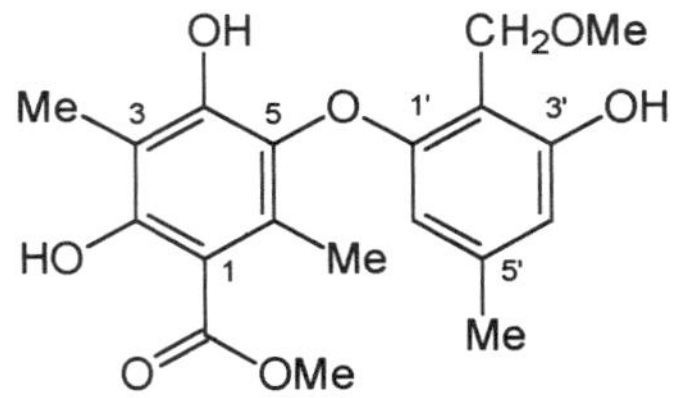

General Characteristics
Colorless powder from dichloromethane-petroleum ether; mp., 204-206°C.

Isolation/Purification
Culture medium from *Phomopsis* sp. was homogenized with a Waring blender, diluted with water and then extracted four times with ethyl acetate. The organic extracts were dried (Na_2SO_4), filtered, and evaporated *in vacuo*. The main compounds were detected in the residue on TLC at R_f values: phomosine A: R_f=0.71; phomosine B: R_f=0.53; phomosine C: R_f=0.48, 5% methanol-methylene chloride detected by UV irradiation at 254nm. Column chromatography on silica gel (methylene chloride-20% ethyl ether) gave four fractions. The second fraction gave material that was further purified by crystallization from dichloromethane-petroleum ether to afford phomosine A. The third fraction was further separated by Chromatotron chromatography (methylene chloride-petroleum ether; 1:1, v/v) into four fractions. The second fraction was purified by thin-layer chromatography (5% methanol-methylene chloride) and crystallization from dichloromethane-petroleum ether to afford additional phomosine A. From the fourth fraction, phomosine B and phomosine C were isolated by the same procedure.

Fungal Source
Phomopsis sp.

Biological Activity
All three metabolites showed moderate fungicidal and antibacterial activity against four fungal and two bacterial (one Gram-positive and one Gram-negative) test organisms. Phomosines B and C also inhibited the algal organism, *Chlorella fusca*.

Spectral Data

UV:

$\lambda_{max}^{Methylene\ Chloride}$ 232(log ϵ = 4.51), 267(4.25), and 312nm (3.74).

IR:

(KBr) 3413(OH), 2953(CH_3), 1647, 1622, 1599, 1456, 1422, 1337, 1300, 1285, 1223, 1088, 1047,and 934cm^{-1}.

^{1}H NMR:

($CDCl_3$) 2.08(3H, s, H-3a); 2.11(3H, s, 5'a-H); 2.44(3H, s, H-6a); 3.47(3H, s, H-2'b); 3.97(3H, s, H-1b); 4.78(2H, s, H-2'a); 5.94(1H, s, H-6'a); 6.46(1H, s, H-4'); 8.69(1H, s, OH); 9.10(1H, s, OH); and 11.94ppm (1H, s, OH).

^{13}C NMR:

($CDCl_3$) 8.3, C-3a (q); 15.8, C-6a (q); 21.5, C-5'a (q); 52.4, C-1b (q); 58.5, C-2'b (q); 64.6, C-2'a (t); 104.3, C-l (s); 107.1, C-6' (d); 111.1, C-3 (s); 111.5, C-2' (s); 111.5, C-4' (d); 132.3, 135.5, C-2, C 5 (2s); 140.9, C-5' (s); 154.7, C-4 (s); 157.2, C-3' (s); 158.5, C-l' (s); 161.1, C-2 (s); and 173.4ppm, C-1a (s).

Mass Spectrum:

362(M$^+$, 20%), 330(62), 298(100), 283(26), and 270*m/e* (18); HREIMS: ($C_{19}H_{22}O_7$) 362.1360*m/e*; calcd, 362.1365.

Reference

K. Krohn, A. Michel, E. Römer, U. Flörke, H.-J. Aust, S. Draeger, B. Schulz, and V. Wray; Biologically Active Metabolites from Fungi 6; Phomosines A-C, Three New Biaryl Ethers from *Phomopsis* sp.; Natural Product Letters, Vol. 6, pp. 309-314(1995).

Common/Systematic Name

Phomosine C

Molecular Formula/Molecular Weight

$C_{17}H_{16}O_7$; MW = 332.08960

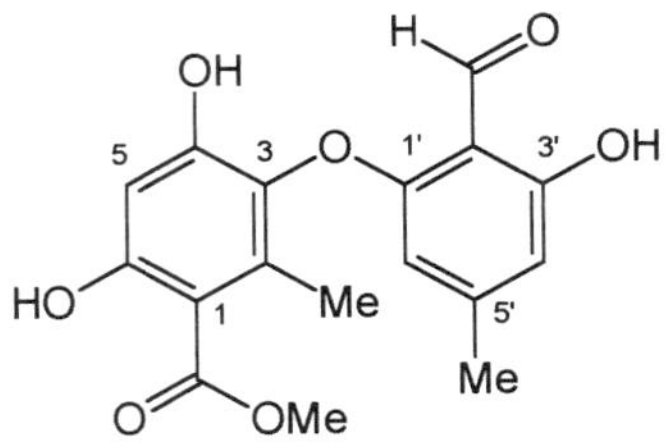

General Characteristics

White powder from dichloromethane-petroleum ether; mp., 192-193°C.

Isolation/Purification

Culture medium from *Phomopsis* sp. was homogenized with a Waring blender, diluted with water and then extracted four times with ethyl acetate. The organic extracts were dried (Na_2SO_4), filtered, and evaporated *in vacuo*. The main compounds were detected in the residue on TLC at R_f values: phomosine A, R_f=0.71; phomosine B, R_f=0.53; phomosine C, R_f=0.48, 5% methanol-methylene chloride detected by UV irradiation at 254nm. Column chromatography on silica gel (methylene chloride-methylene chloride-20% ethyl ether) gave four fractions. The second fraction gave material that was further purified by crystallization from dichloromethane-petroleum ether to afford phomosine A. The third fraction was further separated by Chromatotron chromatography (methylene chloride-petroleum ether; 1:1, v/v) into four fractions. The second fraction was purified by thin-layer chromatography (5% methanol-methylene chloride) and crystallization from dichloromethane-petroleum ether to afford additional phomosine A. From the fourth fraction, phomosine B and phomosine C were isolated by the same procedure.

Fungal Source

Phomopsis sp.

Biological Activity

All three metabolites showed moderate fungicidal and antibacterial activity against four fungal and two bacterial (one Gram-positive and one Gram-negative) test organisms. Phomosines B and C also inhibited the algal organism, *Chlorella fusca*.

Spectral Data

UV:

$\lambda_{max}^{Methylene\ Chloride}$ 232(log ϵ = 4.43), 263(4.00), and 273nm (3.93).

IR:

(KBr) 1420(OH), 3195, 2955, 1647, 1623, 1431, 1329, 1285, 1254, 1198, and 1074cm^{-1}.

^{1}H NMR:

($CDCl_3$) 2.21(3H, s, H-5'a); 2.38(3H, s, H-2a); 3.96(3 H, s, H-1b); 5.93(1H, s, H-6'); 6.42(1H, s, H-4'); 6.46(1H, s, H-5); 9.15(1H, OH); 10.50(1H, s, H-2'a); 11.43(1H, s, OH); and 11.95ppm (1H, s, OH).

^{13}C NMR:

($CDCl_3$) 15.4, C-2a (q); 22.5, C-5'a (q); 52.5, C-lb (q); 103.1, C-5 (d); 105.0, C-l (s); 105.0, C-6' (d); 109.6, C-2' (s); 111.7, C-4' (d); 130.7, 135.8, C-2, C-3 (2s); 151.4 , C-5' (s); 156.4, C-4 (s); 161.8, C-3' (s); 162.8, C-6 (s); 164.3, C-1' (s); 172.5, C-1a (s); and 194.5ppm, C-2a (s).

Mass spectrum:

332(M^+, 100%), 300(71), and 272*m/e* (36); HREIMS: ($C_{17}H_{16}O_7$): 332.0890; calcd, 332.0896.

Reference

K. Krohn, A. Michel, E. Römer, U. Flörke, H.-J. Aust, S. Draeger, B. Schulz, and V. Wray; Biologically Active Metabolites from Fungi 6; Phomosines A-C, Three New Biaryl Ethers from *Phomopsis* sp.; Natural Product Letters, Vol. 6, pp. 309-314(1995).

8

Fumiquinazolines

- Fumiquinazoline A
- Fumiquinazoline B
- Fumiquinazoline C
- Fumiquinazoline D
- Fumiquinazoline E
- Fumiquinazoline F
- Fumiquinazoline G

Common/Systematic Name

Fumiquinazoline A

Molecular Formula/Molecular Weight

$C_{24}H_{23}N_5O_4$; MW = 445.17500

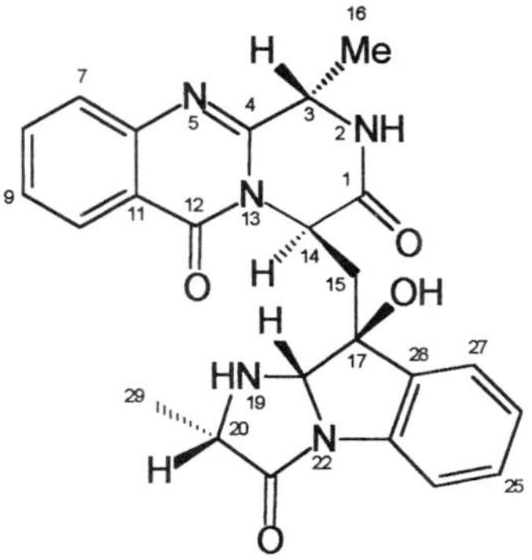

General Characteristics

Fumiquinazoline A was obtained as a pale yellow powder; mp., 178-182°C; $[\alpha]_D$ -214.5° (*c*=0.47, in $CHCl_3$).

Isolation/Purification

The fungal strain was grown in a liquid medium containing 2% glucose, 1% peptone and 0.5% yeast extract in artificial seawater adjusted to pH 7.5 for two weeks at 27°C. The culture was filtered under suction and the mycelium collected was extracted three times with methanol. The combined extracts were evaporated under reduced pressure. The resulting extract was partitioned between methylene chloride and water and removal of solvents gave the ethylene chloride fraction. This fraction was passed through Sephadex LH_{20} using methanol as the eluant. The third fraction was chromatographed on a silica gel column with a methylene chloride-methanol gradient as the eluant and 3 fractions were collected. The methylene chloride eluant yielded fumiquinazoline C after purification by HPLC (methanol-water; 7:3, v/v). The methanol-methylene chloride (1:99, v/v) eluate was purified by HPLC (methanol-water; 7:3, v/v) to afford fumiquinazoline A and fumiquinazoline D. The methanol-methylene chloride (2:98, v/v) eluant gave fumiquinazolines G, F, B, and E after purification by HPLC (methanol-water; 7:3, v/v).

Fungal Source

A strain of *Aspergillus fumigatus* originally isolated from the marine fish *Pseudolabrus japonicus*.

Biological Activity

Exhibited moderate cytotoxicity against cultured P388 cells.

Spectral Data

UV:

λ^{MeOH}_{max} 208(log ϵ = 4.58), 226(4.29), 233(4.44), 256(4.17), 265(4.13), 277(4.01), 305(3.54), and 327nm (3.44).

CD:

(c=1.47 x 10^{-5} mol/dm^{-3} in ethanol) 230($\Delta\epsilon$ -11.82), 245(0), 251(+2.11), 261(0), 278(-3.53), 284(-2.99), 290(-2.65), 297(-2.31), 305(-2.45), 312(-1.90), 316(- 0.20), and 334nm (0).

IR:

3349(OH, NH), 1680(CON), and 1608cm^{-1} (Ar-C-C).

^{1}H NMR:

($CDCl_3$) 66.1(1H, dd, J=0.9, 0.3Hz, NH-2); 4.88(1H, qd, J=7.1, 0.3Hz, H-3); 7.67(1H, dd, J=8.2, 1.0Hz, H-7); 7.75(1H, ddd, J=8.2, 7.0, 1.0Hz, H-8); 7.49(1H, ddd, J=7.9, 7.0, 1.0Hz, H-9); 8.23(1H, dd, J=7.9, 1.0Hz, H-10); 5.97(1H, ddd, J=10.9, 6.0, 0.9Hz, H-14); 2.28(1H, dd, J=13.7, 6.0Hz, H-15_A); 2.51(1H, dd, J=13.7, 10.9Hz, H-15_B); 1.79(1H, d, J=7.1Hz, H-16); 5.49(1H, s, H-18); 2.79(1H, br s, NH-19); 4.22(1H, q, J=6.7Hz, H-20); 7.52(1H, dd, J=7.5, 1.0Hz, H-24); 7.31(1H, td, J=7.5, 1.0Hz, H-25); 7.16(1H, ddd, J=7.5, 6.8, 1.0Hz, H-26); 7.61(1H, dd, J=6.8, 1.0Hz, H-27); 1.35(3H, d, J=6.7Hz, H-29); and 4.89ppm (1H, s, OH).

^{13}C NMR:

($CDCl_3$) 172.36(C-1, q); 49.15(C-3, t); 150.78(C-4, q); 146.87(C-6, q); 127.57(C-7, t); 134.80(C-8, t); 127.45(C-9, t); 126.77(C-10, t); 120.18(C-11, q); 160.48(C-12, q); 52.98(C-14, t); 36.72(C-15, s); 16.75(C-16, p); 80.20(C-17, q); 86.28(C-18, t); 59.01(C-20, t); 170.53(C-21, q); 136.17(C-23, q); 115.01(C- 24, t); 129.76(C-25, t); 125.58(C-26, t); 124.85(C-27, t); 138.59(C-28, q); and 18.63ppm(C-29, p).

Mass Spectrum:

EIMS: 445(M^+, 5%), 428(M^+ - OH, 36), 229(13), 228(4), 217(100), 199(20), and 146*m/e* (22); HREIMS: 445.1769*m/e*; $C_{24}H_{23}N_5O_4$, requires 445.1750.

Reference

C. Takahashi, T. Matsushita, M. Doi, K. Minoura, T. Shingu, Y. Kumeda and A. Numata; Fumiquinazolines A-G, Novel Metabolites of a Fungus Separated from a *Pseudolabrus* Marine Fish; J. Chem. Soc. Perkin Trans. 1, pp. 2345-2353(1995).

Common/Systematic Name

Fumiquinazoline B

Molecular Formula/Molecular Weight

$C_{24}H_{23}N_5O_4$; MW = 445.17500

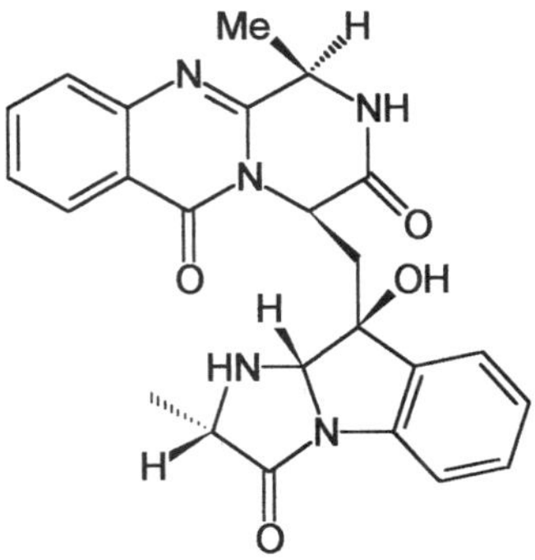

General Characteristics

Fumiquinazoline B was obtained as a pale yellow powder; mp., 174-176°C; $[\alpha]_D$ -196.6° (*c*=0.38, in $CHCl_3$).

Isolation/Purification

The fungal strain was grown in a liquid medium containing 2% glucose, 1% peptone and 0.5% yeast extract in artificial seawater adjusted to pH 7.5 for two weeks at 27°C. The culture was filtered under suction and the mycelium collected was extracted three times with methanol. The combined extracts were evaporated under reduced pressure. The resulting extract was partitioned between methylene chloride and water and removal of solvents gave the ethylene chloride fraction. This fraction was passed through Sephadex LH_{20} using methanol as the eluant. The third fraction was chromatographed on a silica gel column with a methylene chloride-methanol gradient as the eluant and 3 fractions were collected. The methylene chloride eluant yielded fumiquinazoline C after purification by HPLC (methanol-water; 7:3, v/v). The methanol-methylene chloride (1:99, v/v) eluate was purified by HPLC (methanol-water; 7:3, v/v) to afford fumiquinazoline A and fumiquinazoline D. The methanol-methylene chloride (2:98, v/v) eluant gave fumiquinazolines G, F, B, and E after purification by HPLC (methanol-water; 7:3, v/v).

Fungal Source

A strain of *Aspergillus fumigatus* originally isolated from the marine fish *Pseudolabrus japonicus*.

Biological Activity

Exhibited moderate cytotoxicity against cultured P388 cells.

Spectral Data

UV:

λ_{max}^{MeOH} 206(log ϵ = 4.77), 225(4.69), 232(4.65), 256(4.38), 266(4.32), 277(4.24), 305(3.79), and 317nm (3.68).

CD:

(c=2.22 x 10^{-5} mol/dm^{-3} in ethanol) 227($\Delta\epsilon$ -11.04), 246(0), 252(+2.32), 259(0), 280(-7.36), 287(-5.31), 297(-4.36), 305(-4.77), 318(-3.13), and 329nm (0).

IR:

3350(OH, NH), 1673(CON), and 1604cm^{-1} (Ar-C-C).

^{1}H NMR:

($CDCl_3$) 7.34(1H, dd, J=4.9, 0.9Hz, NH-2); 4.72(1H, qd, J=7.2, 4.9Hz, H-3); 7.56(1H, dd, J=8.0, 1.0Hz, H-7); 7.73(1H, ddd, J=8.0, 7.0, 1.0Hz, H-8); 7.45(1H, ddd, J=7.8, 7.0, 1.0Hz, H-9); 8.19(1H, dd, J=7.8, 1.0Hz, H-10); 5.79(1H, ddd, J=11.2, 4.8, 0.9Hz, H-14); 2.48(1H, dd, J=13.3, 4.8Hz, H-15_A); 2.61(1H, dd, J=13.3, 11.2Hz, H-15_B); 1.83(1H, d, J=7.2Hz, H-16); 5.42(1H, br s, H-18); 2.75(1H, br s, NH-19); 4.14(1H, q, J=6.7Hz, H-20); 7.51(1H, dd, J=7.5, 1.0Hz, H-24); 7.30(1H, td, J=7.5, 1.0Hz, H-25); 7.17(1H, td, J=7.5, 1.0Hz, H-26); 7.61(1H, dd, J=7.5, 1.0Hz, H-27); 1.29(3H, d, J=6.7Hz, H-29); and 5.47ppm (1H, s, OH).

^{13}C NMR:

($CDCl_3$) 170.69(C-1, q); 52.73(C-3, t); 150.72(C-4, q); 147.00(C-6, q); 126.88(C-7, t); 134.97(C-8, t); 127.27(C-9, t); 126.88(C-10, t); 120.01(C-11, q); 160.30(C-12, q); 52.01(C-14, t); 38.97(C-15, s); 24.88(C-16, p); 80.20(C-17, q); 80.43(C-18, t); 59.07(C-20, t); 170.56(C-21, q); 136.56(C-23, q); 114.86(C-24, t); 129.73(C-25, t); 125.50(C-26, t); 125.02(C-27, t); 138.62(C-28, q); and 18.14ppm (C-29, p).

Mass Spectrum:

EIMS: 445(M^+, 5%), 229(10), 228(2), 217(100), 199(6), and 146*m/e* (15); HREIMS: 445.1741*m/e*; $C_{24}H_{23}N_5O_4$, requires 445.1750.

Reference

C. Takahashi, T. Matsushita, M. Doi, K. Minoura, T. Shingu, Y. Kumeda and A. Numata; Fumiquinazolines A-G, Novel Metabolites of a Fungus Separated from a *Pseudolabrus* Marine Fish; J. Chem. Soc. Perkin Trans. 1, pp. 2345-2353(1995).

Common/Systematic Name

Fumiquinazoline C

Molecular Formula/Molecular Weight

$C_{24}H_{21}N_5O_4$; MW = 443.15935

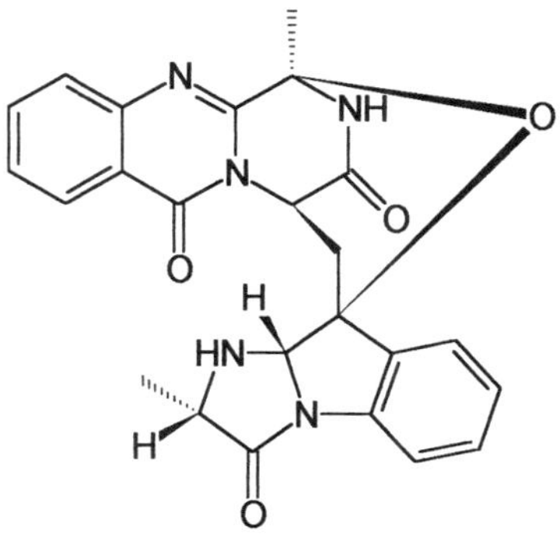

General Characteristics

Fumiquinazoline C was obtained as colorless prisms , 244-246°C; $[\alpha]_D$ -193.7° (*c*=0.31, in $CHCl_3$).

Isolation/Purification

The fungal strain was grown in a liquid medium containing 2% glucose, 1% peptone and 0.5% yeast extract in artificial seawater adjusted to pH 7.5 for two weeks at 27°C. The culture was filtered under suction and the mycelium collected was extracted three times with methanol. The combined extracts were evaporated under reduced pressure. The resulting extract was partitioned between methylene chloride and water and removal of solvents gave the ethylene chloride fraction. This fraction was passed through Sephadex LH_{20} using methanol as the eluant. The third fraction was chromatographed on a silica gel column with a methylene chloride-methanol gradient as the eluant and 3 fractions were collected. The methylene chloride eluant yielded fumiquinazoline C after purification by HPLC (methanol-water; 7:3, v/v). The methanol-methylene chloride (1:99, v/v) eluate was purified by HPLC (methanol-water; 7:3, v/v) to afford fumiquinazoline A and fumiquinazoline D. The methanol-methylene chloride (2:98, v/v) eluant gave fumiquinazolines G, F, B, and E after purification by HPLC (methanol-water; 7:3, v/v).

Fungal Source

A strain of *Aspergillus fumigatus* originally isolated from the marine fish *Pseudolabrus japonicus*.

Biological Activity

Exhibited moderate cytotoxicity against cultured P388 cells.

Spectral Data

UV:

λ_{max}^{MeOH} 207(log ϵ = 4.56), 225(4.48), 260(4.06), 271(4.02), 282(3.98), 304(3.61), and 317nm (3.50).

CD:

(c= 4.02 x 10^{-5} mol/dm^{-3} in ethanol) 226 ($\Delta\epsilon$ -15.84), 238(0), 243(+5.28), 247(+ 3.77), 253(+ 4.90), 269(0), 303(-13.58), 310(-10.18), 314(-10.56), and 328nm (0).

IR:

3343, 3257(NH), 1715(CON), and 1611cm^{-1} (Ar-C-C).

^{1}H NMR:

($CDCl_3$) 8.04(1H, br s, NH-2); 7.78(1H, dd, J=7.4, 1.7Hz, H-7); 7.81(1H, ddd, J=7.4, 6.3, 1.7Hz, H-8); 7.60(1H, ddd, J=7.4, 6.3, 1.7Hz, H-9); 8.35(1H, dd, J=7.4, 1.7Hz, H-10); 5.72(1H, dd, J=10.9, 6.0Hz, H-14); 2.14(1H, dd, J=13.7, 6.0Hz, H-15_A); 2.98(1H, dd, J=13.7, 10.9Hz, H-15_B); 2.06(1H, s, H-16); 5.34(1H, d, J=6.9Hz, H-18); 1.04(1H, dd, J=6.9, 6.7Hz, NH-19); 3.71(1H, qd, J=6.9, 6.7Hz, H- 20); 7.45(1H, dd, J=7.4, 1.0Hz, H-24); 7.32(1H, td, J=7.4, 1.0Hz, H-25); 7.19(1H, td, J=7.4, 1.0Hz, H-26); 7.37(1H, dd, J=7.4, 1.0Hz, H-27); and 1.06ppm (3H, d, J=6.9Hz, H-29).

^{13}C NMR:

($CDCl_3$) 171.02(C-1, q); 84.16(C-3, q); 150.39(C-4, q); 146.32(C-6, q); 128.45(C-7, t); 134.91(C-8, t); 128.56(C-9, t); 126.98(C-10, t); 121.34(C-11, q); 159.53(C-12, q); 51.39(C-14, t); 31.36(C-15, s); 24.43(C-16, p); 87.07(C-17, q); 87.07(C-18, t); 58.61(C-20, t); 170.90(C-21, q); 135.73(C-23, q); 115.46(C-24, t); 130.23(C-25, t); 126.17(C-26, t); 124.88(C-27, t); 138.41(C-28, q); and 18.71ppm (C-29, p).

Mass Spectrum:

HREIMS: 443.1591m/e; $C_{24}H_{21}N_5O_4$, requires 443.1594.

Reference

C. Takahashi, T. Matsushita, M. Doi, K. Minoura, T. Shingu, Y. Kumeda and A. Numata; Fumiquinazolines A-G, Novel Metabolites of a Fungus Separated from a *Pseudolabrus* Marine Fish; J. Chem. Soc. Perkin Trans. 1, pp. 2345-2353(1995).

Common/Systematic Name

Fumiquinazoline D

Molecular Formula/Molecular Weight

$C_{24}H_{21}N_5O_4$; MW = 443.15935

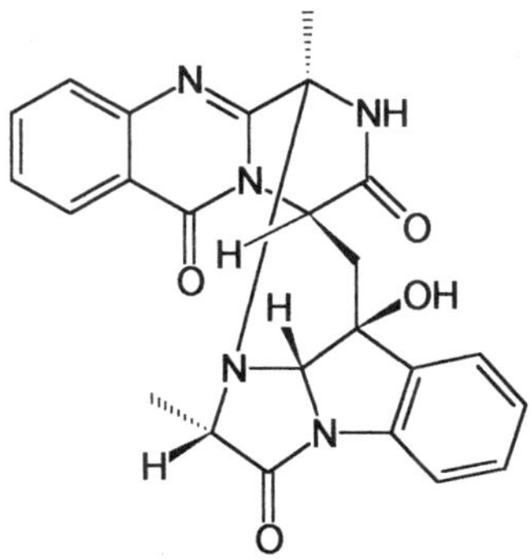

General Characteristics

Fumiquinazoline D was obtained as colorless prisms from acetone, mp., 214-216°C; $[\alpha]_D$ + 68.9° (*c*=0.27, in $CHCl_3$).

Isolation/Purification

The fungal strain was grown in a liquid medium containing 2% glucose, 1% peptone and 0.5% yeast extract in artificial seawater adjusted to pH 7.5 for two weeks at 27°C. The culture was filtered under suction and the mycelium collected was extracted three times with methanol. The combined extracts were evaporated under reduced pressure. The resulting extract was partitioned between methylene chloride and water and removal of solvents gave the ethylene chloride fraction. This fraction was passed through Sephadex LH_{20} using methanol as the eluant. The third fraction was chromatographed on a silica gel column with a methylene chloride-methanol gradient as the eluant and 3 fractions were collected. The methylene chloride eluant yielded fumiquinazoline C after purification by HPLC (methanol-water; 7:3, v/v). The methanol-methylene chloride (1:99, v/v) eluate was purified by HPLC (methanol-water; 7:3, v/v) to afford fumiquinazoline A and fumiquinazoline D. The methanol-methylene chloride (2:98, v/v) eluant gave fumiquinazolines G, F, B, and E after purification by HPLC (methanol-water; 7:3, v/v).

Fungal Source

A strain of *Aspergillus fumigatus* originally isolated from the marine fish *Pseudolabrus japonicus*.

Biological Activity

Exhibited moderate cytotoxicity against cultured P388 cells.

Spectral Data

UV:

λ_{max}^{MeOH} 205(log ϵ = 4.30), 225(4.26), 232(4.24), 254(3.91), 265(3.84), 276(3.77), 304(3.43), and 316nm (3.54).

CD:

(c= 4.33 x 10^{-5} mol/dm^{-3} in ethanol) 232($\Delta\epsilon$ -1.75), 235(0), 247(+6.12), 258(0), 268(- 4.90), 275(- 5.25), 294(- 2.45), 303(-2.80), 310(-2.10), 315(-2.10), and 326nm (0).

IR:

3418(OH, NH), 1703(CON), and 1611cm^{-1} (Ar-C-C).

^{1}H NMR:

($CDCl_3$) 9.16(1H, br s, NH-2); 7.66(1H, dd, J=8.3, 1.2Hz, H-7); 7.75(1H, ddd, J=8.3, 6.8, 1.2Hz, H-8); 7.50(1H, ddd, J=7.9, 6.8, 1.2Hz, H-9); 8.19(1H, dd, J=7.9, 1.2Hz, H-10); 5.65(1H, d, J=10.3Hz, H-14); 2.27(1H, d, J=15.1Hz, H-15_A); 3.38(1H, dd, J=15.1, 10.3Hz, H-15_B); 2.02(1H, s, H-16); 5.52(1H, d, J=1.3Hz, H-18); 3.96(1H, qd, J=6.5, 1.3Hz, H-20); 7.41(1H, dd, J=7.4, 1.0Hz, H-24); 7.23(1H, td, J=7.4, 1.0Hz, H-25); 7.05(1H, td, J=7.4, 1.0Hz, H-26); 7.44(1H, dd, J=7.4, 1.0Hz, H-27); 1.08(3H, d, J=6.5Hz, H-29); and 5.27ppm (1H, br s, OH).

^{13}C NMR:

($CDCl_3$) 172.58(C-1, q); 70.84(C-3, q); 152.14(C-4, q); 146.34(C-6, q); 127.79(C-7, t); 134.83(C-8, t); 127.68(C-9, t); 126.85(C-10, t); 120.35(C-11, q); 160.86(C-12, q); 52.76(C-14, t); 43.44(C-15, s); 18.77(C-16, p); 84.13(C-17, q); 85.59(C-18, t); 59.11(C-20, t); 171.41(C-21, q); 137.60(C-23, q); 115.43(C-24, t); 130.07(C-25, t); 125.77(C-26, t); 124.31(C-27, t); 137.38(C-28, q); and 17.41ppm (C-29, p).

Mass Spectrum:

HREIMS: 443.1588m/e; $C_{24}H_{21}N_5O_4$, requires 443.1594.

Reference

C. Takahashi, T. Matsushita, M. Doi, K. Minoura, T. Shingu, Y. Kumeda and A. Numata; Fumiquinazolines A-G, Novel Metabolites of a Fungus Separated from a *Pseudolabrus* Marine Fish; J. Chem. Soc. Perkin Trans. 1, pp. 2345-2353(1995).

Common/Systematic Name

Fumiquinazoline E

Molecular Formula/Molecular Weight

$C_{24}H_{25}N_5O_5$; MW = 475.18557

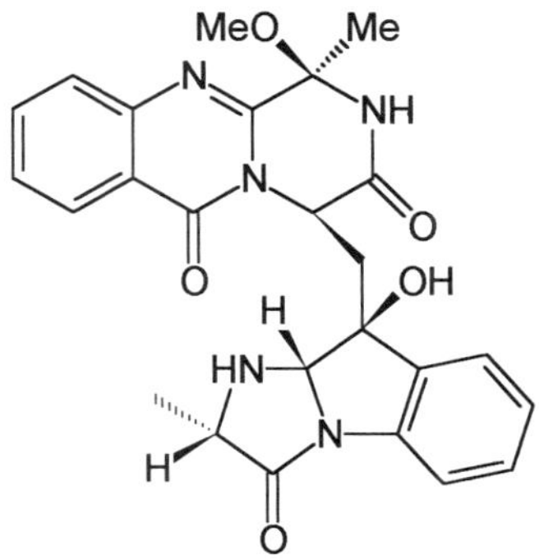

General Characteristics

Fumiquinazoline E was obtained as a pale yellow powder, mp., 168-172^{0}C; $[\alpha]_D$ -143.3° (c=0.18, in $CHCl_3$).

Isolation/Purification

The fungal strain was grown in a liquid medium containing 2% glucose, 1% peptone and 0.5% yeast extract in artificial seawater adjusted to pH 7.5 for two weeks at 27°C. The culture was filtered under suction and the mycelium collected was extracted three times with methanol. The combined extracts were evaporated under reduced pressure. The resulting extract was partitioned between methylene chloride and water and removal of solvents gave the ethylene chloride fraction. This fraction was passed through Sephadex LH_{20} using methanol as the eluant. The third fraction was chromatographed on a silica gel column with a methylene chloride-methanol gradient as the eluant and 3 fractions were collected. The methylene chloride eluant yielded fumiquinazoline C after purification by HPLC (methanol-water; 7:3, v/v). The methanol-methylene chloride (1:99, v/v) eluate was purified by HPLC (methanol-water;7:3,v/v) to afford fumiquinazoline A and fumiquinazoline D. The methanol-methylene chloride (2:98, v/v) eluant gave fumiquinazolines G, F, B, and E after purification by HPLC (methanol-water; 7:3, v/v).

Fungal Source

A strain of *Aspergillus fumigatus* originally isolated from the marine fish *Pseudolabrus japonicus*.

Biological Activity

Exhibited moderate cytotoxicity against cultured P388 cells.

Spectral Data

UV:

λ_{max}^{MeOH} 210 (log ϵ = 4.54), 226 (4.48), 233 (4.44), 256 (4.16), 278 (4.06), 304 (3.62), and 317nm (3.52).

CD:

(c= 4.33 x 10^{-5} mol/dm^{-3} in ethanol) 219($\Delta\epsilon$ -2.69), 221(-2.34), 233(-7.73), 245(0), 251(+ 1.70), 259(0), 278(- 3.98), 290(- 2.87), 296(-2.34), 312(-2.58), 310(-2.05), 314(-1.99), and 329nm (0).

IR:

3427(OH, NH), 1685(CON), and 1608cm^{-1} (Ar-C-C).

^{1}H NMR:

($CDCl_3$) 7.57(1H, br d, NH-2); 7.74(1H, dd, J=7.7, 1.5Hz, H-7); 7.79(1H, ddd, J=8.2, 7.7, 1.5Hz, H-8); 7.53(1H, ddd, J=8.2, 6.8, 1.5Hz, H-9); 8.25(1H, dd, J=6.8, 1.5Hz, H-10); 5.93(1H, ddd, J=8.9, 5.2, 1.0Hz, H-14); 2.34(1H, dd, J=14.4, 5.2Hz, H-15_A); 2.80(1H, dd, J=14.4, 8.9Hz, H-15_B); 1.97(1H, s, H-16); 5.45(1H, s, H-18); 4.16(1H, q, J=6.6Hz, H-20); 7.56(1H, dd, J=7.2, 0.8Hz, H-24); 7.33(1H, ddd, J=8.0, 7.2, 1.0Hz, H-25); 7.16(1H, ddd, J=8.0, 7.2, 0.8Hz, H-26); 7.57(1H, dd, J=7.2, 1.0Hz, H-27); 1.33(3H, d, J=6.6Hz, H-29); 3.33(3H, s, OMe); and 4.55ppm (1H, s, OH-17).

^{13}C NMR:

($CDCl_3$) 172.70(C-1, q); 84.83(C-3, q); 148.17(C-4, q); 146.18(C-6, q); 127.96(C-7, t); 134.82(C-8, t); 127.96(C-9, t); 126.95(C-10, t); 120.60(C-11, q); 161.01(C-12, q); 53.38(C-14, t); 38.91(C-15, s); 20.88(C-16, p); 80.11(C-17, q); 86.29(C-18, t); 59.20(C-20, t); 171.28(C-21, q); 136.78(C-23, q); 115.09(C-24, t); 129.74(C-25, t); 125.16(C-26, t); 124.69(C-27, t); 138.61(C-28, q); 17.85(C-29 p); and 50.80ppm (C-OMe, p).

Mass Spectrum:

FAB: 476(MH^+, 11%), 442(8), 228(18), 217(38), 199(34), 154(100), and 136m/e (90).

Reference

C. Takahashi, T. Matsushita, M. Doi, K. Minoura, T. Shingu, Y. Kumeda and A. Numata; Fumiquinazolines A-G, Novel Metabolites of a Fungus Separated from a *Pseudolabrus* Marine Fish; J. Chem. Soc. Perkin Trans. 1, pp. 2345-2353(1995).

Common/Systematic Name
Fumiquinazoline F

Molecular Formula/Molecular Weight
$C_{21}H_{18}N_4O_2$; MW = 358.14298

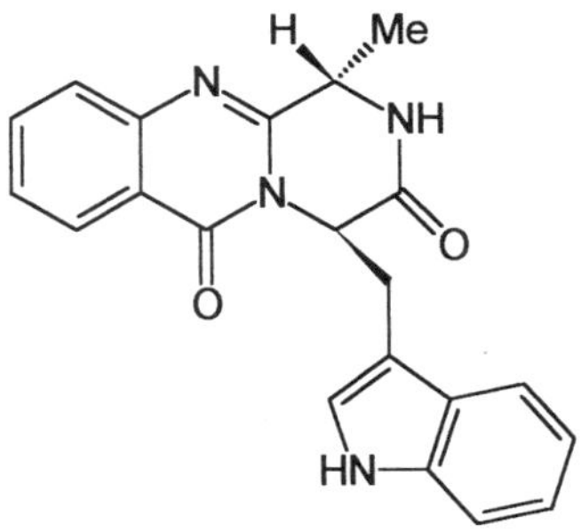

General Characteristics
Fumiquinazoline F was obtained as a pale yellow powder, mp., 88-90°C; $[\alpha]_D$ -411.2° (c=1.36, in $CHCl_3$).

Isolation/Purification
The fungal strain was grown in a liquid medium containing 2% glucose, 1% peptone and 0.5% yeast extract in artificial seawater adjusted to pH 7.5 for two weeks at 27°C. The culture was filtered under suction and the mycelium collected was extracted three times with methanol. The combined extracts were evaporated under reduced pressure. The resulting extract was partitioned between methylene chloride and water and removal of solvents gave the ethylene chloride fraction. This fraction was passed through Sephadex LH_{20} using methanol as the eluant. The third fraction was chromatographed on a silica gel column with a methylene chloride-methanol gradient as the eluant and 3 fractions were collected. The methylene chloride eluant yielded fumiquinazoline C after purification by HPLC (methanol-water; 7:3, v/v). The methanol-methylene chloride (1:99, v/v) eluate was purified by HPLC (methanol-water; 7:3, v/v) to afford fumiquinazoline A and fumiquinazoline D. The methanol-methylene chloride (2:98, v/v) eluant gave fumiquinazolines G, F, B, and E after purification by HPLC (methanol-water; 7:3, v/v).

Fungal Source
A strain of *Aspergillus fumigatus* originally isolated from the marine fish *Pseudolabrus japonicus*.

Biological Activity
Exhibited moderate cytotoxicity against cultured P388 cells.

Spectral Data

UV:

λ_{max}^{MeOH} 207(log ϵ = 4.71), 219(4.73), 270(4.13), 277(4.13), 289(3.99), 306(3.78), and 320nm (3.66).

IR:

3264(NH), 1679(CON), and 1610cm^{-1} (Ar-C-C).

^{1}H NMR:

($CDCl_3$) 6.60(1H, br s, NH-2); 3.14(1H, q, *J*=6.8, 0.3Hz, H-3); 7.60(1H, dd, *J*=7.8, 1.0Hz, H-7); 7.77(1H, td, *J*=7.8, 1.8Hz, H-8); 7.53(1H, td, *J*=7.8, 1.0Hz, H-9); 8.37(1H, dd, *J*=7.8, 1.8Hz, H-10); 5.68(1H, dd, *J*=5.2, 3.6Hz, H-14); 3.64(1H, dd, *J*=15.0, 5.2Hz, H-15_A); 3.71(1H, dd, *J*=15.0, 3.6Hz, H-15_B); 1.37(1H, d, *J*=6.8Hz, H-16); 6.71(1H, d, *J*=2.5Hz, H-18); 8.26(1H, br s, NH-19); 7.30(1H, dd, *J*=8.0, 0.8Hz, H-21); 7.13(1H, td, *J*=8.0, 0.8Hz, H-22); 6.92(1H, td, *J*=8.0, 0.8Hz, H-23); and 7.40ppm (1H, dd, *J*=8.0, 0.8Hz, H-25).

^{13}C NMR:

($CDCl_3$) 169.33(C-1, q); 49.18(C-3, t); 151.68(C-4, q); 147.08(C-6, q); 127.30(C-7, t); 134.70(C-8, t); 127.12(C-9, t); 126.85(C-10, t); 120.24(C-11, q); 160.82(C-12, q); 57.53(C-14, t); 27.04(C-15, s); 19.08(C-16, p); 109.39(C-17, q); 123.55(C-18, t); 135.98(C-20, q); 111.22(C-21, t); 122.57(C-22, t); 120.01(C-23, t); 118.48(C-24, t); and 127.30ppm (C-25, q).

Mass Spectrum:

EIMS: 358(M^+, 3%), 229(4), 228(1), and 130*m/e* (100); HREIMS: 358.1436*m/e*; $C_{21}H_{18}N_4O_2$, requires 358.1430.

Reference

C. Takahashi, T. Matsushita, M. Doi, K. Minoura, T. Shingu, Y. Kumeda and A. Numata; Fumiquinazolines A-G, Novel Metabolites of a Fungus Separated from a *Pseudolabrus* Marine Fish; J. Chem. Soc. Perkin Trans. 1, pp. 2345-2353(1995).

Common/Systematic Name

Fumiquinazoline G

Molecular Formula/Molecular Weight

$C_{21}H_{18}N_4O_2$; MW = 358.14298

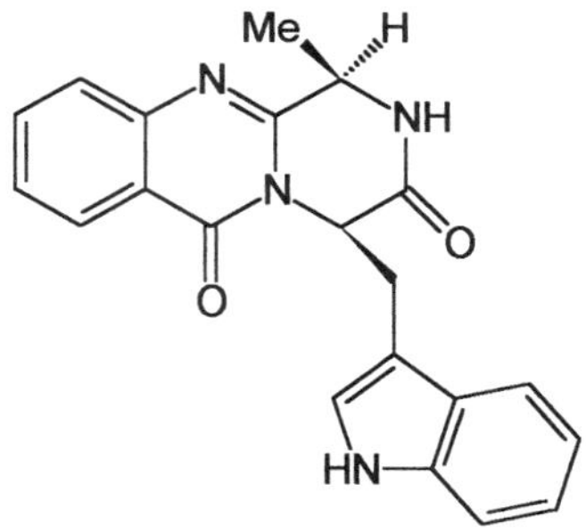

General Characteristics

Fumiquinazoline G was obtained as a pale yellow powder; mp., 119-121°C; $[\alpha]_D$ = - 462.8° (*c*=0.61, in $CHCl_3$).

Isolation/Purification

The fungal strain was grown in a liquid medium containing 2% glucose, 1% peptone and 0.5% yeast extract in artificial seawater adjusted to pH 7.5 for two weeks at 27°C. The culture was filtered under suction and the mycelium collected was extracted three times with methanol. The combined extracts were evaporated under reduced pressure. The resulting extract was partitioned between methylene chloride and water and removal of solvents gave the ethylene chloride fraction. This fraction was passed through Sephadex LH_{20} using methanol as the eluant. The third fraction was chromatographed on a silica gel column with a methylene chloride-methanol gradient as the eluant and 3 fractions were collected. The methylene chloride eluant yielded fumiquinazoline C after purification by HPLC (methanol-water; 7:3, v/v). The methanol-methylene chloride (1:99, v/v) eluate was purified by HPLC (methanol-water; 7:3, v/v) to afford fumiquinazoline A and fumiquinazoline D. The methanol-methylene chloride (2:98, v/v) eluant gave fumiquinazolines G, F, B, and E after purification by HPLC (methanol-water; 7:3, v/v).

Fungal Source

A strain of *Aspergillus fumigatus* originally isolated from the marine fish *Pseudolabrus japonicus*.

Biological Activity

Exhibited moderate cytotoxicity against cultured P388 cells.

Spectral Data

UV:

λ_{max}^{EtOH} 208(log ϵ = 4.61), 220(4.67), 273(4.14), 278(4.13), 288(4.01), 307(3.66), and 323nm (3.49).

IR:

3278(NH), 1680(CON), and 1610cm^{-1} (Ar-C-C).

^{1}H NMR:

($CDCl_3$) 6.60(1H, br s, NH-2); 4.46(1H, qd, *J*=6.0, 4.2Hz, H-3); 7.59(1H, dd, *J*=8.6, 1.0Hz, H-7); 7.80(1H, ddd, *J*=8.6, 7.8, 1.5Hz, H-8); 7.55(1H, td, *J*=7.8, 1.0Hz, H-9); 8.39(1H, dd, *J*=7.8, 1.5Hz, H-10); 5.55(1H, dd, *J*=5.2, 3.6Hz, H-14); 3.71(1H, dd, *J*=15.0, 3.6Hz, H-15_A); 3.78(1H, dd, *J*=15.0, 5.2Hz, H-15_B); 0.58(1H, d, *J*=6.0Hz, H-16); 6.74(1H, d, *J*=2.0Hz, H-18); 8.15(1H, br s, NH-19); 7.27(1H, dd, *J*=8.2, 0.8Hz, H-21); 7.08(1H, ddd, *J*=8.2, 7.0, 1.4Hz, H-22); 6.85(1H, ddd, *J*=8.2, 7.0, 0.8Hz, H-23); and 7.31ppm (1H, dd, *J*=8.2, 1.4Hz, H-24).

^{13}C NMR:

($CDCl_3$) 167.17(C-1, q); 51.73(C-3, t); 151.43(C-4, q); 146.80(C-6, q); 126.89(C-7, t); 134.95(C-8, t); 127.07(C-9, t); 126.99(C-10, t); 120.04(C-11, q); 160.89(C-12, q); 56.93(C-14, t); 27.07(C-15, s); 22.76(C-16, p); 109.32(C-17, q); 123.70(C-18, t); 135.69(C-20, q); 111.07(C-21, t); 122.31(C-22, t); 119.91(C-23, t); 118.59(C-24, t); and 127.83ppm (C-25, q).

Mass Spectrum:

EIMS: 358(M^+, 11%), 229(3), 228(1), and 130*m/e* (100); HREIMS: 358.1428*m/e*; $C_{21}H_{18}N_4O_2$, requires 358.1430.

Reference

C. Takahashi, T. Matsushita, M. Doi, K. Minoura, T. Shingu, Y. Kumeda and A. Numata; Fumiquinazolines A-G, Novel Metabolites of a Fungus Separated from a *Pseudolabrus* Marine Fish; J. Chem. Soc. Perkin Trans. 1, pp. 2345-2353(1995).

9

Ganomastenols

Ganomastenol A
Ganomastenol B
Ganomastenol C
Ganomastenol D

Common/Systematic Name

Ganomastenol A

rel-3α,8,9α-Trihydroxycadina-4,10(15)-diene

Molecular Formula/Molecular Weight

$C_{15}H_{24}O_3$; MW = 252.17254

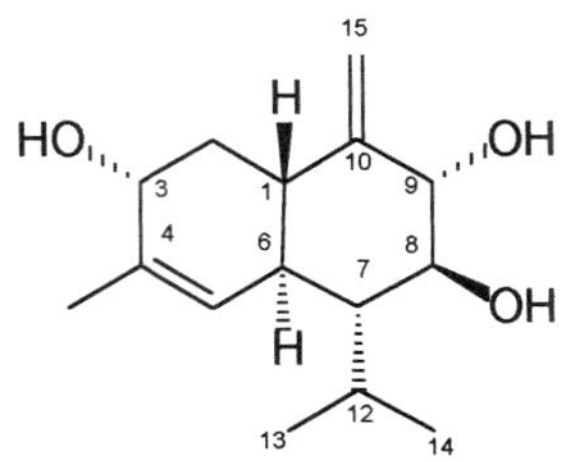

General Characteristics

Isolated as a white powder.

Isolation/Purification

The fungus was cultured on soytone medium. The mycelia were cultured statically at 25°C in the dark for 51 days. After 52 days culture, the mycelia were harvested with nylon cloth and homogenized with methanol and then allowed to stand for 10 days at room temperature. The culture broth, concentrated under reduced pressure and adjusted to pH 2 with 2 M HCl, was extracted with ethyl acetate. The ethyl acetate layer was dried over Na_2SO_4 and then evaporated to dryness to afford the crude extract. After 10 days the methanol-homogenized mycelium was filtered and the residue re-extracted with methanol and the organic solvent removed under reduced pressure. The residue was extracted with $CHCl_3$ and the $CHCl_3$ fraction was dried and evaporated to dryness. The combined $CHCl_3$ extracts of the mycelia and ethyl acetate extract of the culture broth were subjected to silica gel column (Wako-gel C-200) eluted with an ethyl acetate-*n*-hexane solvent system and separated into 6 fractions. Fraction 1 eluted with *n*-hexane and ethyl acetate-*n*-hexane (1:4, v/v); fraction 2 eluted with ethyl acetate-*n*-hexane (1:4, v/v; 200ml); fraction 3 with ethyl acetate-*n*-hexane (1:1, v/v; 500ml); fraction 4 with ethyl acetate-*n*-hexane (1:1, v/v; 100ml); fraction 5 with ethyl acetate-*n*-hexane (1:1, v/v; 940ml); and fraction 6 with ethyl acetate-*n*-hexane (1:1, v/v; 200ml), ethyl acetate-*n*-hexane, (3:2, v/v; 800ml), ethyl acetate (300ml), and methanol (500ml). Repeated purification of fraction 3 by HPLC eluted with 40% acetonitrile in 2% acetic acid yielded purified ganomastenols A, B, C, and D.

Fungal Source

Ganoderma mastoporum.

Spectral Data

IR:

(KBr) 3425cm^{-1} (OH).

^{1}H NMR:

(CDCl$_3$) 1.89(1H, ddd, *J*=12.0, 11.0, 2.5Hz, H-1); 1.48(1H, ddd, *J*=12.0, 12.0, 10.0Hz, H-2β); 2.24(1H, ddd, *J*=12.0, 6.0, 2.5Hz, H-2α); 4.16(1H, dd, *J*=10.0, 6.0Hz, H-3β); 5.61(1H, dd, *J*=1.0, 1.0Hz, H-5); 1.62(1H, ddd, *J*=11.0, 11.0, 1.0Hz, H-6); 1.24(1H, ddd, *J*=11.0, 11.0, 1.0Hz, H-7β); 3.12(1H, dd, *J*=11.0, 10.0Hz, H-8α); 3.80(1H, ddd, *J*=10.0, 1.5, 1.5Hz, H-9β); 1.76(1H, br s, H-11); 2.27(1H, qqd, *J*=7.0, 7.0, 1.0Hz, H-12); 1.00(3H, d, *J*=7.0Hz); 1.09(3H, d, *J*=7.0Hz, H-14); 4.76 91H, dd, *J*=3.0, 1.5Hz, H-15a); and 5.09ppm (1H, dd, *J*=3.0, 1.5Hz, H-15b).

^{13}C NMR:

(CDCl$_3$) 43.1, C-1; 37.2, C-2; 71.6, C-3; 139.4, C-4; 127.3, C-5; 44.9, C-6; 52.7, C-7; 79.0, C-8; 79.1, C-9; 152.2, C-10; 20.1, C-11; 28.0, C-12; 19.9, C-13; 22.1, C-14 and 103.2ppm, C-15.

Mass Spectrum:

FAB-MS: 275*m/e* $(M + Na)^+$; HREIMS: 234.1625*m/e* $(M - H_2O)^+$, $C_{15}H_{24}O_3$, requires 252.1725; EIMS: 234(97%), 191(49), and 173*m/e* (100).

Reference

M. Hirotani, C. Ino, A. Hatano, H. Takayanagi, and T. Furuya; Ganomastenols A, B, C, and D, Cadinene sesquiterpenes from *Ganoderma mastoporum*; Phytochemistry, Vol. 40, pp. 161-165(1995).

Common/Systematic Name

Ganomastenol B

rel-3β,8β,9α-Trihydroxycadina-4,10(15)-diene

Molecular Formula/Molecular Weight

$C_{15}H_{24}O_3$; MW = 252.17254

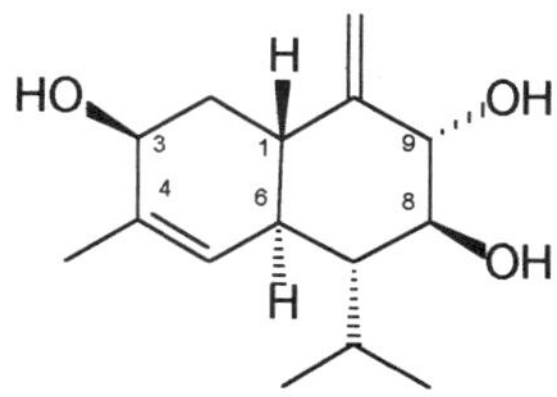

General Characteristics

Isolated as needles; mp., 139-140°C.

Isolation/Purification

The fungus was cultured on soytone medium. The mycelia were cultured statically at 25°C in the dark for 51 days. After 52 days culture, the mycelia were harvested with nylon cloth and homogenized with methanol and then allowed to stand for 10 days at room temperature. The culture broth, concentrated under reduced pressure and adjusted to pH 2 with 2M HCl, was extracted with ethyl acetate. The ethyl acetate layer was dried over Na_2SO_4 and then evaporated to dryness to afford the crude extract. After 10 days the methanol-homogenized mycelium was filtered and the residue re-extracted with methanol and the organic solvent removed under reduced pressure. The residue was extracted with $CHCl_3$ and the $CHCl_3$ fraction was dried and evaporated to dryness. The combined $CHCl_3$ extracts of the mycelia and ethyl acetate extract of the culture broth were subjected to silica gel column (Wako-gel C-200) eluted with an ethyl acetate-*n*-hexane solvent system and separated into 6 fractions. Fraction 1 eluted with *n*-hexane and ethyl acetate-*n*-hexane (1:4, v/v); fraction 2 eluted with ethyl acetate-*n*-hexane (1:4, v/v; 200ml); fraction 3 with ethyl acetate-*n*-hexane (1:1, v/v; 500ml); fraction 4 with ethyl acetate-*n*-hexane (1:1, v/v; 100ml); fraction 5 with ethyl acetate-*n*-hexane (1:1, v/v; 940ml); and fraction 6 with ethyl acetate-*n*-hexane (1:1, v/v; 200ml), ethyl acetate-*n*-hexane (3:2, v/v; 800ml), ethyl acetate (300ml), and methanol (500ml). Repeated purification of fraction 3 by HPLC eluted with 40% acetonitrile in 2% acetic acid yielded purified ganomastenols A, B, C, and D.

Fungal Source

Ganoderma mastoporum.

Spectral Data

IR:

(KBr) 3320(OH) and 2880cm^{-1}.

^{1}H NMR:

(CDCl$_3$) 2.05(1H, ddd, *J*=11.0, 11.0, 2.0Hz, H-1); 1.63(1H, ddd, *J*=13.0, 11.0, 4.0Hz, H-2β); 2.00(1H, ddd, *J*=13.0, 2.0, 2.0Hz, H-2α); 3.99(1H, dd, *J*= 4.0, 2.0Hz, H-3α); 5.72(1H, dd, *J*=1.0, 1.0Hz, H-3β); 1.48(1H, ddd, *J*=11.0, 11.0, 1.0Hz, H-6); 1.31(1H, ddd, *J*=11.0, 11.0, 1.0Hz, H-7β); 3.14(1H, dd, *J*=11.0, 10.0Hz, H-8α); 3.85(1H, ddd, *J*= 10.0, 1.5, 1.5Hz, H-9β); 1.81(1H, br s, H-11); 2.31(1H, qqd, *J*=7.0, 7.0, 1.0Hz, H-12); 1.02(3H, d, *J*=7.0Hz, H-13); 1.09(3H, d, *J*=7.0Hz, H- 14); 4.73 (1H, dd, *J*=3.0, 1.5Hz, H-15a); and 5.08ppm (1H, dd, *J*=3.0, 1.5Hz, H-15b).

^{13}C NMR:

(CDCl$_3$) 37.7, C-1; 36.2, C-2; 68.7, C-3; 137.1, C-4; 128.6, C-5; 44.9, C-6; 55.2, C-7; 79.2, C-8; 79.2, C-9; 152.8, C-10; 21.8, C-11; 27.7, C-12; 19.9, C-13; 22.0, C-14 and 103.1ppm C-15.

Mass Spectrum:

FAB-MS: 275*m/e* $(M + Na)^+$; HREIMS: 234.1614*m/e* $(M - H_2O)^+$, $C_{15}H_{24}O_3$ requires 252.1725; EIMS: 234(10%), 216(25), 173(70), and 145*m/e* (100).

Reference

M. Hirotani, C. Ino, A. Hatano, H. Takayanagi, and T. Furuya; Ganomastenols A, B, C, and D, Cadinene sesquiterpenes from *Ganoderma mastoporum*; Phytochemistry, Vol. 40, pp. 161-165(1995).

Common/Systematic Name

Ganomastenol C

rel-3β,8β,9α-Trihydroxycadina-10(15)-ene

Molecular Formula/Molecular Weight

$C_{15}H_{26}O_3$; MW = 254.18819

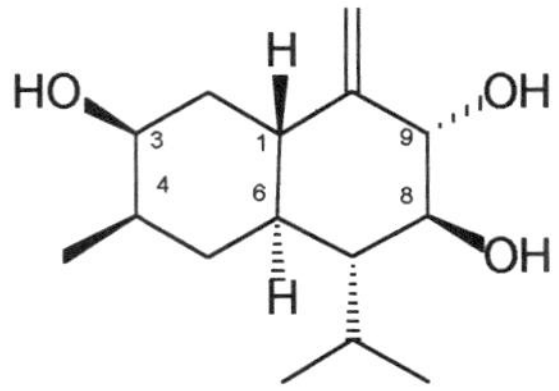

General Characteristics

Isolated as needles; mp., 155.5-157°C.

Isolation/Purification

The fungus was cultured on soytone medium. The mycelia were cultured statically at 25°C in the dark for 51 days. After 52 days culture, the mycelia were harvested with nylon cloth and homogenized with methanol and then allowed to stand for 10 days at room temperature. The culture broth, concentrated under reduced pressure and adjusted to pH 2 with 2 M HCl, was extracted with ethyl acetate. The ethyl acetate layer was dried over Na_2SO_4 and then evaporated to dryness to afford the crude extract. After 10 days the methanol-homogenized mycelium was filtered and the residue re-extracted with methanol and the organic solvent removed under reduced pressure. The residue was extracted with $CHCl_3$ and the $CHCl_3$ fraction was dried and evaporated to dryness. The combined $CHCl_3$ extracts of the mycelia and ethyl acetate extract of the culture broth were subjected to silica gel column (Wako-gel C-200) eluted with an ethyl acetate-*n*-hexane solvent system and separated into 6 fractions. Fraction 1 eluted with *n*-hexane and ethyl acetate-*n*-hexane (1:4, v/v); fraction 2 eluted with ethyl acetate-*n*-hexane (1:4, v/v; 200ml); fraction 3 with ethyl acetate-*n*-hexane (1:1, v/v; 500ml); fraction 4 with ethyl acetate-*n*-hexane (1:1, v/v; 100ml); fraction 5 with ethyl acetate-*n*-hexane (1:1, v/v; 940ml); and fraction 6 with ethyl acetate-*n*-hexane (1:1, v/v; 200ml), ethyl acetate-*n*-hexane (3:2, v/v; 800ml), ethyl acetate (300ml), and methanol (500ml). Repeated purification of fraction 3 by HPLC eluted with 40% acetonitrile in 2% acetic acid yielded purified ganomastenols A, B, C, and D.

Fungal Source

Ganoderma mastoporum.

Spectral Data

IR:

(KBr) 3360(OH) and 2890cm^{-1}.

^{1}H NMR:

(CDCl$_3$) 2.03(1H, ddd, *J*=13.0, 11.0, 2.0Hz, H-1); 1.54(1H, ddd, *J*=13.0, 11.0, 2.5Hz, H-2β); 1.95(1H, ddd, *J*=13.0, 4.0, 2.0Hz, H-2α); 3.85(1H, dd, *J*= 4.0, 2.5Hz, H-3α); 1.47(1H, m, H-4); 1.13(1H, ddd, *J*=13.0, 12.0, 12Hz, H-5); 1.67(1H, ddd, *J*=13.0, 3.5, 3.0Hz, H-5); 0.93(1H, dddd, *J*=13.0, 12.0, 11.0, 3.0Hz, H-6); 1.26(1H, ddd, *J*=12.0, 11.0, 1.5Hz, H-7β); 3.07(1H, dd, *J*=11.0, 9.0Hz, H-8α); 3.79(1H, ddd, *J*= 9.0, 1.5, 1.5Hz, H-9β); 0.96(1H, d, *J*= 7.0Hz, H-11); 2.24(1H, qqd, *J*=7.0, 7.0, 1.0Hz, H-12); 0.98(3H, d, *J*=7.0Hz); 1.04(3H, d, *J*=7.0Hz, H-14); 4.70(1H, dd, *J*=2.5, 1.5Hz, H-15a); and 5.06ppm (1H, dd, *J*=2.5, 1.5Hz, H-15b).

^{13}C NMR:

(CDCl$_3$) 38.7, C-1; 37.8, C-2; 71.1, C-3; 37.6, C-4; 35.4, C-5; 45.2, C-6; 53.8, C-7; 78.9, C-8; 79.2, C-9; 153.3, C-10; 19.3, C-11; 27.7, C-12; 20.3, C-13; 21.6, C-14 and 103.0ppm C-15.

Mass Spectrum:

FAB-MS: 277*m/e* $(M + Na)^+$; HREIMS: 236.1778*m/e* $(M - H_2O)^+$, $C_{15}H_{26}O_3$ requires 254.1881; EIMS: 236(38%), 218(40), 175(100), and 91*m/e* (28).

<u>Reference</u>

M. Hirotani, C. Ino, A. Hatano, H. Takayanagi, and T. Furuya; Ganomastenols A, B, C, and D, Cadinene sesquiterpenes from *Ganoderma mastoporum*; Phytochemistry, Vol. 40, pp. 161-165(1995).

Common/Systematic Name

Ganomastenol D

rel-8β,9α-Dihydroxy-4-hydroxymethylcadina-4,10(15)-diene

Molecular Formula/Molecular Weight

$C_{15}H_{24}O_3$; MW = 252.17254

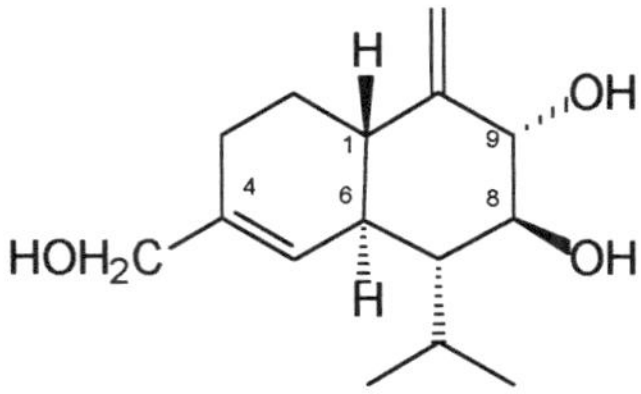

General Characteristics

Isolated as a white powder; mp., 155.5-157°C.

Isolation/Purification

The fungus was cultured on soytone medium. The mycelia were cultured statically at 25°C in the dark for 51 days. After 52 days culture, the mycelia were harvested with nylon cloth and homogenized with methanol and then allowed to stand for 10 days at room temperature. The culture broth, concentrated under reduced pressure and adjusted to pH 2 with 2 M HCl, was extracted with ethyl acetate. The ethyl acetate layer was dried over Na_2SO_4 and then evaporated to dryness to afford the crude extract. After 10 days the methanol-homogenized mycelium was filtered and the residue re-extracted with methanol and the organic solvent removed under reduced pressure. The residue was extracted with $CHCl_3$ and the $CHCl_3$ fraction was dried and evaporated to dryness. The combined $CHCl_3$ extracts of the mycelia and ethyl acetate extract of the culture broth were subjected to silica gel column (Wako-gel C-200) eluted with an ethyl acetate-*n*-hexane solvent system and separated into 6 fractions. Fraction 1 eluted with *n*-hexane and ethyl acetate-*n*-hexane (1:4, v/v); fraction 2 eluted with ethyl acetate-*n*-hexane (1:4, v/v; 200ml); fraction 3 with ethyl acetate-*n*-hexane, 1:1v/v (500ml); fraction 4 with ethyl acetate-*n*-hexane (1:1, v/v; 100ml); fraction 5 with ethyl acetate-*n*-hexane (1:1, v/v; 940ml); and fraction 6 with ethyl acetate-*n*- hexane (1:1, v/v; 200ml), ethyl acetate-*n*-hexane (3:2, v/v; 800ml), ethyl acetate (300ml), and methanol (500ml). Repeated purification of fraction 3 by HPLC eluted with 40% acetonitrile in 2% acetic acid yielded purified ganomastenols A, B, C, and D.

Fungal Source

Ganoderma mastoporum.

Spectral Data

IR:

(KBr) 3360(OH) and 2890cm^{-1}.

^{1}H NMR:

($CDCl_3$) 2.03(1H, ddd, *J*=13.0, 11.0, 2.0Hz, H-1); 1.54(1H, ddd, *J*=13.0, 11.0, 2.5Hz, H-2β); 1.95(1H, ddd, *J*=13.0, 4.0, 2.0Hz, H-2α); 3.85(1H, dd, *J*= 4.0, 2.5Hz, H-3α); 1.47(1H, m, H-4); 1.13(1H, ddd, *J*=13.0, 12.0, 12Hz, H-5); 1.67(1H, ddd, *J*=13.0, 3.5, 3.0Hz, H-5); 0.93(1H, dddd, *J*=13.0, 12.0, 11.0, 3.0Hz, H-6); 1.26(1H, ddd, *J*=12.0, 11.0, 1.5Hz, H-7β); 3.07(1H, dd, *J*=11.0, 9.0Hz, H-8α); 3.79(1H, ddd, *J*=9.0, 1.5, 1.5Hz, H-9β); 0.96(1H, d, *J*=7.0Hz, H-11); 2.24(1H, qqd, *J*=7.0, 7.0, 1.0Hz, H-12); 0.98(3H, d, *J*=7.0Hz); 1.04(3H, d, *J*=7.0Hz, H-14); 4.70(1H, dd, *J*=2.5, 1.5Hz, H-15a); and 5.06ppm (1H, dd, *J*=2.5, 1.5Hz, H-15b).

^{13}C NMR:

($CDCl_3$) 38.7, C-1; 37.8, C-2; 71.1, C-3; 37.6, C-4; 35.4, C-5; 45.2, C-6; 53.8, C- 7; 78.9, C-8; 79.2, C-9; 153.3, C-10; 19.3, C-11; 27.7, C-12; 20.3, C-13; 21.6, C-14 and 103.0ppm, C-15.

Mass Spectrum:

FAB-MS: 277*m/e* $(M + Na)^+$; HREIMS: 236.1778*m/e* $(M - H_2O)^+$, $C_{15}H_{24}O_3$ requires 252.1725; EIMS: 236(38%), 218(40), 175(100), and 91*m/e* (28).

Reference

M. Hirotani, C. Ino, A. Hatano, H. Takayanagi, and T. Furuya; Ganomastenols A, B, C, and D, Cadinene sesquiterpenes from *Ganoderma mastoporum*; Phytochemistry, Vol. 40, pp. 161-165(1995).

10

Memnobotrins

- Memnobotrin A
- Memnobotrin B
- Memnoconone
- Memnoconol

Common/Systematic Name

Memnobotrin A

Molecular Formula/Molecular Weight

$C_{25}H_{33}NO_5$; MW = 427.23587

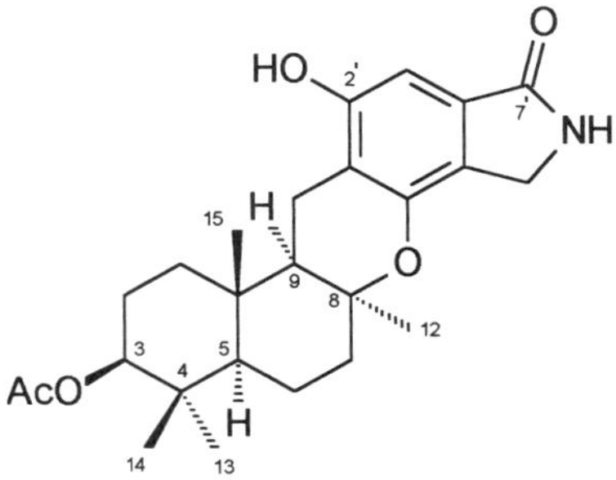

General Characteristics

Crystalline solid; m.p., 240-250°C (dec.); $[\alpha]_D^{20} = +9.6°$ (*c*=1.14, in MeOH).

Fungal Source

Memnoniella echinata (JS6308).

Isolation/Purification

A culture of *M. echinata* grown for 5 weeks on rice was air dried, ground, and extracted with methanol-chloroform, followed by partition between water and chloroform. Chromatography of the chloroform-soluble fraction over polyethyleneimine (methylene chloride with increasing methanol) gave 7 fractions. Fraction 4 was applied to a 2mm Chromatotron plate which was eluted with increasing proportions of methanol in methylene chloride to give memnobotrin A (22.8mg) and memnobotrin B (25.0mg). An earlier fraction from the plate required one further passage through a 2mm Chromatotron plate (gradient elution with 25-50% ethyl acetate-hexane) to yield pure memnoconone (3.7mg). Fraction 5 was dissolved in the minimum methylene chloride-methanol (1:1, v/v), diluted with a small volume of hexane, and the emulsion applied to a silica column. Elution with ethyl acetate-hexane gave a total of 90.2mg of memnoconol.

Spectral Data

UV:

λ_{max}^{MeOH} 217.0 (ϵ= 26,200), 257.5 (5,600), and 300nm (2,300).

IR:

($CHCl_3$) 3596, 3455, 3316, 2931, 2854, 1716, 1692, 1612, 1458, 1368, 1136, and 1071cm^{-1}

^{1}H NMR:

[$(CD_3)_3CO$)] 0.71(3H, s, H-15); 0.84(3H, s, H-13); 0.89(3H, s, H-14); 1.13(1H, m, H-5); 1.19(3H, s, H-12); 1.20(1H, m, H-1B); 1.55(1H, m, H-6B); 157 (1H, m, H-9); 1.61(2H, m, H-2); 1.70(2H, m, H-6A, H-7B); 1.89(1H, dt, *J*=3.4, 13.2Hz, H-1A); 1.98(3H, s, Ac); 2.16(1H, br, d, *J*= 9.60Hz, H-7A); 2.71(1H, ABX, *J*=8.2, 18.8Hz, H-11B); 2.87(1H, AB, *J*=18.8Hz, H-1A); 4.21(2H, br AB, *J*=16.9Hz, H-8'); 4.46(1H, br dd, *J*=6.3, 9.3Hz, H-3); and 6.80ppm (1H, s, H-3').

^{13}C NMR:

[$(CD_3)_3CO$] 38.4, C-1; 24.1, C-2; 80.9, C-3; 38.3, C-4; 54.8, C-5; 18.5, C-6; 40.8, C-7; 76.3, C-8; 49.0, C-9; 38.3, C-10; 18.9, C-11; 27.2, C-12; 17.2, C-13; 28.7, C-14; 14.6, C-15; 114.7, C-1'; 156.3, C-2'; 100.6, C-3'; 132.3, C-4'; 123.6, C-5'; 151.3, C-6'; 171.8, C-7'; 43.0 C-8'; 21.0, Ac-CH_3; and 170.8ppm Ac-CO.

<u>Reference</u>

S. F. Hinkley, J. C. Fettinger, K. Dudley, and B. B. Jarvis; Memnobotrins and Memnoconols: Novel Metabolites from *Memnoniella echinata*; J. Antibiotics, Vol. 52, pp. 988-997 (1999).

Common/Systematic Name

Memnobotrin B

Molecular Formula/Molecular Weight

$C_{27}H_{37}NO_6$; MW = 471.26209

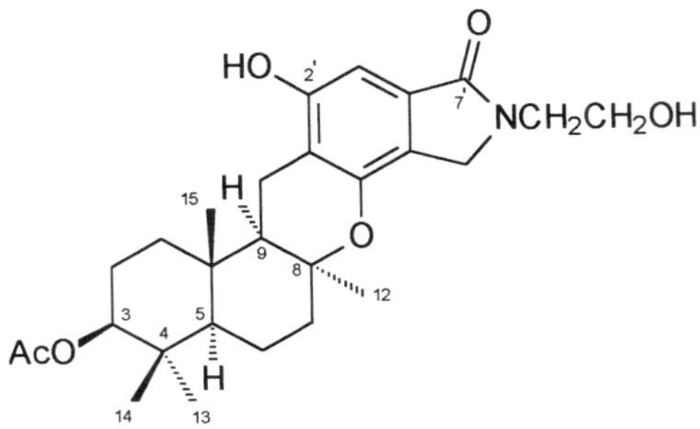

General Characteristics

Cream colored powder; m.p., 186-192°C; $[\alpha]_D^{20}$ = +11.7° (c=1.25, in MeOH).

Fungal Source

Memnoniella echinata (JS6308).

Isolation/Purification

A culture of *M. echinata* grown for 5 weeks on rice was air dried, ground, and extracted with methanol-chloroform, followed by partition between water and chloroform. Chromatography of the chloroform-soluble fraction over polyethyleneimine (methylene chloride with increasing methanol) gave 7 fractions. Fraction 4 was applied to a 2mm Chromatotron plate which was eluted with increasing proportions of methanol in methylene chloride to give memnobotrin A (22.8mg) and memnobotrin B (25.0mg). An earlier fraction from the plate required one further passage through a 2mm Chromatotron plate (gradient elution with 25-50% ethyl acetate-hexane) to yield pure memnoconone (3.7mg). Fraction 5 was dissolved in the minimum methylene chloride-methanol (1:1, v/v), diluted with a small volume of hexane, and the emulsion applied to a silica column. Elution with ethyl acetate-hexane gave a total of 90.2mg of memnoconol.

Biological Activity

Cytotoxic.

Spectral Data

UV:

λ_{max}^{MeOH} 218.5 (ε= 37,200), 259.0 (10,600), and 302nm (3,300).

IR:

(CHCl$_3$) 3598, 3323, 2933, 2855, 1717, 1669, 1616, 1458, 1368, 1317, 1135, and 1071cm^{-1}.

^{1}H NMR:

[(CD$_3$)$_3$CO] 0.69(3H, s, H-15); 0.82(3H, s, H-13); 0.87(3H, s, H-14); 1.13(1H, br d, *J*=9.8Hz, H-5); 1.17(3H, s, H-12); 1.20(1H, m, H-1B); 1.57(1H, m, H-9); 1.61(2H, m, H-2); 1.63(2H, m, H-6); 1.70(1H, m, 7B); 1.90(1H, dt, *J*=3.4, 13.3Hz, H-1A); 1.96(3H, s, Ac); 2.16(1H, br, dd, *J*=2.0, 10.4Hz, H-7A); 2.71(1H, ABX, *J*=8.1, 18.9Hz, H-11B); 2.87(1H, AB, *J*=18.9Hz, H-1A); 3.65(2H, t, *J*=5.4Hz, H-9'); 3.77(2H, t, *J*=5.4Hz, H-10'); 4.36(2H, br AB, *J*=17.0Hz, H-8'); 4.46(1H, br dd, *J*=6.7, 9.8Hz, H-3); and 6.81ppm (1H, s, H-3').

^{13}C NMR:

[(CD$_3$)$_3$CO] 38.4, C-1; 24.1, C-2; 80.9, C-3; 38.3, C-4; 54.7, C-5; 18.5, C-6; 40.8, C-7; 76.4, C-8; 49.0, C-9; 38.7, C-10; 18.8, C-11; 27.2, C-12; 17.1, C-13; 28.6, C-14; 14.6, C-15; 114.4, C-1'; 156.2, C-2'; 100.6, C-3'; 132.5, C-4'; 121.6, C-5'; 151.0, C-6'; 169.6, C-7'; 49.2 C-8'; 46.0, C-9'; 61.2, C-10'; 21.0, Ac-CH$_3$; and 170.8ppm Ac-CO.

Reference

S. F. Hinkley, J. C. Fettinger, K. Dudley, and B. B. Jarvis; Memnobotrins and Memnoconols: Novel Metabolites from *Memnoniella echinata*.; J. Antibiotics, Vol. 52, pp. 988-997 (1999).

Common/Systematic Name

Memnoconone

Molecular Formula/Molecular Weight

$C_{23}H_{30}O_5$; MW = 386.20932

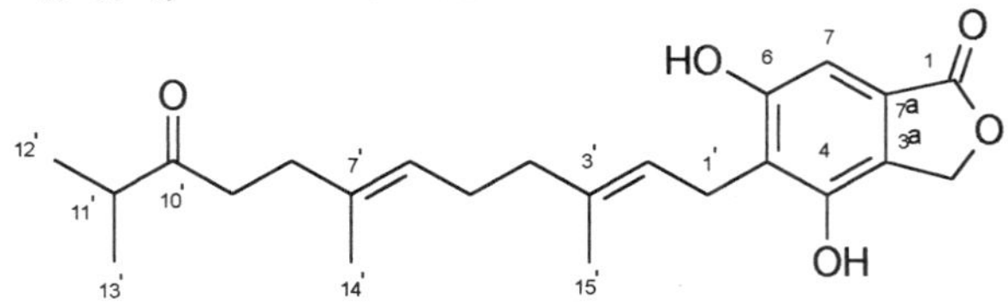

General Characteristics

Light oil.

Fungal Source

Memnoniella echinata (JS6308).

Isolation/Purification

A culture of *M. echinata* grown for 5 weeks on rice was air dried, ground, and extracted with methanol-chloroform, followed by partition between water and chloroform. Chromatography of the chloroform-soluble fraction over polyethyleneimine (methylene chloride with increasing methanol) gave 7 fractions. Fraction 4 was applied to a 2mm Chromatotron plate which was eluted with increasing proportions of methanol in methylene chloride to give memnobotrin A (22.8mg) and memnobotrin B (25.0mg). An earlier fraction from the plate required one further passage through a 2mm Chromatotron plate (gradient elution with 25-50% ethyl acetate-hexane) to yield pure memnoconone (3.7mg). Fraction 5 was dissolved in the minimum methylene chloride-methanol (1:1, v/v), diluted with a small volume of hexane, and the emulsion applied to a silica column. Elution with ethyl acetate-hexane gave a total of 90.2mg of memnoconol.

Biological Activity

Cytotoxic.

Spectral Data

UV:

λ_{max}^{MeOH} 219.0(ϵ= 38,000), 261.0(14,600), and 289nm (2,900).

IR:

($CHCl_3$) 3587, 3435, 3934, 2972, 1761, 1639, 1612, 1462, 1353, 1384, 1355, 1316, and 1124cm^{-1}.

^{1}H NMR:

[$(CD_3)_3CO$] 1.11(6H, s, H-12', H-13'); 1.26(1H, dddd, *J*=4.4, 10.0, 10.1, and 13.6Hz, H-9'A); 1.55(3H, s, H-15'); 1.58(1H, dddd, *J*=1.6, 6.8, 9.9, and 13.6Hz, H-9'B); 1.76(3H, s, H-14'); 1.95(2H, br t, *J*=7.5Hz, H-4'); 2.02(2H, m, H-5'); 2.10(2H, br t, *J*=7.5Hz, H-8'A); 2.49 (2H, m, H-9'); 2.60(1H, hept, *J*=7.0Hz, H-11'); 3.36 (2H, br d, J= 7.1Hz, H-1'); 5.07(1H, dt, *J*=1.1, 6.5Hz, H-6'); 5.22(2H, s, H-3); 5.25(1H, dt, *J*=1.1, 6.8Hz, H-2'); and 6.62ppm (1H, s, H-7).

^{13}C NMR:

[$(CD_3)_3CO$] 173.0, C-1; 70.7, C-3; 103.7, 3a; 163.8, C-4; 114.2, C-5; 155.7, C-6; 101.5, C-7; 147.5, C-7a; 22.1, C-1'; 123.0, C-2'; 135.4, C-3'; 40.3, C-4'; 27.1, C-5'; 125.0, C-6'; 134.9, C-7'; 34.1, C-8'; 39.5, C-9'; 213.7, C-10'; 41.0, C-11'; 18.4, C-12'; 18.4, C-13'; 16.2, C-14'; and 16.1ppm, C-15'.

Reference

S. F. Hinkley, J. C. Fettinger, K. Dudley, and B. B. Jarvis; Memnobotrins and Memnoconols: Novel Metabolites from *Memnoniella echinata*.; J. Antibiotics, Vol. 52, pp. 988-997 (1999).

Common/Systematic Name

Memnoconol

Molecular Formula/Molecular Weight

$C_{23}H_{32}O_6$; MW = 404.21989

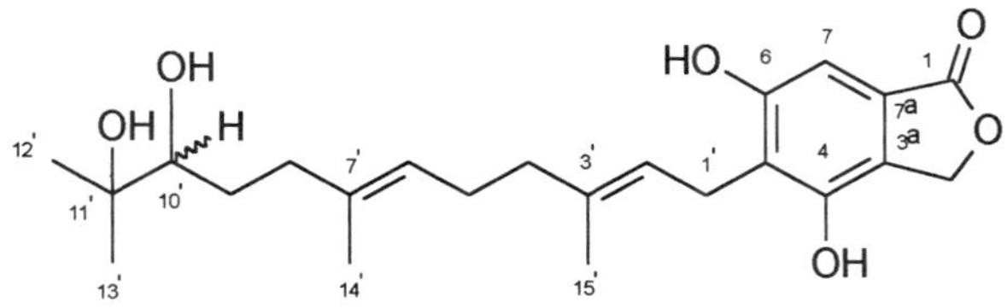

General Characteristics

Light brown powder; m.p., 60-63°C; $[\alpha]_D^{20}$ = -14.0° (*c*=1.08, in MeOH).

Fungal Source

Memnoniella echinata (JS6308).

Isolation/Purification

A culture of *M. echinata* grown for 5 weeks on rice was air dried, ground, and extracted with methanol-chloroform, followed by partition between water and chloroform. Chromatography of the chloroform-soluble fraction over polyethyleneimine (methylene chloride with increasing methanol) gave 7 fractions. Fraction 4 was applied to a 2mm Chromatotron plate which was eluted with increasing proportions of methanol in methylene chloride to give memnobotrin A (22.8mg) and memnobotrin B (25.0mg). An earlier fraction from the plate required one further passage through a 2mm Chromatotron plate (gradient elution with 25-50% ethyl acetate-hexane) to yield pure memnoconone (3.7mg). Fraction 5 was dissolved in the minimum methylene chloride-methanol (1:1, v/v), diluted with a small volume of hexane, and the emulsion applied to a silica column. Elution with ethyl acetate-hexane gave a total of 90.2mg of memnoconol.

Biological Activity

Cytotoxic.

Spectral Data

UV:

λ_{max}^{MeOH} 219.0(ϵ= 28,700), 261.5(11,100), and 290nm (3,000).

IR:

($CHCl_3$) 3587, 3440, 3005, 2978, 2932, 1728, 1637, 1612, 1451, 1353, 1316, 1196, and1161cm^{-1}.

^{1}H NMR:

$[(CD_3)_2CO]$ 1.11(6H, s, H-12', H-13'); 1.26(1H, dddd, *J*=4.4, 10.0, 10.1, and 13.6Hz, H-9'B); 1.55(3H, s, H-15'); 1.58(1H, dddd, *J*=1.6, 6.8, 9.9, and 13.6Hz, H-9'A); 1.76(3H, s, H-14'); 1.87(1H, m, H-8'B); 1.91(2H, br t, *J*=7.4Hz, H-4'); 2.02(2H, m, H-5'); 2.15(1H, br ddd, *J*=4.4, 9.9, and 13.7Hz, H-8'A); 3.18(1H, dd, *J*=1.6, 10.1Hz, H-10'); 3.30(2H, d, *J*=6.9Hz, H-1'); 5.07(1H, br t, *J*=6.5Hz, H-6'); 5.15(2H, s, H-3); 5.20(1H, br t, *J*=6.9Hz, H-2'); and 6.52ppm (1H, s, H-7).

^{13}C NMR:

$[(CD_3)_2CO]$ 172.9, C-1; 70.6, C-3; 103.6, 3a; 163.8, C-4; 115.6, C-5; 155.7, C-6; 101.5, C-7; 147.4, C-7a; 22.1, C-1'; 123.0, C-2'; 135.4, C-3'; 40.3, C-4'; 27.0, C-5'; 124.6, C-6'; 135.7, C-7'; 37.4, C-8'; 30.6, C-9'; 78.4, C-10'; 72.9, C-11'; 25.7, C-12'; 24.9, C-13'; 16.2, C-14'; and 16.1ppm, C-15'.

Reference

S. F. Hinkley, J. C. Fettinger, K. Dudley, and B. B. Jarvis; Memnobotrins and Memnoconols: Novel Metabolites from *Memnoniella echinata*.; J. Antibiotics, Vol. 52, pp. 988-997(1999).

11

Tsugicolines

Tsugicoline A
Tsugicoline B
Tsugicoline C
Tsugicoline D

Common/Systematic Name

Tsugicoline A

Molecular Formula/Molecular Weight

$C_{15}H_{22}O_4$; MW = 266.15181

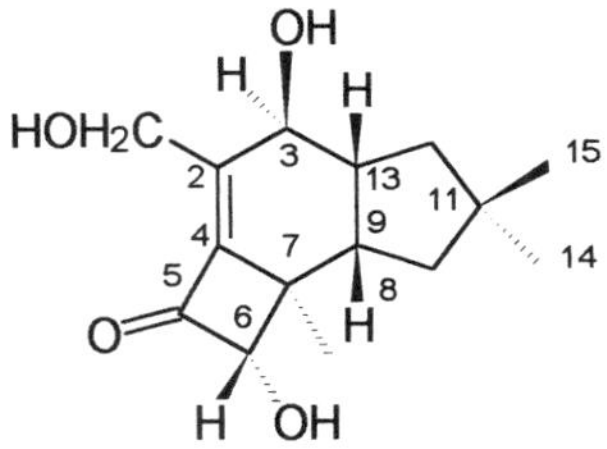

Fungal Source

Laurilia tsugicola = *Echinodontium tsugicola* (CBS 248.51, Centraal Bureau voor Schimmel Cultures, Baarn).

General Characteristics

White crystals from methylene chloride-hexane; mp., 168-170°C; $[\alpha]_D$ - 156° (*c*=0.15, in MeOH) ; triacetate, an oil; $[\alpha]_D$ - 43.2° (*c*=0.1, in $CHCl_3$); acetonide, white crystals from chloroform; mp., 146-148°C.

Isolation/Purification

The culture filtrate which was separated from the mycelium was extracted twice with ethyl acetate. Then the extracts were dried (Na_2SO_4) and evaporated to yield a mixture of sesquiterpenes. The mixture was treated with ethyl ether; the residue was composed of pure tsugicoline A; the mother liquid was chromatographed by flash silica gel column chromatography eluted with hexane-ethyl acetate (2:1, v/v) to give a mixture of tsugicoline B and D that was further purified by preparative TLC using hexane-ethyl acetate (1:2, v/v) and methylene chloride-methanol (15:1, v/v) to yield pure tsugicoline B and D; R_f, 0.10, 0.30 for tsugicoline A, respectively.

Spectral Data

UV:

λ_{max} 260nm (ϵ=8,500).

IR:

(KBr) 3370(OH) and 1730cm^{-1} (carbonyl).

^{1}H NMR:

(acetone-d_6) 4.46(1H, $J_{1a,1b}$=16Hz, $J_{1a,3}$=1.4Hz, H-1a); 4.42(1H, $J_{1b,3}$=1.5Hz, H-1b); 4.23(1H, $J_{3,13}$=8.7Hz, H-3); 4.36(1H, H-6); 1.00(3H, H-8); 2.54(1H, $J_{9,10\alpha}$=10.4Hz, $J_{9,10\beta}$=7.9Hz, $J_{9,13}$=11.5Hz, H-9); 1.51(1H, $J_{10\alpha,10\beta}$=12.4Hz, $J_{10\alpha,15}$=0.8Hz, H-10α); 1.55(1H, $J_{10\beta,12\beta}$=1.8Hz, H-10β); 1.30(1H, $J_{12\alpha,12\beta}$=12.2Hz, $J_{12\alpha,13}$=10.4Hz, $J_{12\alpha,15}$=0.8Hz, H-12α); 1.86(1H, $J_{12\beta,13}$=7.3Hz, H-12β); 2.32(1H, H-13); 1.13(3H, H-14); 1.01(3H, H-15); 3.82(1H, OH-1); 4.57(1H, OH-3); and 5.16ppm (1H, OH-6); ($CDCl_3$) 4.57(1H, H-1a); 4.57(1H, H-1b); 4.24(1H, H-3); 4.39(1H, H-6); 1.02(3H, H-8); 2.51(1H, H-9); 1.48(1H, H-10α); 1.62(1H, H-10β); 1.23(1H, H-12α); 1.88(1H, H-12β); 2.33(1H, H-13); 1.15(3H, H-14); 1.00(3H, H-15); 1.55*(1H, OH-1); 2.15*(1H, OH-3); and 2.95ppm* (1H, OH-6).

* Assignments may be interchanged.

^{13}C NMR:

61.45, t, C-1; 153.02, s, C-2; 74.93, d, C-3; 143.98, s, C-4; 200.15, s, C-5; 90.33, d, C-6; 42.70, s, C-7; 14.66, q, C-8; 47.02, d, C-9; 42.50, t, C-10; 40.89, s, C-11; 47.51, t, C-12; 50.90, d, C-13; 29.79, q, C-14; and 27.23ppm, q, C-15.

Mass Data:

LREIMS: 266*m/e* (M^+); CIMS: (isobutane) 267(MH^+), 249(MH^+ - H_2O, base peak), 231(MH^+ - $2H_2O$), and 203*m/e* (231 - 28); found: C, 67.5, H, 8.3. $C_{15}H_{22}O_4$ requires C, 67.64; H, 8.33%.

<u>Reference</u>

A. Arnone, U. Brambilla, G. Nasini, and O. Vajna de Pava; Isolation and Structure Elucidation of Tsugicolines A-D, Novel Protoilludane Sesquiterpenes from *Laurilia tsugicola*; Tetrahedron; Vol. 51, pp. 13357-13364(1995).

Common/Systematic Name

Tsugicoline B

Molecular Formula/Molecular Weight

$C_{15}H_{22}O_3$; MW = 250.15689

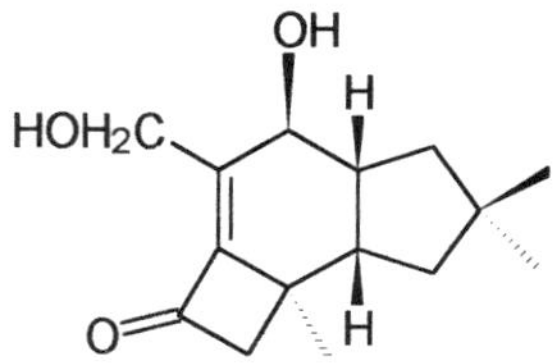

Fungal Source

Laurilia tsugicola = *Echinodontium tsugicola* (CBS 248.51; Centraal Bureau voor Schimmel Cultures, Baarn).

General Characteristics

Obtained as an oil; $[\alpha]_D$ - 71.5° (*c*=4.5, in $CHCl_3$).

Isolation/Purification

The culture filtrate which was separated from the mycelium was extracted twice with ethyl acetate. Then the extracts were dried (Na_2SO_4) and evaporated to yield a mixture of sesquiterpenes. The mixture was treated with ethyl ether; the residue was composed of pure tsugicoline A; the mother liquid was chromatographed by flash silica gel column chromatography eluted with hexane-ethyl acetate (2:1, v/v) to give a mixture of tsugicoline B and D that was further purified by preparative TLC using hexane-ethyl acetate (1:2, v/v) and methylene chloride-methanol (15:1, v/v) to yield pure tsugicoline B and D; R_f, 0.50; 0.30 for tsugicoline B, respectively.

Spectral Data

UV:

λ_{max} 254nm (ϵ=5,100).

IR:

(chloroform) 1730cm^{-1} (conjugated carbonyl).

^{1}H NMR:

($CDCl_3$) 4.54(1H, H-1a); 4.50(1H, $J_{1b,3}$=1.9Hz, H-1b); 4.24(1H, $J_{3,13}$=9.1Hz, H-3); 2.82(1H, H-6); 1.17(3H, H-8); 2.48(1H, $J_{9,10\alpha}$=10.2Hz, $J_{9,10\beta}$=8.3Hz, $J_{9,13}$=11.9Hz, H-9); 1.46(1H, $J_{10\alpha,10\beta}$=12.6Hz, $J_{10\alpha,15}$=0.8Hz, H-10α); 1.56(1H, $J_{10\beta,12\beta}$=1.8Hz, H-10β); 1.22(1H, $J_{12\alpha,12\beta}$=12.3Hz, $J_{12\alpha,13}$=11.3Hz, $J_{12\alpha,15}$=0.8Hz, H-12α); 1.85(1H, $J_{12\beta,13}$=7.2Hz, H-12β); 2.44(1H, H-13); 1.14(3H, H-14); 0.99(3H, H-15); 3.00*(3H, OH-1); and 3.80ppm* (3H, OH-3).

* Assignments may be interchanged.

^{13}C NMR:
61.17, t, C-1; 149.99, s, C-2; 74.51, d, C-3; 148.67, s, C-4; 197.77, s, C-5; 60.31, t, C-6; 36.35, s, C-7; 20.41, q, C-8; 46.40, d, C-9; 41.27, t, C-10; 40.81, s, C-11; 46.56, t, C-12; 52.45, d, C-13; 29.46, q, C-14; and 26.82ppm, q, C-15.

Mass Data:
CIMS: (isobutane) 251(MH^+, 100%), 233(MH^+ - H_2O, 95), 215(38), 205(30), 203(22), 187(28), and 173*m/e* (25); found: C, 71.6, H, 8.7; $C_{15}H_{22}O_3$ requires C, 71.97; H, 8.86%.

Reference

A. Arnone, U. Brambilla, G. Nasini, and O. Vajna de Pava; Isolation and Structure Elucidation of Tsugicolines A-D, Novel Protoilludane Sesquiterpenes from *Laurilia tsugicola*; Tetrahedron, Vol. 51, pp. 13357-13364(1995).

Common/Systematic Name

Tsugicoline C

Molecular Formula/Molecular Weight

$C_{15}H_{24}O_4$; MW = 268.16746

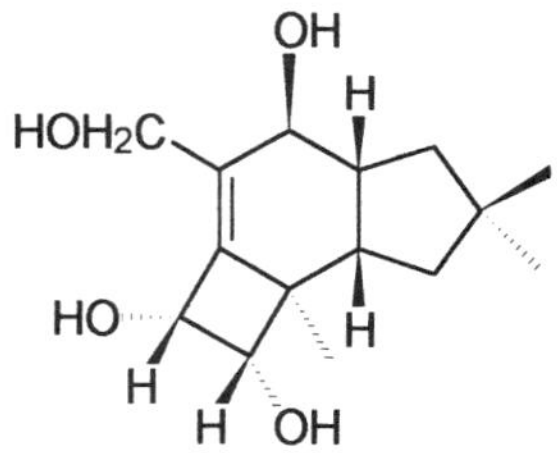

Fungal Source

Laurilia tsugicola = *Echinodontium tsugicola* (CBS 248.51; Centraal Bureau voor Schimmel Cultures, Baarn).

General Characteristics

Obtained as white crystals from methylene chloride-hexane; mp., 74-76°C; $[\alpha]_D$ - 39.6° (*c*=3.00, in $CHCl_3$).

Isolation/Purification

The culture filtrate which was separated from the mycelium was extracted twice with ethyl acetate. Then the extracts were dried (Na_2SO_4) and evaporated to yield a mixture of sesquiterpenes. The mixture was treated with ethyl ether. The residue was composed of pure tsugicoline A. The mother liquid was chromatographed by flash silica gel column chromatography eluted with hexane-ethyl acetate (2:1, v/v) to give a mixture of tsugicoline B and D that was further purified by preparative TLC using hexane-ethyl acetate (1:2, v/v) and methylene chloride-methanol (15:1, v/v) to yield pure tsugicoline B, C, and D; R_f, 0.50; 0.30 for tsugicoline C.

Spectral Data

UV:

λ_{max} 208nm (ϵ=5,600).

IR:

(chloroform) 3400cm^{-1} (OH).

^{1}H NMR:

($CDCl_3$) 4.28(1H, $J_{1a,1b}$=13.4Hz, $J_{1a,3}$=1.0Hz, H-1a); 4.26(1H, $J_{1b,3}$=1.2Hz, H-1b); 4.15(1H, $J_{3,13}$=8.5Hz, H-3); 3.70(1H, H-6); 1.04(3H, H-8); 2.30(1H, $J_{9,10\alpha}$=10.2Hz, $J_{9,10\beta}$=8.2Hz, $J_{9,13}$=12.0Hz, H-9); 1.35(1H, $J_{10\alpha,10\beta}$=12.6Hz, $J_{10\alpha,15}$=0.8Hz, H-10α);

1.39(1H, $J_{10\beta,12\beta}$=1.6Hz, H-10β); 1.17(1H, $J_{12\alpha,12\beta}$=12.6Hz, $J_{12\alpha,13}$=10.2Hz, $J_{12\alpha,15}$=0.8Hz, H-12α); 1.78(1H, $J_{12\beta,13}$=7.2Hz, H-12β); 2.25(1H, H-13); 1.08(3H, H-14); 0.97(3H, H-15); 3.97*(1H, OH-1); 4.50*(1H, 3-OH); and 3.95ppm* (1H, 6-OH).

* Assignments may be interchanged.

^{13}C NMR:

59.437, t, C-1; 139.59, s, C-2; 74.16, d, C-3; 141.03, s, C-4; 70.90, d, C-5; 76.92, d, C-6; 51.03, s, C-7; 15.481, q, C-8; 46.59, d, C-9; 41.82, t, C-10; 40.50, s, C-11; 47.70, t, C-12; 51.58, d, C-13; 29.87, q, C-14; and 27.35ppm, q, C-15.

Mass Data:

CIMS: (isobutane) 269(MH^+, 100%) and 233*m/e* (MH^+ - $2H_2O$, base peak).

Reference

A. Arnone, U. Brambilla, G. Nasini, and O. Vajna de Pava; Isolation and Structure Elucidation of Tsugicolines A-D, Novel Protoilludane Sesquiterpenes from *Laurilia tsugicola*; Tetrahedron, Vol. 51, pp. 13357-13364(1995).

Common/Systematic Name

Tsugicoline D

Molecular Formula/Molecular Weight

$C_{15}H_{20}O_3$; MW = 248.14124

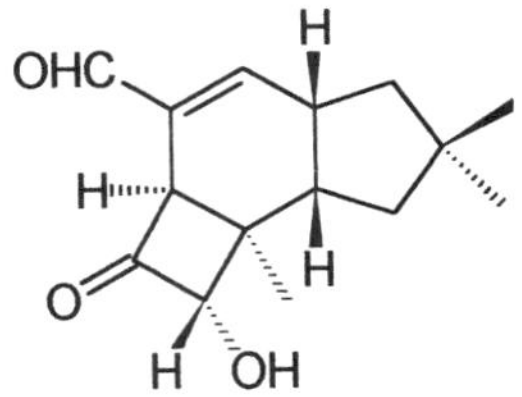

Fungal Source

Laurilia tsugicola = *Echinodontium tsugicola* (CBS 248.51; Centraal Bureau voor Schimmel Cultures, Baarn).

General Characteristics

Obtained as a white solid; mp., 107-110°C; $[\alpha]_D$ + 161.8° (c=0.1, in $CHCl_3$).

Isolation/Purification

The culture filtrate which was separated from the mycelium was extracted twice with ethyl acetate. Then the extracts were dried (Na_2SO_4) and evaporated to yield a mixture of sesquiterpenes. The mixture was treated with ethyl ether; the residue was composed of pure tsugicoline A; the mother liquid was chromatographed by flash silica gel column chromatography eluted with hexane-ethyl acetate (2:1, v/v) to give a mixture of tsugicoline B and D that was further purified by preparative TLC using hexane-ethyl acetate (1:2, v/v) and methylene chloride-methanol (15:1, v/v) to yield pure tsugicoline B and D; R_f, 0.70; 0.30 for tsugicoline D, respectively.

Spectral Data

UV:

λ_{max} 215(ϵ=6,0,50) and 240nm (ϵ=4,800).

IR:

(KBr) 3400(OH), 1780, and 1680cm^{-1} (carbonyl).

^{1}H NMR:

($CDCl_3$) 9.47(1H, H-1a); 6.77(1H, $J_{3,13}$=2.0Hz, H-3); 4.71(1H, H-6); 1.13(3H, H-8); 2.64(1H, $J_{9,10\alpha}$=12.7Hz, $J_{9,10\beta}$=6.9Hz, $J_{9,13}$=7.4Hz, H-9); 1.07(1H, $J_{10\alpha,10\beta}$=12.6Hz, $J_{10\alpha,15}$=~ 0Hz, H-10α); 1.59(1H, $J_{10\beta,12\beta}$=~ 0Hz, H-10β); 1.72(1H, $J_{12\alpha,12\beta}$=13.5Hz, $J_{12\alpha,13}$=2.3Hz, $J_{12\alpha,15}$=~0Hz, H-12α); 2.10(1H, $J_{12\beta,13}$=9.2Hz, H-12β); 3.16(1H, H-13); 1.08(3H, H-14); 1.01(3H, H-15); and 5.14ppm (1H, OH-6).

^{13}C NMR:

193.97, t, C-1; 134.54, s, C-2; 154.21, d, C-3; 54.55, d, C-4; 203.02, s, C-5; 85.83, d, C-6; 38.38, s, C-7; 18.82, q, C-8; 43.02, d, C-9; 37.61, t, C-10; 44.40, s, C-11; 37.61, t, C-12; 47.26, d, C-13; 32.00, q, C-14; and 31.61ppm, q, C-15.

Mass Data:

CIMS: (isobutane) 249(MH^+, 80%), 231(MH^+ - H_2O, 100), 220(20), and 203*m/e* (25); found: C, 72.2, H, 8.0; $C_{15}H_{20}O_3$ requires C, 72.55; H, 8.12%.

Reference

A. Arnone, U. Brambilla, G. Nasini, and O. Vajna de Pava; Isolation and Structure Elucidation of Tsugicolines A-D, Novel Protoilludane Sesquiterpenes from *Laurilia tsugicola*; Tetrahedron, Vol. 51, pp. 13357-13364(1995).

12

Radicinins

Radicinin
Radicinin Diastereomer (2*S**, 3*R**)
Radicinol Diasteromer (2*S**,3*S**,4*S**)
2*S*,3*S*,4*S*-*epi*-Radicinol
Radicinol

Common/Systematic Name

Radicinin; Stemphylone

Molecular Formula/Molecular Weight

$C_{12}H_{12}O_5$; MW = 236.06847

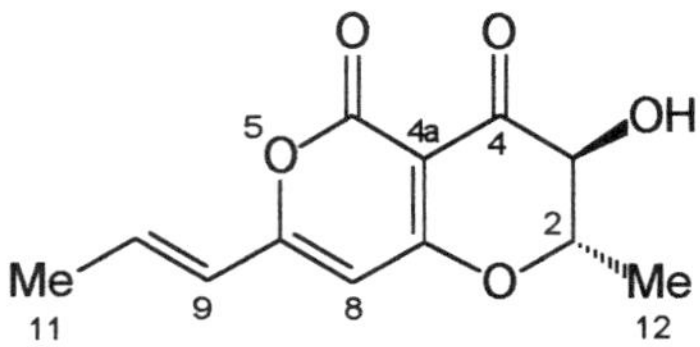

General Characteristics

Needles from methanol; mp., 238-240°C (dec,);$[\alpha]_D^{20}$ -236° (*c*=0.1, in $CHCl_3$).

Isolation/Purification

The fungus was grown without shaking at 24°C for 21 days in the dark in liquid medium made up of glucose (3.0g/L), peptone (3.0g/L) and the extract from 50g/L of malt and water. The culture filtrate was acidified to pH 2.0 with HCl, after which the metabolites in the culture filtrate were extracted with ethyl acetate (3x). The ethyl acetate extracts were dried over Na_2SO_4 and concentrated. The residue was applied to a silica gel column and the column washed with 1500ml of 10% acetone in *n*-hexane, then developed successively with 750ml each 20, 30, and 40% acetone in *n*-hexane. Each 150ml eluate constituted one fraction. Fractions 10 and 11 were combined and evaporated. Recrystallization of the residue from methanol afforded radicinin as needles. The mother liquor was purified by Sephadex LH_{20} column chromatography. The column was washed with 500ml of methanol and fractions consisting of 7ml eluates were collected. Fractions 33-48 were combined and evaporated to dryness. Recrystallization of the residue from methanol afforded radicinin as needles. The diastereoisomer of radicinin (2*S**,3*R**) (R_f=0.38) in the mother liquor was separated from the mixture of the diastereoisomer of radicinol (2*S**,3*S**,4*S**) and *epi*-radicinol (2*S**,3*S**,4*R**) by preparative TLC [acetone-benzene (2:8, v/v) R_f=0.26]. The crude radicinin diastereoisomer was further purified with preparative TLC (ethyl acetate-*n*-hexane; 7:3, v/v) which gave the radicinin diastereoisomer as needles [ethyl acetate-*n*-hexane (7:3, v/v) R_f=0.63]. The diastereoisomer of radicinol (2*S**,3*S**,4*S**) and *epi*-radicinol (2*S**,3*S**,4*R**) and radicinol epoxide were purified after preparative TLC (ethyl acetate-*n*-hexane; 7:3, v/v) of the mixture.

Fungal Source

Bipolaris coicis, a phytopathogen which causes a serious leaf blight on Job's tears (*Coix lachryma-jobi* L), *Alternaria radicina, A. chrysanthemi, A. helianthi, Cochliobolus lunata,* and *Stemphylium radicinum*.

Biological Activity

In a leaf spot assay of Job's tears, radicinin caused necrotic lesions at 0.3µg/leaf but not active at 0.1µg/leaf.

Spectral Data

UV:
λ_{max}^{EtOH} 203(log ϵ = 4.00), 221(4.14), 270(3.66), 280(3.61), and 341nm (4.15).

IR:
(KBr) 3462, 3098, 3034, 2990, 2924, 2918, 1760, 1659, 1605, 1522, 1456, 1435, 1379, 1325, 1228, 1172, and 1056cm^{-1}.

^{1}H NMR:
($CDCl_3$) 4.36(1H, dq, *J*=12.4, 6.3Hz, H-2); 3.98(1H, d, *J*=12.4Hz, H-3); 5.84(1H, s, H-8); 6.03(1H, dq, *J*=15.5, 1.8Hz, H-9); 6.95(1H, dq, *J*=15.5, 7.0Hz, H-10); 1.95(3H, dq, *J*=7.0, 1.8Hz, H-11); and 1.64ppm (3H, d, *J*=6.3Hz, H-12).

^{13}C NMR:
($CDCl_3$) C-2, 80.0; C-3, 72.0; C-4, 188.6; C4a, 97.9; C-5, 156.7; C-7, 164.3; C-8, 98.0; C-8a, 176.3; C-9, 122.6; C-10, 141.0; C-11, 18.8; and C-12, 18.1ppm.

Mass Spectrum:
CIMS (isobutane): 236*m/e* $(M)^{\cdot}$; 236.0682*m/e* exact mass calcd for $C_{12}H_{12}O_5$, 236.0684.

Reference

H. Nakajima, T. Ishida, Y. Otsuka, T. Hamasaki, and M. Ichinoe; Phytotoxins and Related Metabolites Produced by *Bipolaris coicis*, The Pathogen of Job's Tears; Phytochemistry, Vol. 45, pp. 41-45(1997).

Common/Systematic Name

Radicinin Diastereomer (2*S**, 3*R**)

Molecular Formula/Molecular Weight

$C_{12}H_{12}O_5$; MW = 236.06847

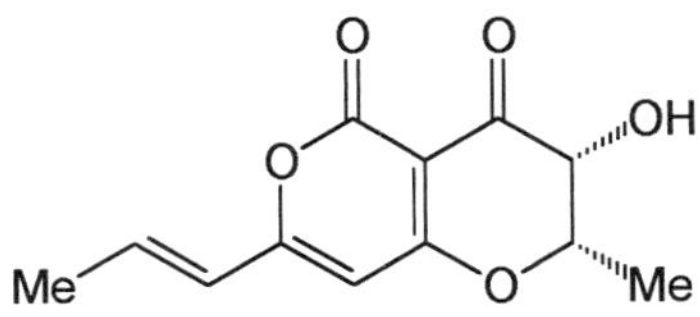

General Characteristics

Colorless needles from methanol; mp., 202-220°C (dec,); $[\alpha]_D^{20}$ = -105° (*c*=0.25, in EtOH).

Isolation/Purification

See radicinin for isolation/purification.

Fungal Source

Bipolaris coicis, a phytopathogen which causes a serious leaf blight on Job's tears (*Coix lachryma-jobi* L).

Biological Activity

In a leaf spot assay of Job's tears, radicinin diastereomer caused necrotic lesions at 1.0μg/leaf but was not active at 0.3μg/leaf.

Spectral Data

UV:

λ_{max}^{EtOH} 203(log ϵ = 4.00), 220(4.14), 269(3.67), 280(3.64), and 338nm (4.14).

IR:

(KBr) 3420, 2928, 2858, 1742, 1655, 1605, 1531, 1458, 1438, 1381, 1263, 1170, 1118, and 1044cm^{-1}.

^{1}H NMR:

($CDCl_3$) 5.07(1H, dq, *J*= 6.0Hz, 6.5Hz, H-2); 4.52(1H, d, *J*=6.0Hz, H-3); 5.83(1H, s, H-8); 6.03(1H, dq, *J*=15.3Hz, 1.3Hz, H-9); 6.96(1H, dq, *J*=15.3Hz, 7.0Hz, H-10); 1.96(3H, dd, *J*=7.0Hz, 1.3Hz, H-11); and 1.35ppm (3H, d, *J*=6.5Hz, H-12).

^{13}C NMR:

($CDCl_3$) C-2, 78.9; C-3, 70.1; C-4, 188.0; C-4a, 97.6; C-5, 156.7; C-7, 164.5; C-8, 98.4; C-8a, 174.9; C-9, 122.6; C-10, 141.0; C-11, 18.8; and C-12, 12.1ppm.

Mass Spectrum:

CIMS (isobutane): 236*m/e*(M)$^-$; 236.0682*m/e* exact mass calcd for $C_{12}H_{12}O_5$, 236.0684

Reference

H. Nakajima, T. Ishida, Y. Otsuka, T. Hamasaki, and M. Ichinoe; Phytotoxins and Related Metabolites Produced by *Bipolaris coicis*, The Pathogen of Job's Tears; Phytochemistry, Vol. 45, pp. 41-45(1997).

Common/Systematic Name

Radicinol diasteromer (2*S**,3*S**,4*S**)

Molecular Formula/Molecular Weight

$C_{12}H_{14}O_5$; MW = 238.08412

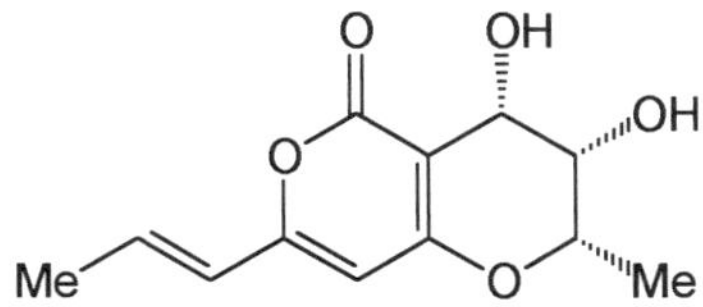

General Characteristics

An oil; $[\alpha]_D^{20}$ -19° (c=0.85, in EtOH).

Isolation/Purification

See radicinin for isolation/purification.

Fungal Source

Bipolaris coicis, a phytopathogen which causes a serious leaf blight on Job's tears (*Coix lachryma-jobi* L).

Biological Activity

In a leaf spot assay of Job's tears, radicinol diasteromer caused no necrotic lesions up to 10μg/ leaf.

Spectral Data

UV:

λ_{max}^{EtOH} 224 (log ϵ = 4.45), 260 (3.51), 271 (3.56), and 315nm (3.95).

IR:

(KBr) 3408, 2988, 2942, 1690, 1618, 15742, 1437, 1383, 1315, 1278, 1214, 1160, 1141, 1071, and 1025cm^{-1}.

^{1}H NMR:

($CDCl_3$) 4.37(1H, dq, J=1.1, 6.3Hz, H-2); 3.88(1H, br, H-3); 4.60(1H, br, H-4OH); 5.79(1H, s, H-8); 5.97(1H, dq, J=15.7, 1.5Hz, H-9); 6.72(1H, dq, J=15.7, 6.8Hz, H-10); 1.91(3H, dd, J=6.8, 1.5Hz, H-11); and 1.50ppm (3H, d, J=6.3Hz, H-12).

^{13}C NMR:

($CDCl_3$) C-2, 72.4; C-3, 69,1; C-4, 63.2; C4a, 99.5; C-5, 165.4; C-7, 158.5; C-8, 99.3; C-8a, 166.6; C-9, 122.6; C-10, 135.2; C-11, 18.4; and C-12, 15.8ppm.

Mass Spectrum:

EIMS: 238(M$^+$, 18%), 181(100), 152(7), 137(8), and 111*m/e* (26); 238.0845*m/e* exact mass calcd for $C_{12}H_{14}O_5$, 238.0841.

Reference

H. Nakajima, T. Ishida, Y. Otsuka, T. Hamasaki, and M. Ichinoe; Phytotoxins and Related Metabolites Produced by *Bipolaris coicis*, The Pathogen of Job's Tears; Phytochemistry, Vol. 45, pp. 41-45(1997).

Common/Systematic Name

2*S*,3*S*,4*S*-*epi*-Radicinol

Molecular Formula/Molecular Weight

$C_{12}H_{14}O_6$; MW = 254.07904

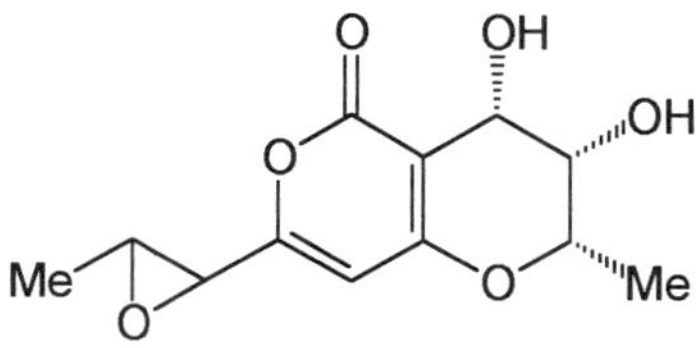

General Characteristics

An oil; $[\alpha]_D^{20}$ -92° (*c*=1.0, in EtOH).

Isolation/Purification

See radicinin for isolation/purification.

Fungal Source

Bipolaris coicis, a phytopathogen which causes a serious leaf blight on Job's tears (*Coix lachryma-jobi* L).

Biological Activity

In a leaf spot assay of Job's tears, *epi*-radicinol caused no necrotic lesions up to 10μg/ leaf.

Spectral Data

UV:

λ_{max}^{EtOH} 215 (log ϵ = 4.34) and 288nm (4.31).

IR:

(Thin film) 3376, 3000, 2930, 1698, 1653, 1580, 1444, 1383, 1212, 1139, 1071, and 1033cm^{-1}.

^{1}H NMR:

($CDCl_3$) 4.37(1H, brq, *J*=6.7Hz, H-2); 3.84(1H, br, H-3); 4.56(1H, d, *J*=2.4Hz, H-4); 6.05(1H, s, H-8); 3.33(1H, d, *J*=1.9Hz, H-9); 3.21(1H, dq, *J*=1.9Hz, 5.4Hz, H-10); 1.42(3H, d, *J*=5.40Hz, H-11); and 1.49ppm (3H, d, *J*=6.7Hz, H-12).

^{13}C NMR:

($CDCl_3$) C-2, 72.6; C-3, 69,1; C-4, 63.3; C-4a, 100.4; C-5, 164.8; C-7, 160.4; C-8, 99.7; C-8a, 165.9; C-9, 55.1; C-10, 57.3; C-11, 17.3; and C-12, 15.7ppm.

Mass Spectrum:

EIMS: 254(M$^+$, 28%), 197(100), 182(10), 153(79), and 139*m/e* (13) ; 254.0795*m/e* exact mass calcd for $C_{12}H_{14}O_6$, 254.0790.

Reference

H. Nakajima, T. Ishida, Y. Otsuka, T. Hamasaki, and M. Ichinoe; Phytotoxins and Related Metabolites Produced by *Bipolaris coicis*, The Pathogen of Job's Tears; Phytochemistry, Vol. 45, pp. 41-45(1997).

Common/Systematic Name

Radicinol

Molecular Formula/Molecular Weight

$C_{12}H_{14}O_5$; MW = 238.08412

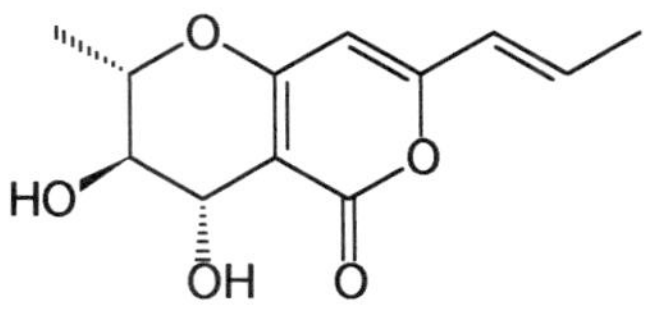

General Characteristics

Colorless viscous oil; $[\alpha]_D^{31}$ -175° (c=1.02, in $CHCl_3$).

Isolation/Purification

A mixture of radicinol and radicinin was obtained from the ethyl acetate extract of the fungal culture after column chromatography using 60% ethyl acetate in *n*-hexane. The mixture was purified using Sephadex LH_{20} with acetone as eluant.

Fungal Source

Cochliobolus lunata (IFO 6288).

Spectral Data

UV:

λ_{max}^{EtOH} 226(ϵ =39,300), 262(3,100), 271(3,200), and 318nm (10,800).

IR:

($CHCl_3$) 3425(OH) and 1680cm^{-1} (α-pyrone).

^{1}H NMR:

($CDCl_3$) 6.72(1H, dq, J=7.0, 16.0Hz, H-10); 3.76(1H, dd, J=6.5, 8.0Hz, H-3); 4.75(2H, bs, 2 OH's); 5.85(1H, s, H-8); 6.02(1H, dq, J=16.0, 2.0Hz, H-9); 1.92(3H, dd, J=7.0, 2.0Hz, H-11); 4.70(1H, d, J=6.5Hz, H-4); 4.23(1H, dq, J=8.0, 6.6Hz, H-2); and 1.52ppm (3H, d, J=6.5Hz, H-12).

^{13}C NMR:

($CDCl_3$) C-2, 76.8; C-3, 72.5; C-4, 68.0; C-4a, 100.6; C-5, 165.4; C-7, 158.9; C-8, 99.1; C-8a, 164.5; C-9, 122.7; C-10, 135.7; C-11, 18.4; and C-12, 17.0ppm.

Mass Spectrum:

HREIMS: 238.082m/e; exact mass calcd for $C_{12}H_{14}O_5$, 238.084.

Reference

M. Nukina and S. Marumo; Radicinol, A New Metabolite of *Cochliobolus lunata*, and Absolute Stereochemistry of Radicinin; Tetrahedron Letters, pp. 3271-3271(1977).

13

Stachybotrylactone and Related Metabolites

Common/Systematic Name

Stachybotrylactone

Molecular Formula/Molecular Weight

$C_{23}H_{30}O_5$; MW = 386.20932

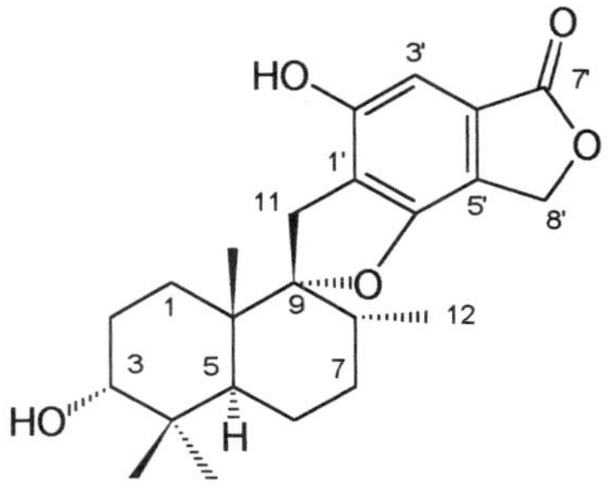

General Characteristics

White or pale yellow crystalline solid; mp., 280°C (dec.); $[\alpha]_D$ -6.4° (*c*=0.09, in acetone).

Isolation/Purification

Rice cultures of *Stachybotrys chartarum* (Egypt 1) were air dried, ground, and extracted with methanol followed by extraction with chloroform. The extracts were combined and evaporated to dryness. The crude extract was dissolved in methanol and filtered through a pad of C_{18} silica gel followed by elution with methanol to give a black gum after removal of solvent. The gum was dissolved in methylene chloride and chromatographed on a PEI silica gel column eluted with methylene chloride-hexane (4:1, v/v), methylene chloride, and 10% methanol in methylene chloride. A combination of preparative HPLC and TLC gave purified satratoxin H, **S**-isosatratoxin H, stachybotrylactone, stachybotrylactone acetate, 2α-acetoxystachybotrylactone acetate and stachybotrylactam.

Fungal Source

Stachybotrys chartarum and *S. cylindrospora.*

Note: Ayer and Miao (1993) believed stachybotrylactone to be an artifact formed from stachybotrydial.

Biological Activity

Cytotoxic and immunosuppressive.

Spectral Data

UV:

$\lambda_{max}^{Acetonitrile}$ 218(ε=28,000), 268(5,3000), and 309nm (2,600).

IR:

(CH_3Cl) 3600-3100, 2939, 1742, 1623, 1469, 1389, 1356, 1332, 954, 943, 772, and 737cm^{-1}.

^{1}H NMR:

($CDCl_3$) 1.90(1H, H-1α); 1.06 (1H, H-1β); 1.60 (1H, H-2α); 1.44(1H, H-2β); 3.32(1H, br s, H-3β); 2.17(1H, dd, *J*=11.6, 2.7Hz, H-5α); 1.46(1H, H-6α); 1.55(1H, H-6β); 1.60 (1H, H-7α); 1.45(1H, H-7β); 1.86(1H, H-8β); 3.26(1H, d, *J*=17.3Hz, H-11a, proton on the side of C-10); 2.90(1H, d, *J*=17.3Hz, H-11b, proton on the side of C-8); 0.72(3H, d, *J*=6.5Hz, H-12α); 0.97(3H, s, H-14β); 0.86(3H, s, H-14β); 1.06(3H, s, H-15β); 6.76(1H, s, H-3'); 5.23(1H, d, *J*=14.7Hz, H-8'a); and 5.17ppm (1H, d, *J*=14.7Hz, H-8'b).

^{13}C NMR:

(acetone-d_6) 24.91, t, C-1; 21.60, t, C-2; 75.21, d, C-3; 38.29, s, C-4; 40.65, d, C-5; 25.91, t, C-6; 31.81, t, C-7; 37.78, d, C-8; 100.00, s, C-9; 43.09, s, C-10; 32.53, t, C-11; 15.86, q, C-12; 28.94, q, C-13; 22.80, q, C-14; 16.36, q, C-15; 120.72, s, C-1'; 156.65, s, C-2'; 103.00, d, C-3'; 119.2, s, C-4'; 128.07, s, C-5'; 155.47, s, C-6'; 171.29, s, C-7'; and 67.84ppm, t, C-8'.

Mass Spectrum:

HREIMS: 386.2095($C_{23}H_{30}O_5$, 53%), 368.1977($C_{23}H_{28}O_4$, 11), 353.1753($C_{22}H_{25}O_4$, 9), 244.0730($C_{14}H_{12}O_4$, 9), 230.0579($C_{13}H_{10}O_4$, 100), 217.049($C_{12}H_9O_4$, 18), 207.1747($C_{14}H_{23}O$, 38), and 189.1642*m/e* ($C_{14}H_{21}$, 35).

References

W. A. Ayer and S. Miao; Secondary Metabolites of the Aspen Fungus *Stachybotrys cylindrospora*; Canad. J. Chem., Vol. 71, pp. 487-493(1993).

B. B. Jarvis, J. Salemme, and A. Morais; *Stachybotrys* Toxins 1. Natural toxins; Vol. 3, pp. 10-16 (1995).

Common/Systematic Name

K-76

Molecular Formula/Molecular Weight

$C_{23}H_{30}O_6$; MW = 402.20424

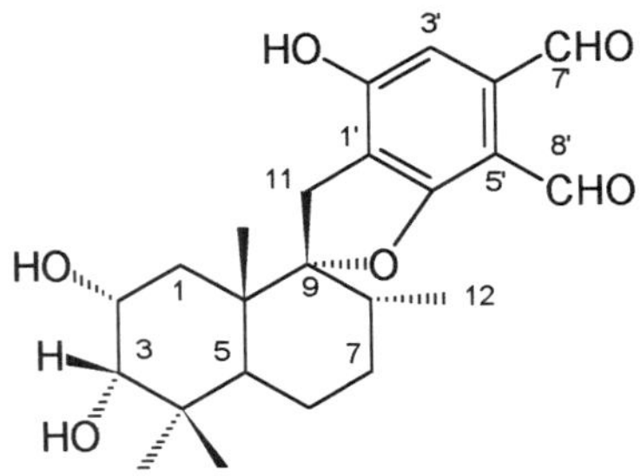

General Characteristics

Crystals; mp., 176°; $[\alpha]_D^{20}$ - 48° (in MeOH).

Fungal Source

Stachybotrys complementi (ATCC 20511).

Biological Activity

Strongly inhibited the complement C_5 step at ca. 10μg/ml *in vitro* and preliminary experiments indicated that it improved the symptoms of experimental glomerulonephritis.

Spectral Data

UV:

λ_{max}^{EtOH} 246(ε=16,500), 307(6,700) and 359nm (5,400).

IR:

(KBr) 1600, 1585, 1385, and 880cm^{-1}.

^{1}H NMR:

(C_6H_5N) 0.82(3H, d, *J*=5.0Hz, H-12); 0.93, 1.04, and 1.27(3H each, s); 3.72(1H, d, *J*=2.0Hz, H-3); 4.30(1H, *J*=20.4Hz, H-2); 7.41(1H, s, H-3'); and 10.75, 11.02ppm (1H each, s, CHO).

X-Ray:

Structure confirmed by X-ray analysis of the *p*-bromobenzenesulfonate.

References

E. J. Corey and J. Das; Total Synthesis of the Complement Inhibitor K-76 in Racemic Form. Structural Assignment to "K-76 monocarboxylic Acid"; J. Am. Chem. Soc., Vol. 104, pp. 5551-5553(1982).

H. Kaise, M. Shinohara, W. Smiyazaki, T. Izawa, Y. Nakano, M. Sugawara, K. Sugiura, and K. Sasaki; Structure of K-76, A Complement Inhibitor Produced by *Stachybotrys complementi nov.* sp. K-76; J. C. S. Chem. Comm., pp. 726-727(1979).

Common/Systematic Name

Stachybotrylactone acetate

Molecular Formula/Molecular Weight

$C_{25}H_{32}O_6$; MW = 428.21989

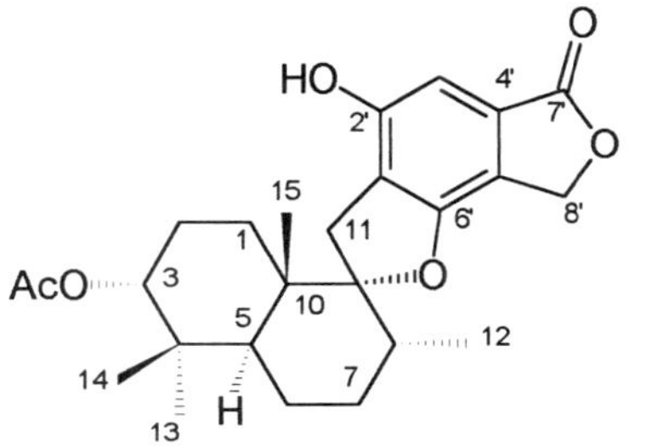

General Characteristics

Crystals; mp., 105-106°C; $[\alpha]_D$ -12° (*c*=0.5, in MeOH).

Isolation/Purification

Rice cultures of *Stachybotrys chartarum* (Egypt 1) were air dried, ground, and extracted with methanol followed by extraction with chloroform. The extracts were combined and evaporated to dryness. The crude extract was dissolved in methanol and filtered through a pad of C_{18} silica gel followed by elution with methanol to give a black gum after removal of solvent. The gum was dissolved in methylene chloride and chromatographed on a PEI silica gel column eluted with methylene chloride-hexane (4:1, v/v), methylene chloride, and 10% methanol in methylene chloride. A combination of preparative HPLC and TLC gave purified satratoxin H, **S**-isosatratoxin H, stachybotrylactone, stachybotrylactone acetate, 2α-acetoxystachybotrylactone acetate and stachybotrylactam.

Fungal Source

Stachybotrys chartarum.

Biological Activity

Cytotoxic and immunosuppressive.

Spectral Data

UV:

$\lambda_{max}^{Acetonitrile}$ 218, 265, and 306nm.

IR:

(CH_3Cl) 3280(OH), 1754(C=0), and 1724cm^{-1} (C = 0).

^{1}H NMR:

($CDCl_3$) 0.74(3H, d, *J*=6.4Hz, H-12); 0.90(3H, s, H-13); 0.91(3H, s, H-14); 0.98(3H, s, H-15); 1.4-1.9(9H, m, H-1, 2, 6, 7, 8); 2.02(3H, s, acetate); 2.05(1H, m, H-5); 2.90 and 3.30(1H each, AB, *J*=17.4, H-11); 4.60(1H, bs, H-3); 5.13 and 5.27(1H each, AB, *J*=14.5, H-8'); and 6.90ppm (1H, s, H-3').

^{13}C NMR:

25.0, C-1; 20.7, C-2; 77.8, C-3; 37.0, C-4; 41.0, C-5; 22.3, C-6; 30.9, C-7; 36.8, C-8; 99.6, C-9; 42.2, C-10; 31.6, C-11; 15.5, C-12; 27.8, C-13; 21.3, C-14; 16.0, C-15; 118.9, C-1'; 153.9, C-2'; 103.3, C-3'; 120.0, C-4'; 127.5, C-5'; 155.7, C-6'; 170.4, C-7'; 67.6, C-8'; 21.9, and 170.5ppm (acetates).

Mass Spectrum:

CIMS (CH_4): 429(7%), 369(12), 299(12), 281(19), and 69*m/e* (100); HREIMS: 428.2195*m/e* for $C_{25}H_{32}O_6$; calcd, 428.2199.

Reference

B. B. Jarvis, J. Salemme and A. Morais; *Stachybotrys* Toxins. 1; Natural Toxins, Vol. 3, pp. 10-16(1995).

Common/Systematic Name

2α-Hydroxystachybotrylactone

Molecular Formula/Molecular Weight

$C_{23}H_{30}O_6$; MW = 402.20424

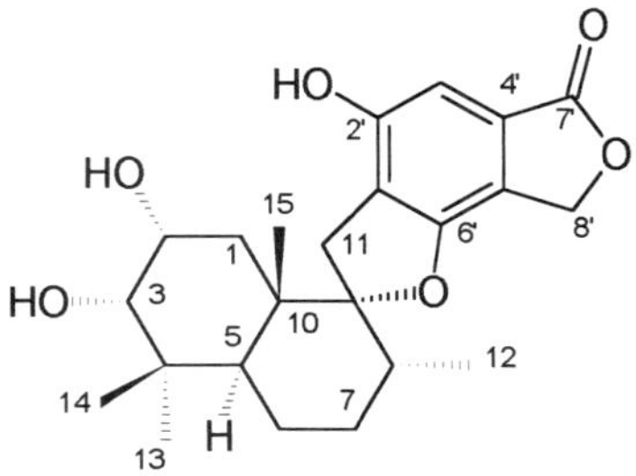

General Characteristics

Amorphous solid; $[\alpha]_D$ - 40° (*c*=1.0, in MeOH).

Fungal Source

Stachybotrys chartarum.

Biological Activity

Cytotoxic and immunosuppressive.

Spectral Data

UV:

$\lambda_{max}^{Acetonitrile}$ 218, 265, and 306nm.

IR:

(CH_3Cl) 3296(OH) and 1750cm^{-1} (C = O).

^{1}H NMR:

($CDCl_3$) 0.67(3H, d, *J*=6.2Hz, H-10); 0.83(3H, s, H-14); 0.97(3H, s, H-13); 1.01(3H, s, H-15); 1.3-1.8(7H, m, H-1, 6, 7, 8); 2.05(1H, m, H-5); 2.85 and 3.2(1H each, AB, *J*=17.3Hz, H-11); 3.40(1H, bs, H-3); 4.02(1H, bd, *J*=11Hz, H-2); 5.10 and 5.24(1H each, AB, *J*=14.9Hz, H-8'); and 6.78ppm (1H, s, H-3').

^{13}C NMR:

30.9, C-1; 66.7, C-2; 78.7, C-3; 39.2, C-4; 38.3, C-5; 20.6, C-6; 30.9, C-7; 36.8, C-8; 98.9, C-9; 43.4, C-10; 33.0, C-11; 15.4, C-12; 28.4, C-13; 21.9, C-14; 16.9, C-15; 119.0, C-1'; 153.9, C-2'; 103.3, C-3'; 120.1, C-4'; 127.1, C-5'; 155.4, C-6'; 172.0, C-7'; and 68.1ppm, C-8'.

Mass Spectrum:
CIMS (CH_4): 403(15%), 299(8), 257(2), 173(100), and 145*m/e* (43); HREIMS: 402.2047*m/e* for $C_{23}H_{30}O_6$; calcd, 402.2042.

Reference

B. B. Jarvis, J. Salemme and A. Morais; *Stachybotrys* Toxins. 1; Natural Toxins, Vol. 3, pp. 10-16(1995).

Common/Systematic Name

2α-Acetoxystachybotrylactone acetate

Molecular Formula/Molecular Weight

$C_{27}H_{34}O_8$; MW = 486.22537

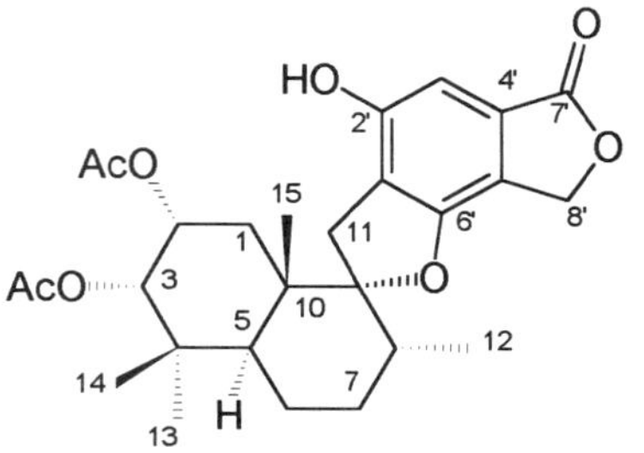

General Characteristics

Amorphous solid; $[\alpha]_D$ -15° (*c*=1.0, in MeOH).

Fungal Source

Stachybotrys chartarum.

Isolation/Purification

The black gummy crude extract derived from a rice culture of *S. chartarum* S-17 was triturated with hexane washes until no further color was extracted. The remaining black gum was partitioned between water and chloroform. The chloroform soluble portion was dried (Na_2SO_4) and concentrated to dryness on the rotary evaporator to give a black gum. The gum was subjected to flash chromatography, over silica gel with a gradient of hexane-CH_2Cl_2-MeOH, and collected in 124 fractions. Fractions 83-84 (3% MeOH-CH_2Cl_2) were combined to give A; fractions 85-87 (3% MeOH/CH_2Cl_2) were combined to give B; fractions 88-89 (3% MeOH/CH_2Cl_2) and 90-99 (4% MeOH/CH_2Cl_2) were combined to give C; fractions 100-103 (5% MeOH/CH_2Cl_2) and fractions 104-110 (6% MeOH/CH_2Cl_2) were combined to give D; fractions 111-112 (6% MeOH-CH_2Cl_2) were combined to give E; fractions 113-115 (10% MeOH-CH_2Cl_2) were combined to give F; and fractions 116-119 were combined to give G. Fraction A was subjected to high speed countercurrent distribution [V_c = 850ml, MeOH (3)-H_2O (2)-CCl_4 (3.5)-CH_2Cl_2 (0.5)-hexane (1), organic mobile phase at 3.2ml/min] to give 10 fractions (F1-F10). Fraction F5 was subjected to preparative TLC (Chromatotron, 2mm plate, 20% hexane in EtOAc) to give pure 2α-acetoxystachybotrylactone acetate.

Biological Activity

Cytotoxic and immunosuppressive.

Spectral Data

UV:
$\lambda_{max}^{Acetonitrile}$ 218, 265, and 306nm.

IR:
(CH_3Cl) 3280(OH) and 1744cm^{-1} (C = O).

^{1}H NMR:
($CDCl_3$) 0.73(3 H, d; J=6.4, H-12); 0.93(3H, s, H-14); 1.00(3H, s, H-13); 1.10(3H, s, H-15); 1.3-1.8(7H, m, H-1, 6, 7, 8); 2.05(1H, m, H-5); 1.90 and 2.05(3H each, s, acetates); 2.95 and 3.35(1H each, AB, J=17.4Hz, H-11); 3.50(1H, bs, H-3); 4.95(1H, bd, J=10Hz, H-2); 5.18 and 5.37(1H each, AB, J=14.5Hz, H-8'); and 6.92ppm (1H, s, H-3').

^{13}C NMR:
($CDCl_3$) 30.7, C-1; 68.3, C-2; 77.0, C-3; 38.2, C-4; 40.6, C-5; 20.4, C-6; 30.6, C-7; 36.8, C-8; 99.0, C-9; 43.6, C-10; 32.0, C-11; 15.5, C-12; 27.7, C-13; 21.6, C-14; 16.9, C-15; 118.8, C-1'; 153.9, C-2'; 103.6, C-3'; 119.9, C-4'; 127.6, C-5'; 155.4, C-6'; 171.6, C-7'; 67.8, C-8'; 21.1, 20.9, 170.4, and 170.5 ppm, acetates.

Mass Spectrum:
EIMS: 486(M^+, 18%), 384(100), 351(3), 279(7), and 230*m/e* (21); HREIMS: 486.2250*m/e* for $C_{27}H_{34}O_8$; calcd, 486.2254.

Reference

B. B. Jarvis, J. Salemme and A. Morais; *Stachybotrys* Toxins. 1; Natural Toxins, Vol. 3, pp. 10-16(1995).

Common/Systematic Name

Stachybotrylactam

Molecular Formula/Molecular Weight

$C_{23}H_{31}NO_4$; MW = 385.22531

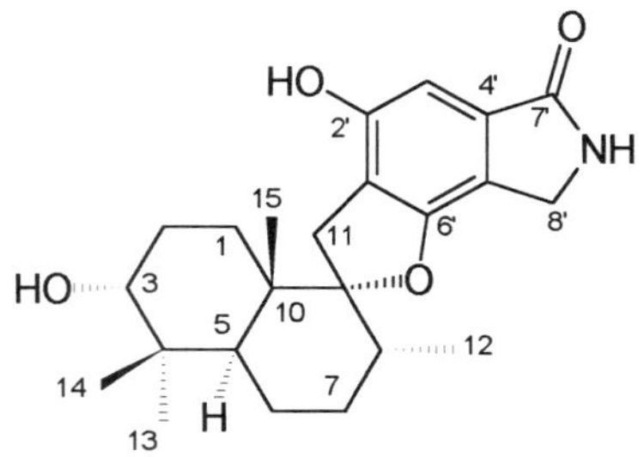

General Characteristics

Amorphous solid.

Fungal Source

Stachybotrys chartarum.

Isolation/Purification

The black gummy crude extract derived from a rice culture of *S. chartarum* S-17 was triturated with hexane washes until no further color was extracted. The remaining black gum was partitioned between water and chloroform. The chloroform soluble portion was dried (Na_2SO_4) and concentrated to dryness on the rotary evaporator to give a black gum. The gum was subjected to flash chromatography, over silica gel with a gradient of hexane-CH_2Cl_2-MeOH, and collected in 124 fractions. Fractions 83-84 (3% MeOH-CH_2Cl_2) were combined to give A; fractions 85-87 (3% MeOH-CH_2Cl_2) were combined to give B; fractions 88-89 (3% MeOH-CH_2Cl_2) and 90-99 (4% MeOH/CH_2Cl_2) were combined to give C; fractions 100-103 (5% MeOH-CH_2Cl_2) and fractions 104-110 (6% MeOH/CH_2Cl_2) were combined to give D; fractions 111-112 (6% MeOH/CH_2Cl_2) were combined to give E; fractions 113-115 (10% MeOH-CH_2Cl_2) were combined to give F; and fractions 116-119 were combined to give G. Fraction D was subjected to reversed-phase MPLC (Rainin, 18g, 8μ, C-18, 4ml/min) with increasing MeOH, starting with 70% MeOH in H_2O, to give several fractions one of which upon reversed-phase HPLC (semipreparative C_{18}, 70% MeOH in H_2O) gave pure stachybotrylactam.

Biological Activity

Cytotoxic and immunosuppressive.

Spectral Data

UV:

$\lambda_{max}^{Acetonitrile}$ 216, 257, and 298nm.

IR:

(CH_3Cl) 3450(NH), 3290(OH), and 1690cm^{-1} (C=O).

^{1}H NMR:

($CDCl_3$) 0.73(3H, d, *J*=6.0Hz, H-12); 0.87(3H, s, H-14); 0.98(3H, s, H-13); 1.03(3H, s, H-15); 1.5-1.9(9H, m, H-1, -2, -6, -7, -8); 2.20(1H, m, H-5); 2.83 and 3.18(1H each, AB, *J*=17.2Hz, H-11); 3.36(1H, bs, H-3); 4.25 and 4.35(1H each, AB, *J*=16.5Hz, H-8'); 6.80(1H, s, H-3'); and 8.0ppm (1H, bs, NH).

^{13}C NMR:

($CDCl_3$) 24.9, C-1; 21.7, C-2; 75.5, C-3; 38.3, C-4; 40.6, C-5; 25.9, C-6; 31.9, C-7; 37.7, C-8; 99.0, C-9; 43.0, C-10; 32.6, C-11; 16.0, C-12; 28.6, C-13; 22.8, C-14; 16.4, C-15; 118.0, C-1'; 153.9, C-2'; 102.3, C-3'; 116.0, C-4'; 135.0, C-5'; 154.7, C-6'; 172.1, C-7'; and 43.3ppm, C-8'.

Mass Spectrum:

EIMS: 386(8%), 385(M$^+$, 23), 279(10), 230(18), 179(15), and 149*m/e* (100);
HREIMS: 385.2215*m/e* for $C_{23}H_{31}NO_4$; calcd, 385.2253.

<u>Reference</u>

B. B. Jarvis, J. Salemme and A. Morais; *Stachybotrys* Toxins. 1; Natural Toxins, Vol. 3, pp. 10-16(1995).

Common/Systematic Name

Stachybotrylactam acetate

Molecular Formula/Molecular Weight

$C_{25}H_{33}NO_5$; MW = 427.23587

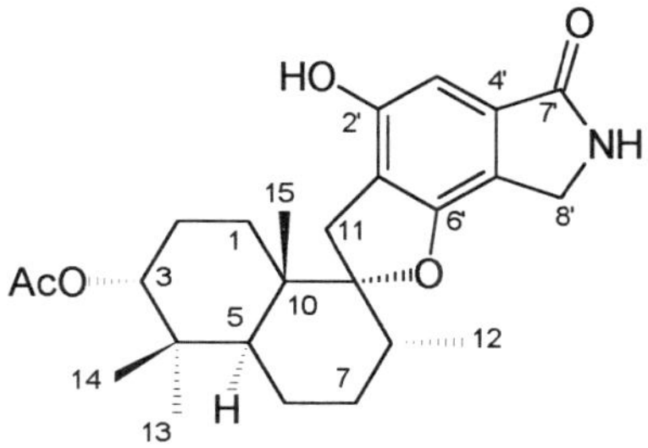

General Characteristics

Amorphous solid.

Fungal Source

Stachybotrys chartarum.

Isolation/Purification

A shake culture of *Stachybotrys complementi* (ATCC 20511) yielded a crude extract from which were isolated stachybotrylactam, stachybotrylactam acetate, and 2α-hydroxystachybotrylactam acetate by a series of chromatographic steps similar to those described for stachybotrylactam.

Biological Activity

Cytotoxic and immunosuppressive.

Spectral Data

UV:

$\lambda_{max}^{Acetonitrile}$ 216, 257, and 298nm.

IR:

(CH_3Cl) 3450(NH), 3248(OH), 1730(C=O), and 1696cm^{-1} (lactam).

^{1}H NMR:

($CDCl_3$) 0.70(3H, d, *J*=6.0Hz, H-12); 0.89(3H, s, H-14); 0.97(3H, s, H-13); 1.23(3H, s, H-15); 1.4-1.9(9H, m, H-1, -2, -6, -7, -8); 1.99(3H, s, acetate); 2.00(1H, m, H-5); 2.84 and 3.19(1H each, AB, *J*=17.0Hz, H-11); 4.22 and 4.38(1H each AB, *J*=15.0Hz, H-8'); 4.58(1H, s, H-6); 6.78(1H, bs, NH); and 6.90ppm (1H, s, H-3').

^{13}C NMR:
(CDCl$_3$) 24.9, C-1; 20.8, C-2; 77.9, C-3; 36.8, C-4; 40.9, C-5; 22.3, C-6; 30.8, C-7; 37.0, C-8; 98.6, C-9; 42.0, C-10; 31.8, C-11; 15.5, C-12; 27.8, C-13; 21.2, C-14; 16.0, C-15; 117.8, C-1'; 153.3, C-2'; 102.3, C-3'; 115.3, C-4'; 135.0, C-5'; 156.4, C-6'; 172.4, C-7'; 43.0, C-8'; 21.7, acetate; and 170.4ppm, acetate.

Mass Spectrum:
HREIMS: 427.2350*m/e* for $C_{25}H_{33}NO_5$; calcd 427.2359.

Reference

B. B. Jarvis, J. Salemme and A. Morais; *Stachybotrys* Toxins. 1; Natural Toxins, Vol. 3, pp. 10-16(1995).

Common/Systematic Name

2α-Acetoxystachybotrylactam acetate

Molecular Formula/Molecular Weight

$C_{27}H_{35}NO_7$; MW = 485.24135

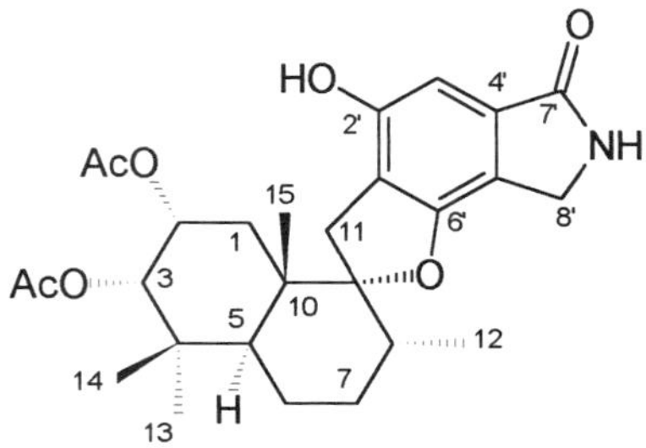

General Characteristics

Amorphous solid; $[\alpha]_D$ -29° (*c*=0.1, in MeOH).

Fungal Source

Stachybotrys chartarum (MRC 1422).

Isolation/Purification

A rice culture of *S. chartarum* yielded 3.2g of crude extract. Verrucarin J, roridin E, and satratoxins F, G, and H were isolated from this extract by a series of chromatographic procedures (see isolation of stachylbotrylactone acetate). Also isolated was 13mg of stachybotrylactone and 25mg of 2α-acetoxystachybotrylactam acetate.

Biological Activity

Cytotoxic and immunosuppressive.

Spectral Data

UV:

$\lambda_{max}^{Acetonitrile}$ 216, 257, and 298nm.

IR:

(CH_3Cl) 3450(NH), 3280(OH), 1744(C=O, acetate), and 1696cm^{-1} (C=O, lactam).

^{1}H NMR:

($CDCl_3$) 0.71(3H, d, *J*=6.4Hz, H-12); 0.93(3H, s, H-14); 1.02(3H, s, H-13); 1.10(3H s, H-15); 1.4-1.8(7H, m, H-1, -6, -7, -8); 2.05(1H, m H-5); 1.90 and 2.07(3H each, s, acetates); 2.90 and 3.24(1H each, AB, *J*=17.0Hz, H-11); 4.25 and 4.42(1H each AB, *J*=16.5Hz, H-8'); 4.95(1H, bs, H-3); 5.21(1H, bd, *J*=11Hz, H-2); 7.01(1H, s, H-3'); and 8.0ppm (1H, bs, NH).

^{13}C NMR:

(CDCl$_3$) 30.5, C-1; 68.2, C-2; 76.7, C-3; 38.1, C-4; 40.5, C-5; 20.4, C-6; 30.7, C-7; 36.7, C-8; 98.1, C-9; 43.5, C-10; 32.0, C-11; 15.4, C-12; 27.7, C-13; 20.9, C-14; 16.9, C-15; 117.6, C-1'; 153.4, C-2'; 102.5, C-3'; 115.3, C-4'; 133.0, C-5'; 156.1, C-6'; 172.0, C-7'; 43.5, C-8'; 21.0, 21.6; and 170.3, 170.6ppm, acetates.

Mass Spectrum:

EIMS: 487(7%), 486(20), 485(60), 383(62), 279(14), and 229*m/e* (24); HREIMS: 485.2404*m/e* for $C_{27}H_{35}NO_7$; calcd, 485.2414).

Reference

B. B. Jarvis, J. Salemme and A. Morais; *Stachybotrys* Toxins. 1; Natural Toxins, Vol. 3, pp. 10-16(1995).

Common/Systematic Name
Stachybotramide

Molecular Formula/Molecular Weight
$C_{25}H_{35}NO_5$; MW = 429.25152

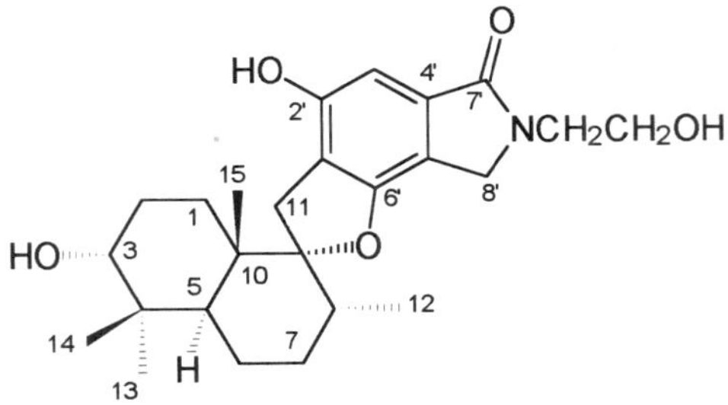

General Characteristics
Crystals; mp., 196-199°C; $[\alpha]_D$ -16° (*c*= 0.1, in MeOH).

Fungal Source
Stachybotrys chartarum and *S. cylindrospora*.

Isolation/Purification
The black gummy crude extract derived from a rice culture of *S. chartarum* S-17 was triturated with hexane washes until no further color was extracted. The remaining black gum was partitioned between water and chloroform. The chloroform soluble portion was dried (Na_2SO_4) and concentrated to dryness on the rotary evaporator to give a black gum. The gum was subjected to flash chromatography, over silica gel with a gradient of hexane-CH_2Cl_2-MeOH, and collected in 124 fractions. Fractions 83-84 (3% MeOH-CH_2Cl_2) were combined to give A; fractions 85-87 (3% MeOH-CH_2Cl_2) were combined to give B; fractions 88-89 (3% MeOH-CH_2Cl_2) and 90-99 (4% MeOH-CH_2Cl_2) were combined to give C; fractions 100-103 (5% MeOH-CH_2Cl_2) and fractions 104-110 (6% MeOH-CH_2Cl_2) were combined to give D; fractions 111-112 (6% MeOH-CH_2Cl_2) were combined to give E; fractions 113-115 (10% MeOH-CH_2Cl_2) were combined to give F; and fractions 116-119 were combined to give G. Fraction F was filtered through a short PEI silica gel column which was eluted with increasing concentrations of MeOH in CH_2Cl_2 to give two fractions. The first fraction was crystallized from EtOAc-hexane to give stachybotramide. Acetylation of stachybotramide gave the triacetate derivative, which was identical to the compound reported by Ayer and Miao [1993].

Biological Activity
Cytotoxic and immunosuppressive.

Spectral Data

UV:

$\lambda_{max}^{Acetonitrile}$ 216, 257, and 300nm.

IR:

(CH_3Cl) 3270(OH), and 1695cm^{-1} (C=O, lactam).

^{1}H NMR:

(pyridin-d_5) 0.84(3H, d, *J*=5.5Hz, H-12); 0.91(3H, s, H-14); 0.98(3H, s, H-13); 1.22(3H s, H-15); 1.20-1.90(9H, m, H-1, -2, -6, -7, -8); 2.05(1H, m, H-5); 3.10 and 3.52(1H each, d, *J*=17.0Hz, H-11); 3.60(1H, br s, H-2); 3.65(2H, m, H-9'); 3.90 (2H, m, H-10'); 4.07 and 4.35 (1Heach, AB, *J*=16.8Hz, H-8'); and 7.35ppm (1H, s, H-3').

^{13}C NMR:

(pyridin-d_5) 25.7, C-1; 24.5, C-2; 74.6, C-3; 38.0, C-4; 40.2, C-5; 21.2, C-6; 31.4, C-7; 37.2, C-8; 98.5, C-9; 42.5, C-10; 32.6, C-11; 15.7, C-12; 28.9, C-13; 22.5, C-14; 16.0, C-15; 117.4, C-1'; 155.2, C-2'; 101.6, C-3'; 113.0, C-4'; 135.0, C-5'; 156.7, C-6'; 168.8, C-7'; 48.3, C-8'; 45.7, C-9'; and 60.3ppm, C-10'.

Mass Spectrum:

HREIMS: 4292534*m/e* for $C_{27}H_{35}NO_7$; calcd, 429.2515.

References

W. A. Ayer and S. Miao; Secondary Metabolites of the Aspen Fungus *Stachybotrys cylindrospora*; Can. J. Chem., Vol. 71, pp. 487-493(1993).

B. B. Jarvis, J. Salemme and A. Morais; *Stachybotrys* Toxins. 1; Natural Toxins, Vol. 3, pp. 10-16(1995).

Common/Systematic Name
Stachybotrydial

Molecular Formula/Molecular Weight
$C_{23}H_{30}O_5$; MW = 386.20932

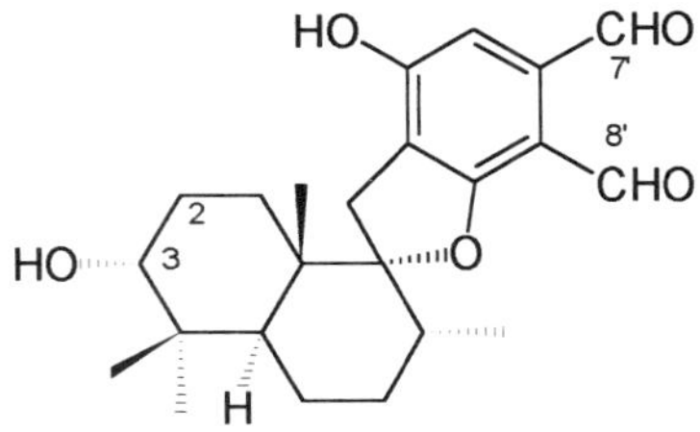

General Characteristics
Crystals; mp., 266°C (dec.).

Fungal Source
Stachybotrys chartarum and *S. cylindrospora.*

Isolation/Purification
The black gummy crude extract derived from a rice culture of *S. chartarum* S-17 was triturated with hexane washes until no further color was extracted. The remaining black gum was partitioned between water and chloroform. The chloroform soluble portion was dried (Na_2SO_4) and concentrated to dryness on the rotary evaporator to give a black gum. The gum was subjected to flash chromatography, over silica gel with a gradient of hexane-CH_2Cl_2-MeOH, and collected in 124 fractions. Fractions 83-84 (3% MeOH-CH_2Cl_2) were combined to give A; fractions 85-87 (3% MeOH-CH_2Cl_2) were combined to give B; fractions 88-89 (3% MeOH-CH_2Cl_2) and 90-99 (4% MeOH-CH_2Cl_2) were combined to give C; fractions 100-103 (5% MeOH-CH_2Cl_2) and fractions 104-110 (6% MeOH-CH_2Cl_2) were combined to give D; fractions 111-112 (6% MeOH-CH_2Cl_2) were combined to give E; fractions 113-115 (10% MeOH/CH_2Cl_2) were combined to give F; and fractions 116-119 were combined to give G. Fraction B was subjected to CCC (V_c = 850ml, MeOH (2)-H_2O(2)-EtOAc(2)-hexane(3), organic mobile phase at 3.2ml/min) to give a major fraction which was subjected to preparative TLC (Chromatotron, 4mm plate, increasing EtOAc in hexane) to yield a semisolid material. This material was subjected to silica gel HPLC (semipreparative column, 2.5% MeOH in CH_2Cl_2 [40%]-hexane [60%], 4ml/min, 0.2g/ injection to give stachybotrylactone and stachybotrydial).

Biological Activity
Cytotoxic and immunosuppressive.

Spectral Data

UV:
$\lambda_{max}^{Acetonitrile}$ 232, 254, 248, and 360nm.

IR:
(CH_3Cl) 3450(OH) and 1690cm^{-1} (C=O).

^{1}H NMR:
($CDCl_3$) 0.72(3H, d, *J*=6.4Hz, H-12); 0.85(3H, s, H-14); 0.98(3H, s, H-13); 0.98(3H, s, H-15); 1.5-2.0(9H, m, H-1, -2, -6, -7, -8); 2.05(1H, dd, *J*=13 and 3Hz); 2.79 and 3.15(1H each, AB, *J*=17.4Hz, H-11); 3.39(1H, bs, H-3); 6.87(1H, s, H-3'); 10.34(1H, s, H-7'); and 10.57ppm (1H, s, H-8').

^{13}C NMR:
($CDCl_3$) 24.6, C-1; 24.0, C-2; 75.7, C-3; 37.5, C-4; 40.0, C-5; 20.8, C-6; 30.3, C-7; 36.9, C-8; 100.6, C-9; 42.1, C-10; 30.9, C-11; 15.4, C-12; 28.2, C-13; 22.2, C-14; 16.0, C-15; 111.0, C-1'; 158.0, C-2'; 109.3, C-3'; 137.9, C-4'; 119.3, C-5'; 167.5, C-6'; 188.7, C-7'; and 193.4ppm, C-8'.

Mass Spectrum:
HREIMS: 386.4878*m/e* for $C_{25}H_{30}O_5$; calcd, 386.4882.

References
W. A. Ayer and S. Miao; Secondary Metabolites of the Aspen Fungus *Stachybotrys cylindrospora*; Can. J. Chem., Vol. 71, pp. 487-493(1993).

B. B. Jarvis, J. Salemme and A. Morais; *Stachybotrys* Toxins. 1; Natural Toxins, Vol. 3, pp. 10-16(1995).

Common/Systematic Name
Stachybotrin A

Molecular Formula/Molecular Weight
$C_{23}H_{31}NO_5$; MW = 401.22022

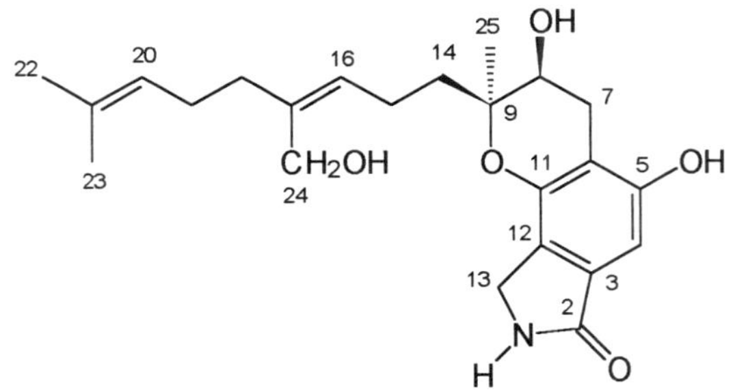

General Characteristics
Isolated as a yellow oil; $[\alpha]_D$ + 8.8° (c=0.612, in MeOH).

Fungal Source
Stachybotrys sp. (ATCC 90017) collected from brackish water in Florida.

Isolation/Purification
The culture filtrate was extracted with ethyl acetate and the organic phase was dried ($MgSO_4$) and concentrated to afford a red oil. The extract was dissolved in acetone and divided into four equal portions. Each portion was subjected to preparative TLC on silica gel GF plates developed twice with 9:1, v/v, chloroform-ethanol. Major bands observed under illumination (254nm) were collected and extracted with methanol. Bands 2 (R_f 0.18) and 4 (R_f 0.36) were further purified with the same TLC conditions to afford stachybotrin A (a yellow oil) and stachybotrin B (as a white solid).

Biological Activity
Stachybotrins A and B each showed activity in disk assays against *Bacillus subtilis* (ATCC 6051) at 10μg/disk (8- and 10-mm zones, respectively). They also inhibited the radial growth of the filamentous fungi *Ascobolus furfuraceus* (NRRL 6460) and *Sordaria fimicola* (NRRL 6459) by 50% in centerpoint inoculation assays at 20 and 10μg/disk, respectively. Disk assays for activity against a strain of *Candida albicans* (ATCC 14053) were negative at 100μg/disk. Stachybotrin A was also evaluated for cytotoxicity against three human solid tumor cell lines (nonsmall carcinoma A-549, breast adenocarcinoma MCF-7, and colon adenocarcinoma HT-29), but afforded only mild activity (ED_{50} values 20-30μg/ml).

Spectral Data

UV:
λ_{max}^{MeOH} 220(ε=17,000), 254(ε=6,400) and 302nm (ε=2,900).

IR:
(neat) 3262, 2918, 1684, 1611, 1462, 1358, 1049, 1025 and 1006cm^{-1}.

^{1}H NMR:
($CDCl_3$) 6.74(1H, s, H-4); 2.65(1H, dd, *J*=17.6, 7.2Hz, H-7); 2.97(1H, dd, *J*=17.6, 5.5Hz, H-7); 3.88(1H, dd, *J*=7.2, 5.5Hz, H-8); 4.24(2H, br s, H-13); 1.69(2H, m, H-14); 2.27 (2H, m, H-15); 5.30(1H, dd, *J*=7.4, 7.4Hz, H-16); 2.08(2H, m, H-18); 2.07(2H, m, H-19); 5.07(1H, dd, *J*=1.4, 1.4Hz, H-20); 1.63(3H, s, H-22); 1.55(3H, s, H-23); 4.08(1H, d, *J*=12.2Hz, H-24); 4.05(1H, d, *J*=12.2Hz, H-24); and 1.26ppm (3H, s, H-25).

^{13}C NMR:
($CDCl_3$) 174.3, C-2; 132.5, C-3; 101 .1, C-4; 158.4, C-5; 113.6, C-6; 27.7, C-7; 68.4, C-8; 80.1, C-9; 150.1, C-11; 123.8, C-12, 44.2, C-13; 38.9, C-14; 22.1, C-15; 128.8, C-16; 139.7, C-17; 36.0, C-18; 27.9, C19; 125.4, C-20; 132.2, C-21; 25.5, C-22; 17.7, C-23; 59.9, C-24; and 18.7ppm, C-25.

Mass Spectrum:
EIMS: 401(M^+, 24%), 383(10), 332(7), 314(4), 248(12), 232(26), 216(18), 190(23), 178(57), 147(19), 121(21), 93(24), and 69*m/e* (base peak); HREIMS: obsd for $C_{23}H_{31}NO_5$, 401.2189; calcd, 401.2202.

HPLC Data

Beckman C_{18} Ultrasphere column; 250 x 4.6 mm; 90:10, v/v, MeOH-water, 1.0ml/min; t_R 2.95 min.

Reference

X. Xu, F. S. de Guzman, and J. B. Gloer; Stachybotrins A and B: Novel Bioactive Metabolites from a Brackish Water Isolate of the Fungus *Stachybotrys* sp.; J. Org. Chem., Vol. 57, pp. 6700-6703(1992).

Common/Systematic Name

Stachybotrin B

Molecular Formula/Molecular Weight

$C_{23}H_{31}NO_4$; MW = 385.22531

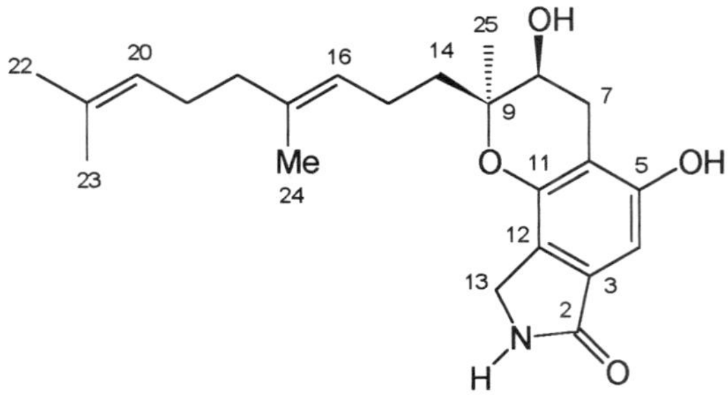

General Characteristics

Isolated as a white solid; mp., 178-180°C; $[\alpha]_D$ + 39.1° (*c*=0.11, in MeOH).

Fungal Source

Stachybotrys sp. (ATCC 90017) collected from brackish water in Florida.

Isolation/Purification

The culture filtrate was extracted with ethyl acetate and the organic phase was dried ($MgSO_4$) and concentrated to afford a red oil. The extract was dissolved in acetone and divided into four equal portions. Each portion was subjected to preparative TLC on silica gel GF plates developed twice with 9:1, v/v, chloroform-ethanol. Major bands observed under illumination (254nm) were collected and extracted with methanol. Bands 2 (R_f 0.18) and 4 (R_f 0.36) were further purified with the same TLC conditions to afford stachybotrin A (a yellow oil) and stachybotrin B (as a white solid).

Biological Activity

Stachybotrins A and B each showed activity in disk assays against *Bacillus subtilis* (ATCC 6051) at 10μg/disk (8- and 10-mm zones, respectively). They also inhibited the radial growth of the filamentous fungi *Ascobolus furfuraceus* (NRRL 6460) and *Sordaria fimicola* (NRRL 6459) by 50% in centerpoint inoculation assays at 20 and 10μg/disk, respectively. Disk assays for activity against a strain of *Candida albicans* (ATCC 14053) were negative at 100μg/disk. Stachybotrin A was also evaluated for cytotoxicity against three human solid tumor cell lines (nonsmall carcinoma A-549, breast adenocarcinoma MCF-7, and colon adenocarcinoma HT-29), but afforded only mild activity (ED_{50} values 20-30μg/ml).

Spectral Data

IR:
(neat) 3293, 2919, 1653, 1608, 1457, 1350, and 1080cm^{-1}.

^{1}H NMR:
($CDCl_3$) 6.74(1H, s, H-4); 2.64(1H, dd, *J*=18.0, 6.0Hz, H-7); 2.98(1H, dd, *J*=18.0, 6.0Hz, H-7); 3.87(1H, dd, *J*=6.0, 6.0Hz, H-8); 4.23(1, d, *J*=18.0Hz, H-13); 4.20(1H, d, *J*=18.0Hz, H-13); 1.67(2H, m, H-14); 2.18(2H, m, H-15); 5.14(1H, m, H-16); 1.95(2H, m, H-18); 2.02(2H, m, H-19); 5.05(1H, m, H-20); 1.63(3H, s, H-22); 1.55(3H, s, H-23); 1.57(3H, s, H-24); and 1.27ppm (3H, s, H-25).

^{13}C NMR:
($CDCl_3$) 174.2, C-2; 132.5, C-3; 100.8, C-4; 158.0, C-5; 113.5, C-6; 27.8, C-7; 68.4, C-8; 80.2, C-9; 150.2, C-11; 124.1, C-12, 44.2, C-13; 38.5, C-14; 22.6, C-15; 125.5, C-16; 136.2, C-17; 40.8, C-18; 27.8, C19; 125.3, C-20; 132.2, C-21; 25.8, C-22; 17.7, C-23; 15.9, C-24; and 18.8ppm, C-25.

Mass Spectrum:
EIMS: 385(M^+, 36%), 311(22), 232(13), 216(16), 190(23), 178(38), 177(30), 147(9), 123(13), 109(15), 95(16), 81(25), and 69*m/e* (base peak); HREIMS: obsd for $C_{23}H_{31}NO_4$, 385.2270*m/e*; calcd, 385.2254.

HPLC Data
Beckman C_{18} Ultrasphere column; 250 x 4.6 mm; 90:10, v/v, MeOH-water; 1.0ml/min; t_R 4.05 min.

Reference
X. Xu, F. S. de Guzman, and J. B. Gloer; Stachybotrins A and B: Novel Bioactive Metabolites from a Brackish Water Isolate of the Fungus *Stachybotrys* sp.; J. Org. Chem., Vol. 57, pp. 6700-6703(1992).

14

Trichothecenes and Related Metabolites

Culmorin
Trichothecene
8β-Hydroxytrichothecene
Trichodermin
Isotrichodermin
7-Hydroxyisotrichodermin
8α-Hydroxyisotrichodermin
7,8-Dihydroxyisotrichodermin
NT-1 Toxin
8-Ketoisotrichodermin
Calonectrin
8-Ketocalonectrin
15-Deacetylcalonectrin
3-Deacetylcalonectrin
7α -Hydroxycalonectrin
8α -Hydroxycalonectrin
7α,8α -Dihydroxycalonectrin
4-Acetoxyscirpenediol
15-Acetoxyscirpenetriol
4,15-Diacetoxyscirpenol
Scirpenetriol
7α-Hydroxydiacetoxyscirpenol
7α,8α-Dihydroxydiacetoxyscirpenol
3,15-Diacetoxyscirpenetriol
3,4,15-Triacetoxyscirpenetriol
T-2 Tetraol
T-2 Toxin
HT-2 Toxin
Acetyl T-2 Toxin
4-Propanyl HT-2 Toxin
3'-Hydroxy T-2 Toxin
3'-Hydroxy HT-2 Toxin
3'-Hydroxy T-2 Triol
Neosolaniol
Isoneosolaniol (Acuminatum)
8-Acetoxyneosolaniol
8-Propanylneosolaniol
8-Butyrylneosolaniol
8-Isobutyrylneosolaniol
15-Deacetylneosolaniol (NT-2 Toxin)
4-Deacetylneosolaniol
Sporotrichiol
4β,8α,15-Triacetoxy-3α,7α-dihydroxy-12,13-epoxytrichothec-9-ene

3-Acetyl-4-deoxynivalenol
Trichodermol
7α-Hydroxytrichodermol
Verrucarol
4,15-Deacetylverrucarol
Crotocin (Antibiotic T)
Crotocol
Trichothecolone
Trichothecin
Trichothecinol A
Trichothecinol B
Trichothecinol C
Trichodermone
Nivalenol
4-Deoxynivalenol (Rd Toxin, Vomitoxin)
3-Acetyl-4-deoxynivalenol
4β,15-Diacetoxynivalenol
4β,15-Diacetyl-7-deoxynivalenol
15-Acetyl-4-deoxynivalenol
3,15-Diacetyl-4-deoxynivalenol
Fusarenon-X (Nivalenol Monoacetate)

Common/Systematic Name
Culmorin

Molecular Formula/Molecular Weight
$C_{15}H_{26}O_2$; MW = 238.19328

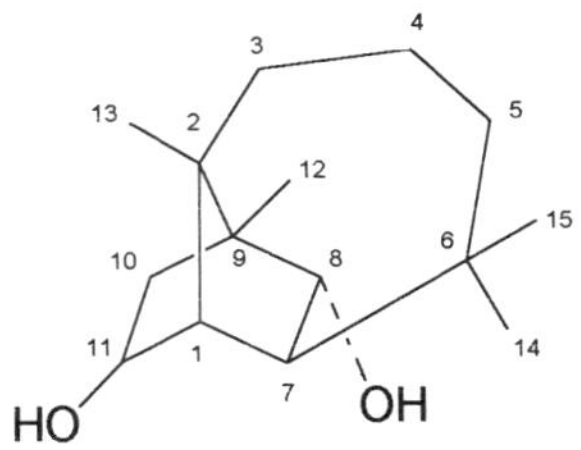

General Characteristics
Colorless needles from tetrahydrofuran-cyclohexane; mp., 178-179°C; $[\alpha]_D^{24}$ - 15° (*c*=0.60, in $CHCl_3$).

Fungal Source
Fusarium roseum (ATCC 28114), *F. culmorum, F. graminearum,* and *F. crookwellense.*

Isolation/Purification
Fusarium roseum cultures were harvested, and the broth was extracted as described by Greenhalgh *et al.* (1984). Some of the oil from the methanol phase after it had been partitioned and concentrated was dissolved in methylene chloride and passed through a Florisil column eluted with 750ml of (A) methylene chloride, (B) 0.5% methanol in methylene chloride, and (C) 5% methanol in methylene chloride. Fraction A afforded an oil from which 3-acetyldeoxynivalenol was obtained. Fractions B and C also afforded yellow oils. The oil which remained in fraction A after removal of 3-acetyldeoxynivalenol was chromatographed on silica gel (Kieselgel 60). The column was eluted first with 10% toluene in methylene chloride and then with 0.5% methanol in methylene chloride, 1.5% methanol in methylene chloride, 3% methanol in methylene chloride, and finally 13% methanol in methylene chloride. Fractions were collected and monitored by TLC; fractions 6-10, 11-12, 13-17, and 18-20 were combined to give mixtures A1, A2, A3, and A4, respectively. Further purification of mixtures A2 and A3 was accomplished with a Chromatotron (Model No. 7924, Harrison Research, Inc.) with a 2mm silica gel plate (Kieselgel 60). Culmorin was isolated from mixture A3 by elution with 50% ethyl acetate in hexane followed by recrystallization from tetrahydrofuran-cyclohexane.

Spectral Data

^{1}H NMR:

(CDCl$_3$) 0.70(3H, H-13); 0.86(3H, H-12); 0.90(3H, H-14); 1.02(3H, H-15); 1.3-2.1(6H, H-3, H-4, H-5, m); 1.64(2H, $J_{10,11}$=6.8Hz, H-10); 1.74(1H, $J_{7,8}$=5.0Hz, H-7); 1.90(1H, $J_{1,11}$=4.5Hz, H-1); 3.86(1H, $J_{2,8}$=8.0Hz, H-8); and 4.35ppm (1H, $J_{10,11}$=6.8, $J_{11,1}$=4.5Hz, H-11).

Mass Spectrum:

HREIMS: 238.1922*m/e* (M^+); calcd for $C_{15}H_{26}O_2$, 238.1922.

References

R. Greenhalgh, R. M. Meier, B. A. Blackwell, J. D. Miller, A. Taylor, and J. W. Apsimon; Minor Metabolites of *Fusarium roseum* (ATCC 28114); J. Agric. Food Chem., Vol. 32, pp. 1261-1264(1984).

D. R. Lauren, A. Ashley, B. A. Blackwell, R. Greenhalgh, J. D. Miller, and G. A. Neish, Trichothecenes Produced by *Fusarium crookwellense* DAOM 193611; J. Agric. Food Chem., Vol. 35, pp. 884-889(1987).

Common/Systematic Name

Trichothecene

12,13-Epoxytrichothec-9-ene

Molecular Formula/Molecular Weight

$C_{15}H_{22}O_2$; MW = 234.16198

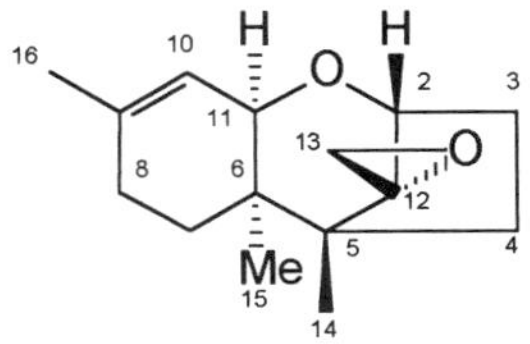

General Characteristics

Crystals from aqueous methanol; mp., 54-57°C.

Fungal Source

Trichothecium roseum.

TLC Data

Preparative TLC using silica gel developed with benzene-ethyl acetate (10:2, v/v).

References

Y. Fujimoto, S. Yokuna, T. Nakamura, T. Morikawa, and T. Tatsuno; Total Synthesis of 12,13-Epoxytrichothec-9-ene; Tetrahedron Letters, pp. 2523-2526(1974).

N. Masouka and T. Kawikawa; A Synthesis of 12,13-Epoxytrichothec-9-ene; Tetrahedron Letters, pp. 1691-1694(1976).

Common/Systematic Name

8β-Hydroxytrichothecene
8β-Hydroxy-12,13-epoxytrichothec-9-ene

Molecular Formula/Molecular Weight

$C_{15}H_{22}O_3$; MW = 250.15689

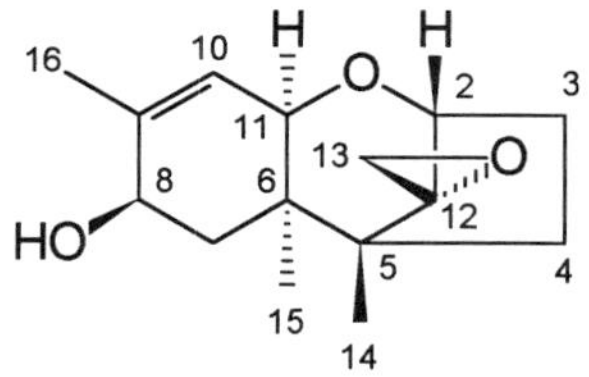

Fungal Source

Fusarium sporotrichioides (MC-72083).

Spectral Data

^{1}H NMR:

($CDCl_3$) 3.65(1H, d, *J*=3.9Hz, H-2); 1.91(1H, m, H-3); 1.57(1H, dd, *J*=13.0, 7.0Hz, H-3); 2.78(1H, dd, *J*=13.0, 7.0Hz, H-4); 1.68(1H, dd, *J*=13.6, 7.0Hz, H-4); 2.03(1H, dd, *J*=12.8, 5.5Hz, H-7); 1.15(1H, dd, *J*=12.5, 9.3Hz, H-7); 4.12(1H, m, H-8); 5.27(1H, m, H-10); 4.66(1H, m, H-11); 3.37(1H, d, *J*=4.1Hz, H-13); 3.06(1H, d, *J*=4.1Hz, H-13); 0.96(3H, s, CH_3-14); 0.96(3H, s, CH_3-15); and 1.77ppm (3H, s, CH_3-16).

^{13}C NMR:

($CDCl_3$) 81.6, C-2; 30.2, C-3; 36.8, C-4; 46.8, C-5; 44.8, C-6; 39.9, C-7; 69.2, C-8; 136.2, C-9; 128.9, C-10; 71.6, C-11; 69.1, C-12; 49.3, C-13; 20.4, C-14; 13.5, C-15; and 18.2ppm, C-16.

Mass Spectrum:

HREIMS: 250.150*m/e* (M^+); calcd for $C_{15}H_{22}O_3$, 250.156.

References

D. G. Corley, G. E. Rottinghaus, and M. S. Tempesta; Novel Trichothecenes from *Fusarium sporotrichioides*; Tetrahedron Letters, Vol. 27, pp. 427-430(1986).

M. E. Savard and B. A. Blackwell; A Compilation of Spectral Characteristics of Secondary Metabolites from *Fusarium* Fungi; In Mycotoxins in Grain; Compounds Other Than Aflatoxin; J. D. Miller and H. L. Trenholm, eds., Eagan Press, St. Paul, pp. 59-257 (1994).

Common/Systematic Name

Trichodermin

4β-Acetoxy-12,13-epoxytrichothec-9-ene

Molecular Formula/Molecular Weight

$C_{17}H_{24}O_4$; MW = 292.16746

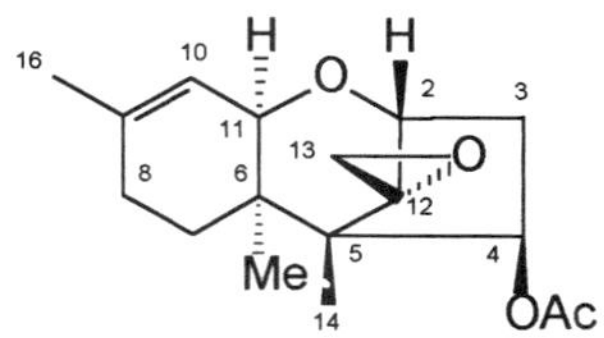

General Characteristics

Synthetic trichodermin; mp., 58-60°C; natural trichodermin crystallized from pentane; mp., 45-46°C; $[\alpha]_D^{20}$ - 11.0° (*c*=1.0, in $CHCl_3$). Insoluble in water; soluble in all common organic solvents.

Fungal Source

Trichoderma lignorum, T. viride, and *Stachybotrys cylindrospora*, a fungal pathogen of aspen (*Populus tremuloides*) that has been found to be strongly antagonistic to the blue-stain fungus, *Ceratocystiopsis crassivaginata*.

Biological Activity

A potent inhibitor of protein synthesis in mammalian cells. Trichodermin inhibited the elongation and/or termination steps in protein synthesis. *In vitro*, it was a potent inhibitor of the peptidyl transferase activity required for elongation and/or termination. LD_{50} in mice dosed SC was 500-1000mg/kg. Trichodermin is also a potent antifungal antibiotic.

Spectral Data

UV:

205nm (ϵ=2,400).

IR:

(KBr) 1730, 1682, 1245, 1225, and 1085cm^{-1}; ($CHCl_3$) 2970, 1735, 1374, 1244, 1220, 1081, 1031, 996, and 970cm^{-1}.

^{1}H NMR:

($CDCl_3$) 3.80, H-2; 1.9-2.5, H-3; 5.60, H-4; 1.9-2.5, H-7; 1.9-2.5, H-8; 5.4, H-10; 3.7, H-11; 2.80, αH-13; 3.10, βH-13; 0.95, H-14; 0.75, H-15; 1.70, H-16; and 2.05ppm, CH_3COO-.

^{13}C NMR:

79.1 d, C-2; 36.7 t, C-3; 75.0 d, C-4; 48.9 s, C-5; 40.4 s, C-6; 24.5 t, C-7; 28.0 t, C-8; 140.1 s, C-9; 118.6 d, C-10; 70.5 d, C-11; 65.5 s, C-12; 47.8 t, C-13; 5.8 q, C-14; 16.0 q, C-15; 23.3 q, C-16; 21.1 q, $\underline{C}H_3COO$-; and 170.8ppm, s, $CH_3\underline{C}OO$.

Mass Spectrum:

HREIMS: 292.1676($C_{17}H_{24}O_4$, Δmmμ=0.2, 100), 277.1441($C_{16}H_{21}O_4$, 78), and 217.1230*m/e* ($C_{14}H_{17}O_2$, 10%).

TLC Data

A. Adsorbent, silica gel G; solvent, chloroform-methanol, 98:2, v/v; R_f, 0.67; detection: H_2SO_4 spraying and heating at 110°C for 5 minutes. B. Adsorbent, silica gel G; solvent: benzene-tetrahydrofuran, 85:15, v/v; R_f, 0.51; detection, H_2SO_4 spraying and heating at 110°C for 5 minutes.

References

R. J. Cole and R. H. Cox; Handbook of Toxic Fungal Metabolites; Academic Press, New York, p. 162 (1981).

W.O. Godtfredsen and S. Vangedal; Trichodermin, A New Antibiotic, Related to Trichothecin; Proc. Chem. Soc., Vol. 19, pp. 188-189(1964).

W. A. Ayer and S. Miao; Secondary Metabolites of the Aspen Fungus *Stachybotrys cylindrospora*; Can. J. Chem., Vol. 71, pp. 487-493(1993).

Common/Systematic Name

Isotrichodermin

3α-Acetoxy-12,13-epoxytrichothec-9-ene

Molecular Formula/Molecular Weight

$C_{17}H_{24}O_4$; MW = 292.16746

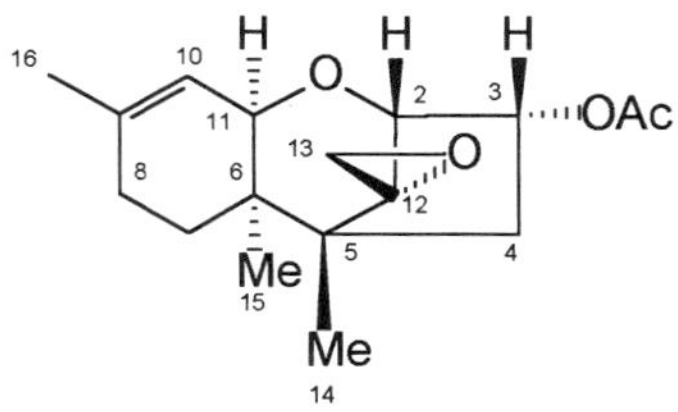

General Characteristics

Colorless crystals; mp, 97-97.5°C; $[\alpha]_D^{24}$ + 9.5° (*c*=0.09, in $CHCl_3$).

Fungal Source

Fusarium culmorum, F. roseum, F. graminearum, and *F. crookwellense.*

Isolation/Purification

Fusarium roseum culture broth was extracted with methylene chloride after being treated with sodium chloride and adjusted to pH 9.3 with sodium hydroxide. The methylene chloride extract was evaporated to dryness and the residue partitioned between aqueous methanol and petroleum ether. Some of the oil from the methanol phase after it had been partitioned and concentrated was dissolved in methylene chloride and passed through a Florisil column eluted with 750ml of (A) methylene chloride, (B) 0.5% methanol in methylene chloride, and (C) 5% methanol in methylene chloride. Fraction A afforded an oil from which 3-acetyldeoxynivalenol was obtained. Fractions B and C also afforded yellow oils. The oil which remained in fraction A after removal of 3-acetyldeoxynivalenol was chromatographed on silica gel (Kieselgel 60). The column was eluted first with 10% toluene in methylene chloride and then with 0.5% methanol in methylene chloride, 1.5% methanol in methylene chloride, 3% methanol in methylene chloride, and finally 13% methanol in methylene chloride. Fractions were collected and monitored by TLC; fractions 6-10, 11-12, 13-17, and 18-20 were combined to give mixtures A1, A2, A3, and A4, respectively. Further purification of mixtures A2 and A3 was accomplished with a Chromatotron (Model No. 7924, Harrison Research, Inc.) with a 2mm silica gel plate (Kieselgel 60). Isotrichodermin was isolated from mixture A2 by elution with 20% ethyl acetate in hexane.

Spectral Data

^{1}H NMR:

($CDCl_3$) 0.74(3H, s, H-15); 0.80(3H, s, H-14); 1.0-2.0(6H, m, H-7, H-4, H-8);

1.71(3H, br s, H-16); 2.11(3H, s, Ac-CH_3); 2.84, 3.07(2H, J_{ab}=4.0Hz, H-13); 3.73(1H, d, $J_{2,3}$=4.6Hz, H-2); 3.96(1H, d, $J_{10,11}$=5.5Hz, H-11); 5.15(1H, dt, J_{24}=10.0, $J_{2,3}$=4.6Hz, H-3); and 5.44ppm (1H, dq, $J_{10,11}$=5.5Hz, $J_{10,16}$=1.5Hz, H-10).

^{13}C NMR:

($CDCl_3$) 78.2, C-2; 71.7, C-3; 38.6, C-4; 45.3, C-5; 40.2, C-6; 24.4, C-7; 28.2, C-8; 139.5, C-9; 119.4, C-10; 71.5, C-11; 65.2, C-12; 48.4, C-13; 11.0, C-14; 15.9, C-15; 23.1, C-16; 20.9, <u>C</u>H_3COO-; and 170.6ppm, <u>C</u>=O.

Mass Spectrum:

HREIMS: 293.174*m/e* (M^+ + 1); calcd for $C_{17}H_{25}O_4$, 293.168.

References

R. Greenhalgh, R. M. Meier, B. A. Blackwell, J. D. Miller, A. Taylor, and J. W. ApSimon; Minor Metabolites of *Fusarium roseum* (ATCC 28114); J. Agric. Food Chem., Vol. 32, pp. 1261-1264(1984).

D. R. Lauren, A. Ashley, B. A. Blackwell, R. Greenhalgh, J. D. Miller, and G. A. Neish; Trichothecenes Produced by *Fusarium crookwellense* DAOM 193611; J. Agric. Food Chem., Vol. 35, pp. 884-889(1987).

Common/Systematic Name

7-Hydroxyisotrichodermin

7α-Hydroxy-3α-acetoxy-12,13-epoxytrichothec-9-ene

Molecular Formula/Molecular Weight

$C_{17}H_{24}O_5$; MW = 308.16237

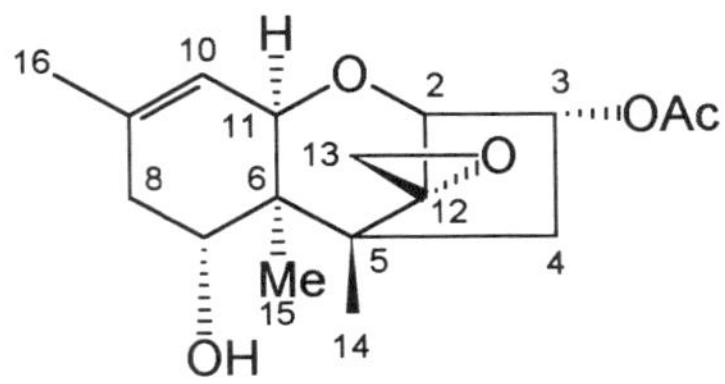

General Characteristics

Crystalline solid from ether-petroleum ethers; mp., 154-155.5°C; $[\alpha]_D^{22}$ -10.6° (*c*=0.095, in $CHCl_3$).

Fungal Source

Fusarium culmorum, F. roseum (ATCC 28114), and *F. crookwellense.*

Isolation/Purification

Fusarium roseum culture broth was extracted with methylene chloride after being treated with sodium chloride and adjusted to pH 9.3 with sodium hydroxide. The methylene chloride extract was evaporated to dryness and the residue partitioned between aqueous methanol and petroleum ether. Some of the oil from the methanol phase after it had been partitioned and concentrated was dissolved in methylene chloride and passed through a Florisil column eluted with 750ml of (A) methylene chloride, (B) 0.5% methanol in methylene chloride, and (C) 5% methanol in methylene chloride. Fraction A afforded an oil which was subjected to medium pressure liquid chromatography on a LiChroprep Si 60 column.The column was eluted with the following solvents: 10% ethyl acetate-hexane; 20% ethyl acetate-hexane; 30% ethyl acetate-hexane; and ethyl acetate. A metabolite eluting in the 10% ethyl acetate fractions was further purified by elution initially with chloroform and then 2% methanol-chloroform. The metabolite was recrystallized from ether-petroleum ether to give a crystalline solid of 7-hydroxyisotrichodermin.

Spectral Data

^{1}H NMR:

($CDCl_3$) 0.82(3H, s, CH_3-15); 1.04(3H, s, CH_3-14); 1.09(1H, 7-OH, *J*=6.3Hz); 1.70(3 H, br s, CH_3-16); 2.10(3H, s, Ac-CH_3); 1.9, 2.2(2H, dd, *J*=17.2, 10.0; 17.2, 6.0Hz, H-8); 2.07, 2.10(2H, m, 2H-4); 3.08, 3.13(2H, d, *J*=4.4, 4.4Hz, H-13); 3.76(1H, d, $J_{2,3}$=4.5Hz, H-2); 4.10(1H, d, $J_{11,10}$=5.4Hz, H-11); 4.46(1H, $J_{7,8}$=5.9, 10.1, $J_{7,10}$=6.3Hz); 5.16(1H, ddd, J=9.8, 5.2, 4.5Hz, H-3); and 5.40ppm (1H, br d, *J*=5.4Hz, H-10).

^{13}C NMR:
(CDCl$_3$) 79.0, C-2; 74.1, C-3; 39.5, C-4; 44.6, C-5; 46.2, C-6; 74.7, C-7; 41.4, C-8; 138.0, C-9; 119.6, C-10; 69.0, C-11; 64.9, C-12; 47.7, C-13; 10.2, C-14; 15.0, C-15; 22.4, C-16; 20.9, <u>C</u>H$_3$COO-; and 170.6ppm, <u>C</u>=O.

Mass Spectrum:
HREIMS: 308.163*m/e* (M$^+$); calcd for $C_{17}H_{24}O_5$, 308.162.

References

R. Greenhalgh, R. M. Meier, B. A. Blackwell, J. D. Miller, A. Taylor, and J. W. ApSimon; Minor Metabolites of *Fusarium roseum* (ATCC 28114); J. Agric. Food Chem., Vol. 34, pp. 115-118(1986).

D. R. Lauren, A. Ashley, B. A. Blackwell, R. Greenhalgh, J. D. Miller, and G. A. Neish; Trichothecenes Produced by *Fusarium crookwellense* DAOM 193611; J. Agric. Food Chem., Vol. 35, pp. 884-889(1987).

Common/Systematic Name

8α-Hydroxyisotrichodermin

8α-Hydroxy-3α-acetoxy-12,13-epoxytrichothec-9-ene

Molecular Formula/Molecular Weight

$C_{17}H_{24}O_5$; MW = 308.16237

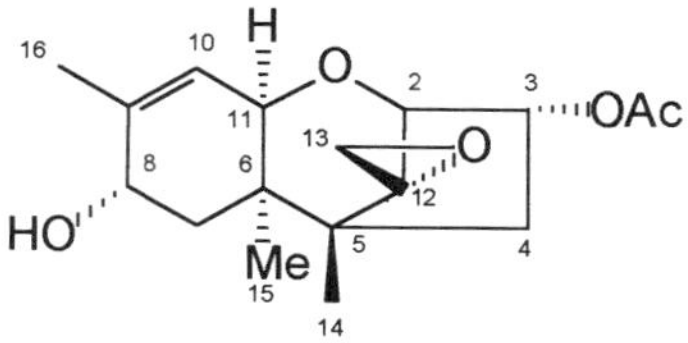

General Characteristics

Crystals from ethyl acetate-hexane; mp., 153-155.5°C; $[\alpha]_D^{21}$ - 18.2° (*c*=0.11, in $CHCl_3$).

Fungal Source

Fusarium culmorum, F. roseum (ATCC 28114), and *F. crookwellense.*

Isolation/Purification

Fusarium roseum culture broth was extracted with methylene chloride after being treated with sodium chloride and adjusted to pH 9.3 with sodium hydroxide. The methylene chloride extract was evaporated to dryness and the residue partitioned between aqueous methanol and petroleum ether. Some of the oil from the methanol phase after it had been partitioned and concentrated was dissolved in methylene chloride and passed through a Florisil column eluted with 750ml of (A) methylene chloride, (B) 0.5% methanol in methylene chloride, and (C) 5% methanol in methylene chloride. Fraction A afforded an oil which was subjected to medium pressure liquid chromatography on a LiChroprep Si 60 column. The column was eluted with the following solvents: 10% ethyl acetate-hexane; 20% ethyl acetate-hexane; 30% ethyl acetate-hexane; and ethyl acetate. An oil eluting in the 10% ethyl acetate fractions was further purified with a Chromatotron eluted with chloroform followed by 5% methanol in chloroform. 8-Hydroxyisotrichodermin and 8-hydroxy-3α-acetoxy-12,13-epoxytrichothec-9-ene were purified by preparative TLC with 7% methanol in chloroform.

Spectral Data

^1H NMR:

($CDCl_3$) 3.72(1H, d, *J*=4.6Hz, H-2); 5.16(1H, ddd, *J*=9.8, 5.5, 4.6Hz, H-3); 2.09(2H, m, *J*=9.8, 5.5Hz, H-4); 1.70(1H, dd, *J*=14.3, 1.4Hz, H-7); 2.21(1H, dd, *J*=14.3, 5.7Hz, H-7); 4.10(1H, br d, *J*=5.7Hz, H-8); 5.59(1H, d, *J*=5.7Hz, H-10); 4.04(1H, d, *J*=5.7Hz, H-11); 2.87(1H, d, *J*=4.1Hz, H-13); 3.06(1H, d, *J*=4.1Hz, H-13); 0.77(3H, s, CH_3-14); 0.98(3H, s, CH_3-15); 1.86(3H, br s, CH_3-16); and 2.11ppm (3H, s, $\underline{C}H_3COO$-).

^{13}C NMR:
(CDCl$_3$) 78.1, C-2; 71.5, C-3; 38.1, C-4; 45.4, C-5; 39.6, C-6; 33.6, C-7; 68.0, C-8; 138.8, C-9; 122.1, C-10; 71.3, C-11; 65.2, C-12; 48.5, C-13; 11.0, C-14; 19.0, C-15; 20.4, C-16; 20.9, $\underline{C}H_3COO$-; and 170.6ppm, $\underline{C}$=O.

Mass Spectrum:
HREIMS: 308.166*m/e* (M^+); calcd for $C_{17}H_{24}O_5$, 308.162.

References

R. Greenhalgh, R.M. Meier, B. A. Blackwell, J. D. Miller, A. Taylor, and J. W. ApSimon; Minor Metabolites of *Fusarium roseum* (ATCC 28114); J. Agric. Food Chem., Vol. 34, pp. 115-118(1986).

D. R. Lauren, A. Ashley, B. A. Blackwell, R. Greenhalgh, J. D. Miller, and G. A. Neish; Trichothecenes Produced by *Fusarium crookwellense* DAOM 193611; J. Agric. Food Chem., Vol. 35, pp. 884-889(1987).

Common/Systematic Name

7,8-Dihydroxyisotrichodermin

7,8-Dihydroxy-3α-acetoxy-12,13-epoxytrichothec-9-ene

Molecular Formula/Molecular Weight

$C_{17}H_{24}O_6$; MW = 324.15729

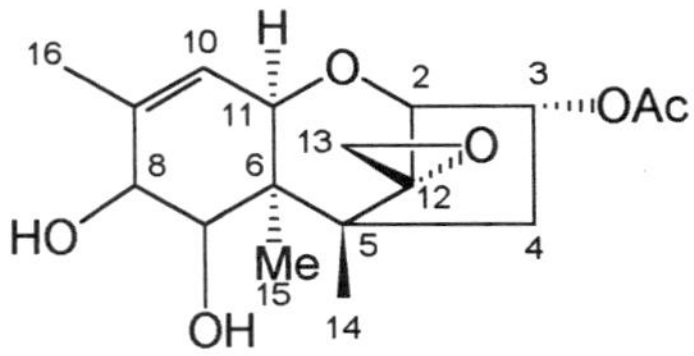

General Characteristics

White solid; mp., 80-84°C.

Fungal Source

Fusarium crookwellense.

Isolation/Purification

The fungal culture filtrate was extracted with ethyl acetate, dried over anhydrous sodium sulfate, and evaporated to dryness to yield a yellow gum. The yellow gum was chromatographed on a silica gel column eluted initially with 10% ethyl acetate-chloroform and increasing the percentage of ethyl acetate. Ethyl acetate eluted an oil that was further purified by preparative HPLC using a cyano-bonded phase column with 3% 2-propanol-hexane as mobile phase to give pure 7,8-dihydroxyisotrichodermin.

Spectral Data

^{1}H NMR:

($CDCl_3$) 3.76(1H, d, *J*=4.5Hz, H-2); 5.17(1H, m, *J*=8.8, 6.9, 4.5Hz, H-3); 2.05(2H, m, *J*α=6.9, 7.8Hz, *J*β=8.8, 7.8Hz, H-4); 4.41(1H, dd, *J*=9.7, 5.5Hz, H-7); 3.98(1H, bt, *J*=6.0Hz, H-8); 5.59(1H, dq, *J*=5.9, 1.6Hz, H-10); 4.16(1H, d, *J*=5.9Hz, H-11); 3.10(1H, d, *J*=4.3Hz, H-13); 3.17(1H, d, *J*=4.3Hz, H-13); 1.06(3H, s, CH_3-14); 0.89(3H, s, CH_3-15); 1.87(3H, br s, CH_3-16); and 2.10ppm (3H, s, $\underline{C}H_3COO$-).

^{13}C NMR:

78.9 C-2; 71.5, C-3; 40.6, C-4; 46.4, C-5; 44.2, C-6; 73.8, C-7; 71.1, C-8; 138.8, C-9; 122.6, C-10; 69.8, C-11; 65.0, C-12; 47.8, C-13; 13.2, C-14; 14.7, C-15; 20.3, C-16; 20.9, $\underline{C}H_3COO$-; and 170.6ppm, $\underline{C}$=O.

Mass Spectrum:

LREIMS: 324(M^+, 27%), 165(24), 148(47), 123(49), 135(61), 95(51), 107(75), and 100*m/e* (100).

Reference

D. R. Lauren, A. Ashley, B. A. Blackwell, R. Greenhalgh, J. D. Miller, and G. A. Neish; Trichothecenes Produced by *Fusarium crookwellense* DAOM 193611; J. Agric. Food Chem., Vol. 35, pp. 884-889(1987).

Common/Systematic Name

NT-1 Toxin

4β,8α-Diacetoxy-3α,15-dihydroxy-12,13-epoxytrichothec-9-ene

Molecular Formula/Molecular Weight

$C_{19}H_{26}O_8$; MW = 382.16277

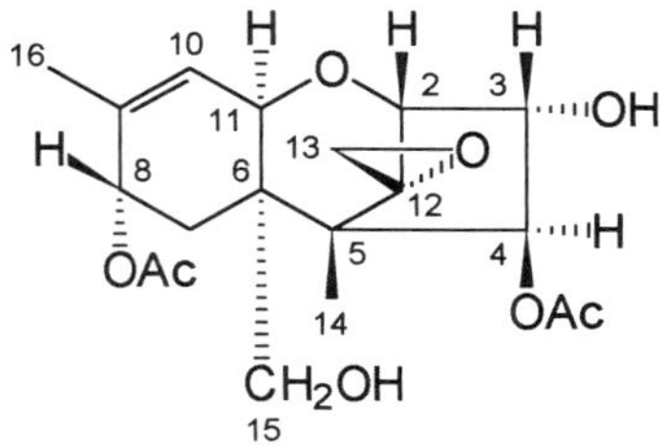

General Characteristics

Crystals from benzene-*n*-hexane; mp., 172.5-173.5°C.

Fungal Source

Fusarium sporotrichioides (strain M-1-1), *F. tricinctum*, *F. equiseti*, and *F. acuminatum*.

Isolation/Purification

Extracted by charcoal absorption and elution with methanol. Extraction of methanol-chloroform soluble materials produced a pale yellow powder. The powder was chromatographed on a silica gel column eluted with *n*-hexane, *n*-hexane-acetone, 12:5, 2:1, 1:1, 1:2 (v/v), acetone and methanol followed by a second silica gel column eluted with benzene-acetone (3:2) and *n*-hexane-acetone (1:1, v/v). NT-1 was crystallized with benzene-*n*-hexane.

Biological Activity

Inhibited uptake of [^{14}C]leucine in protein synthesis with rabbit reticulocytes; ID_{50} at concentrations of 0.23 and 0.25μg/ml by NT-1 and NT-2, respectively. These activities were similar to that of neosolaniol (0.25μg/ml) in the same assay. LD_{50} in rats dosed IP was 1.2mg/Kg.

Spectral Data

IR:

(KBr) 3450, 2940, 1720, and 1230cm^{-1}.

^{1}H NMR:

($CDCl_3$) 3.66(H-2); 4.24(H-3); 5.40(H-4); 1.96(H-7α); 2.34(H-7β); 5.36(H-8); 5.82(H-10); 4.27(H-11); 2.80(H-13α); 3.04(H-13β); 0.84(H-14); 3.60(H-15α); 3.91(H-15β); 1.75(H-16); and 2.09, 2.14ppm (3H each, CH_3CO-).

Mass Data:

LREIMS: 382*m/e* (M^+); found: C, 59.69; H, 6.82; O, 33.49%; calcd for $C_{19}H_{26}O_8$; C, 59.65; H, 6.85; O, 33.50%.

TLC Data

Adsorbent: silica gel; solvent: ethyl acetate-petrol (3:1, v/v); R_f, 0.4; detection: sky-blue fluorescence in UV after spraying with *p*-anisaldehyde and heating.

References

K. Ishii and Y. Ueno; Isolation and Characterization of Two New Trichothecenes from *Fusarium sporotrichioides* Strain M-1-1; Applied and Environmental Microbiology, Vol. 42, pp. 541-543(1981).

A. Visconti, C. J. Mirocha, A. Logrieco, A. Bottalico, and M. Solfrizzo; Mycotoxins Produced by *Fusarium acuminatum*: A New Trichothecene; J. Agric. Food Chem., Vol. 37, pp. 1348-1351(1989).

Common/Systematic Name

8-Ketoisotrichodermin

8-Keto-3α-acetoxy-12,13-epoxytrichothec-9-ene

Molecular Formula/Molecular Weight

$C_{17}H_{22}O_5$; MW = 306.14672

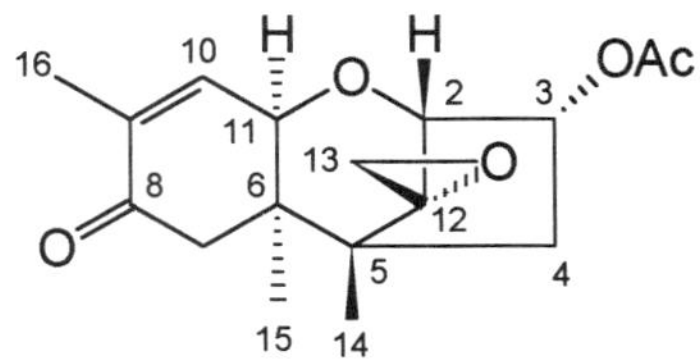

General Characteristics

White solid; mp., 122-124°C.

Fungal Source

Fusarium crookwellense.

Isolation/Purification

The fungal culture filtrate was extracted with ethyl acetate, dried over anhydrous sodium sulfate, and evaporated to dryness to yield a yellow gum. The yellow gum was chromatographed by a silica gel column eluted initially with 10% ethyl acetate-chloroform and increasing the percentage of ethyl acetate. Ethyl acetate eluted an oil that was further purified by preparative HPLC using a cyano-bonded phase column with 3% 2-propanol-hexane as mobile phase.

Spectral Data

^{1}H NMR:

($CDCl_3$) 3.83(1H, d, *J*=4.6Hz, H-2); 5.22(1H, m, *J*=4.6, 10.9, 4.6Hz, H-3); 2.03(2H, dd, *J*α=14.8, 10.9Hz, *J*β=14.8, 4.6Hz, H-4); 2.26(1H, dd, *J*=15.3, 1.1Hz, H-7); 2.87(1H, d, *J*=15.3Hz, H-7); 6.51(1H, dd, *J*=5.7, 1.5Hz, H-10); 4.32(1H, d, *J*=5.7Hz, H-11); 2.86(1H, d, *J*=3.9Hz, H-13); 3.10(1H, d, *J*=3.9Hz, H-13); 0.75(3H, s, CH_3-14); 0.92(3H, d, *J*=1.1Hz,CH_3-15); 1.81(3H, d, *J*=1.5Hz, CH_3-16); and 2.14ppm (3H, s, CH_3COO-).

^{13}C NMR:

($CDCl_3$) 78.5, C-2; 71.4, C-3; 42.1, C-4; 45.4, C-5; 43.4, C-6; 37.8, C-7; 189.0, C-8; 137.7, C-9; 137.6, C-10; 71.6, C-11; 57.5, C-12; 48.1, C-13; 10.6, C-14; 18.3, C-15; 15.3, C-16; 20.8, $\underline{C}H_3COO$-; and 172.5ppm, $\underline{C}$=O.

Mass Spectrum:

LREIMS: 306(M^+, 3%), 216(27), 253(35), 138(92), 123(100), 107(42), and 79*m/e* (49).

Reference

D. R. Lauren, A. Ashley, B. A. Blackwell, R. Greenhalgh, J. D. Miller, and G. A. Neish; Trichothecenes Produced by *Fusarium crookwellense* DAOM 193611; J. Agric. Food Chem., Vol. 35, pp. 884-889(1987).

Common/Systematic Name

Calonectrin

3α,15-Diacetoxy-12,13-epoxytrichothec-9-ene

Molecular Formula/Molecular Weight

$C_{19}H_{26}O_6$; MW = 350.17294

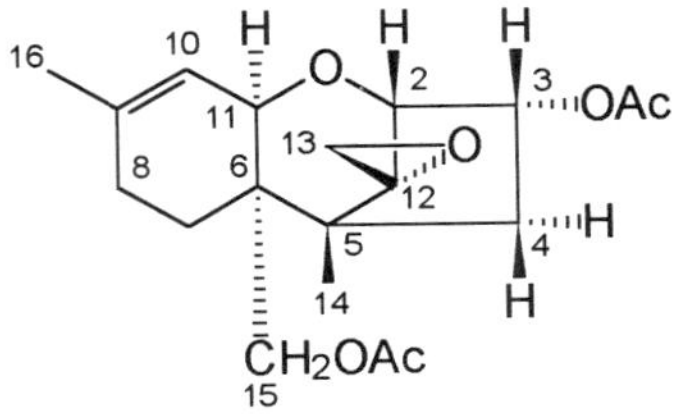

General Characteristics

Prisms from ethyl ether-petroleum ether; mp., 83-85°C; $[\alpha]_D^{27}$ - 14.6° (*c*=1.0, in $CHCl_3$).

Fungal Source

Fusarium culmorum, F. roseum (ATCC 28114), and *Calonectria nivalis.*

Isolation/Purification.

Fusarium roseum culture broth was extracted with methylene chloride after being treated with sodium chloride and adjusted to pH 9.3 with sodium hydroxide. The methylene chloride extract was evaporated to dryness and the residue partitioned between aqueous methanol and petroleum ether. Some of the oil from the methanol phase after it had been partitioned and concentrated was dissolved in methylene chloride and passed through a Florisil column eluted with (A) methylene chloride, (B) 0.5% methanol in methylene chloride, and (C) 5% methanol in methylene chloride. Fraction A afforded an oil which was subjected to medium pressure liquid chromatography on a LiChroprep Si 60 column. The column was eluted with the following solvents: 10% ethyl acetate-hexane; 20% ethyl acetate-hexane; 30% ethyl acetate-hexane; and ethyl acetate. The fractions collected (651) were reduced to 52 samples by combining appropriate fractions. Calonectrin was isolated from an oil eluted in fraction 13 and purified by column chromatography on silica gel eluted with 5% methanol in chloroform.

Spectral Data

IR:

(KBr) 1745, 1725, 1240, and 965cm^{-1}.

^{1}H NMR:

($CDCl_3$) 3.82(2H, d, *J*=12.2Hz, αCH_2-15); 4.06(2H, d, *J*=12.2Hz, βCH_2-15); 0.81(3 H, s, CH_3-14); 1.78-2.19(2H, m, H-7); 1.70(3 H, br s, CH_3-16); 2.01(3H, s, Ac-CH_3);

1.7-2.19(2H, m, H-8); 2.1-2.19(2H, m, H-4); 2.84, 3.08(2H each, d, *J*=4.0, 4.0Hz, 2H-13α and 2H-13β, respectively); 3.74(1H, d, *J*=4.6Hz, H-2); 4.00(1H, d, *J*=5.6Hz, H-11; 5.15(1H, ddd, *J*=9.6, 7.4, 4.6Hz, H-3); 2.01(3H, s, CH_3COO); 2.08(3H, s, CH_3COO); and 5.45ppm (1 H, dq, *J*=5.4, 1.3Hz, H-10).

^{13}C NMR:

($CDCl_3$) 78.0, C-2; 71.2, C-3; 39.35, C-4; 45.3, C-5; 42.9; C-6; 20.9, C-7; 28.1, C-8; 140.3, C-9; 118.9, C-10; 68.0, C-11; 64.9, C-12; 48.4, C-13; 12.0, C-14; 63.5, C-15; 23.1, C-16; 20.9, 21.0, $\underline{C}H_3COO$-; and 170.6, 170.7ppm, $\underline{C}$=O.

References

R. Greenhalgh, D. Lavandier, W. Adams, J. D. Miller, B. A. Blackwell, A. J. McAlees, and A. Taylor; Production and Characterization of Deoxynivalenol and Other Secondary Metabolites of *Fusarium culmorum* (CMI 14764, HLX 1503); J. Agric. Food Chem., Vol. 34, pp. 98-102(1986).

R. Greenhalgh, R.M. Meier, B. A. Blackwell, J. D. Miller, A. Taylor, and J.W. ApSimon; Minor Metabolites of *Fusarium roseum* (ATCC 28114), Part 2; J. Agric. Food Chem., Vol. 34, pp. 115-118(1986).

D. R. Lauren, A. Ashley, B. A. Blackwell, R. Greenhalgh, J. D. Miller, and G. A. Neish; Trichothecenes Produced by *Fusarium crookwellense* DAOM 193611; J. Agric. Food Chem., Vol. 35, pp. 884-889(1987).

R. J. Cole and R. H. Cox; Handbook of Toxic Fungal Metabolites; Academic Press, New York, pp. 192 (1981).

Common/Systematic Name

8-Ketocalonectrin

3α,15-Diacetoxy-12,13-epoxytrichothec-9-en-8-one

Molecular Formula/Molecular Weight

$C_{19}H_{24}O_7$; MW = 364.15220

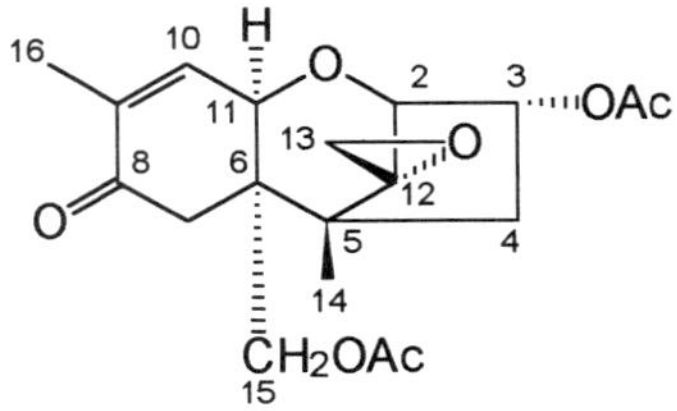

General Characteristics

Isolated as an oil.

Fungal Source

Fusarium culmorum.

Isolation/Purification

Mycelia were extracted with methylene chloride, reduced to dryness, redissolved in methanol-water and partitioned against petroleum ether. The methanol raffinate was evaporated to dryness, redissolved in hot absolute alcohol and hexane added slowly. On cooling the solution deposited crystals of 3-acetyldeoxynivalenol which were removed for further purification. The brown viscous oil from the mother liquor was dissolved and chromatographed on a silica gel column eluted with the following: 25% ethyl acetate in methylene chloride; 2% methanol in methylene chloride; 5% methanol in methylene chloride; and methanol. Fractions containing 8-ketocalonectrin were combined and obtained pure by preparative TLC.

Spectral Data

^{1}H NMR:

($CDCl_3$) 0.81(3H, s, CH_3-14); 1.82(3H, d, $J_{16,10}$=1.6Hz, CH_3-16); 1.96(3H, s, CH_3-15Ac); 2.14(3H, s, CH_3-3Ac); 1.95-2.23(2H, m, H-4); 2.51, 2.85(2H, dd, J_{AB}=16.0Hz, $J_{7\alpha,15}$=1.5Hz, H-7); 2.88, 3.12(2H, d, J_{AB}=3.8Hz, H-13); 3.84(2H, d, $J_{2,3}$=4.6Hz, H-2); 4.07(2H, m, H-15); 4.44(1H, d, $J_{11,10}$=5.1Hz, H-11); 5.23(1H, ddd, $J_{3,2}$=4.6Hz, $J_{3,4}$=5.5, 10.4Hz, H-3); and 6.55ppm (1H, dd, $J_{10,11}$=5.1Hz, $J_{11,16}$=1.6Hz, H-10).

^{13}C NMR:

($CDCl_3$) 78.1, C-2; 71.2, C-3; 38.5, C-4; 45.0, C-5; 47.5; C-6; 38.4, C-7; 198.7, C-8; 138.3, C-9; 137.5, C-10; 68.2, C-11; 65.3, C-12; 48.3, C-13; 11.3, C-14; 64.2, C-15; 15.4, C-16; 20.9, $\underline{C}H_3COO$-; and 170.5ppm, $\underline{C}$=O.

Mass Spectrum:
LREIMS: 364(11%, M^+), 262 (18), 203, (13), 109 (19); 121, and 43*m/e* (100).

Reference

R. Greenhalgh, D. Lavandier, W. Adams, J. D. Miller, B. A. Blackwell, A. J. McAlees, and A. Taylor; Production andCharacterization of Deoxynivalenol and Other Secondary Metabolites of *Fusarium culmorum* (CMI 14764, HLX 1503); J. Agric. Food Chem., Vol. 34, pp. 98-102(1986).

Common/Systematic Name

15-Deacetylcalonectrin

3α-Acetoxy-15-hydroxy-12,13-epoxytrichothec-9-ene

Molecular Formula/Molecular Weight

$C_{17}H_{24}O_5$; MW = 308.16237

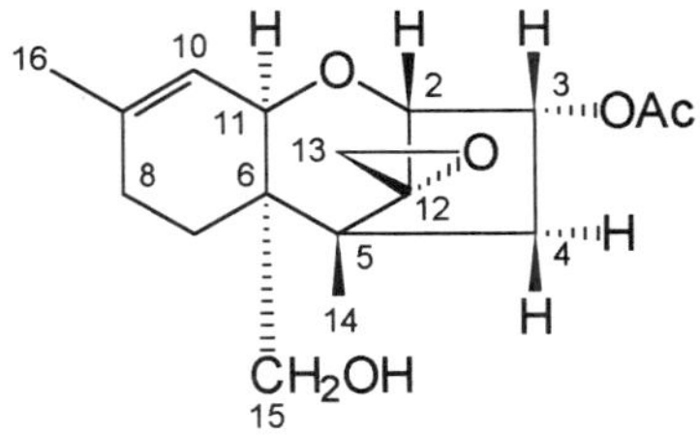

General Characteristics

Colorless prisms from ethyl acetate-hexane; mp., 181-183°C; $[\alpha]_D^{26}$ + 10.2° (*c*=0.8, in $CHCl_3$); prisms from ethyl ether-light petroleum; mp., 184-186°C.

Fungal Source

Fusarium culmorum, F. roseum, F. graminearum, and *Calonectria nivalis.*

Isolation/Purification

Fusarium roseum was cultured, harvested, and the broth extracted as described by Greenhalgh *et al.* (1984). Some of the oil from the methanol phase after it had been partitioned and concentrated was dissolved in methylene chloride and passed through a Florisil column eluted with 750mL of (A) methylene chloride, (B) 0.5% methanol in methylene chloride, and (C) 5% methanol in methylene chloride. Fraction A afforded an oil from which 3-acetyldeoxynivalenol was obtained. Fractions B and C also afforded yellow oils. The oil which remained in fraction A after removal of 3-acetyldeoxynivalenol was chromatographed on silica gel (Kieselgel 60). The column was eluted first with 10% toluene in methylene chloride and then with 0.5% methanol in methylene chloride, 1.5% methanol in methylene chloride, 3% methanol in methylene chloride, and finally 13% methanol in methylene chloride. Fractions were collected and monitored by TLC; fractions 6-10, 11-12, 13-17, and 18-20 were combined to give mixtures A1, A2, A3, and A4, respectively. Further purification of mixtures A2 and A3 was accomplished with a Chromatotron (Model No. 7924, Harrison Research, Inc.) with a 2mm silica gel plate (Kieselgel 60). Isotrichodermin was isolated from mixture A2 by elution with 20% ethyl acetate in hexane. Changing the solvent to 20% ethyl acetate in hexane gave pure 15-deacetylcalonectrin.

Spectral Data

^{1}H NMR:

($CDCl_3$) 3.72(1H, d, $J_{2,3}$=4.68Hz, H-2); 5.13(1H, ddd, J=10, 5.0, 4.6Hz, H-3); 1.73-2.30(2H, m, H-4); 1.73-2.30(2H, m, H-7); 1.73-2.30(2H, m, H-8); 5.46(1H, dd, J=5.3, 1.5Hz, H-10); 3.96(1H, d, J=5.3Hz, H-11); 2.84, 3.07(1H each, d, J=4.0Hz, H-13); 0.90(3H, s, CH_3-14); 3.47(1H, d, J=11.6Hz, H-15); 3.66(1H, ddd, J=11.6, 4.5, 3.2Hz, H-15); 1.71(3H, d, J=1.5Hz, H-16); and 2.09ppm (3H, s, CH_3COO-).

^{13}C NMR:

($CDCl_3$) 78.2, C-2; 71.5, C-3; 39.4, C-4; 45.3, C-5; 44.2, C-6; 20.8, C-7; 28.5, C-8; 140.5, C-9; 119.5, C-10; 68.3, C-11; 65.2, C-12; 48.5, C-13; 12.3, C-14; 62.8, C-15; 23.1, C-16; 20.8, $\underline{C}H_3COO$-; and 170.6ppm, $\underline{C}$=O.

Mass Spectrum:

HREIMS: 309.167*m/e* (M^+ + 1); calcd for $C_{17}H_{25}O_5$, 309.162.

References

R. Greenhalgh, D. Levandier, W. Adams, J. D. Miller, B. A. Blackwell, A. J. McAlees, and A. Taylor; Production and Characterization of Deoxynivalenol and Other Secondary Metabolites of *Fusarium culmorum* (CMI 14764, HLX 1503); J. Agric. Food Chem., Vol. 34, pp. 98-102(1986).

R. Greenhalgh, R. M. Meier, B. A. Blackwell, J. D. Miller, A. Taylor, and J. W. ApSimon; Minor Metabolites of *Fusarium roseum* (ATCC 28114); J. Agric. Food Chem., Vol. 32, pp. 1261-1264(1984).

Common/Systematic Name

3-Deacetylcalonectrin

3α-Hydroxy-15-acetoxy-12,13-epoxytrichothec-9-ene

Molecular Formula/Molecular Weight

$C_{17}H_{24}O_5$; MW = 308.16237

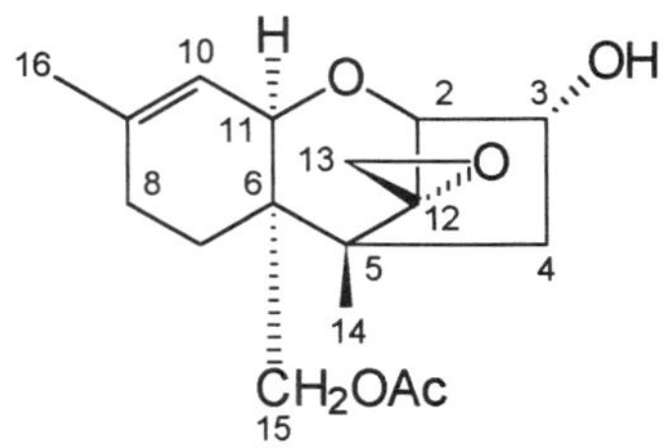

Fungal Source

Fusarium graminearum and *F. culmorum.*

Isolation/Purification

Mycelia were extracted with methylene chloride, reduced to dryness, redissolved in methanol-water and partitioned against petroleum ether. The methanol raffinate was evaporated to dryness, redissolved in hot absolute alcohol and hexane added slowly. On cooling the solution deposited crystals of 3-acetyldeoxynivalenol which were removed for further purification. The brown viscous oil from the mother liquor was chromatographed on a silica gel column eluted with the following: 25% ethyl acetate in methylene chloride; 2% methanol in methylene chloride; 5% methanol in methylene chloride; and methanol. Fractions containing 3-deacetylcalonectrin were combined and further purified by preparative TLC using 10% acetone in chloroform to yield pure 3-deacetylcalonectrin (R_f, 0.62).

Biological Activity

The trichothecenes as a group show a wide range of biological activity such as antibacterial, antiviral, antifungal, and cytostatic activity; some are phytotoxic and all show some degree of animal toxicity, including insecticidal activity. There exists a broad range of toxicity in vertebrate animals and the acute toxicities vary considerably. General gross clinical signs reported for trichothecenes are vomiting, diarrhea, anorexia, ataxia, hematuria, leukocytosis soon followed by severe leukopenia, inflammation of the gastrointestinal tract, degeneration of nerve cells in the central nervous system, degeneration and hemorrhaging of cardiac muscle, and lesions of lymph nodes, testes, and thymus. Topical application or contact with skin causes dermal necrosis. Biochemically, they are potent inhibitors of protein and DNA synthesis in whole-cell and cell-free systems. Some trichothecenes inhibit the initiation step of protein synthesis on polyribosomes and others inhibit the elongation and/or termination step in protein synthesis. The trichothecenes have been strongly implicated in natural intoxications of animals and man.

Spectral Data

^{1}H NMR:

(CDCl$_3$) 0.79(3H, s, CH$_3$-14); 1.70(3H, s, CH$_3$-16); 2.02(3H, s, CH$_3$-15Ac); 1.9-2.3(6H, unresolved m, H-4, -7, -8); 2.82, 3.06(2H, d, $J_{A,B}$=4.0Hz, H-13); 3.48(1H, d, $J_{2,3}$=4.6Hz, H-2); 3.82, 4.06(2H, d, $J_{A,B}$=12.2Hz, H-15); 4.13(1H, d, $J_{11,10}$=5.4Hz, H-11); 4.43(1H, ddd, $J_{3,2}$=4.6, $J_{3,4}$=ca 6, 9.5Hz, H-3); and 5.48ppm (1H, dd, $J_{10,11}$=5.4Hz, $J_{10,16}$ =1.4Hz, H-10).

^{13}C NMR:

(CDCl$_3$) 68.4, C-2; 69.1, C-3; 42.4, C-4; 45.9, C-5; 45.9; C-6; 21.2, C-7; 28.4, C-8; 140.1, C-9; 119.3, C-10; 80.0, C-11; 65.6, C-12; 48.4, C-13; 12.3, C-14; 62.8, C-15; 23.2, C-16; 21.0, CH$_3$COO-; and 170.6ppm, C=O.

Mass Spectrum:

LREIMS: 308(M$^+$), 106(70%), 248(80), 123(82); 220(82), and 91*m/e* (100).

Reference

R. Greenhalgh, D. Lavandier, W. Adams, J. D. Miller, B. A. Blackwell, A. J. McAlees, and A. Taylor; Production and Characterization of Deoxynivalenol and Other Secondary Metabolites of *Fusarium culmorum* (CMI 14764, HLX 1503); J. Agric. Food Chem., Vol. 34, pp. 98-102(1986).

Common/Systematic Name

7α-Hydroxycalonectrin

3α,15-Diacetoxy-7α-hydroxy-12,13-epoxytrichothec-9-ene

Molecular Formula/Molecular Weight

$C_{19}H_{26}O_7$; MW = 366.16785

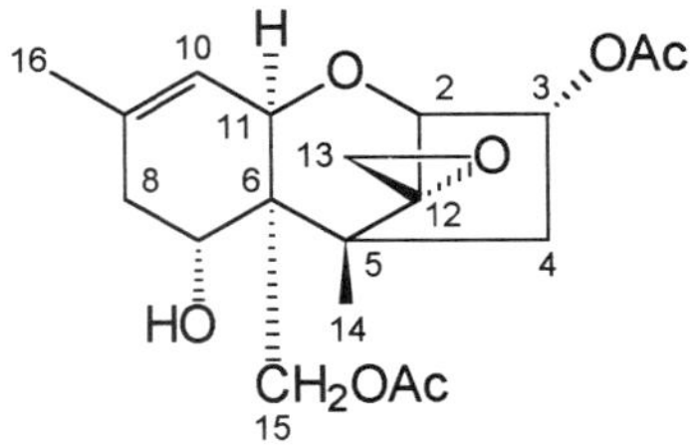

General Characteristics

Crystals from ethyl acetate-hexane; mp., 174-175°C; $[\alpha]_D^{23}$ - 14.3° (*c*=0.14, in $CHCl_3$).

Fungal Source

Fusarium roseum.

Isolation/Purification

Fusarium roseum was cultured, harvested, and the broth was extracted as described by Greenhalgh *et al.* (1984). Some of the oil from the methanol phase after it had been partitioned and concentrated was dissolved in methylene chloride and passed through a Florisil column eluted with 750mL of (A) methylene chloride, (B) 0.5 methanol in methylene chloride, and (C) 5% methanol in methylene chloride. Fraction A afforded an oil from which 3-acetyldeoxynivalenol was obtained. Fractions B and C also afforded yellow oils. The oil which remained in fraction A after removal of 3-acetyldeoxynivalenol was chromatographed on silica gel (Kieselgel 60). The column was eluted first with 10% toluene in methylene chloride and then with 0.5% methanol in methylene chloride, 1.5% methanol in methylene chloride, 3% methanol in methylene chloride, and finally 13% methanol in methylene chloride. Fractions were collected and monitored by TLC (75% ethyl acetate in chloroform; R_f, 0.50); fractions 6-10, 11-12, 13-17, and 18-20 were combined to give mixtures A1, A2, A3, and A4, respectively. Further purification of mixtures A2 was accomplished with a Chromatotron (Model No. 7924, Harrison Research, Inc.) with a 2mm silica gel plate (Kieselgel 60) eluted with chloroform followed by 5% methanol in chloroform. Final purification of 7-hydroxycalonectrin was by preparative TLC using ethyl acetate as developing solvent.

Biological Activity

The trichothecenes as a group show a wide range of biological activity such as antibacterial, antiviral, antifungal, and cytostatic activity; some are phytotoxic and all show some degree of animal toxicity, including insecticidal activity. There exists a broad range of toxicity in vertebrate animals and the acute toxicities vary considerably. General gross clinical signs reported for trichothecenes are vomiting, diarrhea, anorexia, ataxia, hematuria, leukocytosis soon followed by severe leukopenia, inflammation of the gastrointestinal tract, degeneration of nerve cells in the central nervous system, degeneration and hemorrhaging of cardiac muscle, and lesions of lymph nodes, testes, and thymus. Topical application or contact with skin causes dermal necrosis. Biochemically, they are potent inhibitors of protein and DNA synthesis in whole-cell and cell-free systems. Some trichothecenes inhibit the initiation step of protein synthesis on polyribosomes and others inhibit the elongation and/or termination step in protein synthesis. The trichothecenes have been strongly implicated in natural intoxications of animals and man.

Spectral Data

^{1}H NMR:

($CDCl_3$) 3.78(1H, d, $J_{2,3}$=4.4Hz, H-2); 5.17(1H, ddd, J=10, 8.0, 4.5Hz, H-3); 1.97-2.18(2H, m, H-4); 4.55(1H, dd, J=5.9, 11.2Hz, H-7); 1.41(1H, d, J=11.2Hz, OH-7); 1.90-2.0(2H, m, H-8), 2.41(dd, J=17.6, 5.9Hz H-8); 5.38(1H, dd, J=5.4, 1.3Hz, H-10); 4.11(1H, d, J=5.4Hz, H-11); 3.09, 3.23(1H each, d, J=4.4Hz, H-13); 1.14(3H, s, CH_3-14); 4.05(1H, d, J=12.2Hz, H-15); 4.31(1H, m, H-15); 1.72(3H, br s, CH_3-16); and 2.08, 2.09ppm (each 3H, s, CH_3COO-).

^{13}C NMR:

($CDCl_3$) 78.9, C-2; 71.1, C-3; 39.6, C-4; 46.1, C-5; 46.4, C-6; 71.0, C-7; 41.7, C-8; 139.4, C-9; 119.0, C-10; 70.0, C-11; 64.3, C-12; 47.8, C-13; 15.9, C-14; 64.4, C-15; 22.4, C-16; 21.0 and 20.8, $\underline{C}H_3COO$-; and 170.0 and 170.1ppm, $\underline{C}$=O.

Mass Spectrum:

HREIMS: 306.148*m/e* (M^+ - AcOH); calcd for $C_{17}H_{22}O_5$, 306.147.

TLC Data

Silica gel 60 F-254 plates developed with 75% ethyl acetate in chloroform; R_f, 0.50.

References

R. Greenhalgh, D. Levandier, W. Adams, J. D. Miller, B. A. Blackwell, A. J. McAlees and A. Taylor; Production and Characterization of Deoxynivalenol and Other Secondary Metabolites of *Fusarium culmorum* (CMI 14764, HLX 1503); J. Agric. Food Chem., Vol. 34, pp. 98-102(1986).

R. Greenhalgh, R. M. Meier, B. A. Blackwell, J. D. Miller, A. Taylor, and J. W. ApSimon; Minor Metabolites of *Fusarium roseum* (ATCC 28114); J. Agric. Food Chem., Vol. 32, pp. 1261-1264(1984).

Common/Systematic Name

8α-Hydroxycalonectrin

3α,15-Diacetoxy-8α-hydroxy-12,13-epoxytrichothec-9-ene

Molecular Formula/Molecular Weight

$C_{19}H_{26}O_7$; MW = 366.16785

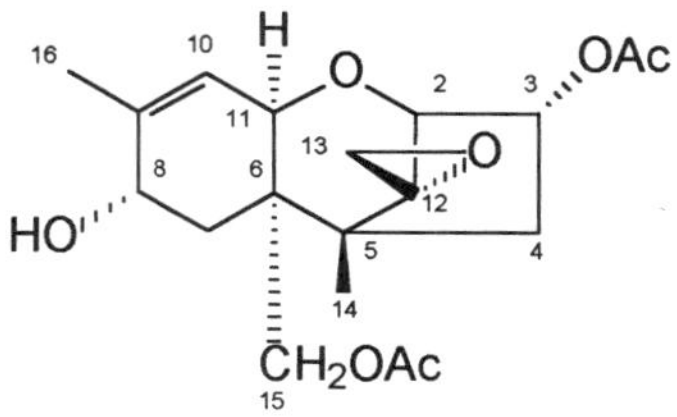

General Characteristics

Crystals; mp., 168-170°C; $[\alpha]_D^{21}$ - 6.67° (*c*=0.15, in $CHCl_3$).

Fungal Source

Fusarium roseum, F. culmorum, and *F. graminearum.*

Isolation/Purification

Mycelia were extracted with methylene chloride, reduced to dryness, redissolved in methanol-water and partitioned against petroleum ether. The methanol raffinate was evaporated to dryness, redissolved in hot absolute alcohol and hexane added slowly. On cooling the solution deposited crystals of 3-acetyldeoxynivalenol which were removed for further purification. The brown viscous oil from the mother liquor was chromatographed on a silica gel column eluted with the following: 25% ethyl acetate in methylene chloride; 2% methanol in methylene chloride; 5% methanol in methylene chloride; and methanol. Fractions containing 8-hydroxycalonectrin were combined and the mixture was separated by preparative TLC (developed with 1% ethanol in ethyl ether; R_f, 0.27) to yield pure 8-hydroxycalonectrin.

Biological Activity

The trichothecenes as a group show a wide range of biological activity such as antibacterial, antiviral, antifungal, and cytostatic activity; some are phytotoxic and all show some degree of animal toxicity, including insecticidal activity. There exists a broad range of toxicity in vertebrate animals and the acute toxicities vary considerably. General gross clinical signs reported for trichothecenes are vomiting, diarrhea, anorexia, ataxia, hematuria, leukocytosis soon followed by severe leukopenia, inflammation of the gastrointestinal tract, degeneration of nerve cells in the central nervous system, degeneration and hemorrhaging of cardiac muscle, and lesions of lymph nodes, testes, and thymus. Topical application or contact with skin causes dermal necrosis. Biochemically, they are potent inhibitors of protein and DNA synthesis in whole-cell and cell-free systems. Some trichothecenes inhibit the initiation step of protein synthesis on polyribosomes and others inhibit the elongation and/or termination step in protein synthesis. The trichothecenes have been strongly implicated in natural intoxications of animals and man.

Spectral Data

^{1}H NMR:

($CDCl_3$) 3.73(1H, d, $J_{2,3}$=4.6Hz, H-2); 5.15(1H, ddd, J=10, 5.1, 5.0Hz, H-3); 2.23-2.28(2H, m, H-4); 1.95(1H, d, J=14.6Hz, H-7), 2.19(1H, dd, J=14.6, 10.8Hz, H-7); 4.08-4.18(2H, m, H-8), 5.58(dd, J=5.7, 1.9Hz H-10); 4.08-4.18(1H, m, H-11); 2.86, 3.08(1H each, d, J=4.0Hz, H-13); 0.83(3H, s, CH_3-14); 4.08-4.18(2H, m, H-15); 1.85(3H, d, J=0.6Hz, CH_3-16); and 2.03, 2.11ppm (each 3H, s, CH_3COO-).

^{13}C NMR:

($CDCl_3$) 77.8, C-2; 71.1, C-3; 39.1, C-4; 45.4, C-5; 42.3, C-6; 30.0, C-7; 67.8, C-8; 139.5, C-9; 121.5, C-10; 67.0, C-11; 64.9, C-12; 48.6, C-13; 11.9, C-14; 65.0, C-15; 20.5, C-16; 20.9 and 21.8, $\underline{C}H_3COO$-; and 170.3 and 170.4ppm, $\underline{C}$=O.

Mass Spectrum:

HREIMS: 306.145*m/e* (M^+ - AcOH); calcd for $C_{17}H_{22}O_5$, 306.147.

TLC Data

Silica gel 60 F_{254} plates developed with 75% ethyl acetate in chloroform; R_f, 0.37.

References

R. Greenhalgh, D. Levandier, W. Adams, J. D. Miller, B. A. Blackwell, A. J. McAlees, and A. Taylor; Production and Characterization of Deoxynivalenol and Other Secondary Metabolites of *Fusarium culmorum* (CMI 14764, HLX 1503); J. Agric. Food Chem., Vol. 34, pp. 98-102(1986).

R. Greenhalgh, R. M. Meier, B. A. Blackwell, J. D. Miller, A. Taylor, and J. W. ApSimon; Minor Metabolites of *Fusarium roseum* (ATCC 28114); J. Agric. Food Chem., Vol. 32, pp. 1261-1264(1984).

Common/Systematic Name

7α,8α-Dihydroxycalonectrin

3α,15-Diacetoxy-7α,8α-dihydroxy-12,13-epoxytrichothec-9-ene

Molecular Formula/Molecular Weight

$C_{19}H_{26}O_8$; MW = 382.16277

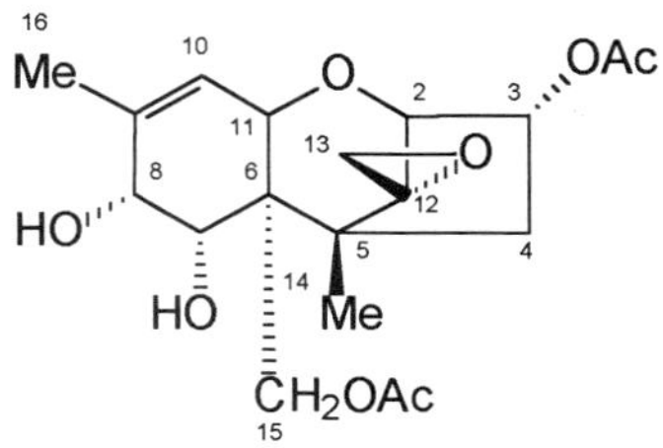

General Characteristics

Needles from ethyl ether; mp., 190-192°C; $[\alpha]_D^{26}$ + 7.2° (*c*=0.07, in $CHCl_3$).

Fungal Source

Fusarium roseum (ATCC 28114), *F. culmorum*, and *F. graminearum*.

Isolation/Purification

Fusarium roseum was cultured, harvested, and the broth was extracted as described by Greenhalgh *et al.* (1984). Some of the oil from the methanol phase after it had been partitioned and concentrated was dissolved in methylene chloride and passed through a Florisil column eluted with 750mL of (A) methylene chloride, (B) 0.5 methanol in methylene chloride, and (C) 5% methanol in methylene chloride. Fraction A afforded an oil from which 3-acetyldeoxynivalenol was obtained. Fractions B and C also afforded yellow oils. The oil which remained in fraction A after removal of 3-acetyldeoxynivalenol was chromatographed on silica gel (Kieselgel 60). The column was eluted first with 10% toluene in methylene chloride and then with 0.5% methanol in methylene chloride, 1.5% methanol in methylene chloride, 3% methanol in methylene chloride, and finally 13% methanol in methylene chloride. Fractions were collected and monitored by TLC (75% ethyl acetate in chloroform; R_f, 0.31); fractions 6-10, 11-12, 13-17, and 18-20 were combined to give mixtures A1, A2, A3, and A4, respectively. Further purification of mixtures A2 and A3 was accomplished with a Chromatotron (Model No. 7924, Harrison Research, Inc.) with a 2mm silica gel plate (Kieselgel 60). 3α,15-diacetoxy-7α,8β-dihydroxy-12,13-epoxytrichothec-9-ene was isolated from mixture A3 by elution with 50% ethyl acetate in hexane followed by recrystallization from ethyl ether.

Spectral Data

^{1}H NMR:
(CDCl$_3$) 1.12(3H, H-14); 1.86(3H, H-16, $J_{10,16}$=1.0Hz); 2.02(3H, AC-CH$_3$); 2.10(3H, AC-CH$_3$); 2.13, 2.34(2H, H-4, $J_{4,3}$=11.1, 4.6Hz); 2.71(1H, 8-OH, $J_{8,OH}$=8.0Hz); 3.0(1H, 7-OH, $J_{7,OH}$=9.7Hz); 3.09, 3.20(2H, H-13, J_{ab}=4.3Hz); 3.77(1H, H-2, $J_{2,3}$=4.4Hz); 3.99(1H, H-8, $J_{7,8}$=5.8, $J_{8,OH}$=7.5Hz); 4.14, 4.44(2H, H-15, J_{ab}=12.3Hz); 4.32(1H, H-11, $J_{11,10}$=5.8Hz); 4.50(1H, H-7, $J_{7,OH}$=9.6Hz, $J_{7,8}$=5.4Hz); 5.15(1H, H-3, $J_{3,2}$=4.4Hz, $J_{3,4}$=4.5, 11.1Hz); and 5.58ppm (1H, H-10, $J_{10,11}$=5.8Hz, $J_{10,16}$=0.9Hz).

^{13}C NMR:
(CDCl$_3$) 78.5, C-2; 70.4, C-3; 41.3, C-4; 46.0, C-5; 46.2, C-6; 70.2, C-7; 71.0, C-8; 139.3, C-9; 122.1, C-10; 69.7, C-11; 64.6, C-12; 47.8, C-13; 15.0, C-14; 63.3, C-15; 21.1, C-16; 20.9, 20.3, $\underline{C}H_3COO$-; and 170.4, 170.0ppm, $\underline{C}$=O.

Mass Spectrum:
HREIMS: 383.179*m/e* (M$^+$ + 1); calcd for $C_{19}H_{27}O_8$, 383.171.

References

R. Greenhalgh, R. M. Meier, B. A. Blackwell, J. D. Miller, A. Taylor, and J. W. ApSimon; Part 2. Minor Metabolites of *Fusarium roseum* (ATCC 28114); J. Agric. Food Chem., Vol. 32, pp. 115-118(1984).

R. Greenhalgh, R. M. Meier, B. A. Blackwell, J. D. Miller, A. Taylor, and J. W. ApSimon; Minor Metabolites of *Fusarium roseum* (ATCC 28114); J. Agric. Food Chem., Vol. 32, pp. 1261-1264(1984).

M. E. Savard and B. A. Blackwell; A Compilation of Spectral Characteristics of Secondary Metabolites from *Fusarium* Fungi; In Mycotoxins in Grain; Compounds Other Than Aflatoxin; J. D. Miller and H. L. Trenholm, eds., Eagan Press, St. Paul, pp. 59-257 (1994).

Common/Systematic Name

4-Acetoxyscirpenediol

4β-Acetyl-3α,15-dihydroxy-12,13-epoxytrichothec-9-ene

Molecular Formula/Molecular Weight

$C_{17}H_{24}O_6$; MW = 324.15729

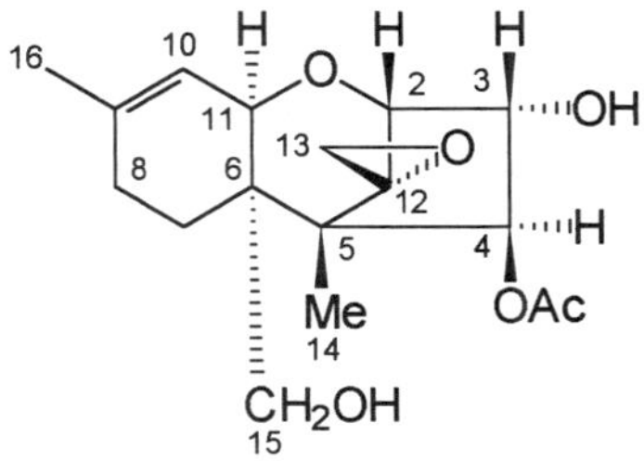

General Characteristics

Amorphous solid from benzene-hexane; mp., 100-110°C.

Fungal Source

Fusarium roseum (NRRL 1181), *F. sulphureum,* and *F. sambucinum* (NRRL 13495).

Isolation/Purification

The mycelium was extracted with ethyl acetate, followed by silica gel column chromatography eluted with benzene-acetone (2:1, v/v), acetone, and methanol. 4-Acetoxyscirpenediol was purified by preparative TLC using silica gel G plates developed with hexane-acetone (1:1, v/v).

Biological Activity

4-Acetoxyscirpenediol caused dermal necrosis in white rats. The trichothecenes as a group show a wide range of biological activity such as antibacterial, antiviral, antifungal, and cytostatic activity; some are phytotoxic and all show some degree of animal toxicity, including insecticidal activity. There exists a broad range of toxicity in vertebrate animals and the acute toxicities vary considerably. General gross clinical signs reported for trichothecenes are vomiting, diarrhea, anorexia, ataxia, hematuria, leukocytosis soon followed by severe leukopenia, inflammation of the gastrointestinal tract, degeneration of nerve cells in the central nervous system, degeneration and hemorrhaging of cardiac muscle, and lesions of lymph nodes, testes, and thymus. Topical application or contact with skin causes dermal necrosis. Biochemically, they are potent inhibitors of protein and DNA synthesis in whole-cell and cell-free systems. Some trichothecenes inhibit the initiation step of protein synthesis on polyribosomes and others inhibit the elongation and/or termination step in protein synthesis. The trichothecenes have been strongly implicated in natural intoxications of animals and man.

Spectral Data

IR:

3450, 2950, 1720, 1435, 1375, 1240, 1165, 1110, 1080, 1050, and 960cm^{-1}.

^{1}H NMR:

($CDCl_3$) 3.68(1H, d, *J*=4.8Hz, H-2); 4.26(1H, dd, *J*=3.1, 4.1Hz, H-3); 5.53(1H, d, *J*=3.1Hz, H-3); 1.7-2.2(4H, m, H-7 and H-8); 5.58(1H, br d, *J*=5.0Hz, H-10); 4.20(1H, br d, *J*=5.0Hz, H-11); 2.78(1H, d, *J*=4.0Hz, H-13); 3.06(1H, d, *J*=4.0Hz, H-13); 0.86(3H, s, CH_3-14); 3.64, 3.69(2H, d, *J*=12.0Hz, CH_2-15); 1.74(3H,br s, CH_3-16); and 2.170ppm (3H, s, CH_3-Ac).

Mass Data:

LREIMS: 306(M^+ - H_2O), 278, 234, 219, and 43*m/e*; TMS ether: 468(M^+); anal. calcd for $C_{17}H_{24}O_6$: C, 62.95; H, 7.46%; found: C, 60.93; H, 6.65%.

References

K. Ishii, S. V. Pathre, and C. J. Mirocha; Two New Trichothecenes Produced by *Fusarium roseum*; J. Agric. Food Chem., Vol. 26, pp. 649-653(1978).

K. E. Richardson, G. E. Toney, C. A. Haney, and P. B. Hamilton; Occurrence of Scirpentriol and Its Seven Acetylated Derivatives in Culture Extracts of *Fusarium sambucinum* NRRL 13495; J. Food Protect., Vol. 52, pp. 871-876(1989).

D. R. Sanson, D. G. Corley, C. L. Barnes, S. Searles, E. O. Schlemper, and M. S. Tempesta; New Mycotoxins from *Fusarium sambucinum*; J. Org. Chem., Vol. 54, pp. 4313-4318(1989).

M. E. Savard and B. A. Blackwell; A Compilation of Spectral Characteristics of Secondary Metabolites from *Fusarium* Fungi; In Mycotoxins in Grain; Compounds Other Than Aflatoxin; J. D. Miller and H. L. Trenholm, eds., Eagan Press, St. Paul, pp. 59-257 (1994).

Common/Systematic Name

15-Acetoxyscirpenetriol

15-Acetoxy-3α,4β-dihydroxy-12,13-epoxytrichothec-9-ene

Molecular Formula/Molecular Weight

$C_{17}H_{24}O_6$; MW = 324.15729

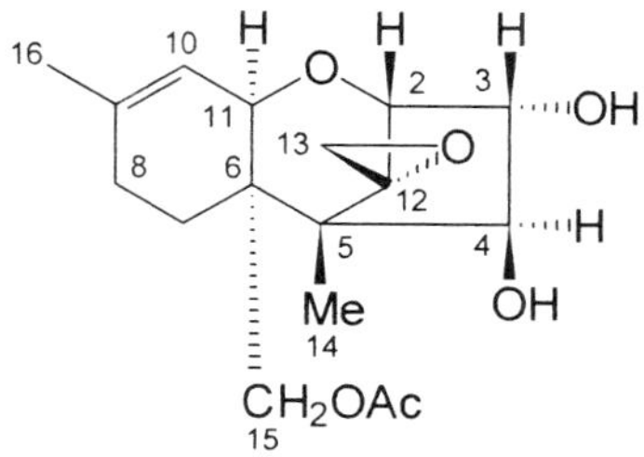

General Characteristics

Crystals from isooctane-ethyl acetate; mp., 172-173°C.

Fungal Source

Fusarium roseum and *F. sambucinum*.

Isolation/Purification

The dried cultures were moistened with water to a moisture content of 30% and extracted with ethyl acetate. The extract was concentrated to a gum and redissolved in acetonitrile and partitioned against petroleum ether; the petroleum ether layer was discarded. The acetonitrile layer was concentrated and then chromatographed on a column of silica gel. The components were eluted off the column with ethyl acetate-*n*-hexane (1:3 to 1:7, v/v), ethyl acetate-methanol (5:1, v/v), and methanol. Each 100ml fraction was tested for toxicity by topical application to the shaved skin of the white rat. Fractions 4 through 12 were toxic and were pooled and rechromatographed on a column of silica gel using chloroform-methanol (98:2, v/v) as the eluting solvent. The fractions from this column were tested for toxicity and the one found toxic was purified by preparative TLC on silica gel G, developed in chloroform-methanol (98:5, v/v) and made visible by charring with concentrated H_2SO_4. The monoacetoxyscirpenol was crystallized from methylene chloride-petroleum ether. Two recrystallizations from isooctane-ethyl acetate gave an analytical sample.

Biological Activity

Clinical signs in birds ingesting the toxin were bilateral inflammation of the beak area and gastrointestinal hemorrhaging. Application to shaved skin of rat resulted in hyperkeratosis and petechial hemorrhaging. The LD_{50} in 20-day-old white female weanling rats dosed SC was 0.752mg/kg. A single 20kg female pig injected IV with 20mg monoacetoxyscirpenol (1mg/kg) exhibited emesis within 0.5 hr, lethargy, a staggered gait, and death within 13 hr.

Spectral Data

IR:
(KBr) 3400,1715, and 1250 cm^{-1}.

^{1}H NMR:
($CDCl_3$) 3.60(1H,d, *J*=4.6Hz, H-2); 4.21(1H, dd, *J*=2.7, 4.6Hz, H-3); 4.26(1H, br d, *J*=2.7Hz, H-4); 1.76(1H, dd, *J*=11.3, 4.8Hz, H-7); 2.01(1H, m, H-7); 1.98-2.00(2H, m, H-8); 5.46(1H, d, *J*=5.4Hz, H-10); 3.92(1H, br d, *J*=5 4Hz, H-11); 2.73(1H, d, *J*=3.9Hz, H-13); 3.01(1H, d, *J*=3.9Hz, H-13); 0.79(3H,s, CH_3-14); 3.87(1H, d, *J*=12.3Hz, H-15); 4.18(1H, d, *J*=12.3Hz, H-15); 1.70(3H, br s, CH_3-16); and 2.04ppm (s, CH_3COO-).

^{13}C NMR:
($CDCl_3$) 78.9, C-2; 80.0, C-3; 81.9, C-4; 49.2, C-5; 43.5, C-6; 21.1, C-7; 28.0, C-8; 140.7, C-9; 118.4, C-10; 68.0, C-11; 64.7, C-12; 46.9, C-13; 6.9, C-14; 63.6, C-15; 23.2, C-16; 21.3, $\underline{C}H_3COO$-; and 170.8ppm, $CH_3\underline{C}OO$-.

Mass Data:
264(36), 205(100), 191(9), 189(11), 187(30), and 177*m/e* (24); anal. calcd for $C_{17}H_{24}O_6$: C, 62.96; H, 7.41%; found: C, 63.42; H, 7.61%.

TLC Data
Adsorbent: silica gel G; Solvent: chloroform-methanol (90:10, v/v); R_f, 0.37. Detection: H_2SO_4 or *p*-anisaldehyde spraying and heating at 110° for 10 min. Purple to brown color with H_2SO_4; purple color with *p*-anisaldehyde.

GLC Data
Liquid phase: 3% OV-1 on Gas Chrom Q (100-120 mesh); TMS, 9-10 min.; retention time: trifluoroacetate, 5-6 min. (Derivative for GLC: trimethylsilyl ether or trifluoroacetate).

References
R. J. Cole and R. H. Cox; Handbook of Toxic Fungal Metabolites; Academic Press, New York, p.168(1981).

S. V. Pathre, C. J. Mirocha, C. M. Christensen, and J. Behrens; Monoacetoxyscirpenol. A New Mycotoxin Produced by *Fusarium roseum* Gibbosum; J. Agric. Food Chem., Vol. 24, pp. 97-103(1976).

K. E. Richardson, G. E. Toney, C. A. Haney, and P. B. Hamilton; Occurrence of Scirpentriol and Its Seven Acetylated Derivatives in Culture Extracts of *Fusarium sambucinum* NRRL 13495; J. Food Protection, Vol. 52, pp.871-876(1989).

M. E. Savard and B. A. Blackwell; A Compilation of Spectral Characteristics of Secondary Metabolites from *Fusarium* Fungi; In Mycotoxins in Grain; Compounds Other Than Aflatoxin; J. D. Miller and H. L. Trenholm, eds., Eagan Press, St. Paul, pp. 59-257(1994).

Common/Systematic Name

4,15-Diacetoxyscirpenol; Anguidine
4β,15-Diacetyl-3α-hydroxy-12,13-epoxytrichothec-9-ene

Molecular Formula/Molecular Weight

$C_{19}H_{26}O_7$; MW = 366.16785

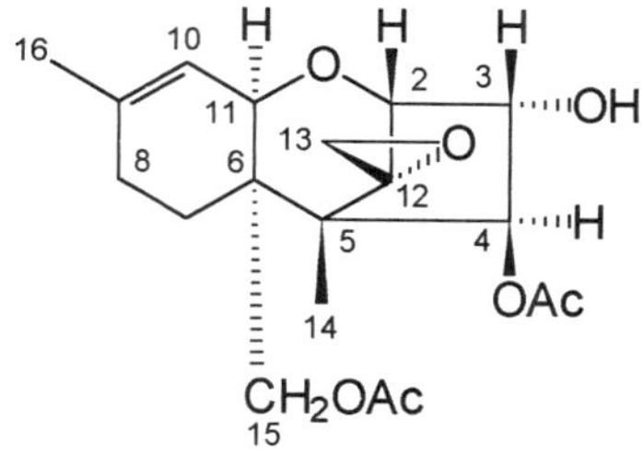

General Characteristics

Crystals from ether; mp., 162-164°C. Benzoate: prisms from ethanol; mp., 178°C; $[\alpha]_D^{24}$ - 27° (*c*=1.28).

Fungal Source

Fusarium roseum (NRRL 1181), *F. sambucinum* (NRRL 13495) = *Gibberella pulicaris*, *F. tricinctum*, *F. equiseti*, *F. lateritium*, *F. graminearum*, *F. semitectum*, *F. sulphureum*, *F. diversisporum*, *F. scirpi*, and *Gibberella intricans*.

Isolation/Purification

The mycelium was extracted with ethyl acetate, followed by silica gel column chromatography eluted with benzene-acetone (2:1, v/v), acetone, and methanol. 4,15-Diacetoxyscirpenol was purified by repetitive preparative TLC using silica gel G plates developed with hexane-acetone (1:1, v/v).

Biological Activity

The LD_{50} in mice dosed IP was 23.0mg/kg; LD_{50} in chicken embryo test was 0.09μg per egg. ID_{50} of protein synthesis in rabbit reticulocytes (whole cell) was 0.03μg/ml; cell-free was 5.0μg/ml; tumor cells were 0.30μg/ml; rat liver (cell-free) was >50μg/ml. Dermal toxicity to rabbit, mouse, and guinea pig. Diacetoxyscirpenol was also highly phytotoxic.

Spectral Data

^{1}H NMR:

($CDCl_3$) 3.65(1H, d, *J*=4.9Hz, H-2); 4.10(1H, dd, *J*=2.9, 4.9Hz, H-3); 5.11(1H, d, *J*=2.9Hz, H-4); 2.00(1H, d, *J*=11Hz, H-7); 1.71(1H, d, *J*=11.0Hz, H-7); 1.93(2H, m, H-8); 5.50(1H, d, *J*=5.3Hz, H-10); 4.02(1H, d, *J*=5.3Hz, H-11); 3.00(1H, d, *J*=4.0Hz, H-13); 2.74(1H, d, *J*= 4.0Hz, H-13); 0.79(3H, s, CH_3-14); 4.10, 3.90(2H, d, *J*=12.3Hz, CH_2-15); 1.68(3H, s, CH_3-16); and 2.00, 2.09ppm (3H, s, CH_3-Ac).

^{13}C NMR:

79.0, d, C-2; 76.3, d, C-3; 83.0, d, C-4; 49.1, s, C-5; 44.2, s, C-6; 21.1, t, C-7; 27.9, t, C-8; 139.4, s, C-9; 119.3, d, C-10; 67.4, d, C-11; 64.8, s, C-12; 46.6, t, C-13; 6.8, q, C-14; 63.4, t, C-15; 23.2, q, C-16; 21.1, q, and 21.1, q, $\underline{C}H_3C = O$; 170.3, s, and 170.3, s, $CH_3\underline{C} = O$.

Mass Data:

LREIMS (TMS derivative): 439(M^+ + 1), 438(M^+), 324, 379(base peak), 319, 301, 289, and 229*m/e*.

TLC Data

Adsorbent: Kieselgel G; solvent: chloroform-methanol, 97:3 (v/v); R_f, 0.55; detection: H_2SO_4 spraying and heating at 110°C for 5 min. Adsorbent: alumina; solvent: chloroform-methanol, 98:2 (v/v); R_f, 0.86; detection: H_2SO_4 spraying and heating at 110°C for 5 min.

GLC Data

Support: Shimalite W; liquid phase: OV-17 (1.5%); retention time: 5.95; relative retention time: (relative to nivalenol) 1.67.

References

R. J. Cole and R. H. Cox; Handbook of Toxic Fungal Metabolites; Academic Press, New York, pp. 171-172(1981).

K. E. Richardson, G. E. Toney, C. A. Haney and P. B. Hamilton; Occurrence of Scirpentriol and Its Seven Acetylated Derivatives in Culture Extracts of *Fusarium sambucinum* NRRL 13495; J. Food Protect., Vol. 52, pp. 871-876(1989).

M. E. Savard and B. A. Blackwell; A Compilation of Spectral Characteristics of Secondary Metabolites from *Fusarium* Fungi; In Mycotoxins in Grain; Compounds Other Than Aflatoxin; J. D. Miller and H. L. Trenholm, eds., Eagan Press, St. Paul, pp.59-257 (1994).

Common/Systematic Name

Scirpenetriol

3α,4β,15-Trihydroxy-12,13-epoxytrichothec-9-ene

Molecular Formula/Molecular Weight

$C_{15}H_{22}O_5$; MW = 282.14672

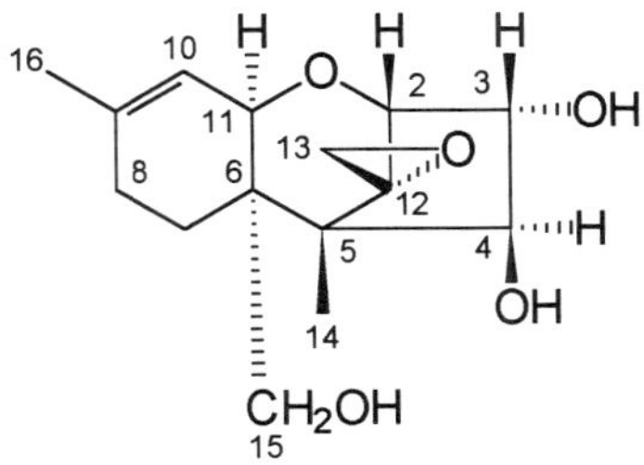

General Characteristics

Prisms from ethyl acetate; mp., 193°C; $[\alpha]_D^{23}$ 0° (*c*=1.27, in acetone).

Fungal Source

Fusarium roseum and *F. equiseti.*

Isolation/Purification

The dried cultures were rehydrated to a moisture content of 30% and extracted with ethyl acetate. The extract was concentrated to a gum and redissolved in acetonitrile and partitioned against petroleum ether; the petroleum ether layer was discarded. The acetonitrile layer was concentrated and then chromatographed on a column of silica gel. The components were eluted off the column with ethyl acetate-*n*-hexane (1:3 to 1:7, v/v), ethyl acetate-methanol (5:1, v/v), and methanol. Each 100ml fraction was tested for toxicity by topical application to the shaved skin of the white rat. Fractions 4 through 12 were toxic and were pooled and rechromatographed on a column of silica gel using chloroform-methanol (98:2, v/v) as the eluting solvent. Scirpenetriol was purified by preparative TLC on silica gel G, developed in chloroform-methanol (98:5, v/v) and made visible by charring with concentrated H_2SO_4.

Biological Activity

LD_{50} in rats dosed IP was 0.81mg/kg (single dose).

Spectral Data

UV:

End absorption.

IR:

(Nujol) 3480, 3455, 3405, 1676, and 830cm^{-1}.

^{1}H NMR:

3.78, H-2; 4.08, H-3; 4.12, H-4; NR, H-7; NR, H-8; NR, H-10; NR, H-11; 2.70, H-13α; 3.05, H-13β; 0.90, H-14; 3.59, H-15; and 1.72ppm, H-16.

References

P. W. Brian, A. W. Dawkins, J. F. Grove, H. G. Hemming, D. Lowe, and G. L. F. Norris; Phytotoxic Compounds Produced by *Fusarium equiseti*; J. Exp. Botany, Vol. 12, pp. 116-123(1966).

R. J. Cole and R. H. Cox; Handbook of Toxic Fungal Metabolites; Academic Press, New York, p. 160 (1981).

S. V. Pathre, C. J. Mirocha, C. M. Christensen, and J. Behrens; Monoacetoxyscirpenol. A New Mycotoxin Produced by *Fusarium roseum* Gibbosum; J. Agric. Food Chem., Vol. 24, p. 97(1976)

Common/Systematic Name

7α-Hydroxydiacetoxyscirpenol

3α,7α-Dihydroxy-4β,15α-diacetoxy-12,13-epoxytrichothec-9-ene

Molecular Formula/Molecular Weight

$C_{19}H_{26}O_8$; MW = 382.16277

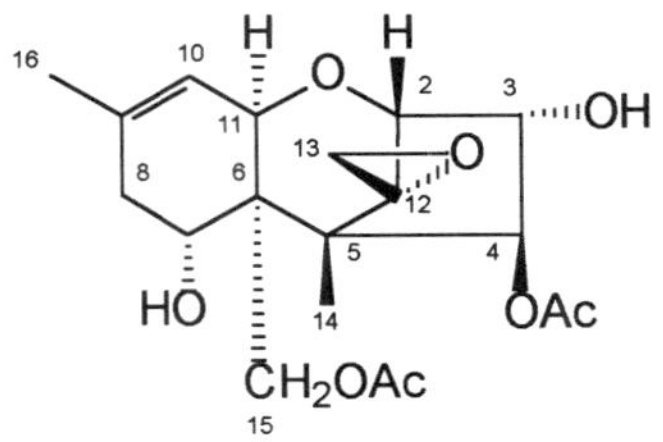

General Characteristics

Needles from chloroform-hexane; mp., 201-203°C; tetraacetoxy derivative, needles from benzene-*n*-hexane; mp., 147-149°C.

Fungal Source

Fusarium lateritium and *Fusarium* spp. (K-5036).

Isolation/Purification

The culture filtrate was mixed with activated charcoal, the charcoal washed with water and the materials adsorbed to the charcoal eluted with methanol. The methanol extract was concentrated and chloroform added which resulted in a precipitate. The chloroform-methanol was filtered and the filtrate evaporated to dryness. The residue was extracted with hot acetone, the acetone soluble materials were chromatographed on a silica gel column eluted with benzene-acetone 5:2, 2:1, 1:1 (v/v), acetone and methanol. The fractions were monitored by TLC (Kieselgel G) and the fractions containing 7α-hydroxydiacetoxyscirpenol were combined and chromatographed on a silica gel column eluted with *n*-hexane-acetone, 1:1 (v/v); the metabolite at R_f0.5 was crystallized from chloroform-*n* hexane to give needles of 7α-hydroxydiacetoxyscirpenol.

Biological Activity

The LD_{50} to mice dosed IP was about 3.5mg/kg; ID_{50} of protein synthesis in rabbit reticulocytes was 0.3μg/ml.

Spectral Data

UV:

End absorption.

IR:

(KBr) 3500, 2950, 1720, 1380, 1280, and 1060cm^{-1}.

^1H NMR:

(CDCl$_3$) 3.70(H-2); 4.25(H-3); 5.20(H-4); 4.62(H-7); 2.00(H-8α); 2.43(H-8β); 5.50(H-10); 4.25(H-11); 3.07(H-13α); 3.17(H-13β); 1.13(H-14); 4.24(H-15α); 4.42(H-15β); 1.75(H-16); and 2.07, 2.15ppm (CH_3CO-).

Mass Data:

LREIMS: 364(M^+ - 18), 322(M^+ - 60), 304, and 263*m/e*; found: C, 59.25; H, 6.78%; $C_{19}H_{26}O_8$ requires: C, 59.65; H, 6.85%.

TLC Data

Adsorbent: silica gel; solvent: acetone-hexane (1:1, v/v); R_f, 0.5; detection: spraying with 20% H_2SO_4 and heating at 110°C.

References

R. J. Cole and R. H. Cox; Handbook of Toxic Fungal Metabolites; Academic Press, New York, p. 190(1981).

K. Ishii; Two New Trichothecenes Produced by *Fusarium* sp.; Phytochemistry, Vol. 14, pp. 2469-2471(1975).

Common/Systematic Name

7α,8α-Dihydroxydiacetoxyscirpenol
3α,7α,8α-Trihydroxy-4β,15α-diacetoxy-12,13-epoxytrichothec-9-ene

Molecular Formula/Molecular Weight

$C_{19}H_{26}O_9$; MW = 398.15768

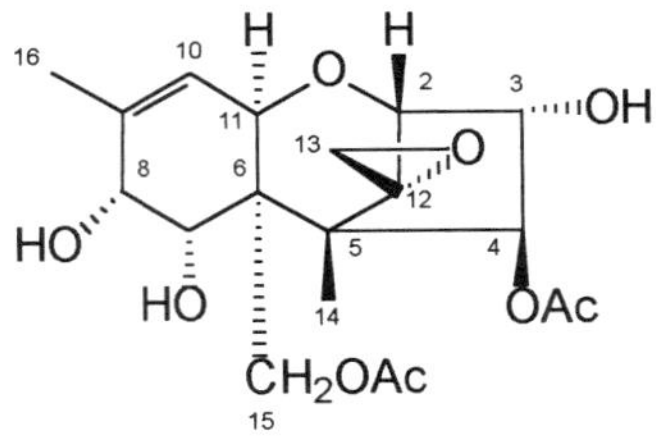

General Characteristics

Needles from ethanol-ether-*n*-hexane; mp., 167-169°C.

Fungal Source

Fusarium lateritium, and *F.* spp. (K-5036).

Isolation/Purification

The culture filtrate was mixed with activated charcoal, the charcoal washed with water and the materials adsorbed to the charcoal eluted with methanol. The methanol extract was concentrated; chloroform was added which resulted in a precipitate. The chloroform-methanol was filtered and the filtrate evaporated to dryness. The residue was extracted with hot acetone, the acetone soluble materials were chromatographed on a silica gel column eluted with benzene-acetone 5:2, 2:1, 1:1 (v/v), acetone and methanol. The fractions were monitored by TLC (Kieselgel G) and the fractions containing 7α-hydroxydiacetoxyscirpenol were combined and chromatographed on a silica gel column eluted with *n*-hexane-acetone (1:1, v/v); the metabolite at R_f 0.38 was crystallized from EtOH-ether-*n* hexane to give needles of 7α,8α-dihydroxydiacetoxyscirpenol.

Biological Activity

The LD_{50} to mice dosed IP was about 6.0mg/kg; ID_{50} of protein synthesis in rabbit reticulocytes was 0.6μg/ml.

Spectral Data

UV:

End absorption.

IR:

(KBr) 3500, 2950, 1750, 1390, 1260, and 1050cm^{-1}.

^{1}H NMR:

(CDCl$_3$) 3.70(H-2); 4.20(H-3); 5.45(H-4); 4.01(H-7); 4.50(H-8); 5.65(H-10); 4.50(H-11); 3.05(H-13α); 3.15(H-13β); 1.10(H-14); 4.29(H-15α); 4.50(H-15β); 1.85(H-16); and 2.02, 2.13ppm (C$\underline{H_3}$CO-).

TLC Data

Adsorbent, silica gel; solvent, acetone-*n*-hexane (1:1, v/v); R_f, 0.38; detection, spraying with 20% H_2SO_4 and heating at 110°C.

References

R. J. Cole and R. H. Cox; Handbook of Toxic Fungal Metabolites; Academic Press, New York, p. 191 (1981).

K. Ishii; Two New Trichothecenes Produced by *Fusarium* sp.; Phytochemistry, Vol. 14, pp. 2469-2471(1975).

Common/Systematic Name

3,15-Diacetoxyscirpenetriol

3α,15-Diacetyl-4β-hydroxy-12,13-epoxytrichothec-9-ene

Molecular Formula/Molecular Weight

$C_{19}H_{26}O_7$; MW = 366.16785

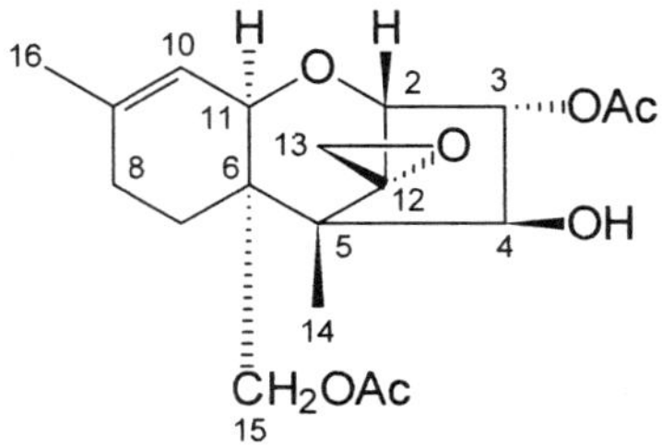

General Characteristics

Colorless glass.

Fungal Source

Fusarium sambucinum.

Isolation/Purification

Fungal cultures were extracted with chloroform-acetone (85:15, v/v), allowed to sit over night, filtered,and the solid residue was re-extracted with acetone. The acetone extract was combined with the chloroform-acetone extract, concentrated under vacuum, and the non-polar materials were removed by hexane drip. The solvent was decanted, concentrated and chromatographed by flash chromatography with toluene, toluene-acetone (4:1, 2:1, 1:1, v/v), acetone, and acetone-methanol (1:1, v/v). The toluene-acetone (4:1, v/v) fraction was further purified by flash chromatography eluting with toluene-acetone (4:1, v/v) This resulted in purified 3,15-diacetoxyscirpenol

Biological Activity

The trichothecenes as a group show a wide range of biological activity such as antibacterial, antiviral, antifungal, and cytostatic activity; some are phytotoxic and all show some degree of animal toxicity, including insecticidal activity. There exists a broad range of toxicity in vertebrate animals and the acute toxicities vary considerably. General gross clinical signs reported for trichothecenes are vomiting, diarrhea, anorexia, ataxia, hematuria, leukocytosis soon followed by severe leukopenia, inflammation of the gastrointestinal tract, degeneration of nerve cells in the central nervous system, degeneration and hemorrhaging of cardiac muscle, and lesions of lymph nodes, testes, and thymus. Topical application or contact with skin causes dermal necrosis. Biochemically, they are potent inhibitors of protein and DNA synthesis in whole-cell and cell-free systems. Some trichothecenes inhibit the initiation step of protein synthesis on polyribosomes and others inhibit the elongation and/or termination step in protein synthesis. The trichothecenes have been strongly implicated in natural intoxications of animals and man.

Spectral Data

UV:

λ_{max}^{ACN} 199nm (ϵ=8,200, π to π^* transition).

IR:

(film) 3403 and 1731cm^{-1} (C=O).

^{1}H NMR:

($CDCl_3$) 3.81(1H, d, *J*=4.9Hz, H-2); 4.85(1H, dd, *J*=2.9, 4.9Hz, H-3); 4.31(1H, d, *J*=2.9Hz, H-4); 1.7-2.1; 5.47(1H, b d, *J*=5.5Hz, H-10); 3.75(1H, b d, *J*=5.5Hz, H-11); 2.79(1H, H-13); 3.05(1H, d, *J*=4.0Hz, H-13); 0.87(3H, s, CH_3-14); 3.90(1H, CH_2-15); 4.13(1H, d, *J*=12.3Hz, CH_2-15); 1.73(3H, b s, CH_3-16); and 2.05, 2.20ppm (3H each, s, CH_3-Ac).

^{13}C NMR:

77.6, C-2; 83.5, C-3; 79.1, C-4; 48.9, C-5; 43.6, C-6; 20.9, C-7; 28.0, C-8; 141.0, C-9; 118.2, C-10; 68.1, C-11; 64.0, C-12; 46.8, C-13; 6.7,C-14; 63.5, C-15; 23.2, C-16; 21.0, and 21.2, $\underline{C}H_3C = O$; not observed due to small sample size, $CH_3\underline{C} = O$.

Mass Data:

HREIMS: 307.154*m/e*; calcd for $C_{17}H_{23}O_5$ (M^+ - OAc); 307.174; LREIMS: 307(M^+ - OAc, 5%), 205(68), 124(base peak), 105(97), and 81*m/e* (55).

Reference

D. R. Sanson, D. G. Corley, C. L. Barnes, S. Searles, E. O. Schlemper, M. S. Tempesta, and G. E. Rottinghaus; New Mycotoxins from *Fusarium sambucinum*; J. Org. Chem., Vol. 54, pp. 4313-4318(1989).

Common/Systematic Name

3,4,15-Triacetoxyscirpenetriol

3α,4β,15-Triacetoxy-12,13-epoxytrichothec-9-ene

Molecular Formula/Molecular Weight

$C_{21}H_{28}O_8$; MW = 408.17842

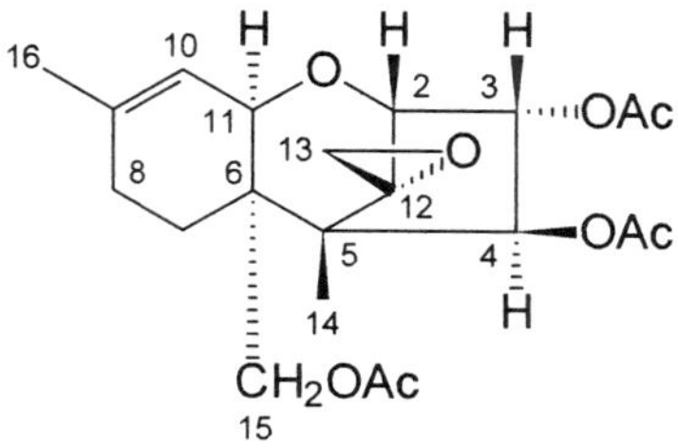

General Characteristics

Colorless crystals from benzene-*n*-hexane; mp., 124-126°C.

Fungal Source

Fusarium sulphureum (MRC-514).

Isolation/Purification

Fungal cultures were extracted with chloroform-methanol (1:1, v/v), concentrated, and partitioned between 90% methanol-*n*-hexane. The aqueous methanol solution was concentrated and partitioned between chloroform and water. The chloroform solution was dried, filtered, evaporated to dryness, and chromatographed on a silica gel H column eluted with chloroform-methanol (19:1, v/v). The first fraction was filtered through a short alumina column (activity II-III) using chloroform; the yellow oil obtained was recrystallized from benzene-*n*-hexane to give colorless crystals of triacetoxyscirpenol.

Spectral Data

^{1}H NMR:

($CDCl_3$) 0.76(3H, s, C-14 Me); 1.71(3H, s, C-16 Me); 2.04(3H, s, C-15 OAc); 2.09(3H, s, C-3 OAc); 2.12(3H, s, C-4 OAc); 2.77; 3.05(1H,each d, $J_{13,14}$=4Hz C-13 H); 3.84(1H, d, $J_{2,3}$=5 Hz, C-2 H); 3.99(d, 1H, d, $J_{10,11}$=5Hz, C-11 H); 4.03 and 4.25(11H, each d, $J_{15,15}$=12Hz, C-15 H); 5.17(1H, dd, $J_{3,4}$=3.5Hz, $J_{2,3}$=5Hz, C-3 H); 5.46(1H, br d, $J_{10,11}$=5Hz, C-10 H); and 5.74ppm (1H, d, $J_{3,4}$=3.5Hz, C-4 H).

Mass Data:

Found: C, 61.89; H, 6.68%; calcd for $C_{21}H_{28}O_8$: C, 61.75; H, 6.91%.

References

R. J. Cole and R. H. Cox; Handbook of Toxic Fungal Metabolites; Academic Press, New York, p. 201(1981).

P. S. Steyn, R. Vleggaar, C. J. Rabie, N. P. J. Kriek, and J. S. Harington; Trichothecene Mycotoxins from *Fusarium sulphureum*; Phytochemistry, Vol. 17, pp. 949-951(1978).

Common/Systematic Name

T-2 Tetraol

3α,4β,8α,15-Tetrahydroxy-12,13-epoxytrichothec-9-ene

Molecular Formula/Molecular Weight

$C_{15}H_{22}O_6$; MW = 298.14164

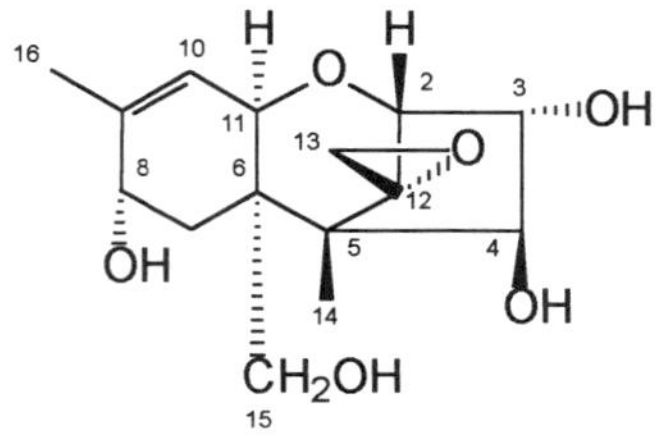

Fungal Source

Fusarium poae and *F. sporotrichioides.*

Spectral Data

UV:

End absorption.

IR:

(KBr) 3400, 2930, 1625, 1450, and 1380cm^{-1}.

^{1}H NMR:

($CDCl_3$) 3.60(1H, d, *J*=4.8Hz, H-2); 4.07(1H, dd, *J*=4.8, 3.3Hz, H-3); 4.12(1H, d, *J*=3.3Hz, H-4); 1.97(1H, dt, *J*=14.4, 1.6Hz, αH-7); 2.16(1H, dd, *J*=14.4, 5.3Hz, βH-7); 5.52(1H, dq, *J*=5.7, 1.5Hz, H-10); 3.80(1H, d, *J*=5.7Hz, H-11); 2.89(1H, d, *J*=4.1Hz, H-13); 2.76(1H, d, *J*=4.1Hz, H-13); 0.84(3H, s, CH_3-14); 3.72(1H, d, *J*=2.4Hz, H-15); 3.40(1H, d, *J*=12.4Hz, H-15); and 1.82ppm (3H, s, CH_3-16).

^{13}C NMR:

78.5, C-2; 79.1, C-3; 80.0, C-4; 48.0, C-5; 45.1, C-6; 28.5, C-7; 64.8, C-8; 138.1, C-9; 121.6, C-10; 67.6, C-11; 64.3, C-12; 45.1, C-13; 6.3, C-14; 61.0, C-15; and 19.9ppm, C-16. ($CDCl_3$) 80.6, C-2; 80.8, C-3; 82.3, C-4; 50.4, C-5; 45.9, C-6; 29.9, C-7; 67.0, C-8; 141, C-9; 122.6, C-10; 70.0, C-11; 65.8, C-12; 47.2, C-13; 7.3, C-14; 63.1, C-15 and 20.7ppm, C-16.

TLC Data

Adsorbent: silica gel G or H; solvent: ethanol-ethyl acetate-acetone, 1:4:4, v/v/v; R_f, 0.52; detection: H_2SO_4 spraying and heating at 150°C for 5 min.

References

R. J. Cole and R. H. Cox; Handbook of Toxic Fungal Metabolites; Academic Press, New York, p. 162 (1981).

R. A. Ellison and F. N. Kotsonis; Carbon-13 Nuclear Magnetic Resonance Assignments in the Trichothecene Mycotoxins; J. Org. Chem., Vol. 41, p. 576(1976).

E. B. Smalley and F. M. Strong; Toxic Trichothecenes. In Mycotoxins; I. F. H. Purchase, ed.; pp.199-228, Elsevier Scientific Pub. Co., New York (1974).

M. E. Savard and B. A. Blackwell; A Compilation of Spectral Characteristics of Secondary Metabolites from *Fusarium* Fungi; In Mycotoxins in Grain; Compounds Other Than Aflatoxin; J. D. Miller and H. L. Trenholm, eds., Eagan Press, St. Paul, pp. 59-257 (1994).

Common/Systematic Name

T-2 Toxin

3α-Hydroxy-4β,15-diacetoxy-8α-[3-methylbutyryloxy]-12,13-epoxytrichothec-9-ene

Molecular Formula/Molecular Weight

$C_{24}H_{34}O_9$; MW = 466.22028

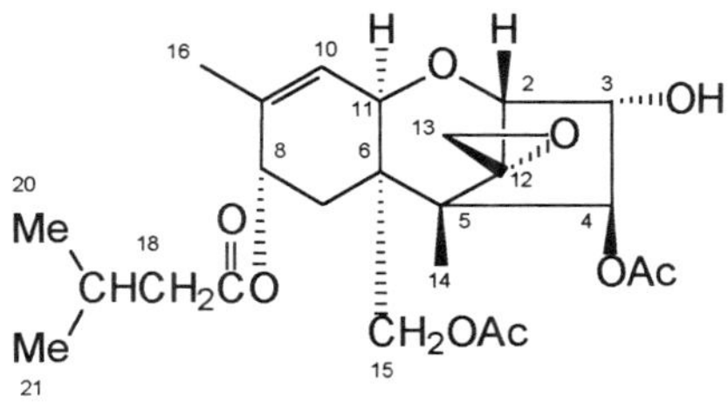

General Characteristics

White needles from benzene-Skellysolve B; mp., 151-152°C; $[\alpha]_D^{26}$ + 15° (*c*=2.58, in EtOH). Acetate derivative: amorphous solid from ether-pentane; $[\alpha]_D^{30}$ +27° (*c*=0.9, in 95% EtOH).

Fungal Source

Fusarium tricinctum, F. culmorum (F. roseum), F. solani, F. poae, F. sporotrichioides, and *Trichoderma lignorum.*

Biological Activity

Acute LD_{50} in rats and swine dosed orally was 4mg/kg; LD_{50} in mice dosed IP was 3.04mg/kg; LD_{50} in chicks dosed orally was 1.84mg/kg; ID_{50} of rabbit reticulocytes (whole cell) was 0.03μg/ml; ID_{50} of rabbit reticulocytes (cell-free) was 0.15μg/ ml. T-2 toxin inhibited the initiation step of protein synthesis on polyribosomes. It had emetic properties when administered orally, IP or IV. Minimum SC dosage to induce vomiting in ducklings was 0.1mg/kg; in cat, 0.1-0.2mg/kg. Major gross clinical signs in cats from T-2 toxin were emesis, vomiting, diarrhea, anorexia, ataxia of the hind legs, discharge from the eyes, and ejection of hemorrhagic fluid. Consecutive administration at sublethal dosages caused a marked decrease in white cells. Necropsy showed extensive cellular damage in the bone marrow, intestine, spleen, and lymph nodes. Also evident were meningeal hemorrhage of the brain, bleeding in the lungs, and vacuolic degeneration of the renal tubes. T-2 caused dermal necrosis when applied to the surface of the skin. It caused primary oral lesions in animals ingesting it.

Spectral Data

UV:

End absorption.

^{1}H NMR:

($CDCl_3$) 3.68(1H, d, *J*=4.9Hz, H-2); 4.13(1H, ddd, *J*=4.9, 2.8, 2.8Hz, H-3); 3.18(1H, d, *J*=2.8Hz, 3-OH); 5.24(1H, d, *J*=2.8Hz, H-4); 2.38(1H, dd, *J*=15.1, 5.8Hz, αH-7); 1.87(1H, dd, *J*=15.3, 1.5Hz, βH-7); 5.27(1H, d, *J*=5.8Hz, H-8); 5.72(1H, dt, *J*=5.8, 1.2Hz, H-10); 4.33(1H, d, *J*=5.8Hz, H-11); 3.04(1H, d, *J*=3.9Hz, H-13); 2.78(1H, d, *J*=3.9Hz, H-13); 0.79(3H, s, CH_3-14); 4.04(1H, d, *J*=12.6Hz, αH-15); 4.27(1H, d, *J*=12.6Hz, βH-15); 1.72(3H, br s, CH_3-16); 2.10(2H, m, H-18); 2.01(1H, m, H-19); 0.94, 0.93(3H each, d, *J*=6.5Hz, 20 and 21 CH_3); and 2.01, 2.12ppm (3H each, s, CH_3COO-).

^{13}C NMR:

78.7, C-2; 78.2, C-3; 84.3, C-4; 48.3, C-5; 42.9, C-6; 27.7, C-7; 68.0, C-8; 136.3, C-9; 123.8, C-10; 67.3, C-11; 64.2, C-12; 47.0, C-13; 6.6, C-14; 64.5, C-15; 20.1, C-16; 172.7, C-17; 43.4, C-18; 25.6, C-19; 22.2, C-20 and C-21; 20.8(3H, $\underline{C}H_3COO$-); and 170.2, 170.5ppm, (3H each, $CH_3\underline{C}OO$-).

TLC Data

A. Adsorbent: silica gel G; solvent: chloroform-methanol, 98:2, v/v; R_f, 0.40; detection: H_2SO_4 spraying and heating at 110°C for 5 minutes. B. Adsorbent: alumina; solvent: chloroform-methanol, 98:2, v/v; R_f, 0.88; detection: H_2SO_4 spraying and heating at 110°C for 5 minutes.

GLC Data (TMS derivatives)

Support: Shimalite W; liquid phase: OV-17 (1.5 %); retention time 8.55; relative retention time: (relative to nivalenol) 2.40.

References

J. R. Bamberg and F. M. Strong; Mycotoxins of the Trichothecene Family Produced by *Fusarium tricinctum* and *Trichoderma lignorum*; Phytochemistry, Vol. 8, pp. 2405-2410(1969).

R. J. Cole and R. H. Cox; Handbook of Toxic Fungal Metabolites; Academic Press, New York, pp. 185-186(1981).

M. E. Savard and B. A. Blackwell; A Compilation of Spectral Characteristics of Secondary Metabolites from *Fusarium* Fungi; In Mycotoxins in Grain; Compounds Other Than Aflatoxin; J. D. Miller and H. L. Trenholm, eds., Eagan Press, St. Paul, pp. 59-257 (1994).

Common/Systematic Name

HT-2 Toxin

3α,4β-Dihydroxy-15-acetoxy-8α-[3-methylbutyryloxy]-12,13-epoxytrichothec-9-ene

Molecular Formula/Molecular Weight

$C_{22}H_{32}O_8$; MW = 424.20972

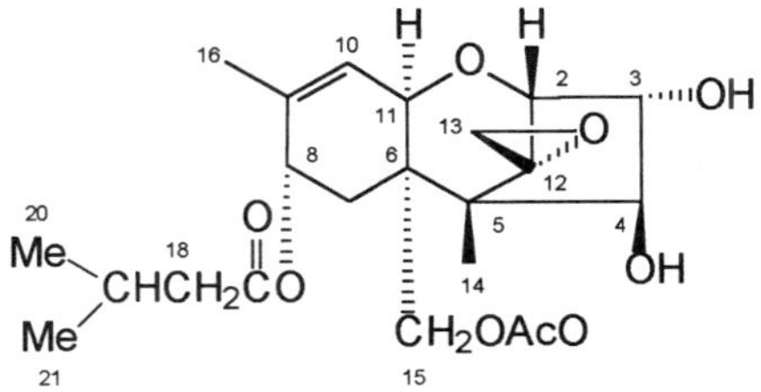

General Characteristics

Pale yellow oil.

Fungal Source

Fusarium sporotrichioides, *F. poae*, and *F. culmorum*.

Biological Activity

LD_{50} dosed IP to mice was 9.0mg/kg; LD_{50} in chicken embryo assay was 0.5μg per egg. ID_{50} of protein synthesis in rabbit reticulocytes (whole cell) was 0.03μg/ml. It inhibited the initiation step in protein synthesis. It also caused dermal necrosis similar to that of T-2.

Spectral Data

IR:

3400, 2950, 1720, 1635, and 1240cm^{-1}.

^{1}H NMR:

($CDCl_3$) 3.60(1H, d, *J*=4.9Hz, H-2); 4.22(1H, m, H-3); 4.13(1H, br d, *J*=3.0Hz, H-4); 2.00(1H, dt, *J*=15.0, 1.5Hz, αH-7); 2.32(1H, dd, *J*=15.0, 5.7Hz, βH-7); 5.25(1H, br d, *J*=5.1Hz, H-8); 5.73(1H, br d, *J*=6.0Hz, H-10); 4.36(1H, br d, *J*=6.0Hz, H-11); 2.74(1H, d, *J*=4.0Hz, H-13); 3.00(1H, d, *J*=4.0Hz, H-13); 0.75(3H, s, CH_3-14); 3.97(1H, d, *J*=12.5Hz, αH-15); 4.29(1H, d, *J*=12.5Hz, βH-15); 1.71(3H, s, CH_3-16); 2.05-2.10(1H, m, H-19); 0.93, 0.92(3H each, d, *J*=6.4Hz, 20- and 21-CH_3); and 2.01ppm (3H, s, CH_3COO-).

^{13}C NMR:

78.7, C-2; 80.6, C-3; 81.6, C-4; 48.9, C-5; 42.5, C-6; 27.6, C-7; 68.1, C-8; 136.4, C-9; 123.7, C-10; 67.3, C-11; 64.7, C-12; 46.9, C-13; 6.9, C-14; 64.5, C-15; 20.3, C-16; 172.7, C-17; 43.6, C-18; 25.7, C-19; 22.4, C-20 and C-21; 21.1(3H, <u>C</u>H_3COO-); and

170.4ppm, (3H, $CH_3\underline{C}OO$-).

Mass Spectrum:
LREIMS: 424(M^+), 322, 249, 203, 121, 105, 85, and 57*m/e* (base peak).

TLC Data

A. Adsorbent: silica gel G; solvent: chloroform-methanol, 98:2, v/v; R_f, 0.09; detection: H_2SO_4 spraying and heating at 110°C for 5 min. B. Adsorbent: alumina; solvent: chloroform-methanol, 98:2, v/v; R_f, 0.32; detection: H_2SO_4 spraying and heating at 110°C for 5 min.

References

J. R. Bamberg and F. M. Strong; Mycotoxins of the Trichothecene Family Produced by *Fusarium tricinctum* and *Trichoderma lignorum*; Phytochemistry, Vol. 8, pp. 2405-2410 (1969).

R. J. Cole and R. H. Cox; Handbook of Toxic Fungal Metabolites; Academic Press, New York, pp. 181-182(1981).

M. E. Savard and B. A. Blackwell; A Compilation of Spectral Characteristics of Secondary Metabolites from *Fusarium* Fungi; In Mycotoxins in Grain; Compounds Other Than Aflatoxin; J. D. Miller and H. L. Trenholm, eds., Eagan Press, St. Paul, pp. 59-257 (1994).

Common/Systematic Name

Acetyl T-2 Toxin

3α,4β,15-Triacetoxy-8α-[3-methylbutyloxy]-12,13-epoxytrichothec-9-ene

Molecular Formula/Molecular Weight

$C_{26}H_{36}O_{10}$; MW = 508.23085

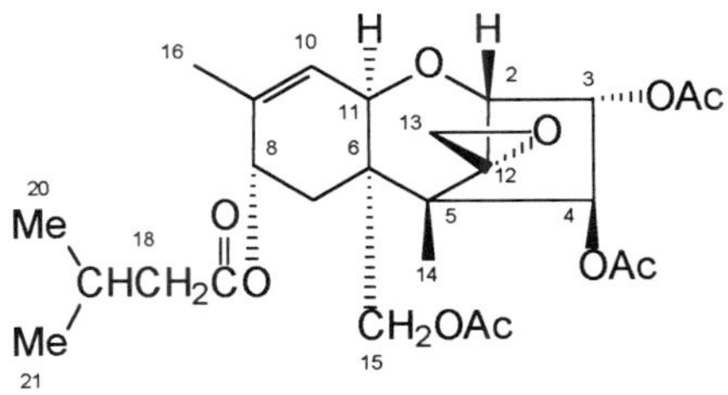

General Characteristics

An oil.

Fungal Source

Fusarium poae (NRRL 3287).

Biological Activity

Acetyl T-2 toxin was much less toxic than T-2 toxin in pigeons. It caused emesis at higher dosages (18.2mg/kg oral). No deaths occurred at this dosage level.

Spectral Data

UV:

End absorption.

^{1}H NMR:

($CDCl_3$) 3.78, H-2; 5.07, H-3; 5.85, H-4; 1.85-2.1, H-7; 5.20, H-8; 5.65, H-10; 4.14, H-11; 2.75, αH-13; 2.95, βH-13; 0.65, H-14; 4.00, αH-15; 4.27, βH-15; 1.66, H-16;1.93, H-18; 2.0, H-19; 0.96, H-20; 0.96, H-21; and 2.03ppm, (3H, CH_3-COO-).

^{13}C NMR:

76.2, C-2; 78.7, C-3; 78.2, C-4; 47.7, C-5; 42.0, C-6; 26.7, C-7; 67.2, C-8; 135.0, C-9; 124.0, C-10; 66.3, C-11; 63.6, C-12; 41.4, C-13; 6.1, C-14; 63.6, C-15; 19.4, C-16; 172.2, C-17; 42.4, C-18; 25.3, C-19; 21.7, C-20; 21.7, C-21; 170.6, $CH_3\underline{C}O$; and 20.3ppm, $\underline{C}H_3CO$.

TLC Data

Adsorbent: Brinkman F_{254} silica gel; solvent: ethyl acetate-ethanol, 6:1, v/v; R_f, 0.74; detection: a quenching spot under UV light.

References

R. J. Cole and R. H. Cox; Handbook of Toxic Fungal Metabolites; Academic Press, New York, pp. 185-186(1981).

M. E. Savard and B. A. Blackwell; A Compilation of Spectral Characteristics of Secondary Metabolites from *Fusarium* Fungi; In Mycotoxins in Grain; Compounds Other Than Aflatoxin; J. D. Miller and H. L. Trenholm, eds., Eagan Press, St. Paul, pp. 59-257 (1994).

Common/Systematic Name

4-Propanyl HT-2

4β-Propanyl-3α-hydroxy-15-acetoxy-8α-[3-methylbutyryloxy]-12,13-epoxytrichothec-9-ene

Molecular Formula/Molecular Weight

$C_{25}H_{36}O_9$; MW = 480.23593

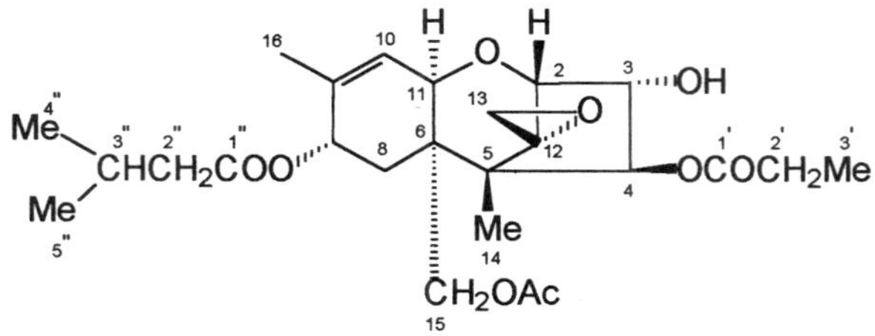

General Characteristics

Isolated as white needles; mp., 141-142°C.

Fungal Source

Fusarium sporotrichioides (MC-72083) and *F. sambucinum.*

Isolation/Purification

Fungal cultures were extracted with chloroform-acetone (85:15, v/v), followed by Florisil column chromatography eluted with benzene-hexane (2:1, v/v), methylene chloride, and chloroform-methanol (95:5, v/v) to give an oil highly enriched with trichothecenes. The oil was further purified by normal phase preparative HPLC using benzene-acetone followed by preparative RPTLC to yield several trichothecenes including 4-propanyl HT-2 toxin.

Spectral Data

IR:

(film) 3430(OH), 1741, and 1730cm^{-1} (ester).

^{1}H NMR:

($CDCl_3$) 6.24(1H, t, *J*=1.5Hz, H-2); 3.10(1H, d, *J*=18.2, H-4), 2.03(1H, d, *J*=18.2Hz, H-4); 1.95(1H, dd, *J*=15.0, 4.6Hz, H-7); 1.79(1H, d, *J*=15.0Hz, H-7); 1.45(2H, m, *J*=4.6Hz, H-8); 5.05(1H, br s, H-10); 4.11(1H, br s, H-11); 4.55(1H, d, *J*=17.3Hz, H-13); 4.34(1H, d, *J*=17.3Hz, H-13); 1.24(3H, s, CH_3-14); 0.84(3H, s, CH_3-15); and 1.61ppm (3H, br s, CH_3-16).

^{13}C NMR:

($CDCl_3$) 129.5, C-2; 208.4, C-3; 50.4, C-4; 53.1, C-5; 41.9, C-6; 29.9, C-7; 27.4, C-8; 135.7, C-9; 125.0, C-10; 71.3, C-11; 188.0, C-12; 61.0, C-13; 22.4, C-14; 13.1, C-

15; and 22.5ppm C-16.

Mass Spectrum:
CIMS: 470.236*m/e* (M^+); calcd for $C_{25}H_{36}O_9$, 470.235.

References

D. G. Corley, G. E. Rottinghaus, J. K. Tracy, and M. S. Tempesta; New Trichothecene Mycotoxins of *Fusarium sporotrichioides* (MC- 72083); Tetrahedron Letters, pp. 4133-4136(1986).

M. E. Savard and B. A. Blackwell; A Compilation of Spectral Characteristics of Secondary Metabolites from *Fusarium* Fungi; In Mycotoxins in Grain; Compounds Other Than Aflatoxin; J. D. Miller and H. L. Trenholm, eds., Eagan Press, St. Paul, pp. 59-257 (1994).

Common/Systematic Name

3'-Hydroxy T-2 toxin

3α-Hydroxy-4β,15-diacetoxy-8α-[3-hydroxy-3-methylbutyryloxy]-12,13-epoxytrichothec-9-ene

Molecular Formula/Molecular Weight

$C_{24}H_{34}O_{10}$; MW = 482.21520

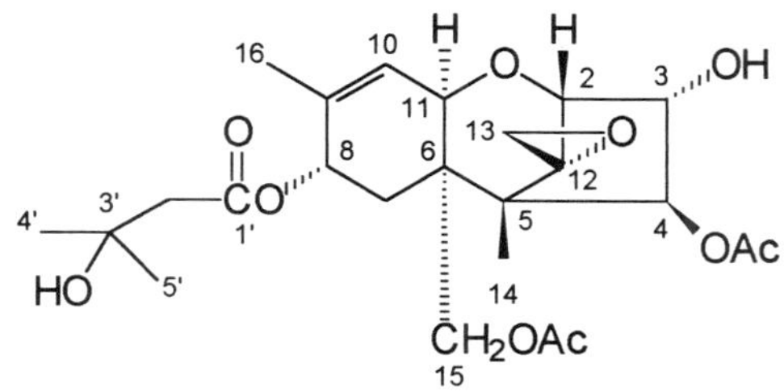

General Characteristics

An oil.

Fungal Source

Fusarium sporotrichioides (MC-72083 and DAOM 165006).

Isolation/Purification

Fungal material was extracted with ethyl ether, chromatographed in two equal portions on a column containing activated LiChroprep Si-60 eluted with methylene chloride, methylene chloride-methanol (79:1, v/v), methylene chloride-methanol (59:11, v/v), methylene chloride-methanol (24:1, v/v), methylene chloride-methanol (4:1, v/v), and methanol. Appropriate fractions were combined to give seven fractions. Fraction five was further purified, first by activated LiChroprep Si-60 eluted with methylene chloride containing increasing amounts of ethyl acetate followed by preparative HPLC using 9% isopropanol-hexane to yield 3'-hydroxy T-2 toxin as an oil.

Spectral Data

UV:

End absorption.

^{1}H NMR:

($CDCl_3$) 3.67(1H, d, *J*=4.9Hz, H-2); 4.14(1H, dd, *J*=4.9, 2.9Hz, H-3); 5.27(1H, d, *J*=2.9Hz, H-4); 2.40(1H, dd, *J*=15.0, 5.2Hz, αH-7); 1.90(1H, br d, *J*=15.0Hz, βH-7); 5.26(1H, d, *J*=5.3Hz, H-8); 5.79(1H, br d, *J*=5.9Hz, H-10); 3.04(1H, d, *J*=3.9Hz, H-13); 2.78(1H, d, *J*=3.9Hz, H-13); 0.78(3H, s, CH_3-14); 4.04(1H, d, *J*=2.6Hz, αH-15);

4.26(1H, d, *J*=12.6Hz, βH-15); 1.73(3H, br s, CH_3-16); 2.42(2H, s, 2'-CH_2); 1.27(3H, s, 4' and 5'-CH_3); and 2.02, 2.12ppm (3H each, s, CH_3COO-).

^{13}C NMR:

78.8, C-2; 78.4, C-3; 84.5, C-4; 48.4, C-5; 42.9, C-6; 27.7, C-7; 68.5, C-8; 135.8, C-9; 124.3, C-10; 67.2, C-11; 64.2, C-12; 47.1, C-13; 6.7, C-14; 64.6, C-15; 20.2, C-16; 172.8, C-1'; 46.6, C-2'; 69.1, C-3'; 29.0, 29.5, C-4', C-5'; 20.9, 21.0(3H each, $\underline{C}H_3COO$-); and 170.4, 172.6ppm, (3H each, $CH_3\underline{C}OO$-).

Mass Spectrum:

CIMS: (methane, positive ion) (TFA derivative) 601(M^+ + 1), 561, 541, 501, 451, 403, 401(base peak), 341, 311, 281, 215, 207, 151, and 115*m/e*. EIMS: 185(48%), 180(45), 105(57), 121(100), and 59*m/e* (92).

TLC Data

Silica gel. Solvent system A: Benzene-acetone (12:7, v/v), R_f0.48; solvent system B: toluene-ethyl acetate-formic acid (6:3:1, v/v/v); R_f, 0.19. Solvent system C: chloroform-methanol (9:1, v/v); R_f, 0.59.

References

R. Greenhaugh, B. A. Blackwell, M. Savard, J. D. Miller, and A. Taylor; Secondary Metabolites Produced by *Fusarium sporotrichioides* DAOM 165006 in Liquid Culture; J. Agric. Food Chem., Vol. 36, pp.216-219(1988).

M. E. Savard and B. A. Blackwell; A Compilation of Spectral Characteristics of Secondary Metabolites from *Fusarium* Fungi; In Mycotoxins in Grain; Compounds Other Than Aflatoxin; J. D. Miller and H. L. Trenholm, eds., Eagan Press, St. Paul, pp. 59-257 (1994).

A. Visconti, C. J. Mirocha, A. Bottalico, and J. Chelkowski; Trichothecene Mycotoxins Produced by *Fusarium sporotrichioides* Strain P-11; Mycotoxin Research, Vol. 1, pp. 3-10(1985).

T. Yoshizawa, T. Sakamoto, Y. Ayano, and C. J. Mirocha; 3'-Hydroxy T-2 and 3' Hydroxy HT-2 Toxins: New Metabolites of T-2 Toxin, A Trichothecene Mycotoxin, In Animals; Agric. Biol. Chem., Vol. 46, pp. 2613-2615(1982).

Common/Systematic Name

3'-Hydroxy HT-2 toxin

3α,4β-Dihydroxy-15-acetoxy-8α-[3-hydroxy-3-methylbutyryloxy]-12,13-epoxytrichothec-9-ene

Molecular Formula/Molecular Weight

$C_{22}H_{32}O_9$; MW = 440.20463

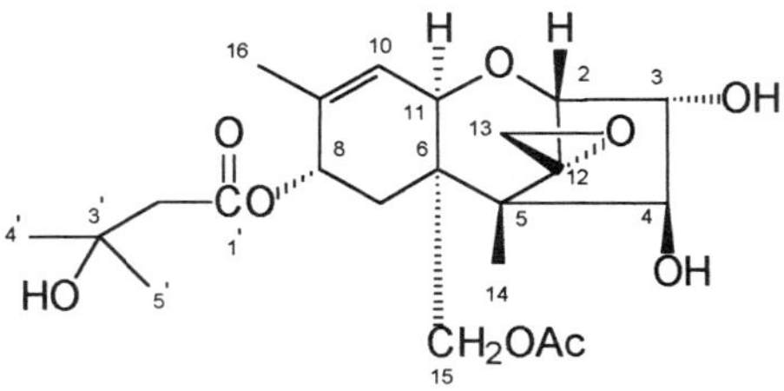

Fungal Source

Fusarium acuminatum misidentified as *F. heterosporum*. The *F. acuminatum* was isolated from *Claviceps paspali* honey dew on *Paspalum distichum*.

Isolation/Purification

Fungal cultures were extracted with chloroform; the crude chloroform extract was chromatographed on a column containing silica gel eluted with toluene, ethyl ether, ethyl acetate, acetone, and methanol. The acetone fraction was further purified on a silica gel column eluted with a linear gradient from ethyl acetate to acetone. The 3'-hydroxy HT-2 toxin-containing fractions were combined, reduced in volume and the toxin was precipitated from solution.

Biological Activity

The LD_{50} value for day-old chicks dosed orally was 8.5mg/kg; the toxin was inhibitory in the wheat coleoptile assay down to 10^{-5} M; ED_{50} values for dermal toxicity on back skin of rabbits was >1.28μg compared to < 0.16μg for T-2 toxin in the same assay.

Spectral Data

UV:

End absorption.

^{1}H NMR:

($CDCl_3$) 3.28(1H, *J*=4.6Hz, H-2); 4.02(1H, H-3); 4.02(1H, H-4); 2.09(2H, H-7); 5.18(1H, H-8); 5.65(1H, *J*=5.2Hz, H-10); 4.10(1H, H-11); 2.66(1H, *J*=4.0Hz, H-13); 2.88(1H, *J*=4.0Hz, H-13); 0.65(3H, s, CH_3-14); 3.84(1H, *J*=12.0Hz, H-15); 4.10(1H, *J*=12.0Hz, H-15); 1.67(3H, s, CH_3-16); 2.31(2H, s, 2'-CH_2); 1.19(3H each, s, 4', 5'-CH_3); and 1.99ppm (3H, s, CH_3COO-).

^{13}C NMR:

78.43, d, C-2; 78.87, d, C-3; 79.45, d, C-4; 47.95, s, C-5; 41.90, s, C-6; 26.40, t, C-7; 67.58, d, C-8; 134.43, s, C-9; 124.19, d, C-10; 66.22, d, C-11; 64.28, s, C-12; 45.44, t, C-13; 6.93, q, C-14; 63.85, t, C-15; 19.81, q, C-16; 169.89, s, C-1'; 47.86, t, C-2'; 68.05, s, C-3'; 29.17, 29.37, C-4', C-5'; 20.83, s, $\underline{C}H_3COO$-; and 169.89ppm, s, $CH_3\underline{C}OO$-.

Mass Spectrum:
CIMS: 441(M^+ + 1), 423, 405, 381, 363, 263, 203, and 121*m/e*. EIMS: 381, 203, and 121*m/e*.

Reference

R. J. Cole, J. W. Dorner, R. H. Cox, B. M. Cunfer, H. G. Cutler, and B. P. Stuart; The Isolation and Identification of Several Trichothecene Mycotoxins from *Fusarium heterosporum*; J. Nat. Prod., Vol. 44, pp. 321-330(1981).

Common/Systematic Name

3'-Hydroxy T-2 triol

3α,4β,15-Trihydroxy-8α-[3-hydroxy-3-methylbutyryloxy]-12,13-epoxytrichothec-9-ene

Molecular Formula/Molecular Weight

$C_{20}H_{30}O_8$; MW = 398.19407

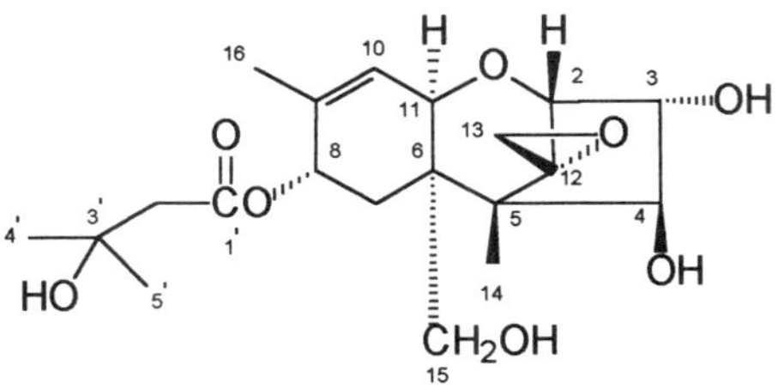

Fungal Source

Fusarium acuminatum misidentified as *F. heterosporum*. The *F. acuminatum* was isolated from *Claviceps paspali* honey dew on *Paspalum distichum*.

Isolation/Purification

Fungal cultures were extracted with chloroform; the crude chloroform extract was chromatographed on a column containing silica gel eluted with toluene, ethyl ether, ethyl acetate, acetone, and methanol. The acetone fraction was further purified on a silica gel column eluted with a linear gradient from ethyl acetate to acetone. The 3'-hydroxy T-2 triol-containing fractions were combined, reduced in volume and final purification was on a C_{18} reversed-phase column eluted with a linear gradient from 10-50% acetonitrile-water.

Biological Activity

The toxin was inhibitory in the wheat coleoptile assay down to10^{-5} M; ED_{50} values for dermal toxicity on back skin of rabbits was >1.28μg compared to < 0.16μg for T-2 toxin in the same assay.

Spectral Data

UV:

End absorption.

^{1}H NMR:

($CDCl_3$) 3.21(1H, d, *J*=4.8Hz, H-2); 3.84(1H, *J*=4.8, 2.9Hz, H-3); 4.42(1H, *J*=2.9Hz, H-4); 2.05(2H, H-7); 5.15(1H, *J*=5.8Hz, H-8); 5.63(1H, *J*=5.4Hz, H-10); 4.05(1H, *J*=5.4Hz, H-11); 2.83(1H, *J*=4.2Hz, H-13); 2.61, 2.83(2H, *J*=4.2Hz, H-13); 0.68(3H, s, CH_3-14); 4.24(1H, *J*=12.0Hz, H-15); 3.64(1H, *J*=12.0Hz, H-15); 1.66(3H, s, CH_3-16); 2.40(2H, s, 2'-CH_2); and 1.20ppm (3H, s, 4', 5'-CH_3).

^{13}C NMR:

78.49, d, C-2; 79.18, d, C-3; 79.18, d, C-4; 48.06, s, C-5; 43.37, s, C-6; 26.66, t, C-7; 68.12, d, C-8; 133.93, s, C-9; 124.76, d, C-10; 66.45, d, C-11; 64.75, s, C-12; 45.58, t, C-13; 6.92, q, C-14; 61.37, t, C-15; 19.78, q, C-16; 170.11, s, C-1'; 47.81, t, C-2'; 67.91, s, C-3'; 29.08, q, C-4', and 29.64ppm, q, C-5'

Reference

R. J. Cole, J. W. Dorner, R. H. Cox. B. M. Cunfer, H. G. Cutler, and B. P. Stuart; The Isolation and Identification of Several Trichothecene Mycotoxins from *Fusarium heterosporum*; J. Nat. Prod., Vol. 44, pp. 321-330(1981).

Common/Systematic Name

Neosolaniol; Solaniol

4β,15α-Diacetoxy-3α,8α-dihydroxy-12,13-epoxytrichothec-9-ene

Molecular Formula/Molecular Weight

$C_{19}H_{26}O_8$; MW = 382.16277

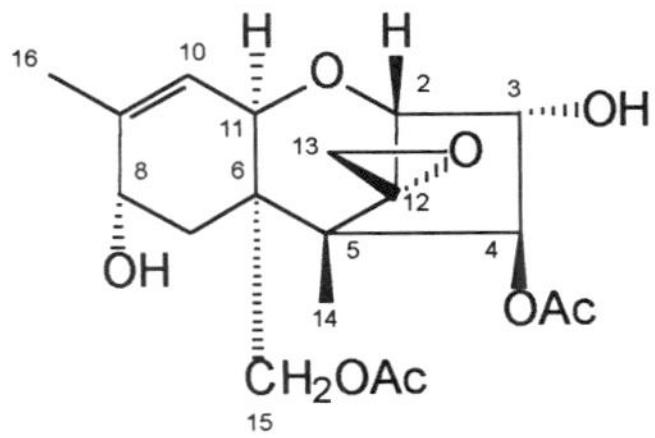

General Characteristics

Crystals from ethyl acetate-*n*-hexane; mp., 170-172°C.

Fungal Source

Fusarium culmorum, F. solani, F. poae, F. sporotrichioides, F. lateritium, F. equiseti, and *F. averaceum.*

Biological Activity

LD_{50} to mice dosed IP was 14.5mg/kg; LD_{50} in chicken embryo test was 5.0μg per egg. ID_{50} of protein synthesis in rabbit reticulocytes (whole cell) was 0.25μg/ml; rat liver (cell-free) was 20μg/ml. Clinical signs in animals receiving a fatal dose were marked cellular degeneration and karyorrhexis in actively dividing cells of thymus, lymph nodes, spleen, bone marrow, intestine, and testes reflecting the so-called "radiomimetic" property. Minimum dose for skin-irritant toxicity to rabbits was 1.0μg.

Spectral Data

^{1}H NMR:

($CDCl_3$) 3.66(1H, d, *J*=4.9Hz, H-2); 4.14(1H, dd, *J*=4.9, 2.9Hz, H-3); 5.25(1H, d, *J*=2.9Hz, H-4); 1.89(1H, dd, *J*=14.5, 1.4Hz, H-7); 2.33(1H, dd, *J*=14.5, 5.7Hz, H-7); 4.10(1H, d, *J*=5.7Hz, H-8); 5.65(1H, d, *J*=5.9Hz, H-10); 4.25(1H, d, *J*=5.9Hz, H-11); 2.78(1H, d, *J*=4.0Hz, H-13); 3.04(1H, d, *J*=4.0Hz, H-13); 0.83(3H,s, CH_3-14); 4.29(1H, d, *J*=12.6Hz, H-15); 4.21(1H, d, *J*=12.6Hz, H-15); 1.82(3H, s, CH_3-16); and 2.02, 2.13ppm (3H each, s, CH_3COO-).

^{13}C NMR:

78.7, C-2; 78.4, C-3; 84.7, C-4; 48.7, C-5; 43.4, C-6; 30.4, C-7; 66.7, C-8; 139.6, C-9; 121.1, C-10; 67.7, C-11; 64.4, C-12; 47.2, C-13; 6.7, C-14; 64.8, C-15; 19.9, C-16; 21.4 and 21.0 (3H each, <u>C</u>H_3COO-); 169.8 and 172.0ppm (3H each, CH_3<u>C</u>OO-).

TLC Data

Adsorbent: Kieselgel G; solvent: ethyl acetate-*n*-hexane, 3:1 (v/v); R_f, 0.15; detection: H_2SO_4 spraying and heating at 110°C for 5 min.

GLC Data

Solid Support: Shimalite W; liquid phase: OV-17 (1.5%); retention time: 7.50 (relative to nivalenol).

References

R. J. Cole and R. H. Cox; Handbook of Toxic Fungal Metabolites; Academic Press, New York, p. 177(1981).

M. Mesilaakso, M. Moilanen, and E. Rahkamaa; ^{1}H and ^{13}C NMR Analysis of Some Trichothecenes; Arch. Environ. Contam. Toxicol., Vol. 18, pp. 365-373(1989).

M. E. Savard and B. A. Blackwell; A Compilation of Spectral Characteristics of Secondary Metabolites from *Fusarium* Fungi; In Mycotoxins in Grain; Compounds Other Than Aflatoxin; J. D. Miller and H. L. Trenholm, eds., Eagan Press, St. Paul, pp. 59-257 (1994).

Common/Systematic Name

Isoneosolaniol; Acuminatum; 8α,15-Diacetoxy-T-2 tetraol
8α,15-Diacetoxy-3α,4β-dihydroxy-12,13-epoxytrichothec-9-ene

Molecular Formula/Molecular Weight

$C_{19}H_{26}O_8$; MW = 382.16277

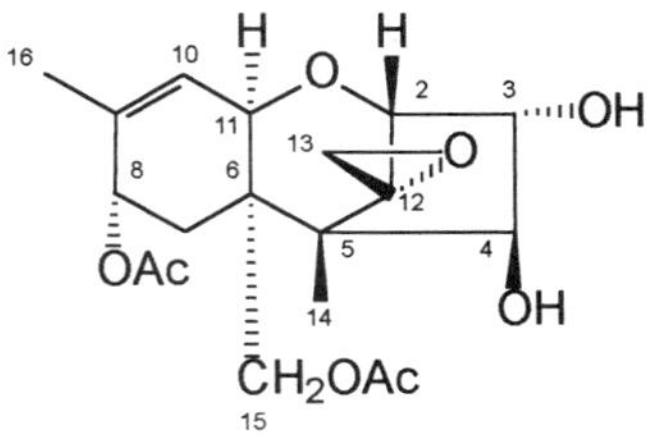

Fungal Source

Fusarium acuminatum, F. tricinctum, F. compactum, and *F. equiseti.*

Isolation/Purification

Extraction was performed with MeOH-1% aqueous NaCl (55:45, v/v); after filtration, the residue was extracted with the MeOH-NaCl solution. The filtrate was concentrated, defatted with *n*-hexane and then extracted with methylene chloride. The methylene chloride extract was dried over anhydrous Na_2SO_4 and concentrated to dryness. The residue was reconstituted with MeOH and chromatographed on a silica gel 60 column eluted sequentially with CH_2Cl_2, CH_2Cl_2-MeOH (95:5, v/v), CH_2Cl_2-MeOH (90:10, v/v), CH_2Cl_2-MeOH (80:20, v/v), and MeOH. Eighteen fractions were collected and tested by TLC for trichothecenes. The compounds of major interest that were positive for trichothecenes accumulated in fractions F6 and F7. Fraction F6 contained acuminatin which was further purified by preparative HPLC using an RP_{18} column with MeOH-H_2O (40:60, v/v) as mobile phase.

Biological Activity

Highly toxic to brine shrimp larvae (*Artemia salina*) and inhibited the growth of tomato seedlings.

Spectral Data

^{1}H NMR:

($CDCl_3$) 3.64(1H, d, *J*=4.9Hz, H-2); 4.17(1H, dd, *J*=4.9, 3.0Hz, H-3); 4.94(1H, d, *J*=3.0Hz, H-4); 2.06(1H, dt, *J*=14.3, 1.6Hz, αH-7); 2.19(1H, dd, *J*=14.3, 5.2Hz, βH-7); 4.12(1H, m, H-8); 5.65(1H, dq, *J*=5.8, 1.5Hz, H-10); 3.88(1H, d, *J*=5.8Hz, H-11); 2.79(1H, d, *J*=4.0Hz, H-13); 3.02(1H, d, *J*=4.0Hz, H-13); 0.89(3H, s, CH_3-14); 3.48(1H, d, *J*=12.6Hz, H-15); 3.76(1H, d, *J*=12.6Hz, H-15); 1.85(3H, br s, CH_3-16); and 2.13 ppm (3H, s, CH_3COO-).

^{13}C NMR:

78.7, C-2; 78.3, C-3; 84.9, C-4; 49.1, C-5; 44.9, C-6; 27.9, C-7; 66.8, C-8; 139.0, C-9; 122.0, C-10; 68.5, C-11; 64.4, C-12; 47.0, C-13; 7.0, C-14; 62.2, C-15; 20.59, C-16; 21.0, $\underline{C}H_3COO$-; and 172.8ppm $CH_3\underline{C}OO$-.

References

K. Ishii and Y. Ueno; Isolation and Characterization of Two New Trichothecenes from *Fusarium sporotrichioides* Strain M-1-1; Applied and Environmental Microbiology; Vol. 42, pp. 541-543(1981).

M. E. Savard and B. A. Blackwell; A Compilation of Spectral Characteristics of Secondary Metabolites from *Fusarium* Fungi; In Mycotoxins in Grain; Compounds Other Than Aflatoxin; J. D. Miller and H. L. Trenholm, eds., Eagan Press, St. Paul, pp. 59-257 (1994).

A. Visconti, C. J. Mirocha, A. Logrieco, A. Bottalico, and M. Solfrizzo; Mycotoxins Produced by *Fusarium acuminatum*: A New Trichothecene; J. Agric. Food Chem., Vol. 37, pp. 1348-1351(1989).

Common/Systematic Name
8-Acetoxyneosolaniol
4β,8α,15-Triacetoxy-3α-hydroxy-12,13-epoxytrichothec-9-ene

Molecular Formula/Molecular Weight
$C_{21}H_{28}O_9$; MW = 424.17333

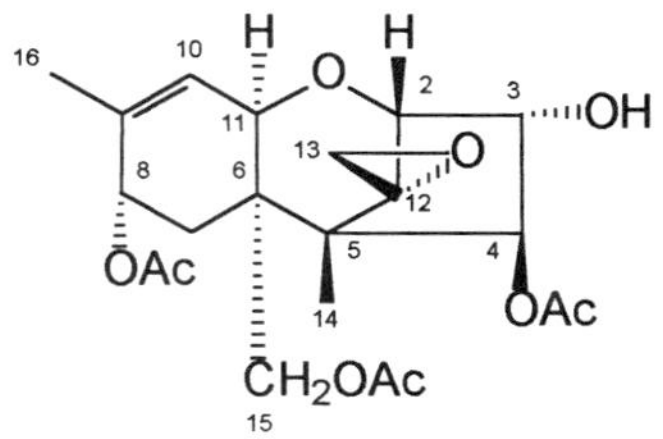

Fungal Source
Fusarium acuminatum, F. tricinctum, F. compactum, and *F. roseum.*

Isolation/Purification
Extraction was performed with MeOH-1% aqueous NaCl (55:45); after filtration, the residue was extracted with the MeOH-NaCl solution. The filtrate was concentrated, defatted with *n*-hexane, and extracted with methylene chloride. The methylene chloride extract was dried over anhydrous Na_2SO_4 and concentrated to dryness. The residue was reconstituted with MeOH and chromatographed on a silica gel 60 column eluted sequentially with CH_2Cl_2, CH_2Cl_2-MeOH (95:5, v/v), CH_2Cl_2-MeOH (90:10, v/v), CH_2Cl_2-MeOH (80:20, v/v), and MeOH. Eighteen fractions were collected and tested by TLC for trichothecenes. The compounds of major interest that were positive for trichothecenes accumulated in fractions F6 and F7. Fraction F6 contained 8-acetoxyneosolaniol which was further purified by preparative HPLC using an RP_{18} column with MeOH-H_2O (40:60, v/v) as mobile phase.

Biological Activity
Highly toxic to brine shrimp larvae (*Artemia salina*) and inhibited the growth of tomato seedlings. LD_{50} in day-old cockerels dosed via crop intubation was 0.789mg/kg; LD_{50} of T-2 toxin (dosed simultaneously) was 1.84mg/kg. Also, showed inhibition in wheat coleoptile assay down to 10^{-6} M. It showed a linear, rather than a curvilinear, response.

Spectral Data

^{1}H NMR:
($CDCl_3$) 3.67(1H, d, *J*=4.9Hz, H-2); 4.12(1H, dd, *J*=4.9, 2.9Hz, H-3); 5.21(1H, d, *J*=2.9Hz, H-4); 1.97(1H, d, *J*=15.1Hz, αH-7); 2.35(1H, dd, *J*=15.1, 5.7Hz, βH-7); 5.24(1H, d, *J*=5.7Hz, H-8); 5.79(1H, d, *J*=5.9Hz, H-10); 4.28(1H, d, *J*=5.9Hz, H-11); 2.77(1H, d, *J*=4.0Hz, H-13); 3.03(1H, d, *J*=4.0Hz, H-13); 0.80(3H, s, CH_3-14);

4.05(1H, d, *J*=12.5Hz, H-15); 4.26(1H, d, *J*=12.5Hz, H-15); 1.73(3H, s, CH_3-16); and 2.00, 2.01, 2.12ppm (3H, s, CH_3COO-).

^{13}C NMR:

78.7, C-2; 78.4, C-3; 84.6, C-4; 48.6, C-5; 43.0, C-6; 27.4, C-7; 68.5, C-8; 136.2, C-9; 123.8, C-10; 67.4, C-11; 64.3, C-12; 47.2, C-13; 7.0, C-14; 64.4, C-15; 20.3, C-16; 21.0, 21.1, 21.1(3H each, $\underline{C}H_3COO$-); and 172.6, 170.5, 170.0ppm (3H each, $CH_3\underline{C}OO$-).

Mass Data:

Positive CIMS (TFA derivative), 521(8%), 461 (10), 401 (100), and 341*m/e* (10).

TLC Data

A. Benzene-acetone, 12:7 (v/v); R_f, 0.6. B: Chloroform-methanol, 9:1 (v/v); R_f, 0.85. C: Toluene-ethyl acetate-formic acid, 6:3:1 (v/v/v); R_f, 0.28.

GLC Data

(TFA derivative) DB5 capillary column, with covalently bonded liquid phase; injector temperature, 275°C; detector temperature, 300°C; and temperature programming from 150-280°C at 10°/min. followed by 5 min. at 280°C; retention time, 10.51 min.

References

R. J. Cole and R. H. Cox; Handbook of Toxic Fungal Metabolites; Academic Press, New York, p. 178(1981).

K. Ishii and Y. Ueno; Isolation and Characterization of Two New Trichothecenes from *Fusarium sporotrichioides* Strain M-1-1; Applied and Environmental Microbiology, Vol. 42, pp. 541-543(1981).

M. E. Savard and B. A. Blackwell; A Compilation of Spectral Characteristics of Secondary Metabolites from *Fusarium* Fungi; In Mycotoxins in Grain; Compounds Other Than Aflatoxin; J. D. Miller and H. L. Trenholm, eds., Eagan Press, St. Paul, pp. 59-257 (1994).

A. Visconti, C. J. Mirocha, A. Logrieco, A. Bottalico and M. Solfrizzo; Mycotoxins Produced by *Fusarium acuminatum*: A New Trichothecene; J. Agric. Food Chem., Vol. 37, pp. 1348-1351(1989).

Common/Systematic Name

8-Propionylneosolaniol

8α-Propanyl-3α-hydroxy-4β,15-diacetoxy-12,13-epoxytrichothec-9-ene

Molecular Formula/Molecular Weight

$C_{22}H_{30}O_9$; MW = 438.18898

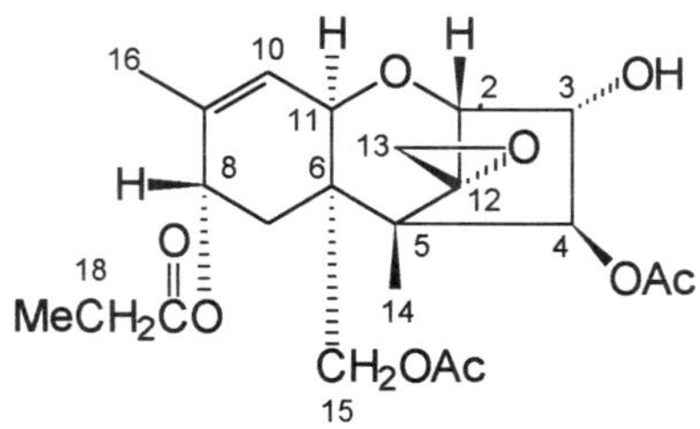

General Characteristics

Crystals; mp., 182-183°C.

Fungal Source

Fusarium sporotrichioides (MC-72083 and DAOM 165006).

Isolation/Purification

Fungal material was extracted with ethyl ether, chromatographed in two equal portions on a column containing activated LiChroprep Si-60 eluted with methylene chloride, methylene chloride-methanol (79:1, v/v), methylene chloride-methanol (59:11, v/v), methylene chloride-methanol (24:1, v/v), methylene chloride-methanol (4:1, v/v), and methanol. Appropriate fractions were combined to give seven fractions. Further purification was achieved by preparative HPLC using various isocratic solvent systems of 2-propanol-hexane. Fraction three was further purified by preparative HPLC using 5% isopropanol-hexane followed by 3% isopropanol-hexane to yield crystalline 8-propionyl-neosolaniol in pure form.

Biological Activity

The trichothecenes as a group show a wide range of biological activity such as antibacterial, antiviral, antifungal, and cytostatic activity; some are phytotoxic and all show some degree of animal toxicity, including insecticidal activity. There exists a broad range of toxicity in vertebrate animals and the acute toxicities vary considerably. General gross clinical signs reported for trichothecenes are vomiting, diarrhea, anorexia, ataxia, hematuria, leukocytosis soon followed by severe leukopenia, inflammation of the gastrointestinal tract, degeneration of nerve cells in the central nervous system, degeneration and hemorrhaging of cardiac muscle, and lesions of lymph nodes, testes, and thymus. Topical application or contact with skin causes dermal necrosis. Biochemically, they are potent inhibitors of protein and DNA synthesis in whole-cell and cell-free systems. Some trichothecenes inhibit the initiation step of protein synthesis on polyribosomes and others inhibit the elongation and/or termination step in protein synthesis. The trichothecenes have been strongly implicated in natural intoxications of animals and humans.

Spectral Data

^{1}H NMR:

($CDCl_3$) 3.68($J_{2,3}$=4.9Hz, H-2); 4.12($J_{3,2}$=4.9, $J_{3,4}$=2.8Hz, H-3); 5.27($J_{4,3}$=2.8Hz, H-4); 1.93(J_{AB}=15.1Hz, H-70; 2.38($J_{7,8}$=5.8Hz, H-7); 5.27($J_{8,7}$=5.8Hz, H-8); 5.80($J_{10,11}$= 6.0Hz, $J_{10,16}$=1.2Hz, H-10); 4.33($J_{11,10}$=6.0Hz, H-11); 2.78(J_{AB}=3.9Hz, H-13); 3.04(H-13); 0.79(H-14); 4.03(J_{AB}=12.6Hz, H-15); 4.27(H-15); 1.72($J_{16,10}$=1.2Hz, H-16); 2.28(2H, q, $J_{2',3'}$=7.5Hz, H-2'); 1.13(1H, t, $J_{3',2'}$=7.5Hz, H-3'); 2.01; and 2.13ppm (CH_3-Ac).

^{13}C NMR:

78.7, C-2; 78.2, C-3; 84.3, C-4; 48.3, C-5; 42.9, C-6; 27.7, C-7; 68.0, C-8; 136.3, C-9; 123.8, C-10; 67.3, C-11; 64.2, C-12; 47.0, C-13; 6.6, C-14; 64.5, C-15; 20.1, C-16; 174.1, C-17; 27.6, C-18; 8.9, C-19; 20.8, 20.1(3H, $\underline{C}H_3COO$-); and 170.2, 170.5ppm (3H each, $CH_3\underline{C}OO$-).

Mass Spectrum:

EIMS: (lacked a significant M^+) 185(35%), 180(61), 121(89), 105(48), and 57*m/e* (100).

GLC Data

DB-5 fused capillary column (20m x 0.32mm i.d., 0.25μm film); temperature programmed from 140-260°C at 15°/min using helium as carrier gas.

References

R. Greenhaugh, B. A. Blackwell, M. Savard, J. D. Miller, and A. Taylor; Secondary Metabolites Produced by *Fusarium sporotrichioides* DAOM 165006 in Liquid Culture; J. Agric. Food Chem., Vol. 36, pp. 216-219(1988).

M. E. Savard and B. A. Blackwell; A Compilation of Spectral Characteristics of Secondary Metabolites from *Fusarium* Fungi; Plant Research Centre, Agriculture Canada, Ottawa, Ontario, K1A 0C6.

Common/Systematic Name

8-Butyrylneosolaniol

8α-Butyryloxy-3α-hydroxy-4β,15-diacetoxy-12,13-epoxytrichothec-9-ene

Molecular Formula/Molecular Weight

$C_{23}H_{32}O_9$; MW = 452.20463

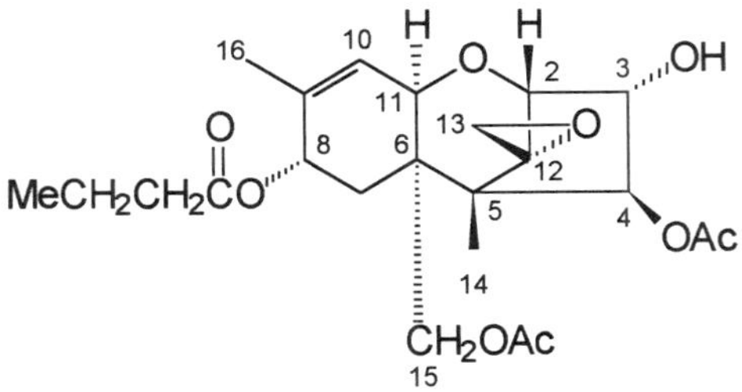

General Characteristics

Isolated as an oil.

Fungal Source

Fusarium sporotrichioides (MC-72083 and DAOM 165006).

Isolation/Purification

Fungal material was extracted with ethyl ether and chromatographed in two equal portions on a column containing activated LiChroprep Si-60 eluted with methylene chloride, methylene chloride-methanol (79:1, v/v), methylene chloride-methanol (59:11, v/v), methylene chloride-methanol (24:1, v/v), methylene chloride-methanol (4:1, v/v), and methanol. Appropriate fractions were combined to give seven fractions. Further purification was achieved by preparative HPLC using various isocratic solvent systems of 2-propanol-hexane. Fraction three was further purified by preparative HPLC using 5% isopropanol-hexane followed by 3% isopropanol-hexane. Pure 8-butyrylneosolaniol was obtained as an oil.

Biological Activity

The trichothecenes as a group show a wide range of biological activity such as antibacterial, antiviral, antifungal, and cytostatic activity; some are phytotoxic and all show some degree of animal toxicity, including insecticidal activity. There exists a broad range of toxicity in vertebrate animals and the acute toxicities vary considerably. General gross clinical signs reported for trichothecenes are vomiting, diarrhea, anorexia, ataxia, hematuria, leukocytosis soon followed by severe leukopenia, inflammation of the gastrointestinal tract, degeneration of nerve cells in the central nervous system, degeneration and hemorrhaging of cardiac muscle, and lesions of lymph nodes, testes, and thymus. Topical application or contact with skin causes dermal necrosis. Biochemically, they are potent inhibitors of protein and DNA synthesis in whole-cell and cell-free systems. Some trichothecenes inhibit the initiation step of protein synthesis on polyribosomes and others inhibit the elongation and/or termination step in protein synthesis. The trichothecenes have been strongly implicated in natural intoxications of animals and humans.

Spectral Data

^{1}H NMR:

(CDCl$_3$) 3.68($J_{2,3}$=4.9Hz, H-2); 4.13($J_{3,2}$=4.9Hz, $J_{3,4}$=2.9Hz, H-3); 5.27($J_{4,3}$=2.9Hz, H-4); 1.91(J_{AB}=15.9Hz, H-7); 2.39($J_{7,8}$=5.3Hz, H-7); 5.27($J_{8,7}$=5.5Hz, H-8); 5.79($J_{10,11}$= 4.9Hz, H-10); 4.30($J_{11,10}$=4.9Hz, H-11); 2.78(J_{AB}=3.9Hz, H-13); 3.04(H-13); 0.79(H-14); 4.03(J_{AB}=12.5Hz, H-15); 4.27(H-15); 1.72($J_{16,10}$=1.2Hz, H-16); 2.33(2H, q, $J_{2',3'}$=7.4Hz, H-2'); 1.64($J_{2',3'}$=$J_{3',4'}$=7.4Hz, H-3'); 0.93($J_{4',3'}$=7.4Hz, H-4'); 2.01; and 2.13ppm (CH$_3$-Ac).

Mass Spectrum:

EIMS: (lacked a significant M$^+$) 185(26%), 180(45), 121(100), 105(48), and 71*m/e* (80).

GLC Data

DB-5 fused capillary column (20m x 0.32mm i.d., 0.25μm film); temperature programmed from 140-260°C at 15°/min using helium as carrier gas.

References

R. Greenhaugh, B. A. Blackwell, M. Savard, J. D. Miller, and A. Taylor; Secondary Metabolites Produced by *Fusarium sporotrichioides* DAOM 165006 in Liquid Culture; J. Agric. Food Chem., Vol. 36, pp. 216-219(1988).

M. E. Savard and B. A. Blackwell; A Compilation of Spectral Characteristics of Secondary Metabolites from *Fusarium* Fungi; In Mycotoxins in Grain; Compounds Other Than Aflatoxin; J. D. Miller and H. L. Trenholm, eds., Eagan Press, St. Paul, pp. 59-257 (1994).

Common/Systematic Name

8-Isobutyrylneosolaniol

3α-Hydroxy-4β,15-diacetoxy-8α-[(2-methylpropionyl)oxy]-12,13-epoxytrichothec-9-ene

Molecular Formula/Molecular Weight

$C_{23}H_{32}O_9$; MW = 452.20463

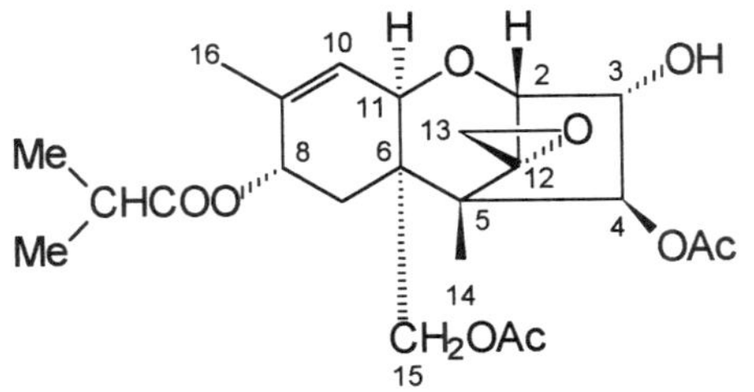

Fungal Source

Fusarium sporotrichioides (MC-72083 and DAOM 165006).

Isolation/Purification

Fungal material was extracted with ethyl ether, chromatographed in two equal portions on a column containing activated LiChroprep Si-60 eluted with methylene chloride, methylene chloride-methanol (79:1, v/v), methylene chloride-methanol (59:11, v/v), methylene chloride-methanol (24:1, v/v), methylene chloride-methanol (4:1, v/v), and methanol. Appropriate fractions were combined to give seven fractions. Further purification was achieved by preparative HPLC using various isocratic solvent systems of 2-propanol-hexane. Fraction three was further purified by preparative HPLC using 5% isopropanol-hexane followed by 3% isopropanol-hexane. Pure 8-isobutyrylneosolaniol was obtained after double development preparative TLC using hexane-acetone-formic acid (65:33:2, v/v/v; R_f 0.42).

Biological Activity

The trichothecenes as a group show a wide range of biological activity such as antibacterial, antiviral, antifungal, and cytostatic activity; some are phytotoxic and all show some degree of animal toxicity, including insecticidal activity. There exists a broad range of toxicity in vertebrate animals and the acute toxicities vary considerably. General gross clinical signs reported for trichothecenes are vomiting, diarrhea, anorexia, ataxia, hematuria, leukocytosis soon followed by severe leukopenia, inflammation of the gastrointestinal tract, degeneration of nerve cells in the central nervous system, degeneration and hemorrhaging of cardiac muscle, and lesions of lymph nodes, testes, and thymus. Topical application or contact with skin causes dermal necrosis. Biochemically, they are potent inhibitors of protein and DNA synthesis in whole-cell and cell-free systems. Some trichothecenes inhibit the initiation step of protein synthesis on polyribosomes and others inhibit the elongation and/or termination step in protein synthesis. The trichothecenes have been strongly implicated in natural intoxications of animals and humans.

Spectral Data

^{1}H NMR:

(CDCl$_3$) 3.69($J_{2,3}$=4.9Hz, H-2); 4.14($J_{3,2}$=4.9Hz, $J_{3,4}$=2.9Hz, H-3); 5.35($J_{4,3}$=2.9Hz, H-4); 1.83(J_{AB}=15.0Hz, H-7); 2.40(H-7); 5.26($J_{8,7}$=5.6Hz, H-8); 5.80($J_{10,11}$=5.4Hz, H-10); 4.38($J_{11,10}$=5.4Hz, H-11); 2.78(J_{AB}=3.9Hz, H-13); 3.05(H-13); 0.79(H-14); 4.02(J_{AB}=12.6Hz, H-15); 4.31(H-15); 1.73($J_{16,10}$=1.2Hz, H-16); 2.45(2H, q, $J_{2',3'}$=$J_{2',4'}$=7.4Hz, H-2'); 1.16($J_{2',3'}$=7.0Hz, H-3'); 1.16($J_{2',4'}$=7.0Hz, H-4'); 2.01; and 2.13ppm (CH$_3$-Ac).

Mass Spectrum:

EIMS: (lacked a significant M$^+$) 195(38%), 191(62), 180(60), 121(100), 105(57), and 71*m/e* (98).

GLC Data

DB-5 fused capillary column (20m x 0.32mm i.d., 0.25μm film); temperature programmed from 140-260°C at 15°/min using helium as carrier gas.

References

R. Greenhaugh, B. A. Blackwell, M. Savard, J. D. Miller, and A. Taylor; Secondary Metabolites Produced by *Fusarium sporotrichioides* DAOM 165006 in Liquid Culture; J. Agric. Food Chem., Vol. 36, pp. 216-219(1988).

M. E. Savard and B. A. Blackwell; A Compilation of Spectral Characteristics of Secondary Metabolites from *Fusarium* Fungi; In Mycotoxins in Grain; Compounds Other Than Aflatoxin; J. D. Miller and H. L. Trenholm, eds., Eagan Press, St. Paul, pp. 59-257 (1994).

Common/Systematic Name

15-Deacetylneosolaniol; NT-2 Toxin; 4-Acetyl-T-2 tetraol
4β-Acetoxy-3α,8α,15-trihydroxy-12,13-epoxytrichothec-9-ene

Molecular Formula/Molecular Weight

$C_{17}H_{24}O_7$; MW = 340.15220

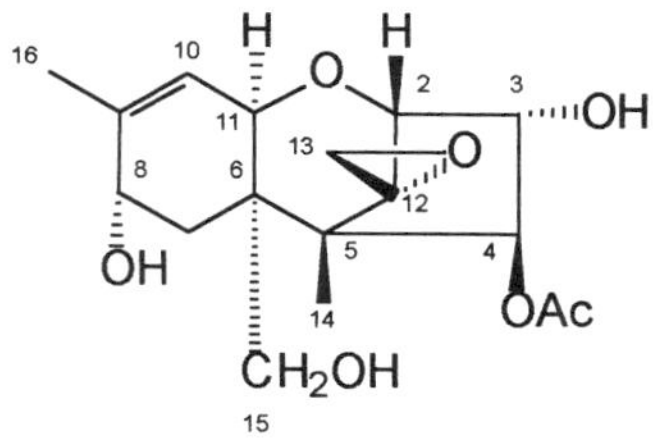

General Characteristics

Needles from ethyl acetate-*n*-hexane; mp., 172-173°C.

Fungal Source

Fusarium sporotrichioides (strain M-1-1), *F. tricinctum*, *F. compactum*, and *F. averaceum*.

Isolation/Purification

Extracted by charcoal absorption and elution with methanol. Extraction of methanol-chloroform soluble materials produced a pale yellow powder. The powder was chromatographed on a silica gel column eluted with *n*-hexane, *n*-hexane-acetone (12:5, 2:1, 1:1, 1:2, v/v), acetone and methanol followed by a second silica gel column eluted with benzene-acetone (3:2, v/v), and *n*-hexane-acetone (1:1, v/v). NT-2 was crystallized with ethyl acetate-*n*-hexane.

Biological Activity

Inhibited uptake of [^{14}C]leucine in protein synthesis with rabbit reticulocytes; ID_{50} at concentrations of 0.23 and 0.25μg/ml by NT-1 and NT-2, respectively. These activities were similar to that of neosolaniol (0.25μg/ml) in the same assay.

Spectral Data

IR:

(KBr) 3380, 2960, 1720, 1370, 1240, and 1025cm^{-1}.

^{1}H NMR:

($CDCl_3$) 3.64(1H, d, *J*=4.9Hz, H-2); 4.17(1H, dd, *J*=4.9, 3.0Hz, H-3); 4.94(1H, d, *J*=3.0Hz, H-4); 2.06(1H, dt, *J*=14.3, 1.6Hz, αH-7); 2.19(1H, dd, *J*=14.3, 5.2Hz, βH-7); 4.12(1H, m, H-8); 5.65(1H, dq, *J*=5.8, 1.5Hz, H-10); 3.88(1H, d, *J*=5.8Hz, H-11);

2.79(1H, d, *J*=4.0Hz, H-13); 3.02(1H, d, *J*=4.0Hz, H-13); 0.89(3H,s, CH_3-14); 3.48(1H, d, *J*=12.6Hz, H-15); 3.76(1H, d, *J*=12.6Hz, H-15); 1.85(3H, br s, CH_3-16); and 2.13 ppm (3H, s, CH_3COO-).

^{13}C NMR:

78.7, C-2; 78.3, C-3; 84.9, C-4; 49.1, C-5; 44.9, C-6; 27.9, C-7; 66.8, C-8; 139.0, C-9; 122.0, C-10; 68.5, C-11; 64.4, C-12; 47.0, C-13; 7.0, C-14; 62.2, C-15; 20.59, C-16; 21.0, CH_3COO-; and 172.8ppm, 3H, $CH_3\underline{C}OO$-.

Mass Data:

LREIMS: 340*m/e* (M^+); found: C, 60.04; H, 7.10; O, 32.86%; calcd for $C_{17}H_{24}O_7$; C, 59.97; H, 7.11; O, 32.92%.

References

K. Ishii and Y. Ueno; Isolation and Characterization of Two New Trichothecenes from *Fusarium sporotrichioides* Strain M-1-1; Applied and Environmental Microbiology, Vol. 42, pp. 541-543(1981).

M. E. Savard and B. A. Blackwell; A Compilation of Spectral Characteristics of Secondary Metabolites from *Fusarium* Fungi; In Mycotoxins in Grain; Compounds Other Than Aflatoxin; J. D. Miller and H. L. Trenholm, eds., Eagan Press, St. Paul, pp. 59-257 (1994).

A. Visconti, C. J. Mirocha, A. Logrieco, A. Bottalico and M. Solfrizzo; Mycotoxins Produced by *Fusarium acuminatum*: A New Trichothecene; J. Agric. Food Chem., Vol. 37, pp. 1348-1351(1989).

Common/Systematic Name

4-Deacetylneosolaniol

3α,4β,8α-Trihydroxy-15-acetoxy-12,13-epoxytrichothec-9-ene

Molecular Formula/Molecular Weight

$C_{17}H_{24}O_7$; MW = 340.15220

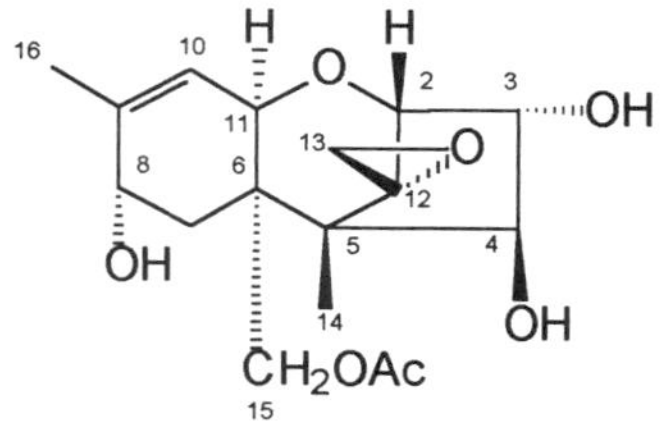

Fungal Source

Fusarium acuminatum misidentified as *F. heterosporum*. The *F. acuminatum* was isolated from *Claviceps paspali* honey dew on *Paspalum distichum*.

Isolation/Purification

Fungal cultures were extracted with chloroform; the crude chloroform extract was chromatographed on a column containing silica gel eluted with toluene, ethyl ether, ethyl acetate, acetone, and methanol. The acetone fraction was further purified on a silica gel column eluted with a linear gradient from ethyl acetate to acetone. The 15-acetoxy T-2 triol-containing fractions were combined, reduced in volume and final purification was on a C_{18} reversed-phase column eluted with a linear gradient from 50% acetonitrile to water.

Biological Activity

The toxin was inhibitory in the wheat coleoptile assay down to10^{-3} M; ED_{50} values for dermal toxicity on back skin of rabbits was >1.28μg compared to < 0.16μg for T-2 toxin in the same assay. The LD_{50} value for day-old chicks dosed orally was > 10mg/kg.

Spectral Data

UV:

End absorption.

^{1}H NMR:

($CDCl_3$) 3.24(1H, J=4.9Hz, H-2); 3.89(1H, H-3); 4.06(1H, H-4); 2.06(2H, H-7); 5.19(1H, H-8); 5.40(1H, H-10); 4.03(1H, H-11); 2.84(1H, J=4.1Hz, H-13); 2.61(1H, J=4.1Hz, H-13); 0.67(3H, s, CH_3-14); 3.89, 4.03(2H, H-15); 1.72(3H, s, CH_3-16); and 1.97ppm (3H, s, CH_3COO).

^{13}C NMR:

($CDCl_3$) 78.48, d, C-2; 79.01, d, C-3; 79.49, d, C-4; 47.86, s, C-5; 42.57, s, C-6; 30.09, t, C-7; 64.82, d, C-8; 138.93, s, C-9; 120.38, d, C-10; 66.65, d, C-11; 64.61, s, C-12; 45.58, t, C-13; 6.78, q, C-14; 64.61, t, C-15; 20.34, q, C-16; 20.82, q, $\underline{C}H_3COO$) and 169,60ppm, s, $CH_3\underline{C}OO$.

Mass Spectrum:
EIMS: 340(M^+), 322, 203, 175, and 121*m/e* (base peak).

Reference

R. J. Cole, J. W. Dorner, R. H. Cox, B. M. Cunfer, H. G. Cutler, and B. P. Stuart; The Isolation and Identification of Several Trichothecene Mycotoxins from *Fusarium heterosporum*; J. Nat. Prod., Vol. 44, pp. 321-330(1981).

Common/Systematic Name
Sporotrichiol

Molecular Formula/Molecular Weight
$C_{20}H_{30}O_6$; MW = 366.20424

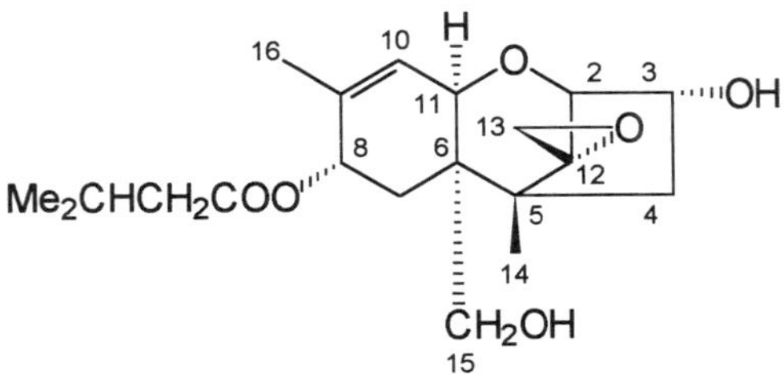

General Characteristics
Isolated as an oil.

Fungal Source
Fusarium sporotrichioides (MC-72083).

Isolation/Purification
Fungal cultures were extracted with chloroform-acetone (85:15, v/v), followed by Florisil column chromatography eluted with benzene-hexane (2:1, v/v), methylene chloride, and chloroform-methanol (95:5, v/v) to give an oil highly enriched with trichothecenes. The oil was further purified by normal phase preparative HPLC using benzene-acetone followed by preparative RPTLC to yield several trichothecenes including sporol and sporotrichiol.

Spectral Data

IR:
(thin film) 3422(OH) and 1726cm^{-1} (ester).

^{1}H NMR:
($CDCl_3$) 3.49(1H, d, H-2); 4.49(1H, m, H-3); 2.05-2.25(2H, m, H-4); 1.96(1H, d, H-7); 2.30(1H, dd, H-7); 5.50(1H, d, H-8); 5.79(1H, d, H-10); 4.17(1H, d, H-11); 2.57(1H, d, *J*=4.1Hz, H-13); 3.06(1H, d, *J*=4.1Hz, H-13); 0.87(3H, s, CH_3-14); 3.53(1H, d, *J*=12.7Hz, H-15); 3.70(1H, d, *J*=12.7Hz, H-15); 1.75(3H, s, CH_3-16); 2.21(2H, m, H-18); 2.05-2.30(1H, m, H-19); and 0.95ppm (3H each, d, *J*=7.0Hz, CH_3-20 and -21).

^{13}C NMR:
($CDCl_3$) 79.6 C-2; 69.1, C-3; 42.1, C-4; 45.8, C-5; 43.3, C-6; 26.8, C-7; 68.4, C-8; 135.7, C-9; 125.4, C-10; 68.1, C-11; 65.1, C-12; 48.5, C-13; 12.44, C-14; 63.1, C-15; 20.4, C-16; 171.9, C-17; 43.7, C-18, 25.7, C-19; and 22.3ppm, C-20 and C-21.

Mass Spectrum:
HREIMS: 366.204*m/e*; calcd for $C_{20}H_{30}O_6$, 366.206.

References

D. G. Corley, G. E. Rottinghaus, and M. S. Tempesta; Novel Trichothecenes from *Fusarium sporotrichioides*; Tetrahedron Letters, Vol. 27, pp. 427-430(1986).

M. E. Savard and B. A. Blackwell; A Compilation of Spectral Characteristics of Secondary Metabolites from *Fusarium* Fungi; In Mycotoxins in Grain; Compounds Other Than Aflatoxin; J. D. Miller and H. L. Trenholm, eds., Eagan Press, St. Paul, pp. 59-257 (1994).

Common/Systematic Name

4β,8α,15-Triacetoxy-3α,7α-dihydroxy-12,13-epoxytrichothec-9-ene

Molecular Formula/Molecular Weight

$C_{21}H_{28}O_{10}$; MW = 440.16825

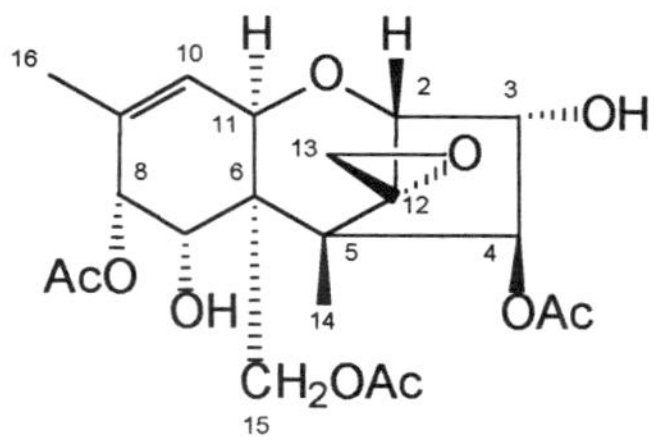

General Characteristics

Crystals; mp., 185-188°C.

Fungal Source

Fusarium equiseti.

Biological Activity

LD_{50} in rats dosed IP was 1.2mg/kg.

Reference

R. J. Cole and R. H. Cox; Handbook of Toxic Fungal Metabolites; Academic Press, New York, p. 200(1981).

Common/Systematic Name

3α-Acetoxy-15-hydroxy-12,13-epoxytrichothec-9-en-8-one

Molecular Formula/Molecular Weight

$C_{17}H_{22}O_6$; MW = 322.14164

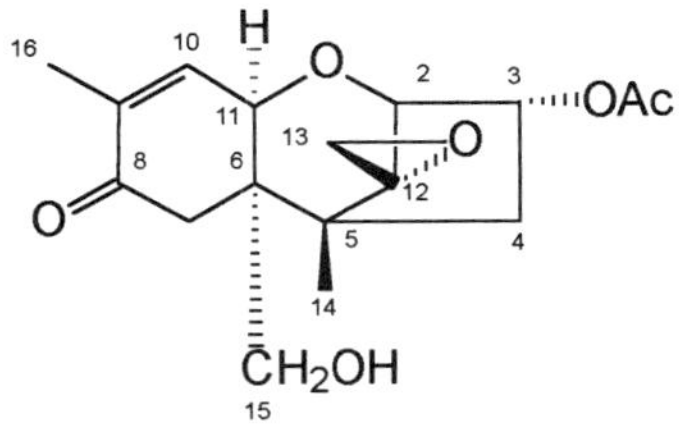

General Characteristics

Colorless needles; mp., 202-203°C; $[\alpha]_D^{26}$ +41.7° (*c*=0.40, in $CHCl_3$).

Fungal Source

Fusarium roseum (ATCC 28114).

Isolation/Purification

Fusarium roseum cultures were harvested and the broth was extracted as described by Greenhalgh *et al.* (1984). Some of the oil from the methanol phase after it had been partitioned and concentrated was dissolved in methylene chloride and passed through a Florisil column eluted with 750ml of (A) methylene chloride, (B) 0.5% methanol in methylene chloride, and (C) 5% methanol in methylene chloride. Fraction A afforded an oil from which 3-acetyldeoxynivalenol was obtained. Fractions B and C also afforded yellow oils. The oil which remained in fraction A after removal of 3-acetyldeoxynivalenol was chromatographed on silica gel (Kieselgel 60). The column was eluted first with 10% toluene in methylene chloride and then with 0.5% methanol in methylene chloride, 1.5% methanol in methylene chloride, 3% methanol in methylene chloride, and finally 13% methanol in methylene chloride. Fractions were collected and monitored by TLC; fractions 6-10, 11-12, 13-17, and 18-20 were combined to give mixtures A1, A2, A3, and A4, respectively. Further purification of mixtures A2 and A3 was accomplished with a Chromatotron (Model No. 7924, Harrison Research, Inc.) with a 2mm silica gel plate (Kieselgel 60). 3α-Acetoxy-15-hydroxy-12,13-epoxytrichothec-9-en-8-one was isolated from mixture A2 by elution with 20% ethyl acetate in hexane followed by rechromatography using the same solvent.

Spectral Data

^1H NMR:

($CDCl_3$) 0.83(3H, H-14); 1.80(3H, H-16, $J_{16,10}$=1.4Hz); 2.12(3H, AC-CH_3); 2.40, 2.17(2H, H-4, J_{ab}=12.8Hz, $J_{4,3}$=4.4Hz); 2.86, 2.42(2H, H-7, J_{ab}=16.8Hz); 2.86,

3.09(2H, H-13, J_{ab}=3.9Hz); 3.64(2H, H-15); 3.81(1H, H-2, $J_{2,3}$=4.6Hz); 4.52(1H, H-11, $J_{11,10}$=5.7Hz); 5.18(1H, H-3, $J_{3,2}$=4.6Hz, $J_{3,4}$=10.2, 4.4Hz); and 6.55 ppm (1H, H-10, $J_{10,11}$=5.7Hz, $J_{10,16}$=1.4Hz).

^{13}C NMR:
($CDCl_3$) 78.1, C-2; 71.2, C-3; 38.5, C-4; 45.0, C-5; 47.5, C-6; 38.3, C-7; 198.7, C-8; 138.3, C-9; 137.7, C-10; 68.2, C-11; 65.3, C-12; 48.3, C-13; 11.2, C-14; 64.1, C-15; 15.3, C-16; 20.9, <u>C</u>H_3COO-; and 170.5ppm, <u>C</u>=O.

Mass Spectrum:
HREIMS: 323.149*m/e* (M^+ + 1); calcd for $C_{17}H_{23}O_6$, 323.150.

References

R. Greenhalgh, R.M. Meier, B. A. Blackwell, J. D. Miller, A. Taylor, and J. W. ApSimon; Minor Metabolites of *Fusarium roseum* (ATCC 28114); J. Agric. Food Chem., Vol. 32, pp. 1261-1264(1984).

D. R. Lauren, A. Ashley, B. A. Blackwell, R. Greenhalgh, J. D. Miller, and G. A. Neish; Trichothecenes Produced by *Fusarium crookwellense* DAOM 193611; J. Agric. Food Chem., Vol. 35, pp. 884-889(1987).

Common/Systematic Name

3-Acetyl-4-deoxynivalenol

3α-Acetoxy-7α,15-dihydroxy-12,13-epoxytrichothec-9-en-8-one

Molecular Formula/Molecular Weight

$C_{17}H_{22}O_7$; MW = 338.13655

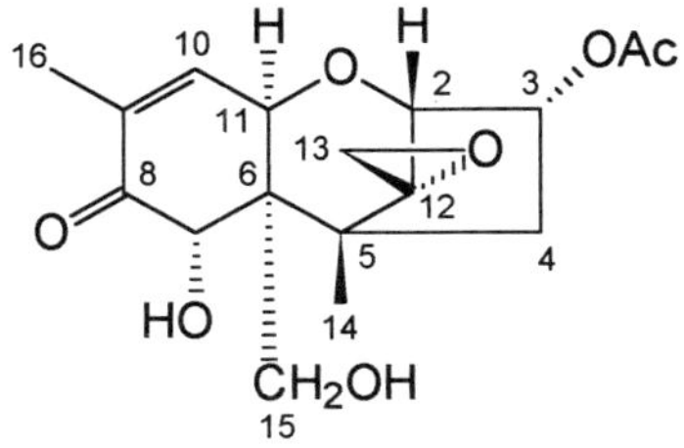

General Characteristics

Colorless needles from ethyl ether-*n*-pentane; mp.,185.5-186°C; $[\alpha]_D^{20}$ + 43.0° (*c*=1.3, in EtOH); $[\alpha]_D^{25}$ + 40.5°; tetracetate; mp., 168-170°C.

Isolation/Purification

Fungal mycelium was extracted with methylene chloride, concentrated and the residue dissolved in methanol. The methanol phase was extracted with petroleum ether and evaporated to dryness. The residue was chromatographed on a silica gel column eluted with chloroform-ethanol (50:1, v/v) and then chloroform-ethanol (400:1, v/v). 3-Acetyl-4-deoxynivalenol was recrystallized from hot ethyl ether.

Fungal Source

Fusarium culmorum (HLX 1503; ATCC 28114), *F. graminearum* (HLX 1506), and *F. roseum.*

Biological Activity

LD_{50} in male ddS strain of mice dosed IP was 76.7mg/kg; females, 49.9mg/kg; ducklings, 37mg/kg. Minimum SC dosage to induce vomiting in ducklings was 10.0 mg/kg; dogs, S.C., 0.2mg/kg. Inhibited *Tetrahymena pyriformis*, 29.0μg/ml.

Spectral Data

UV:

λ_{max}^{EtOH} 219nm (ϵ=5,900).

IR:

(KBr) 3480, 3400, 1720, and 1680cm^{-1}.

Spectral Data

UV:
λ_{max}^{MeOH} 220nm (ϵ=7,100).

IR:
(Nujol) (needles) 3500, 3420, 1740, 1683, and 1668cm^{-1}; (needles or plates) 3480 br, 1750, 1690, 1672, and 1660cm^{-1}.

^{1}H NMR:
($CDCl_3$) 6.10(1H, d, *J*=4.5Hz, H-2); 4.72(1H, m, H-3); ca. 7.75(2H, m, H-4); 5.12(1H, d, *J*=1.5Hz, H-7); 3.36(1H, dd, *J*=5.5, 1.5Hz, H-10); 5.29(1H, d, *J*=5.5Hz, H-11); 6.84(2H, s, H-13); 8.81(1H, s, H-14); 6.14(2H, d, *J*=1.5Hz, H-15); 8.12(3H, s, H-16); 7.90(3H, OAc); and 6.15, 8.0ppm (1H each, OH).

Mass Data:
HREIMS: 338.1360, $C_{17}H_{22}O_7$ requires 338.1365; found: C, 60.4; H, 7.0%; $C_{17}H_{22}O_7$ requires C, 60.35; H, 6.55%.

Reference

M. M. Blight and J. F. Grove; New Metabolic Products of *Fusarium culmorum*: Toxic Trichothec-9-en-8-ones and 2-Acetylquinazolin-4(*3H*)-one; J. C. S. Perkin I, pp. 1691-1693(1974).

Common/Systematic Name

Trichodermol

4β-Hydroxy-12,13-epoxytrichothec-9-ene

Molecular Formula/Molecular Weight

$C_{15}H_{22}O_3$; MW = 250.15689

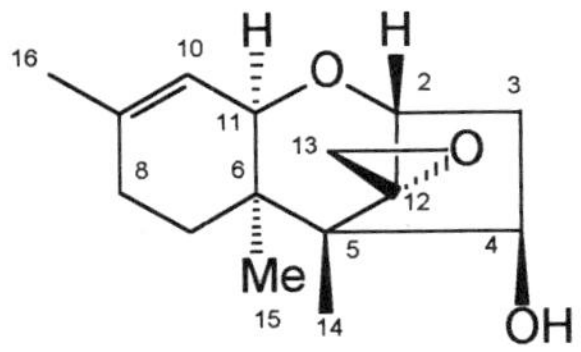

General Characteristics

Needle crystals from light petroleum; mp., 116-119°C; crystals from ether-*n*-hexane; mp., 117.5°-118°C; $[\alpha]_D^{20}$ - 33.5°(*c*=1.0, in $CHCl_3$).

Fungal Source

Myrothecium roridum, Trichoderma polysporum, T. sporulosum, and *Hypocrea austro-grandis.*

Spectral Data

UV:

End absorption.

^1H NMR:

($CDCl_3$) 3.51, H-2; 1.7-2.5, H-3; 4.3, H-4; 1.7-2.5, H-7; 1.7-2.5, H-8; 5.41, H-10; 3.81, H-11; 2.95, H-12; 0.80, H-14; 0.85, H-15; and 1.70ppm, H-16.

^{13}C NMR:

($CDCl_3$) 78.8, C-2; 40.2, C-3; 74.0, C-4; 49.2, C-5; 39.8, C-6; 24.5, C-7; 28.0, C-8; 140.1, C-9; 118.8, C-10; 70.4, C-11; 65.8, C-12; 47.6, C-13; 6.2, C-14; 15.8, C-15; and 23.2ppm, C-16.

Mass Data:

HREIMS: 250.1569($C_{15}H_{22}O_3$), 235.1335($C_{14}H_{19}O_3$), 207.1384($C_{13}H_{19}O_2$), and 188.1200*m/e* ($C_{13}H_{16}O$).

TLC Data

A. Adsorbent: silica gel G. Solvent: chloroform-methanol, 98:2, v/v; R_f, 0.36; detection: H_2SO_4 spraying and heating at 110°C for 5 minutes. B. Adsorbent: alumina. Solvent: chloroform-methanol, 98:2, v/v; R_f, 0.86; detection: H_2SO_4 spraying and heating for 5 minutes.

References

W. A. Ayer and S. Miao; Secondary Metabolites of the Aspen Fungus *Stachybotrys cylindrospora*; Can. J. Chem., Vol. 71, pp. 487-493(1993).

J. R. Hanson, T. Marten, and M. Siverns; Studies in Terpenoid Biosynthesis. Part XII. Carbon-13 Nuclear Magnetic Resonance Spectra of the Trichothecenes and the Biosynthesis of Trichothecolone from [2-^{13}C]Mevalonic Acid; J. Chem. Soc. Perkin I, pp. 1033-1036(1974).

Common/Systematic Name

7α-Hydroxytrichodermol

4β,7α-Dihydroxy-12,13-epoxytrichothec-9-ene

Molecular formulamolecular Weight

$C_{15}H_{22}O_4$; MW = 266.15181

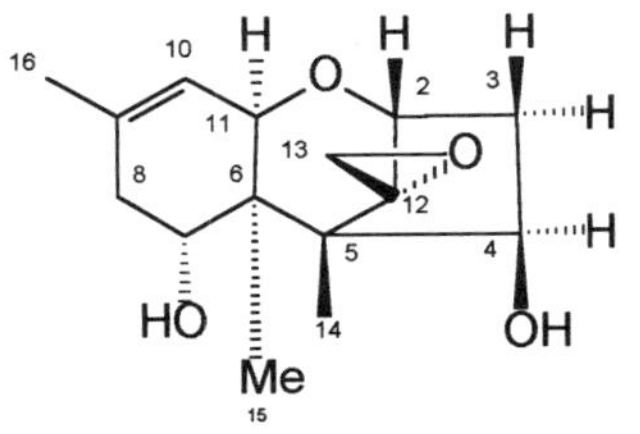

General Characteristics

Amorphous colorless solid; $[\alpha]_D$ = +2.4° (*c*=0.76, in MeOH).

Plant Source

Myrothecium roridum.

Isolation/Purification

An aqueous shake culture of *Myrothecium roridum* (M4582) as filtered through Whatman # 1 filter paper, and the filtrate was extracted three times with ethyl acetate. The mycelia remaining from filtration were soaked in methanol overnight and filtered. The methanol filtrate was concentrated *in vacuo* until only an aqueous phase remained which was extracted three times with ethyl acetate. The ethyl acetate extracts were pooled and concentrated *in vacuo* to yield 4g of gum. The gum was subjected to filtration chromatography (50g of silica gel) with increasing amounts of ethyl acetate in hexane to yield five fractions: 1 (800mg, eluted with hexane), 2 (200mg, eluted with 10% ethyl acetate in hexane), 3 (400mg, eluted with 30% ethyl acetate in hexane), 4 (500mg, eluted with 50 to 70% ethyl acetate in hexane), and 5 (1.5g, eluted with ethyl acetate). Fractions 3 and 4 were subjected to purification on a Chromatotron (2-mm silica gel plates, ethyl acetate-hexane) to yield, after recrystallization (ethyl acetate-hexane), 25mg of trichodermol and 50 mg of 7α-hydroxytrichodermol. 7α-Hydroxytrichodermol also was isolated from rice culture: *ca.* 200mg/kg of rice.

Spectral Data

^{1}H NMR:

($CDCl_3$) 0.86(3H, s, H-14); 1.09(3H, s, H-15); 1.69(3H, s, H-16); 1.8 to 2.1(2H, m, H-3β and H-8β); 2.24(1H, dd, *J*=12.6 and 6.0Hz, H-8α); 3.06 and 3.1 0(1H each, AB, *J*=4.3 Hz, H-13); 3.61(1H, d, *J*=5.5Hz, H-11); 3.82(1H, d, *J*=5.0Hz, H-2); 4.26(1H, dd, *J*=7.6 and 4.0Hz, H-4); 4.46(1H, dd, *J*=12.0 and 6.0Hz, H-7); and 5.36ppm (1H, br d, *J*=5Hz, H-10).

Mass Spectrum:
HREIMS: 266.1526*m/e* found for $C_{15}H_{22}O_4$; calcd 266.1512.

Reference

B. B. Jarvis, Y.-W. Lee, C. S. Yatawara, D. B. Mazzocchi, J. L. Flippen-Anderson, R. Gilardi, and C. George; 7α-Hydroxytrichodermol, A New Trichothecene from *Myrothecium* roridum; Appl. Environ. Microbiol., Vol. 50, pp. 225-228(1985).

Common/Systematic Name

Verrucarol

4β,15-Dihydroxy-12,13-epoxytrichothec-9-ene

Molecular Formula/Molecular Weight

$C_{15}H_{22}O_4$; MW = 266.15181

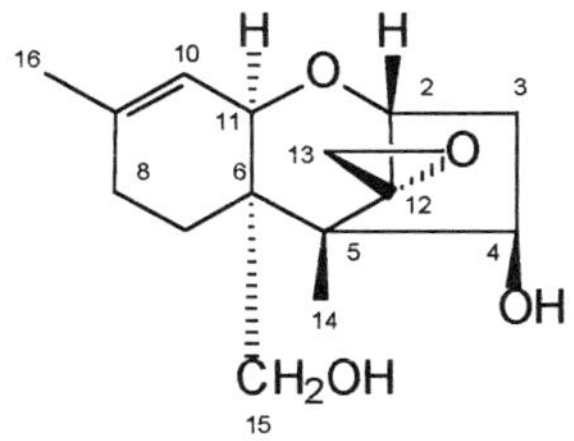

General Characteristics

Crystals from ether-methylene chloride; mp., 158-159°C; fine needles from acetone-ether; mp., 155-156°C; $[\alpha]_D^{22}$ -39° (*c*=1.069, in $CHCl_3$). Di-*O*-acetylverrucarol, colorless needles from acetone-ether-petroleum ether; mp., 148-150°C; $[\alpha]_D^{25}$ -17° (*c*=1.22, in $CHCl_3$). Di-*O*-benzoylverrucarol, crystals from ether-petroleum ether; mp., 151-152°C; $[\alpha]_D^{24}$ - 64° (*c*=1.130, in acetone). Dihydroverrucarol, crystals from acetone-ether-petroleum ether; mp., 149-151°C; $[\alpha]_D^{25}$ - 6° (*c*=1.101, in $CHCl_3$).

Fungal Source

Formed as one of the products of alkaline hydrolysis of verrucarin A which is produced by *Myrothecium verrucaria*.

Spectral Data

UV:

λ_{max}^{EtOH} 195nm (ε=7,900).

IR:

(CH_2Cl_2) 3610, 3570, 1675, 1380, 1335, 1079, 1045, 965, and 820cm^{-1}.

^{1}H NMR:

3.70, H-2; 1.7-2.5, H-3; 4.7, H-4; 1.7-2.5, H-7; 1.7-2.5, H-8; 5.45, H-10; 3.80, H-11; 2.95, H-12; 0.92, H-14; 3.70, H-15; and 1.72ppm, H-16.

^{13}C NMR:

78.5, C-2; 39.5, C-3; 74.0, C-4; 48.7, C-5; 43.7, C-6; 20.9, C-7; 28.0, C-8; 140.4, C-9; 118.7, C-10; 66.4, C-11; 65.6, C-12; 47.4, C-13; 6.8, C-14; 62.1, C-15; and 22.9ppm, C-16.

TLC Data

A. Adsorbent: silica gel G. Solvent: chloroform-methanol (98:2, v/v); R_f, 0.06; detection: H_2SO_4 spraying and heating at 110°C for 5 minutes. B. Adsorbent: alumina. Solvent: chloroform-methanol (98:2, v/v); R_f, 0.34; detection: H_2SO_4 spraying and heating at 110°C for 5 minutes.

References

J. Gutzwiller and C. Tamm; Uber die Verrucarine und Roridine. Struktur von Verrucarol; Helv. Chim. Acta, Vol. 46, pp. 1786-1790(1963).

J. Gutzwiller and C. Tamm; Uber die Struktur von Verrucarin A; Helv. Chim. Acta, Vol. 48, pp. 157-176(1965).

Common/Systematic Name

4,15-Diacetylverrucarol

4β,15-Diacetoxy-12,13-epoxytrichothec-9-ene

Molecular Formula/Molecular Weight

$C_{19}H_{26}O_6$; MW = 350.17294

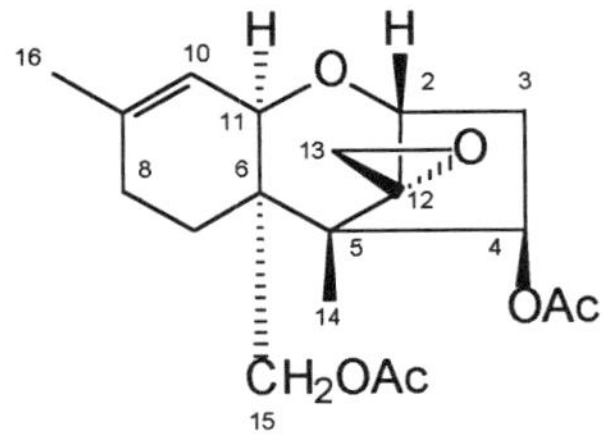

General Characteristics

White prisms from benzene-methanol; mp., 147-148°C; $[\alpha]_D^{25}$ - 14° (*c*=1.01, in MeOH). Readily soluble in most organic solvents such as methanol, acetone, chloroform, ether, and benzene; sparingly soluble in hexane and petroleum ether.

Fungal Source

Myrothecium spp.

Biological Activity

Antifungal activity against *Trichophyton asteroides* (ED_{50}, 0.1μg/ml) and *T. interdigitale* (ED_{50}, 10μg/ml).

Spectral Data

^{1}H NMR:

($CDCl_3$) 3.80(H-2); NR(H-3); 3.24(H-4); NR(H-7); NR(H-8); 5.39(H-10); 3.75(H-11); 2.79(H-13α); 3.09(H-13β); 0.79(H-14); 4.05(H-15α); 4.15(H-15β); and 1.70ppm (H-16).

^{13}C NMR:

($CDCl_3$) 79.0, C-2; 36.7, C-3; 75.4, C-4; 48.9, C-5; 43.4, C-6; 21.4, C-7; 28.1, C-8; 138.7, C-9; 119.7, C-10; 66.8, C-11; 65.2, C-12; 47.3, C-13; 6.8, C-14; 63.7, C-15; 23.0, C-16; 20.2; 2 each $\underline{C}H_3CO$; and 169.6, 169ppm $CH_3\underline{C}O$.

References

R. J. Cole and R. H. Cox; Handbook of Toxic Fungal Metabolites; Academic Press, New York, p. 189 (1981).

M. Okuchi, M. Itoh, Y. Kaneko, and S. Doi; A New Antifungal Substance Produced by *Myrothecium*; J. Agric. Biol. Chem. Jpn., Vol. 32, pp. 394(1968).

Common/Systematic Name

Crotocin; Antibiotic T

Molecular Formula/Molecular Weight

$C_{19}H_{24}O_5$; MW = 332.16237

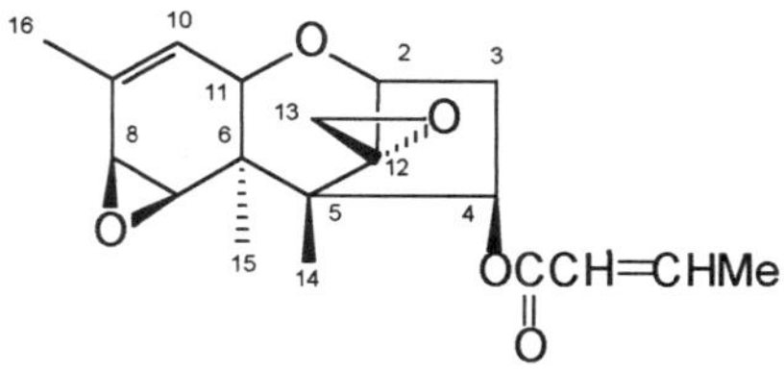

General Characteristics

Colorless prisms from methanol; mp., 126-128°C; needles from ether-benzene; mp., 116-118°C; $[\alpha]_D^{25}$ + 7.17° (*c*=3.98, in $CHCl_3$).

Fungal Source

Cephalosporium crotocinigenum and *Trichothecium roseum*.

Biological Activity

LD_{50} of crotocin in mice dosed IV was 700mg/kg; fungistatic; negligible antitumor activity.

Spectral Data

UV:

λ_{max} 211(ϵ=21,800) and 209nm.

IR:

1710 and 1640cm^{-1}.

^{13}C NMR:

($CDCl_3$) 74.3, C-2; 36.2, C-3; 78.5, C-4; 47.7, C-5; 41.3, C-6; 58.1, C-7; 50.4, C-8; 137.2, C-9; 122.9, C-10; 69.4, C-11; 65.9, C-12; 46.8, C-13; 6.2, C-14; 15.9, C-15; 21.0, C-16; 166.4, C-17; 120.2, C-18; 146.5, C-19; and 14.8ppm, C-20.

TLC Data

Adsorbent, silica gel; solvent, ethanol-ethyl acetate-acetone, 1:4:4, v/v/v; R_f, 0.67; detection: 50% H_2SO_4 spraying and heating at 110°C for 5 minutes.

References

B. A. Achilladelis and J. R. Hanson; Minor Terpenoids of *Trichothecium roseum*; Phytochemistry, Vol. 8, p. 765 (1969).

R. J. Cole and R. H. Cox; Handbook of Toxic Fungal Metabolites; Academic Press, New York, p. 195 (1981).

J. Gyimesi and A. Melera; On the Structure of Crotocin, an Antifungal Antibiotic; Tetrahedron Letters, p. 1665 (1967).

Common/Systematic Name
Crotocol
4β-Hydroxy-7,8,12,13-diepoxytrichothec-9-ene

Molecular Formula/Molecular Weight
$C_{15}H_{20}O_4$; MW = 264.13616

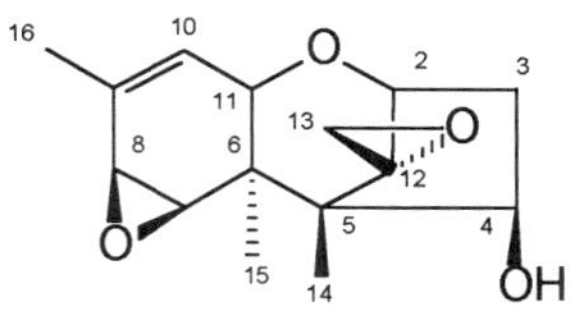

General Characteristics
Crystals; mp., 154°C; $[\alpha]_D^{20}$ - 6.4° (*c*=2.01, in $CHCl_3$); acetate derivative; mp., 128°C.

Fungal Source
Formed upon mild alkaline hydrolysis of crotocin.

Spectral Data

UV:
λ_{max} 210nm (ϵ=4,830).

TLC Data
Adsorbent: silica gel; solvent, ethanol-ethyl acetate-acetone, 1:4:4, v/v/v; R_f, 0.50; detection: 50% H_2SO_4 spraying and heating at 110°C for 5 minutes.

References
R. J. Cole and R. H. Cox; Handbook of Toxic Fungal Metabolites; Academic Press, New York, p. 196 (1981).

J. Gyimesi and A. Melera; On the Structure of Crotocin an Antifungal Antibotic; Tetrahedron Letters, p. 1665 (1967).

Common/Systematic Name

Trichothecolone

4β-Hydroxy-12,13-epoxytrichothec-9-en-8-one

Molecular Formula/Molecular Weight

$C_{15}H_{20}O_4$; MW = 264.13616

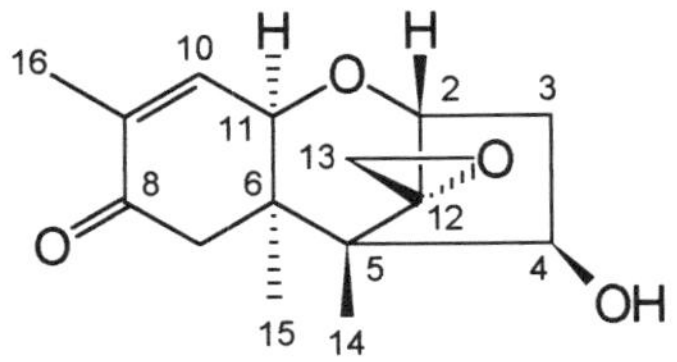

General Characteristics

Colorless needles from benzene-light petroleum; mp., 183-184°C; $[\alpha]_D^{19.5}$ + 22.5° (*c*=1.0, in $CHCl_3$); $[\alpha]_D^{8}$ + 17.0° (*c*=1.0, in EtOH). Acetyl derivative, prisms from methanol; mp., 148-149°C; 2,4-dinitrophenylhydrazone, deep orange rods from chloroform-ethanol; mp., 261-262°C.

Fungal Source

Fusarium roseum and *Trichothecium roseum*. Also, hydrolysis product of trichothecin.

Spectral Data

UV:

λ_{max}^{MeOH} 226nm (ε=8,000); acetate derivative: λ_{max}^{MeOH} 227nm (ε=8,000).

IR:

3560 and 1680cm^{-1}.

^{1}H NMR:

($CDCl_3$) 3.90(1H, H-2); 1.93(1H, H-3); 2.43(1H, H-3); 4.35(1H, H-4); 6.49(1H, H-10); 3.94(1H, H-11); 2.81, 3.12(2H, H-13); 1.00(3H, CH_3-15); and 1.80ppm (3H, s, CH_3-16).

^{13}C NMR:

70.2, C-2; 40.2, C-3; 79.6, C-4; 49.5, C-5; 43.6, C-6; 42.3, C-7; 199.4, C-8; 138.5, C-9; 137.7, C-10; 73.1, C-11; 66.0, C-12; 47.3, C-13; 6.2, C-14; 15.6, CH_3-15; and 18.5ppm, CH_3-16.

References

R. J. Cole and R. H. Cox; Handbook of Toxic Fungal Metabolites; Academic Press, New York, p. 222 (1981).

M. E. Savard and B. A. Blackwell; A. Compilation of Spectral Characteristics of Secondary Metabolites from *Fusarium* Fungi; In Mycotoxins in Grain; Compounds Other Than Aflatoxin; J. D. Miller and H. L. Trenholm, eds., Eagan Press, St. Paul, pp. 59-257 (1994).

Common/Systematic Name

Trichothecin

4β-Crotonoyloxy-12,13-epoxytrichothec-9-en-8-one

Molecular Formula/Molecular Weight

$C_{19}H_{24}O_5$; MW = 332.16237

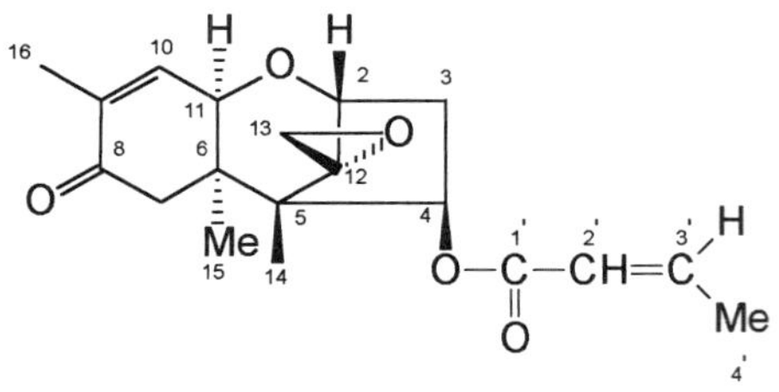

General Characteristics

Crystals; mp., 118°C; $[\alpha]_D^{10}$ + 44° (*c*=1.0, in $CHCl_3$).

Fungal Source

Fusarium roseum.

Biological Activity

LD_{50} in mice dosed IV was ~300mg/kg; ID_{50} of protein synthesis in rabbit reticulocytes (whole cell) was 0.15μg/ml. Inhibited the elongation or termination steps in protein synthesis on polyribosomes.

Spectral Data

UV:

λ_{max}^{MeOH} 215nm (ϵ=19,000).

^{1}H NMR:

3.95(1H, H-2); 2.0-2.5(2H, H-3); 5.70(1H, H-4); 2.0-2.5(2H, H-7); 6.50(1H, H-10); 3.95(1H, H-11); 2.80(1H, H-13a); 3.10(1H, H-13b); 1.05(3H, H-14); 0.80(3H, H=15); 1.80(3H, H-16); 5.80(1H, H-2'); 6.30(1H, H-3'); and 2.10ppm (3H, H-4').

^{13}C NMR:

($CDCl_3$) 73.3, d, C-2; 36.9, t, C-3; 79.5, d, C-4; 49.0, s, C-5; 43.7, s, C-6; 42.1, t, C-7; 198.5, s, C-8; 138.1, s, C-9; 137.0, d, C-10; 1,70.1, d, C-11; 65.4, s, C-12; 47.4, t, C-13; 5.7, q, C-14; 15.4, q, C-15; 18.5, q, C-16; 166.1, s, C-1'; 120.3, d, C-2'; 145.9, d, C-3'; and 15.4ppm, q, C-4'.

<u>TLC Data</u>

A. Adsorbent, silica gel G; solvent, chloroform-methanol, 98:2, v/v; R_f, 0.66; detection: H_2SO_4 spraying and heating at 110°C for 5 minutes. B. Adsorbent, silica gel G; solvent, benzene-tetrahydrofuran, 85:15, v/v; R_f, 0.53; detection, H_2SO_4 spraying and heating at 110°C for 5 minutes.

<u>GLC Data</u>

Support, Shimalite W; liquid phase, OV-17 (1.5%); retention time: 8.55min.; relative retention time (relative to nivalenol): 2.40 minutes.

<u>Reference</u>

R. J. Cole and R. H. Cox; <u>Handbook of Toxic Fungal Metabolites</u>; Academic Press, New York, p. 217(1981).

Common/Systematic Name

Trichothecinol A

Molecular Formula/Molecular Weight

$C_{19}H_{24}O_6$; MW = 348.15729

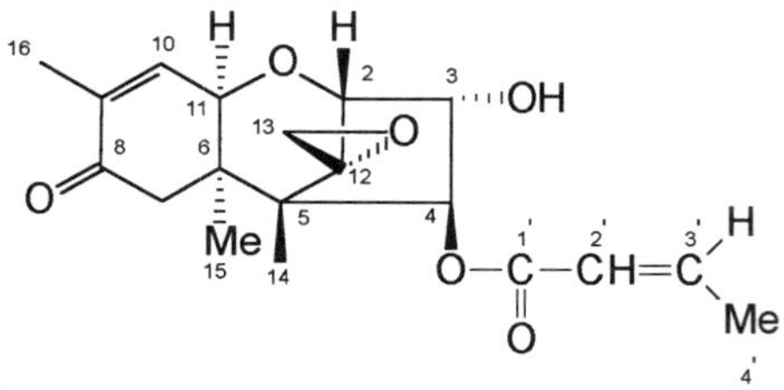

General Characteristics

$[\alpha]_D^{18}$ +81.5° (*c*=0.70, in MeOH).

Fungal Source

Trichothecium roseum (TMI-32358 Supplied from the Tottori Mycological Institute; Tottori, Japan).

Biological Activity

Trichothecinol A was quite a potent antitumor promoter on Epstein-Barr virus early antigen activation induced by the tumor promoter 12-*O*-tetradecanoylphorbol13-acetate in Raji cells in comparison with β-carotene.

Spectral Data

UV:

λ_{max}^{MeOH} 218nm (ϵ=1.4 x 10^4).

IR:

($CHCl_3$) 3450, 1720, and 1680 cm^{-1}.

^1H NMR:

($CDCl_3$) 3.78(d, *J*=5.0Hz, H-2); 4.29(ddd, *J*=2.6, 3.0, 5.0Hz, H-30); 4.99(d, *J*=3.0Hz, H-4); 2.31(dd, *J*=1.6, 15.2Hz, H-7α); 2.95(dd, *J*=1.2, 15.2Hz, H-7β); 6.595(dq, *J*=1.4, 5.8Hz, H-10); 4.41(dd, *J*=0.8, 5.8Hz, H-11); 2.81(d, *J*=3.9Hz, H-13 *pro-R*); 3.08(d, *J*=3.9Hz, H-13 *pro*-S); 0.77(s, 5-Me); 1.05(d, *J*=1.2Hz, 6-Me); 1.84(dd, *J*=0.8, 1.4Hz, 9-Me); 3.50(d, *J*=2.6Hz, 3-OH); 5.88(dq, *J*=1.8, 11.5Hz, H-2'); 6.45(dq, *J*=7.3, 11.5Hz, H-3'); and 2.17ppm (dd, *J*=1.8, 7.3Hz, 3'-Me).

^{13}C NMR:

($CDCl_3$) 79.30(d, C-2); 78.77(d, C-3); 83.17(d, C-4); 48.87(s, C-5); 44.39(s, C-6); 42.03(t, C-7); 198.46(s, C-8); 137.77(s, C-9); 137.24(d, C-10); 70.97(d, C-11); 64.50(s, C-12); 46.63(t, C-13); 5.90(q, C-14); 18.40(q, C-15); 15.33(q, C-16);

167.81(s, C-l'); 119.89(d, C-2'); 147.05(d, C-3'); and 15.57ppm (q, C-4').

Mass Spectrum:
HR-CIMS: 349.1656*m/e*; MH^+; calcd mass, 349.1651.

Reference

A. Iida, K. Konishi, H. Kubo, K. Tomioka, H. Tokuda, and H. Nishino; Trichothecinols A, B, C, Potent anti-Tumor Promoting Sesquiterpenoids from the Fungus *Trichothecium roseum*; Tetrahedron Letters, Vol. 37, pp-9219-9220.

Common/Systematic Name
Trichothecinol B

Molecular Formula/Molecular Weight
$C_{19}H_{26}O_5$; MW = 334.17802

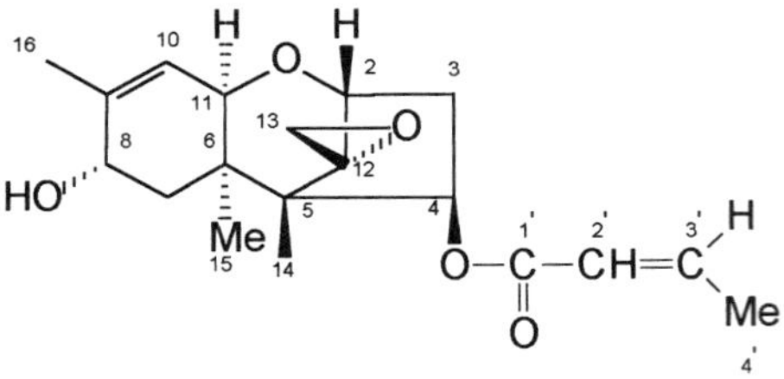

General Characteristics
$[\alpha]_D^{19}$ -14.1° (c=0.10, in MeOH).

Fungal Source
Trichothecium roseum (TMI-32358 Supplied from the Tottori Mycological Institute; Tottori, Japan).

Biological Activity
Trichothecinol B was quite a potent antitumor promoter on Epstein-Barr virus early antigen activation induced by the tumor promoter 12-*O*-tetradecanoylphorbol 13-acetate in Raji cells in comparison with β-carotene.

Spectral Data
UV:
λ_{max}^{MeOH} 210nm (ϵ=1.5 x 10^4).

IR:
(neat) 3450 and 1720cm^{-1}.

^{1}H NMR:
($CDCl_3$) 2.58 (dd, J=7.8, 15.5Hz, H-3α); 2.04 (ddd, J=3.6, 5.2, 15.5Hz, H-3β); 4.15 (d, J=5.8Hz, H-3β). Compare spectrum with trichothecinol A.

^{13}C NMR:
($CDCl_3$) 36.91 (t, C-3) and 67.83ppm (d, C-8). Compare spectrum with trichothecinol A.

Mass Spectrum:
HR-CIMS: 335.1859m/e; MH$^+$, calcd mass, 335.1858.

Reference

A. Iida, K. Konishi, H. Kubo, K. Tomioka, H. Tokuda, and H. Nishino; Trichothecinols A, B, C, Potent Anti-Tumor Promoting Sesquiterpenoids from the Fungus *Trichothecium roseum*; Tetrahedron Letters, Vol. 37, pp-9219-9220, 1996.

Common/Systematic Name

Trichothecinol C

Molecular Formula/Molecular Weight

$C_{19}H_{26}O_6$; MW = 350.17294

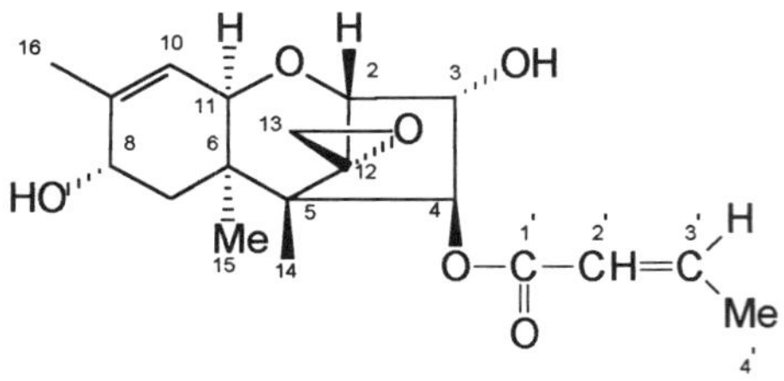

General Characteristics

$[\alpha]_D^{18}$ +28.8° (*c*=0.2, in MeOH).

Fungal Source

Trichothecium roseum (TMI-32358 Supplied from the Tottori Mycological Institute; Tottori, Japan).

Biological Activity

Trichothecinol C was quite a potent anti-tumor promoter on Epstein-Barr virus early antigen activation induced by the tumor promoter 12-*O*-tetradecanoylphorbol 13-acetate in Raji cells in comparison with β-carotene.

Spectral Data

UV:

λ_{max}^{MeOH} 211nm (ϵ= 1.2 x 10^4).

IR:

($CHCl_3$) 3420 and 1705cm^{-1}.

^{1}H NMR:

($CDCl_3$) 4.22(ddd, *J*=2.7, 3.0, 4.9Hz, H-3β); and 4.13ppm (d, *J*=4.9Hz, H-8β). Compare spectrum with trichothecinol A.

^{13}C NMR:

($CDCl_3$) 78.81(d, C-3) and 67.73ppm (d, C-8). Compare spectrum with trichothecinol A.

Mass Spectrum:

HR-CIMS: 351.1805*m/e*; MH$^+$, calcd mass, 351.1807.

Reference

A. Iida, K. Konishi, H. Kubo, K. Tomioka, H. Tokuda, and H. Nishino; Trichothecinols A, B, C, Potent anti-Tumor Promoting Sesquiterpenoids from the Fungus *Trichothecium roseum*; Tetrahedron Letters, Vol. 37, pp-9219-9220 (1996).

Common/Systematic Name

Trichodermone
4-Keto-12,13-epoxytrichothec-9-ene

Molecular Formula/Molecular Weight

$C_{15}H_{20}O_3$; MW = 248.14124

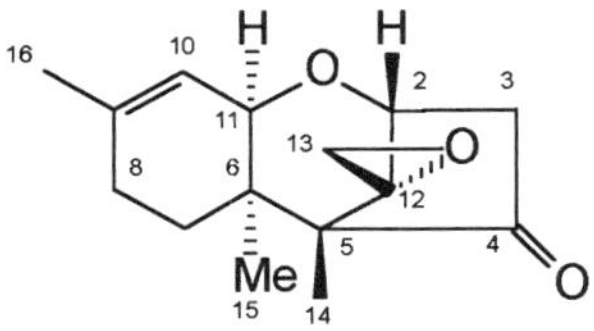

General Characteristics

Crystals from ether-hexane; mp., 154-155°C; $[\alpha]_D^{20}$ - 42.3° (*c*=1.0, in $CHCl_3$).

Fungal Source

Obtained from the oxidation of trichodermin.

Spectral Data

UV:

λ_{max}^{EtOH} 205nm (ϵ=2,800).

IR:

(KBr) 1735cm^{-1}.

^{1}H NMR:

($CDCl_3$) 4.22(1H, H-2); 2.80(2H, H-3); 2.01(2H, H-7); 2.01(2H, H-8); 5.41(1H, H-10); 4.38(1H, H-11); 3.15(2H, H-13); 0.84(3H, CH_3-14); 0.39(3H,CH_3-15); and 1.70ppm (3H, s, CH_3-16).

^{13}C NMR:

76.2, C-2; 42.0, C-3; 214.9, C-4; 55.3, C-5; 42.7, C-6; 23.9, C-7; 27.9, C-8; 140.9, C-9; 118.7, C-10; 71.4, C-11; 65.3, C-12; 50.1, C-13; 5.4, C-14; 15.4, C-15; and 23.4ppm, C-16.

Reference

R. J. Cole and R. H. Cox; Handbook of Toxic Fungal Metabolites; Academic Press, New York, p. 224(1981).

Common/Systematic Name

Nivalenol

3α,4β,7α,15-Tetrahydroxy-12,13-epoxytrichothec-9-en-8-one

Molecular Formula/Molecular Weight

$C_{15}H_{20}O_7$; MW = 312.12090

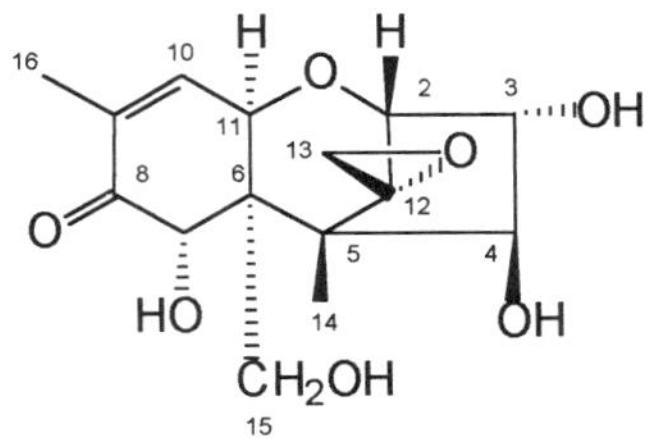

General Characteristics

Crystals from methanol; mp., 80-90°C; dried in presence of P_2O_5 in reduced pressure; mp., 222-223°C (dec.); $[\alpha]_D^{24}$ + 21.54° (*c*=1.3, in EtOH); tetraacetate; mp., 168-170°C.

Fungal Source

Fusarium nivale (Fn-2B) = *F. sporotrichioides, F. graminearum,* and *F. crookwellense.*

Biological Activity

LD_{50} in mice dosed IP was 50μg/g (injured proliferating cells) and in chick embryo, 4.0μg/egg. Minimum SC dosage to induce vomiting in ducklings was 1.0 mg/kg. 1-10μg/ml inhibited uptake of [^{14}C]leucine and [^{14}C]thymidine into protein and DNA in Ehrlich ascites tumor cells. However, uptake of [^{14}C]uracil into RNA was not affected. Inhibition of protein synthesis occurred before inhibition of DNA synthesis. It inhibited the initiation step of protein synthesis on polyribosomes. ID_{50} in rabbit reticulocytes was 3.0μg/ml (whole cell); 0.5μg/ml (cell free); rat liver was 8.0μg/ml (whole cell); and tumor cell was 6.0μg/ml (whole cell). Dermally toxic in rabbit and guinea pig. Emetic to laboratory animals; in ducklings emetic at 1mg/kg (S.C.). Caused cell degeneration of bone marrow, lymph nodes, intestines, testes and thymus.

Spectral Data

UV:

λ_{max}^{MeOH} 218nm (ε=7,500); tetraacetate, 227nm (ε=7,900).

^{1}H NMR:

($CDCl_3$) 3.61(1H, d, *J*=4.8Hz, H-2); 4.14(1H, dd, *J*=4.8, 3.4Hz, H-3); 4.43(2H, d, *J*=3.4Hz, H-4); 4.81(1H, s, H-7); 6.57(1H, dd, *J*=6.0, 1.5Hz, H-10); 4.72(1H, d, *J*=6.0Hz, H-11); 3.01(1H, d, *J*=4.4Hz, H-13); 2.97(1H, d, *J*=4.4Hz, H-13); 1.08(3H, s, CH_3-14); 3.74, 3.79(2H, d, *J*=12.1Hz, CH_2OH-15); and 1.84ppm (3H, d, *J*=1.5Hz, CH_3-16).

^{13}C NMR:

81.6, C-2; 81.3, C-3; 80.8, C-4; 50.6, C-5; 54.5, C-6; 75.1, C-7; 201.5, C-8; 137.1, C-9; 139.2, C-10; 71.0, C-11; 66.0, C-12; 46.3, C-13; 8.3, C-14; 61.5, C-15; and 15.2ppm, CH_3-16.

TLC Data

A: Adsorbent, Kieselgel G; solvent, chloroform-methanol, 5:1 v/v; R_f, 0.45; detection, brown color after H_2SO_4 spraying and heating at 110°C for 5 minutes. B: Adsorbent, silica gel G; solvent, ethyl acetate-toluene, 3:1 v/v; R_f, 0.09; detection; brown color after H_2SO_4 spraying and heating at 110°C for 5 minutes.

GLC Data

Support, Shimalite W; liquid phase, OV-17 (1.5%); retention time, 3.55 minutes.

References

R. J. Cole and R. H. Cox; Handbook of Toxic Fungal Metabolites; Academic Press, New York, pp. 206-207(1981).

M. E. Savard and B. A. Blackwell; A Compilation of Spectral Characteristics of Secondary Metabolites from *Fusarium* Fungi; In Mycotoxins in Grain; Compounds Other Than Aflatoxin; J. D. Miller and H. L. Trenholm, eds., Eagan Press, St. Paul, pp. 59-257 (1994).

R. F. Vesonder and P. Golinski; Metabolites of *Fusarium*; In Fusarium Mycotoxins, Taxonomy and Pathogenicity; J. Chelkowski, ed.; Elsevier Pub. Co., New York, pp. 13-23(1989).

Common/Systematic Name

4-Deoxynivalenol; Rd Toxin; Vomitoxin

3α,7α,15-Trihydroxy-12,13-epoxytrichothec-9-en-8-one

Molecular Formula/Molecular Weight

$C_{15}H_{20}O_6$; MW = 296.12599

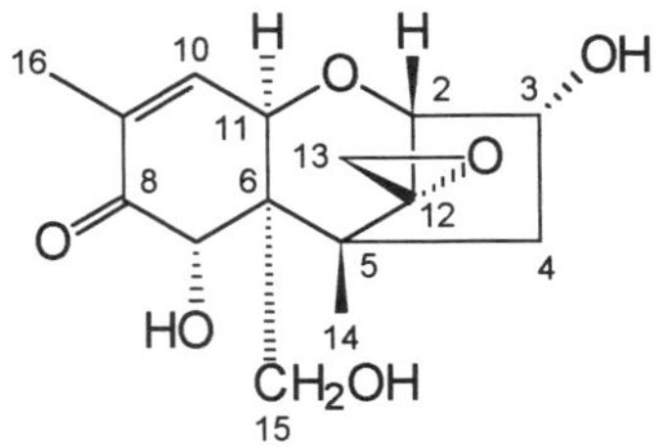

General Characteristics

Needles from ethyl acetate-petroleum ether; mp., 151-153°C and 176-178°C (bound water); semicarbazone derivative; mp., 199-201°C; triacetate, colorless needles from ethyl acetate-petroleum ether; mp., 155-157°C; $[\alpha]_D^{25}$ + 6.35° (*c*=0.07, in EtOH).

Fungal Source

Fusarium graminearum, F. culmorum, and *F. roseum.*

Isolation/Purification

Contaminated corn was extracted with aqueous methanol, concentrated and allowed to sit for 4 hours at 4°C. The supernatant liquid was recovered, and basic and acidic components were removed from the neutral components. The neutral material was chromatographed on a Florisil column eluted with chloroform-methanol, 50:50 and 25:75, v/v. The deoxynivalenol containing fractions were further fractionated by flash chromatography, preparative TLC (silica gel F_{254} developed with chloroform-methanol-water, 80:20:0.1, v/v/v) and Sephadex LH-20 column chromatography.

Biological Activity

LD_{50} in male mice (ddY strain) dosed IP was 70mg/kg; females, 49.4mg/kg; ducklings (10 day old) 27mg/kg. Also, inhibited the multiplication of culture cells of *Tetrahymena pyriformis* at same level as fusarenon-X (4.6μg/ml); ID_{50} in rabbit reticulocytes was 2μg/ml(whole cells); caused emesis in swine (7mg/60lb via intubation), duckling (10 day old, 10mg/kg), dogs (0.1mg/kg, s.c.) and food refusal in swine at 40mg/kg.

Spectral Data

UV:

λ_{max}^{EtOH} 218nm(ε=4,500); semicarbazone derivative, 268nm (ε=18,200).

IR:

(KBr) 3470, 3430, 3350, and 1680cm^{-1}.

^{1}H NMR:

($CDCl_3$) 3.62(1H, d, *J*=4.5Hz, H-2); 4.53(1H, dt, *J*=10.7, 4.5Hz, H-3); 2.21(1H, dd, *J*α=14.8, 4.5Hz, H-4); 2.07(1H, dd, *J*β=14.8, 10.7Hz, H-4); 4.83(1H, d, *J*=2.0Hz, H-7); 6.61(1H, dq, *J*=5.9, 1.5Hz, H-10); 4.80(1H, d, *J*=5.9Hz, H-11); 3.07(1H, d, *J*=4.3Hz, H-13); 3.15(1H, d, *J*=4.3Hz, H-13); 1.13(3H, s, CH_3-14); 3.73, 3.89(2H, d, *J*=11.7Hz, CH_2OH-15); and 1.86ppm (3H, br s, CH_3-16).

^{13}C NMR:

80.6, C-2; 68.5, C-3; 43.0, C-4; 46.0, C-5; 52.1, C-6; 74.3, C-7; 200.1, C-8; 135.7, C-9; 138.3, C-10; 70.2, C-11; 65.7, C-12; 47.3, C-13; 14.1, C-14; 61.4, C-15; and 15.01ppm, CH_3-16.

TLC Data

A: Adsorbent, silica gel G; solvent, chloroform-methanol, 97:3, v/v; R_f, 0.09; detection, H_2SO_4 spraying and heating at 110°C for 5 minutes. B: Adsorbent; silica gel G; solvent, ethyl acetate-toluene, 3:1, v/v; R_f, 0.21; detection, H_2SO_4 spraying and heating at 110°C for 5 minutes.

References

R. J. Cole and R. H. Cox; Handbook of Toxic Fungal Metabolites; Academic Press, New York, pp. 202-203(1981).

M. E. Savard and B. A. Blackwell; A Compilation of Spectral Characteristics of Secondary Metabolites from *Fusarium* Fungi; Plant Research Centre, Agriculture Canada, Ottawa, Ontario, K1A 0C6.

R. F. Vesonder, A. Ciegler, and A. H. Jensen; Isolation of the Emetic Principle from *Fusarium*-Infected Corn; Applied Microbiology, Vol. 26, pp. 1008-1010(1973).

R. F. Vesonder and P. Golinski; Metabolites of *Fusarium*; In Fusarium Mycotoxins, Taxonomy and Pathogenicity; J. Chelkowski, ed.; Elsevier Pub. Co., New York, pp. 13-23(1989).

Common/Systematic Name

3-Acetyl-4-deoxynivalenol

3α-Acetoxy-7α,15-dihydroxy-12,13-epoxytrichothec-9-en-8-one

Molecular Formula/Molecular Weight

$C_{17}H_{22}O_7$; MW = 338.13655

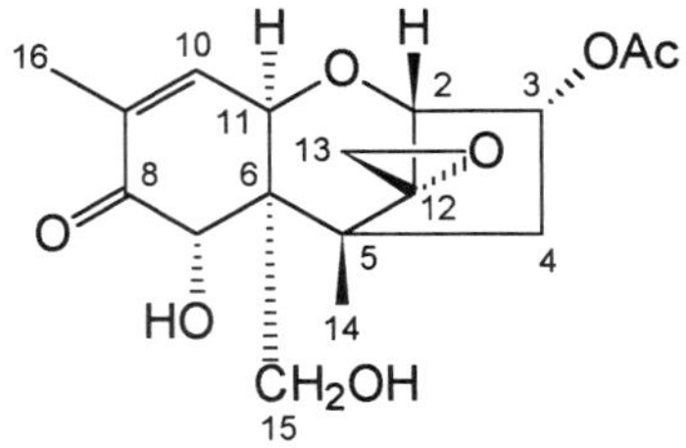

General Characteristics

Colorless needles from ethyl ether-*n*-pentane; mp.,185.5-186°C; $[\alpha]_D^{20}$ + 43.0° (*c*=1.3, in EtOH); $[\alpha]_D^{25}$ + 40.5°; tetraacetate; mp., 168-170°C.

Isolation/Purification

Fungal mycelium was extracted with methylene chloride, concentrated and the residue dissolved in methanol. The methanol phase was extracted with petroleum ether and evaporated to dryness. The residue was chromatographed on a silica gel column eluted with chloroform-ethanol (50:1, v/v) and then chloroform-ethanol (400:1, v/v). 3-Acetyl-4-deoxynivalenol was recrystallized from hot ethyl ether.

Fungal Source

Fusarium culmorum (HLX 1503; ATCC 28114), *F. graminearum* (HLX 1506), and *F. roseum*.

Biological Activity

LD_{50} in male ddS strain of mice dosed IP was 76.7mg/kg; females, 49.9mg/kg; ducklings, 37mg/kg. Minimum SC dosage to induce vomiting in ducklings was 10.0 mg/kg; dogs, S.C., 0.2mg/kg. Inhibited *Tetrahymena pyriformis*, 29.0μg/ml.

Spectral Data

UV:

λ_{max}^{EtOH} 219nm (ε=5,900).

IR:

(KBr) 3480, 3400, 1720, and 1680cm^{-1}.

^{1}H NMR:

(CDCl$_3$) 3.87(1H, d, *J*= 4.5Hz, H-2); 5.18(1H, dt, *J*=11.2, 4.5Hz, H-3); 2.35(1H, dd, *J*α=15.1, 4.5Hz, H-4); 2.12(1H, dd, *J*β=15.1, 11.2Hz, H-4); 4.79(1H, d, *J*=2.1Hz, H-7); 6.56(1H, dq, *J*=5.9, 1.5Hz, H-10); 4.66(1H, d, *J*=5.9Hz, H-11); 3.08(1H, d, *J*α=4.3Hz, H-13); 3.14(1H, d, *J*=4.3Hz, H-13); 1.12(3H, s, CH$_3$-14); 3.75(α), 3.79(β) (2H, d, *J*=11.7Hz, CH$_2$OH-15); 1.85(3H, d, *J*=1.5Hz, CH$_3$-16) ;and 2.10ppm (3H, s, CH$_3$COO-).

^{13}C NMR:

79.1, C-2; 71.3, C-3; 40.5, C-4; 45.9, C-5; 52.0, C-6; 74.5, C-7; 199.8, C-8; 135.8, C-9; 138.4, C-10; 70.2, C-11; 65.1, C-12; 47.5, C-13; 14.1, C-14; 62.2, C-15; 15.2, CH$_3$-16; 20.9, CH$_3$-Ac; and 170.3ppm (CH$_3$C=O).

Mass Data:

LREIMS: 338(M$^+$), 278, 290, 248, 241, 231, 223(100), 203, 189, 181, and 175*m/e;* anal. calcd for $C_{17}H_{22}O_7$: C, 60.3; H, 6.6; O, 33.1%; found C, 60.1; H, 6.9; O, 32.9%.

TLC Data

A: Adsorbent, silica gel G; chloroform-methanol, 93:7 v/v; R$_f$, 0.40; detection, H_2SO_4 spraying and heating at 110°C for 5 minutes. B: Adsorbent, silica gel G; solvent, ethyl acetate-toluene, 3:1 v/v; R$_f$, 0.43; detection, H_2SO_4 spraying and heating at 110°C for 5 minutes.

References

R. J. Cole and R. H. Cox; Handbook of Toxic Fungal Metabolites; Academic Press, New York, p. 209(1981).

R. Greenhalgh, A. W. Hanson, J. D. Miller, and A. Taylor; Production and X-ray Crystal Structure of 3α-Acetoxy-7α,15-dihydroxy-12,13-epoxytrichothec-9-en-8-one; J. Agric. Food Chem., Vol. 32, pp. 948-952(1984).

M. E. Savard and B. A. Blackwell; A Compilation of Spectral Characteristics of Secondary Metabolites from *Fusarium* Fungi; In Mycotoxins in Grain; Compounds Other Than Aflatoxin; J. D. Miller and H. L. Trenholm, eds., Eagan Press, St. Paul, pp. 59-257 (1994).

R. F. Vesonder and P. Golinski; Metabolites of *Fusarium*; In Fusarium Mycotoxins, Taxonomy and Pathogenicity; J. Chelkowski, ed.; Elsevier Pub. Co., New York, pp. 13-23(1989).

Common/Systematic Name

4β,15-Diacetylnivalenol

4β,15-Diacetoxy-3α,7α-dihydroxy-12,13-epoxytrichothec-9-en-8-one

Molecular Formula/Molecular Weight

$C_{19}H_{24}O_9$; MW = 396.14203

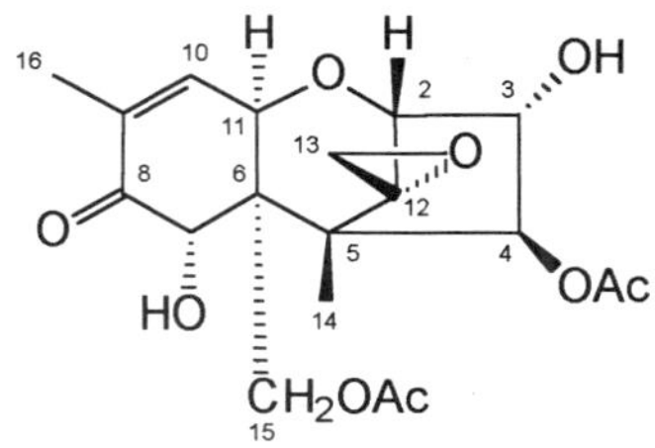

General Characteristics

Crystals from acetone-*n*-hexane; mp., 135-136°C; $[\alpha]_D^{26}$ + 64.3° (*c*=1.0, in EtOH); $[\alpha]_D^{25}$ + 72° (in acetone).

Isolation/Purification

The fungal culture filtrate was extracted with ethyl acetate, dried over anhydrous sodium sulfate, and evaporated to dryness to yield a yellow gum. The yellow gum was chromatographed by a silica gel column eluted initially with 10% ethyl acetate-chloroform and increasing the percentage of ethyl acetate. Ethyl acetate eluted an oil that was further purified by preparative HPLC using a cyano-bonded phase column with 3% 2-propanol-hexane as mobile phase.

Fungal Source

Fusarium sporotrichioides, F. crookwellense, F. scirpi (CMI 45490), and *Gibberella intricans* = *F. equiseti.*

Biological Activity

Caused skin necrosis and emesis in laboratory animals (emetic in ducklings); S. C., 0.4mg/kg; LD_{50} in male mice (ddY strain) dosed IP was 3.5mg/kg; chick embryo, 0.9mg/egg; ID_{50} in rabbit reticulocytes, 0.10μg/ml (whole cell).

Spectral Data

UV:

λ_{max}^{MeOH} 220nm (ε=6,200).

IR:

(KBr) 3420-3450, 2980-2920, 1735, 1680, 1235, and 1040cm^{-1}.

^{1}H NMR:

($CDCl_3$) 3.82(1H, d, *J*=4.7Hz, H-2); 4.22(1H, ddd, *J*=4.8, 3.1, 2.7Hz, H-3); 3.25(1H, d, *J*=2.7Hz, OH-3); 5.16(1H, d, *J*=3.1Hz, H-4); 4.86(1H, d, *J*=2.0Hz, H-7); 3.80(1H, d, *J*=2.0Hz, OH-7); 6.63(1H, dd, *J*=5.9, 1.6Hz, H-10); 4.72(1H, d, *J*=5.9Hz, H-11); 3.07(1H, d, *J*=4.3Hz, H-13); 3.08(1H, d, *J*=4.3Hz, H-13); 1.09(3H, s, CH_3-14); 4.19, 4.32(2H, d, *J*=12.3Hz, CH_2OAc-15); 1.88(3H, d, *J*=1.6Hz, CH_3-16); 1.90(3H, s, CH_3Ac-15); and 2.14ppm (3H, s, CH_3COO-).

^{13}C NMR:

79.7, C-2; 78.4, C-3; 83.9, C-4; 49.4, C-5; 52.2, C-6; 73.2, C-7; 198.9, C-8; 136.0, C-9; 138.3, C-10; 69.3, C-11; 64.3, C-12; 46.1, C-13; 7.6, C-14; 61.8, C-15; 15.3, CH_3-16; 20.6, $\underline{C}H_3$-Ac-15; 21.0, $\underline{C}H_3$-Ac-4; and 170.0, 172.7ppm ($CH_3\underline{C}$=O).

Mass Spectrum:

LREIMS: 396(M^+), 366, 336, 294, 277, 247, 189, 179(100), 151, 137, and 123*m/e*.

References

R. J. Cole and R. H. Cox; Handbook of Toxic Fungal Metabolites; Academic Press, New York, p. 221(1981).

D. R. Lauren, A. Ashley, B. A. Blackwell, R. Greenhalgh, J. D. Miller, and G. A. Neish; Trichothecenes Produced by *Fusarium crookwellense* DAOM 193611; J. Agric. Food Chem., Vol. 35, pp. 884-889(1987).

M. E. Savard and B. A. Blackwell; A Compilation of Spectral Characteristics of Secondary Metabolites from *Fusarium* Fungi; In Mycotoxins in Grain; Compounds Other Than Aflatoxin; J. D. Miller and H. L. Trenholm, eds., Eagan Press, St. Paul, pp. 59-257 (1994).

R. F. Vesonder and P. Golinski; Metabolites of *Fusarium*; In Fusarium Mycotoxins, Taxonomy and Pathogenicity; J. Chelkowski, ed.; Elsevier Pub. Co., New York, pp. 13-23(1989).

Common/Systematic Name

4β,15-Diacetyl-7-deoxynivalenol

4β,15-Diacetoxy-3α-hydroxy-12,13-epoxytrichothec-9-en-8-one

Molecular Formula/Molecular Weight

$C_{19}H_{24}O_8$; MW = 380.14712

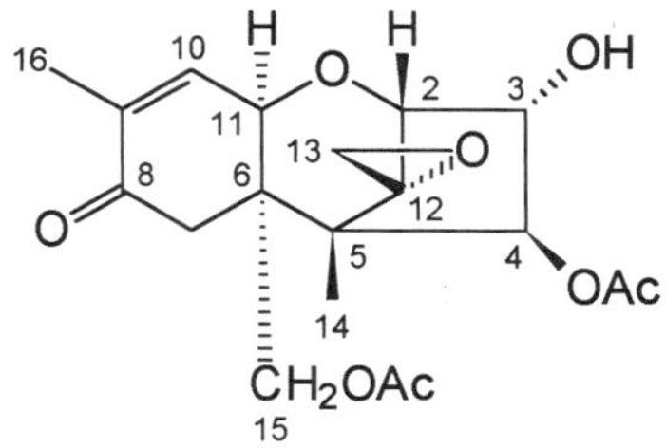

Fungal Source

Fusarium sporotrichioides and *F. crookwellense.*

Isolation/Purification

The fungal culture filtrate was extracted with ethyl acetate, dried over anhydrous sodium sulfate, and evaporated to dryness to yield a yellow gum. The yellow gum was chromatographed by a silica gel column eluted initially with 10% ethyl acetate-chloroform and increasing the percentage of ethyl acetate. Ethyl acetate eluted an oil that was further purified by preparative HPLC using a cyano-bonded phase column with 3% 2-propanol-hexane as mobile phase.

Biological Activity

The trichothecenes, as a group, show a wide range of biological activity such as antibacterial, antiviral, antifungal, and cytostatic activity; some are phytotoxic and all show some degree of animal toxicity, including insecticidal activity. There exists a broad range of toxicity in vertebrate animals and the acute toxicities vary considerably. General gross clinical signs reported for trichothecenes are vomiting, diarrhea, anorexia, ataxia, hematuria, leukocytosis soon followed by severe leukopenia, inflammation of the gastrointestinal tract, degeneration of nerve cells in the central nervous system, degeneration and hemorrhaging of cardiac muscle, and lesions of lymph nodes, testes, and thymus. Topical application or contact with skin causes dermal necrosis. Biochemically, they are potent inhibitors of protein and DNA synthesis in whole-cell and cell-free systems. Some trichothecenes inhibit the initiation step of protein synthesis on polyribosomes and others inhibit the elongation and/or termination step in protein synthesis. The trichothecenes have been strongly implicated in natural intoxications of animals and humans.

Spectral Data

^{1}H NMR:

(CDCl$_3$) 3.77(1H, d, *J*=4.9Hz, H-2); 4.21(1H, ddd, *J*=4.9, 2.9, 2.6Hz, H-3); 3.21(1H, d, *J*=2.6Hz, OH-3); 5.06(1H, d, *J*=2.9Hz, H-4); 2.46(1H, dd, *J*=15.9, 1.6Hz, H-7); 2.92(1H, dd, *J*=15.9, 1.6Hz, H-7); 6.59(1H, dd, *J*=5.9, 1.5Hz, H-10); 4.51(1H, d, *J*=5.9Hz, H-11); 2.79(1H, d, *J*=3.9Hz, H-13); 3.07(1H, d, *J*=3.9Hz, H-13); 0.80(3H, s, CH$_3$-14); 4.10, 4.17(2H, d, *J*=12.4Hz, CH$_2$OAc-15); 1.82(3H, d, *J*=1.5Hz, CH$_3$-16); 1.97(3H, s, CH$_3$Ac-15); and 2.14ppm (3H, s, CH$_3$COO-).

^{13}C NMR:

79.0, C-2; 78.5, C-3; 83.8, C-4; 47.5, C-5; 48.8, C-6; 38.2, C-7; 196.7, C-8; 138.9, C-9; 136.9, C-10; 68.4, C-11; 64.4, C-12; 46.7, C-13; 6.1, C-14; 64.5, C-15; 15.3, CH$_3$-16; 20.8, $\underline{C}H_3$-Ac-15; 20.5, $\underline{C}H_3$-Ac-4; and 170.2, 172.7ppm (CH$_3\underline{C}$=O).

Mass Spectrum:

LREIMS: 380(M$^+$), 338, 320, 292, 278, 247, 189, 173, 121, 109, and 43*m/e* (100).

References

D. R. Lauren, A. Ashley, B. A. Blackwell, R. Greenhalgh, J. D. Miller, and G. A. Neish; Trichothecenes Produced by *Fusarium crookwellense* DAOM 193611; J. Agric. Food Chem., Vol. 35, pp. 884-889(1987).

M. E. Savard and B. A. Blackwell; A Compilation of Spectral Characteristics of Secondary Metabolites from *Fusarium* Fungi; In Mycotoxins in Grain; Compounds Other Than Aflatoxin; J. D. Miller and H. L. Trenholm, eds., Eagan Press, St. Paul, pp. 59-257 (1994).

Common/Systematic Name

15-Acetyl-4-deoxynivalenol

15-Acetoxy-3α,7α-dihydroxy-12,13-epoxytrichothec-9-en-8-one

Molecular Formula/Molecular Weight

$C_{17}H_{22}O_7$; MW = 338.13655

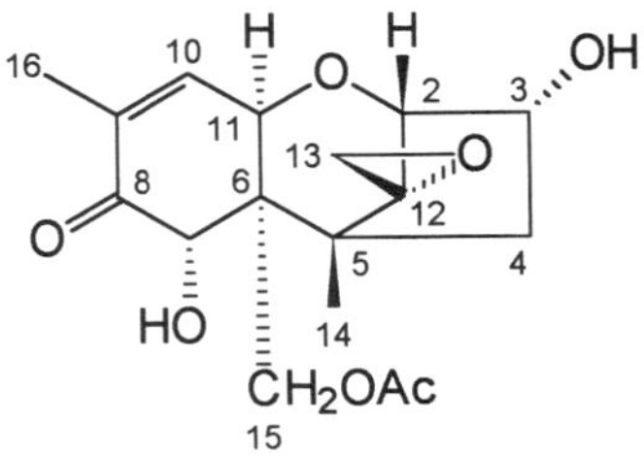

General Characteristics

Crystals; mp., 142-145°C; $[\alpha]_D^{19}$ + 79° (in $CHCl_3$).

Fungal Source

Fusarium graminearum (DAOM 17; 8148).

Biological Activity

The trichothecenes as a group show a wide range of biological activity such as antibacterial, antiviral, antifungal, and cytostatic activity; some are phytotoxic and all show some degree of animal toxicity, including insecticidal activity. There exists a broad range of toxicity in vertebrate animals and the acute toxicities vary considerably. General gross clinical signs reported for trichothecenes are vomiting, diarrhea, anorexia, ataxia, hematuria, leukocytosis soon followed by severe leukopenia, inflammation of the gastrointestinal tract, degeneration of nerve cells in the central nervous system, degeneration and hemorrhaging of cardiac muscle, and lesions of lymph nodes, testes, and thymus. Topical application or contact with skin causes dermal necrosis. Biochemically, they are potent inhibitors of protein and DNA synthesis in whole-cell and cell-free systems. Some trichothecenes inhibit the initiation step of protein synthesis on polyribosome and others inhibit the elongation and/or termination step in protein synthesis. The trichothecenes have been strongly implicated in natural intoxications of animals and humans.

Spectral Data

^{1}H NMR:

($CDCl_3$) 3.60(1H, d, J=4.4Hz, H-2); 4.50(1H, ddd, J=10.6, 4.4, 4.5Hz, H-3); 2.20(1H, dd, $J\alpha$=14.8, 4.5Hz, H-4); 2.07(1H, dd, $J\beta$=14.8, 10.6Hz, H-4); 4.81(1H, d, J=1.9Hz, H-7); 6.58(1H, dq, J=5.8, 1.3Hz, H-10); 4.87(1H, d, J=5.8Hz, H-11); 3.11(1H, d, $J\alpha$=4.2Hz, H-13); 3.06(1H, d, J=4.2Hz, H-13); 1.04(3H, s, CH_3-14); 4.21(2H, s, CH_2OAc-15); 1.86(3H, br s, CH_3-16) and 1.85ppm (3H, s, CH_3COO-).

^{13}C NMR:

80.7, C-2; 68.9, C-3; 43.3, C-4; 46.4, C-5; 51.4, C-6; 73.5, C-7; 199.4, C-8; 135.5, C-9; 138.6, C-10; 70.1, C-11; 65.4, C-12; 47.3, C-13; 13.8, C-14; 62.2, C-15; 15.3, CH_3-16; 20.6, $\underline{C}H_3$-Ac; and 170.1ppm ($CH_3\underline{C}$=O).

References

M. E. Savard and B. A. Blackwell; A Compilation of Spectral Characteristics of Secondary Metabolites from *Fusarium* Fungi; In Mycotoxins in Grain; Compounds Other Than Aflatoxin; J. D. Miller and H. L. Trenholm, eds., Eagan Press, St. Paul, pp. 59-257 (1994).

R. F. Vesonder and P. Golinski; Metabolites of *Fusarium*; In Fusarium Mycotoxins, Taxonomy and Pathogenicity; J. Chelkowski, ed.; Elsevier Pub. Co., New York, pp. 13-23(1989).

Common/Systematic Name

3,15-Diacetyl-4-deoxynivalenol

3α,15α-Diacetoxy-7α-hydroxy-12,13-epoxytrichothec-9-en-8-one

Molecular Formula/Molecular Weight

$C_{19}H_{24}O_8$; MW = 380.14712

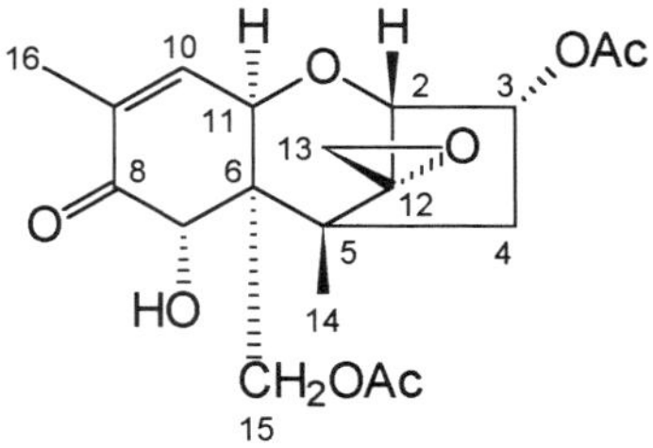

General Characteristics

Crystals from ethyl acetate-hexane; mp., 119-120°C.

Fungal Source

Fusarium roseum (ATCC 28114) and *F. graminearum*.

Spectral Data

^{1}H NMR:

($CDCl_3$) 3.90(1H, d, *J*=4.5Hz, H-2); 5.22(2H, ddd, *J*=11.2, 4.5, 4.4Hz, H-3); 2.17(1H, dd, *J*=11.2, 15.1Hz, H-4); 2.30(1H, dd, *J*=15.1, 4.4Hz, H-4); 3.81(1H, d, *J*=1.6Hz, H-7); 3.76(1H, d, *J*=1.6Hz, OH-7); 6.57(1H, dd, *J*=5.8, 1.6Hz, H-10); 4.70(1H, d, *J*=5.8Hz, H-11); 3.10(1H, d, *J*=4.3Hz, H-13); 3.15(1H, d, *J*=4.3Hz, H-13); 1.09(3H, s, CH_3-14); 4.22, 4.28(2H, d, *J*=12.0Hz, CH_2OAc-15); 1.89(3H, d, *J*=0.8Hz, CH_3-16); 1.88(3H, s, CH_3Ac-15); and 2.13ppm (3H, s, CH_3COO-).

^{13}C NMR:

78.9, C-2; 71.1, C-3; 40.4, C-4; 45.8, C-5; 51.5, C-6; 73.4, C-7; 199.2, C-8; 135.6, C-9; 138.4, C-10; 70.1, C-11; 64.9, C-12; 47.4, C-13; 13.6, C-14; 62.1, C-15; 15.3, CH_3-16; 20.9, $\underline{C}H_3$-Ac-15; 20.6, $\underline{C}H_3$-Ac-4; and 170.2, 170.7ppm ($CH_3\underline{C}$=O).

Mass Spectrum:

LREIMS: 380(M^+), 320, 291, 231, 203, 181, and 163*m/e*.

References

R. Greenhalgh, R. M. Meier, B. A. Blackwell, J. D. Miller, A. Taylor, and J. W. ApSimon; Part 2. Minor Metabolites of *Fusarium roseum* (ATCC 28114); J. Agric. Food Chem., Vol. 32, pp. 115-118(1986).

M. E. Savard and B. A. Blackwell; A Compilation of Spectral Characteristics of Secondary Metabolites from *Fusarium* Fungi; In Mycotoxins in Grain; Compounds Other Than Aflatoxin; J. D. Miller and H. L. Trenholm, eds., Eagan Press, St. Paul, pp. 59-257 (1994).

Common/Systematic Name

Fusarenon-X; Nivalenol monoacetate; Fusarenon

4β-Acetoxy-3α,7α,15α-trihydroxy-12,13-epoxytrichothec-9-en-8-one

Molecular Formula/Molecular Weight

$C_{17}H_{22}O_8$; MW = 354.12145

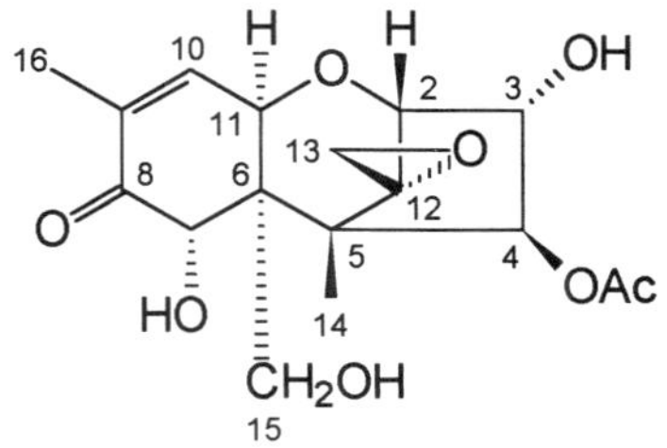

General Characteristics

Hexagonal bipyramid crystals from dichloromethane-*n*-pentane; mp., 91-92°C; crystals from dichloroethane; mp., 181-182°C; $[\alpha]_D^{25}$ + 58° (*c*=1.0, in MeOH.)

Fungal Source

Fusarium nivale, Fn-2B = *sporotrichioides, F. crookwellense, F. graminearum,* and *F. equiseti.*

Isolation/Purification

The toxin in the fungal broth was absorbed on active carbon, followed by elution with methanol. After evaporation of the solvent, 5 volumes of chloroform were added to the methanol extract. The methanol-chloroform soluble fraction, herein referred to as crude toxin, was chromatographed on Kieselgel. Development with chloroform-methanol (97:3 to 5:1, v/v) yielded a highly toxic fraction that eluted before the nivalenol fraction. Rechromatography on Kieselgel with chloroform-acetone (5:1, v/v) gave a white powder. This material, when crystallized from dichloromethane-*n*-pentane, gave hexagonal bipyramid crystals.

Biological Activity

Application of 0.2-1.0μg to dehaired back skin of rabbit, guinea pig, and mouse caused cytotoxic effects on epidermis, dermis, and hair follicles; no change in the subcutaneous tissues or muscle fibers. LD_{50} in male mice (ddY strain) dosed IP (0.9% saline) was ~3.3 mg/kg; nonlethal doses produced mucoidal secretion around the eye one week after treatment. LD_{50} in chick embryos, 2.6mg/egg; ID_{50} in rabbit reticulocytes, 0.25μg/ml (whole cell); 0.5μg/ml (cell free); tumor cells, 6.0μg/ml (whole cell); and rat liver, 8.0μg/ml (cell free). Emetic, minimum S.C. dose to induce vomiting in ducklings was 0.4-0.5 mg/kg; in cats, 0.3-0.5 mg/kg; and in pigeons, 0.5-1.0 mg/kg (IV and PO).

Spectral Data

UV:
λ_{max}^{MeOH} 220nm (ε=6,500).

^{1}H NMR:
($CDCl_3$) 3.79(1H, d, *J*=4.7Hz, H-2); 4.32(2H, m, H-3); 5.53(1H, d, *J*=3.4Hz, H-4); 4.83(1H, d, *J*=2.0Hz, H-7); 3.71(1H, d, *J*=2.0Hz, OH-7); 6.66(1H, d, *J*=6.0Hz, H-10); 4.81(1H, d, *J*=6.0Hz, H-11); 3.04(1H, d, *J*=4.2Hz, H-13); 3.09(1H, d, *J*=4.2Hz, H-13); 1.08(3H, s, CH_3-14); 3.59(1H, dd, *J*=12.5, 4.7Hz, H-15); 4.01(1H, br d, *J*=12.5Hz, H-15); 1.88(3H, br s, CH_3-16); and 2.14ppm (3H, s, CH_3COO-).

^{13}C NMR:
77.5, C-2; 80.0, C-3; 83.5, C-4; 49.4, C-5; 52.9, C-6; 75.8, C-7; 199.6, C-8; 135.9, C-9; 138.3, C-10; 69.1, C-11; 64.7, C-12; 46.3, C-13; 7.8, C-14; 61.6, C-15; 15.2, CH_3-16; 21.0, $\underline{C}H_3$-Ac-15; and 172.9ppm ($CH_3\underline{C}$=O).

Mass Data:
Found: C, 57.62; H, 6.22; O, 36.16%; calcd for C, 57.62; H, 6.22; O, 36.16%.

TLC Data

A. Adsorbent: silica gel G; Solvent: chloroform-methanol, 97:3, v/v; R_f, 0.19; detection: purple to yellow-green with H_2SO_4 spraying and heating at 110°C for 5 minutes. B. Adsorbent: silica gel G; solvent: toluene-ethyl acetate, 1:3, v/v; R_f, 0.36; detection: purple to yellow-green with H_2SO_4 spraying and heating at 110°C for 5 minutes.

GLC Data

Support: Shimalite W; liquid phase: OV-17 (1.5%); retention time: 3.95; relative retention time (relative to nivalenol): 1.11.

References

R. J. Cole and R. H. Cox; Handbook of Toxic Fungal Metabolites; Academic Press, New York, p. 213 (1981).

M. E. Savard and B. A. Blackwell; A Compilation of Spectral Characteristics of Secondary Metabolites from *Fusarium* Fungi; In Mycotoxins in Grain; Compounds Other Than Aflatoxin; J. D. Miller and H. L. Trenholm, eds., Eagan Press, St. Paul, pp. 59-257 (1994).

Y. Sugiura, Y. watanabe, T. Tanaka, S. Yamamoto, and Y. Ueno; Occurrence of *Gibberella zoeae* Strains That Produce Both Nivalenol and Deoxynivalenol; Appl. Environ. Microbiol.; Vol. 56, pp. 3047-3051(1990).

Y. Ueno, I. Ueno, T. Tatsuno, K. Okubo, and H. Tsunoda; Fusarenon-X, A Toxic Principle of *Fusarium nivale* - Culture Filtrate; Experientia, Vol. 25, pp. 1062 (1969).

15

Modified Trichothecenes

2-Deoxy-11-*epi*-12-acetyl-3α-hydroxysambucoin
2-Deoxy-11-*epi*-3α-hydroxysambucoin
Trichodiol A
Trichodiene
FS-1
FS-2
FS-3
FS-4
3-Ketoapotrichothecene
3α-Hydroxyapotrichothecene
3β-Hydroxyapotrichothecene

Common/Systematic Name

2-Deoxy-11-*epi*-12-acetyl-3α-hydroxysambucoin

Molecular Formula/Molecular Weight

$C_{17}H_{26}O_4$; MW = 294.18311

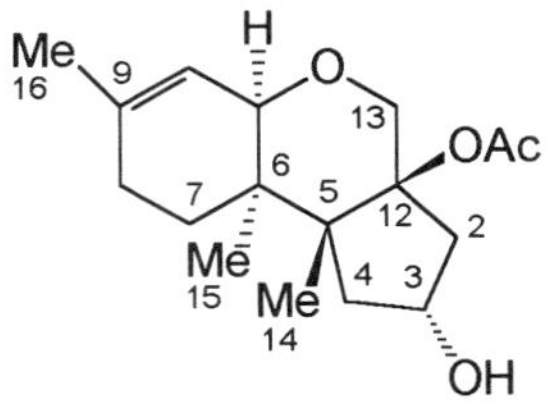

General Characteristics

Isolated as an oil.

Fungal Source

Fusarium sporotrichioides isolated from Ethiopian wheat.

Isolation/Purification

F. sporotrichioides was cultured on ground corn grits and the fermented corn grits were blended with chloroform-acetone (85:15, v/v) and the mixture allowed to stand overnight. After filtration the remaining solid residue was blended with acetone; the mixture was filtered and the acetone extract and the chloroform-acetone extract were combined and concentrated under reduced pressure, which yielded a dark green oil. The oil was dissolved in 2 liters benzene-*n*-hexane (2:1, v/v) and aliquots were applied to Florisil columns. Columns were eluted successively with benzene-*n*-hexane (2:1, v/v), methylene chloride, chloroform-acetone (9:1, v/v), and acetone. The residue from the chloroform-acetone fraction was recrystallized from acetone-*n*-hexane to yield a mixture of trichothecenes. Reversed-phase flash column chromatography of the solid trichothecene mixture using MeOH-H_2O-acetic acid (35:20:1, v/v/v) yielded neosolaniol, NT-1, 8-acetylneosolaniol, 8-propionyl-neosolaniol, 8-isobutyrylneosolaniol, 8-*n*-butyrylneosolaniol, T-2 toxin, 8-*n*-pentanoyl-neosolaniol, and 8-*n*-hexanoylneosolaniol. The acetone fraction was dissolved in benzene-acetone (2:1, v/v) and subjected to Florisil column chromatography. The column was eluted successively with benzene-acetone (2:1, v/v), chloroform-acetone (4:1, v/v), and acetone. The residue from the acetone fraction was chromatographed using flash column chromatography, eluting with solvent mixtures of increasing polarity: benzene-acetone (65:35, v/v), benzene-acetone (57:63, v/v), acetone, acetone-methanol (1:1, v/v), and MeOH. Fractions were collected and similar fractions were combined. The polar fractions of the silica gel column chromatography were combined, concentrated at reduced pressure, and subjected to reversed-phase column chromatography eluting with methanol-water-acetic acid (35:20:1, v/v/v). Similar fractions were combined. Acuminatin, FS-1, scirpenol, T-2 tetraol, T-2 triol, 15-acetylscirpenol, DON (deoxynivalenol), 8α-hydroxytrichothecolone, verrucarol, 2-deoxy-11-*epi*-3α-hydroxysambucoin and 2-deoxy-11-*epi*-12-acetyl-3α-hydroxysambucoin were isolated in pure form.

Biological Activity

2-Deoxy-11-*epi*-3α-hydroxysambucoin and 2-deoxy-11-*epi*-12-acetyl-3α-hydroxysambucoin were screened for relative cytotoxicity in cultured baby hamster kidney (BHK-21) cells and found to be non-toxic (LC_{100} =1000 ng/ml).

Spectral Data

IR:

(NaCl) 1736(acetyl group) and 3408cm^{-1} (OH group).

^{1}H NMR:

($CDCl_3$) 1.40(1H, dd, *J*=14.9, 2.0Hz, H-2); 2.32(1H, dd, *J*=14.9, 8.4Hz, H-2); 4.4(1H, m, H-3); 1.91(1H, m, H-4); 2.12(1H, m, H-4); 1.68(1H, dd, *J*=5.5, 2.0Hz, H-7); 1.95(1H, dd, *J*=9.0, 2.0Hz, H-7); 1.95-2.0(2H, m, 2H-8); 5.45(1H, dd, *J*=6.0, 1.0Hz, H-10); 3.6(1H, bs, H-11); 3.58(1H, d, *J*=15.1Hz, H-13); 3.75(1H, d, *J*=15.1Hz, H-13); 0.96(3H, s, H-14); 0.73(3H, s, H-15); 1.68(3H, s, H-16); and 2.05ppm (3H, s, $COCH_3$).

^{13}C NMR:

($CDCl_3$) 45.9, t, C-2; 67.5, d, C-3; 44.8, t, C-4; obscured by solvent, C-5; 35.2, s, C-6; 24.5, t, C-7; 29.2, t, C-8; 140.4, s, C-9; 120.8, d, C-10; 75.9, d, C-11; 86.9, s, C-12; 74.5, t, C-13; 16.8, q, C-14; 16.3, q, C-15; 23.0, q, C-16; and 22.4ppm, q, $CO\underline{C}H_3$. ($\underline{C}OCH_3$, not observed).

Mass Spectrum:

CIMS (TFA derivative): 391(M^+ + 1, 10%), 331(17), 301(38), 277(22), 217(55), and 111*m/e* (100).

Reference

D. M. Fort, C. L. Barnes, M. S. Tempestra, H. H. Casper, E. Bekele, A. A. Rottinghaus, and G. E.Rottinghaus; Two New Modified Trichothecenes from *Fusarium sporotrichioides*; J. Natural Products, Vol. 56, pp.1890-1897(1993).

Common/Systematic Name

2-Deoxy-11-*epi*-3α-hydroxysambucoin

Molecular Formula/Molecular Weight

$C_{15}H_{24}O_3$; MW = 252.17254

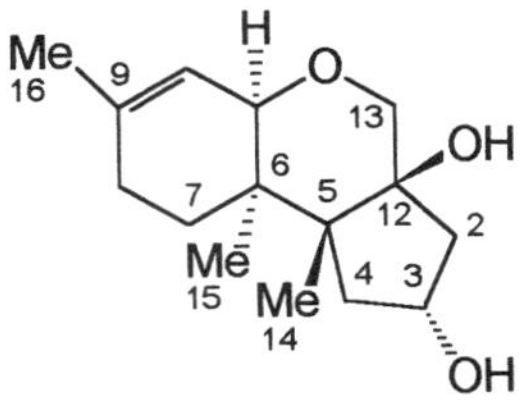

General Characteristics

Colorless crystals from methanol-H_2O; mp., 177-178°C.

Fungal Source

Fusarium sporotrichioides isolated from Ethiopian wheat.

Isolation/Purification

F. sporotrichioides was cultured on ground corn grits at 10°C for 28 days and the fermented corn grits were blended with chloroform-acetone (85:15, v/v) and the mixture allowed to stand overnight. After filtration, the remaining solid residue was blended with acetone. The mixture was filtered and the solid autoclaved and discarded. The acetone and the chloroform-acetone extract were combined and concentrated under reduced pressure, which yielded a dark green oil. The oil was dissolved in 2 liters benzene-*n*-hexane (2:1, v/v), and aliquots were applied to Florisil columns. Columns were eluted successively with benzene-*n*-hexane (2:1, v/v), methylene chloride, chloroform-acetone (9:1, v/v), and acetone. The residue from the chloroform-acetone fraction was recrystallized from acetone-*n*-hexane to yield a mixture of trichothecenes. Reversed-phase flash column chromatography of the solid trichothecene mixture using methanol-water-acetic acid (35:20:1, v/v/v) yielded neosolaniol, NT-1, 8-acetylneosolaniol, 8-propionyl-neosolaniol, 8-isobutyrylneosolaniol, 8-*n*-butyrylneosolaniol, T-2 toxin, 8-*n*-pentanoylneosolaniol, and 8-*n*-hexanoylneosolaniol. The acetone fraction was dissolved in benzene-acetone (2:1, v/v) and subjected to Florisil column chromatography. The column was eluted successively with benzene-acetone (2:1, v/v), chloroform-acetone (4:1, v/v), and acetone. The residue from the acetone fraction was chromatographed using flash column chromatography, eluting with solvent mixtures of increasing polarity: benzene-acetone (65:35, v/v), benzene-acetone (57:63, v/v), acetone, acetone-methanol (1:1, v/v), and MeOH. Fractions were collected and similar fractions were combined. The polar fractions of the silica gel column chromatography were combined, concentrated at reduced pressure, and subjected to reversed-phase column chromatography eluting with methanol-water-acetic acid (35:20:1, v/v/v). Similar fractions were combined. Acuminatin, FS-1, scirpenol, T-2 tetraol, T-2 triol, 15-acetylscirpenol, DON (deoxynivalenol), 8α-hydroxytrichothecolone, verrucarol, 2-deoxy-11-*epi*-3α-hydroxysambucoin and 2-deoxy-11-*epi*-12-acetyl-3α-hydroxysambucoin were isolated in pure form.

Biological Activity

2-Deoxy-11-epi-3α-hydroxysambucoin and 2-deoxy-11-epi-12-acetyl-3α-hydroxysambucoin were screened for relative cytotoxicity in cultured baby hamster kidney (BHK-21) cells and found to be non-toxic (LC_{100} = 1000ng/ml).

Spectral Data

IR:

(NaCl) 3412cm^{-1} (OH group).

^{1}H NMR:

($CDCl_3$) 1.46(1H, dd, *J*=15.0, 2.4Hz, H-2); 2.28(1H, dd, *J*=15.0, 9.4Hz, H-2); 4.44(1H, ddd, *J*=15.6,7.8, 2.4Hz, H-3); 1.85(1H, m, H-4); 2.02(1H, m, H-4); 1.53 (1H, dd, *J*=13.3, 2.0Hz, H-7); 1.91(1H, dd, *J*=8.0, 2.0Hz, H-7); 1.95-2.0(2H, m, H-8); 5.52(1H, dd, *J*=5.6, 0.8Hz, H-10); 3.69(1H, bs, H-11); 3.66(1H, d, *J*=12.6Hz, H-13); 3.95(1H, d, *J*=12.6Hz, H-13); 0.97(3H, s, 3H-14); 0.71(3H, s, H-15); and 1.70ppm (3H, s, H-16).

^{13}C NMR:

($CDCl_3$) 44.1, t, C-2; 67.0, d, C-3; 44.2, t, C-4; 48.6, s, C-5; 35.0, s, C-6; 24.3, t, C-7; 28.2, t, C-8; 139.5, s, C-9; 119.5, d, C-10; 75.1, d, C-11; 77.6, s, C-12; 74.0, t, C-13; 16.6, q, C-14; 16.1, q, C-15; and 23.0ppm, q, C-16.

Mass Spectrum:

LREIMS (TMSi derivative): 396(M^+, 1%), 378(4), 258(100), 108(63), and 73*m/e* (60); CIMS (TMSi derivative): 397(M^++ 1, 18%), 381(15), 307(22), 291(100), 263(42), 217(53), 199(32), 73*m/e* (21); and CIMS (TFA derivative): 445(M^+ + 1, 45%), 445(45), 331(100), 217(13), 115(67), and 93*m/e* (80).

Reference

D. M. Fort, C. L. Barnes, M. S. Tempestra, H. H. Casper, E. Bekele, A. A. Rottinghaus, and G. E. Rottinghaus; Two New Modified Trichothecenes from *Fusarium sporotrichioides*; J. Natural Products, Vol. 56, pp.1890-1897(1993).

Common/Systematic Name

Trichodiol A

Molecular Formula/Molecular Weight

$C_{15}H_{24}O_3$; MW = 252.17254

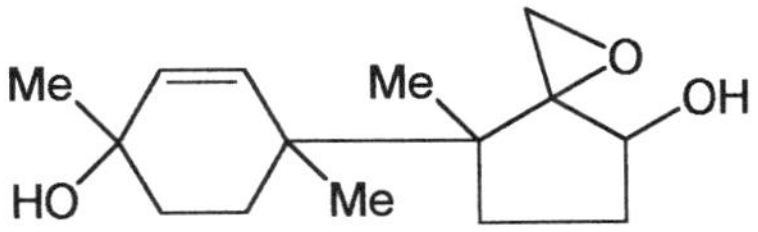

General Characteristics

Colorless crystals from ether-hexane; mp., 81-83°C; $[\alpha]_D$ = +52° ($CHCl_3$).

Isolation/Purification

The ethyl acetate extract of the fermentation broth from *Trichothecium roseum* was saponified with 10% ethanolic KOH at room temperature. The mixture was concentrated to *ca.* 1/3 volume below 40°C under reduced pressure. This material was extracted with ether and the extract washed with water, dried and the solvent evaporated to dryness. Repeated column chromatography of the nonsaponifiable material using Wakogel C-200 (60% ether-benzene) gave trichodiol A which crystallized from ether-hexane to give a pure sample.

Fungal Source

Trichothecium roseum.

Spectral Data

UV:

λ_{max}^{EtOH} End absorption, 210nm (ε= 360).

IR:

($CHCl_3$) 3460cm^{-1} (OH).

^{1}H NMR:

($CDCl_3$) The NMR spectrum revealed the presence of three tertiary methyl groups (singlets at 0.86, 0.96, and 1.15ppm, 3H each), a CH_2OH group (3.48, 4.06, 2H, Abq, J = 12.0Hz) attached to a non-hydrogen atom, and a –C$\underline{H}$=C$\underline{H}$- group (5.46, 5.73ppm, 2H, Abq, J = 10Hz). Both carbon atoms are attached to quaternary carbon atoms and a methine proton (3.17ppm, 1H, bs). The signals at 3.48 and 4.06ppm shifted to 4.33 and 4.54ppm upon acetylation.

Mass Data:

HREIMS: 234.162($C_{15}H_{22}O_2$, M^+ - H_2O, calcd. 234.162), 127.074($C_7H_{11}O_2$, calcd 127.076), 125.099($C_8H_{13}O$, calcd 125.097), 108.095(C_8H_{12}, calcd 108.094), 107.088(C_8H_{11}, calcd 107.086), 109.065(C_7H_9O, calcd 109.065), 96.056*m/e* (C_6H_8O, calcd 96.058). Found: O, 18.84; $C_{15}H_{24}O_3$ requires O, 19.02%.

Reference

S. Nozoe and Y. Machida; The Structures of Trichodiol and Trichodiene; Tetrahedron, Vol. 28, pp. 5105-5111(1972).

Common/Systematic Name

Trichodiene

Molecular Formula/Molecular Weight

$C_{15}H_{24}$; MW = 204.18780

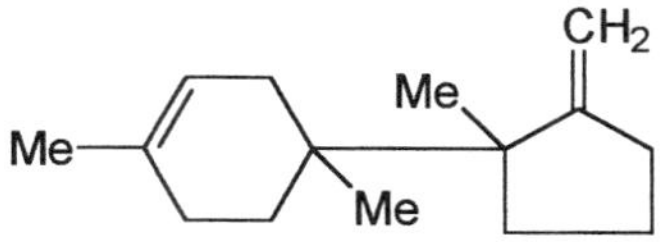

General Characteristics

Colorless oily material; $[\alpha]_D = +21°$ ($CHCl_3$).

Isolation/Purification

The mycelium from the fermentation of *T. roseum* was suspended in warm acetone for 3 hours. After filtration, the mycelium was resuspended in acetone and allowed to stand overnight at room temperature and then filtered. The combined acetone extracts were concentrated to *ca.* $^1/_3$ volume, to which water was added. Extraction with ethyl acetate followed by successive washing with water, drying, and removal of solvent afforded a brown residue, which was saponified with 10% KOH at room temperature to obtain the nonsaponifiable material. Column chromatographic separation was first afforded using ether-benzene. The first fraction (100% benzene) was further chromatographed using a $AgNO_3$ impregnated silica gel column (hexane elution) to obtain pure trichodiene.

Fungal Source

Trichothecium roseum.

Spectral Data

IR:

($CHCl_3$) 3065, 1645, and 890cm^{-1}.

^{1}H NMR:

($CDCl_3$) The NMR spectrum revealed the presence of singlets at 0.85 and 1.04 ppm due to two tertiary methyl groups, a broad singlet at 1.63ppm due to an olefinic methyl group, a multiplet at 5.23ppm due to an olefinic proton, and two broad singlets at 4.71 and 4.92ppm due to olefinic protons.

Mass Spectrum:

EIMS: 204(M^+, $C_{15}H_{24}$); intense peaks at 189, 161, 133, 121, 119, 109 (base peak C_8H_{13}), 95 (C_7H_{11}), 93, and 67*m/e*.

Reference

S. Nozoe and Y. Machida; The Structures of Trichodiol and Trichodiene; Tetrahedron, Vol. 28, pp. 5105-5111(1972).

Common/Systematic Name

FS-1

Molecular Formula/Molecular Weight

$C_{15}H_{22}O_3$; MW = 250.15689

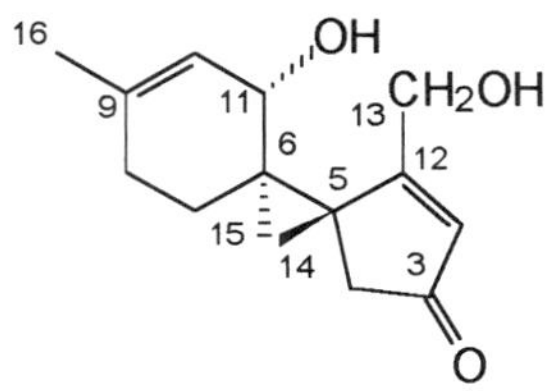

General Characteristics

Isolated as an oil.

Fungal Source

Fusarium sporotrichioides (MC-72083) and *F. sambucinum.*

Isolation/Purification

Fungal cultures were extracted with chloroform-acetone (85:15, v/v), followed by Florisil column chromatography eluted with benzene-hexane, 2:1 (v/v), methylene chloride, and chloroform-methanol (95:5, v/v) to give an oil highly enriched with trichothecenes. The oil was further purified by normal phase preparative HPLC using benzene-acetone followed by preparative reversed-phase TLC to yield several trichothecenes including FS-1.

Spectral Data

IR:

(thin film) 1684(enone) and 3352cm^{-1} (OH).

^{1}H NMR:

($CDCl_3$) 6.24(1H, t, *J*=1.5Hz, H-2); 3.10(1H, d, *J*=18.2Hz, H-4), 2.03(1H, d, *J*=18.2Hz, H-4); 1.95(1H, dd, *J*=15.0, 4.6Hz, H-7); 1.79(1H, d, *J*=15.0Hz, H-7); 1.45(2H, m, *J*=4.6Hz, H-8); 5.05(1H, br s, H-10); 4.11(1H, br s, H-11); 4.55(1H, d, *J*=17.3Hz,
H-13); 4.34(1H, d, *J*=17.3Hz, H-13); 1.24(3H, s, CH_3-14); 0.84(3H, s, CH_3-15); and 1.61ppm (3H, br s, CH_3-16).

^{13}C NMR:

($CDCl_3$) 129.5, C-2; 208.4, C-3; 50.4, C-4; 53.1, C-5; 41.9, C-6; 29.9, C-7; 27.4, C-8; 135.7, C-9; 125.0, C-10; 71.3, C-11; 188.0, C-12; 61.0, C-13; 22.4, C-14; 13.1, C-15; and 22.5ppm; C-16.

Mass Spectrum:
HREIMS: 250.150*m/e* (M^+); calcd for $C_{15}H_{22}O_3$, 250.156; LREIMS: 250, 232, 219, 204, 167(base peak), 126, 107, 84, and 55*m/e*.

References
D. G. Corley, G. E. Rottinghaus, J. K. Tracy, and M. S. Tempesta; New Trichothecene Mycotoxins of *Fusarium sporotrichioides* (MC- 72083); Tet. Lett., pp. 4133-4136 (1986).

M. E. Savard and B. A. Blackwell; A Compilation of Spectral Characteristics of Secondary Metabolites from *Fusarium* Fungi; In Mycotoxins in Grain; Compounds Other Than Aflatoxin; J. D. Miller and H. L. Trenholm, eds., Eagan Press, St. Paul, pp. 59-257 (1994).

Common/Systematic Name

FS-2

Molecular Formula/Molecular Weight

$C_{15}H_{24}O_3$; MW = 252.17254

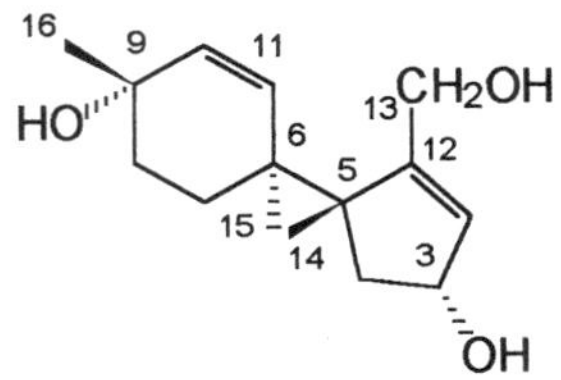

Fungal Source

Fusarium sporotrichioides (MC-72083).

Isolation/Purification

Fungal cultures were extracted with chloroform-acetone (85:15, v/v), followed by acetone. The combined extracts were concentrated to yield a dark red oil which was treated with *n*-hexane to remove non-polar materials. The resulting orange-red oil was further purified by Florisil column chromatography eluted with benzene-hexane, 2:1 (v/v), methylene chloride, and chloroform-methanol (95:5, v/v) followed by acetone. The latter two were combined to give an oil highly enriched with trichothecenes. Flash chromatography followed by normal phase preparative HPLC using toluene-acetone and preparative reversed-phase TLC yielded several purified trichothecenes including FS-2.

Spectral Data

UV:

$\lambda_{max}^{Acetonitrile}$ 194.5nm (ϵ=12,000; two ene π to π^* transitions).

^{1}H NMR:

($CDCl_3$) 5.75(1H, dd, *J*=1.5, 3.3Hz, H-2); 4.79(1H, m, H-3), 2.10(1H, m, H-4); 1.75(1H, m, H-7); 1.31(1H, m, H-7); 1.98, 1.73(2H, m, H-8); 5.58(1H, d, *J*=10.2Hz, H-10); 5.67(1H, dd, *J*=1.7, 10.2Hz, H-11); 4.35(1H, br d, *J*=14.5Hz, H-13); 4.23(1H, br d, *J*=14.5Hz, H-13); 1.09(3H, s, CH_3-14); 0.95(3H, s, CH_3-15); and 1.27ppm (3H, s, CH_3-16).

^{13}C NMR:

($CDCl_3$) 133.0, C-2; 73.4, C-3; 47.4, C-4; 54.6, C-5; 40.0, C-6; 27.8, C-7; 35.0, C-8; 65.7, C-9; 135.6, C-10; 133.2, C-11; 154.0, C-12; 60.7, C-13; 21.3, C-14; 22.0, C-15; and 30.9ppm (C-16).

Mass Spectrum:
HREIMS: 252.173*m/e* (M^+); calcd for $C_{15}H_{24}O_3$, 252.173. CIMS: 253(M^+ + 1, 2%), 235(M^+ - OH, 50), 127(cleavage of C-6/C-6 bond, 85), 125(90), 109(127 - H_2O, 100), and 107*m/e* (125 - H_2O, 50),

References

D. G. Corley, G. E. Rottinghaus, J. K. Tracy, and M. S. Tempesta; New Trichothecene Mycotoxins of *Fusarium sporotrichioides* (MC- 72083); Tet. Lett., pp. 4133-4136 (1986).

M. E. Savard and B. A. Blackwell; A Compilation of Spectral Characteristics of Secondary Metabolites from *Fusarium* Fungi; In Mycotoxins in Grain; Compounds Other Than Aflatoxin; J. D. Miller and H. L. Trenholm, eds., Eagan Press, St. Paul, pp. 59-257 (1994).

Common/Systematic Name

FS-3

Molecular Formula/Molecular Weight

$C_{15}H_{20}O_3$; MW = 248.14124

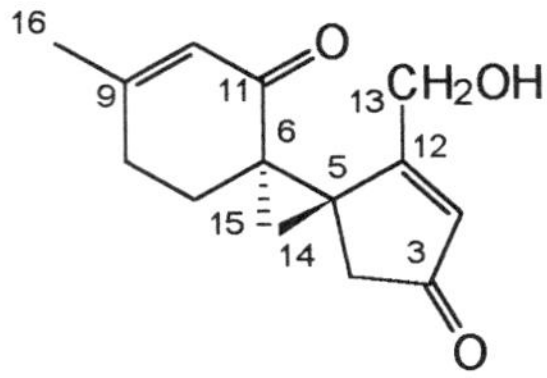

General Characteristics

Isolated as a colorless glass.

Fungal Source

Fusarium sambucinum.

Isolation/Purification

Fungal cultures were extracted with chloroform-acetone (85:15, v/v), allowed to sit overnight, filtered and the solid residue re-extracted with acetone. The acetone extract was combined with the chloroform-acetone extract, concentrated under vacuum, and the non-polar materials were removed by hexane drip. The solvent was decanted, concentrated and chromatographed by flash chromatography with toluene, toluene-acetone 4:1, 2:1, 1:1 (v/v), acetone, and acetone-methanol, 1:1 (v/v). The toluene-acetone (4:1, v/v) fraction was further purified by flash chromatography eluting with toluene-acetone (4:1v/v). This resulted in purified diacetoxyscirpenol, 3,15-diacetoxyscirpenol, 3,4,15-triacetoxyscirpenol, neosolaniol, sambucoin, 4-monoacetoxyscirpenol, 15-monoacetoxyscirpenol, and FS-3.

Spectral Data

UV:

$\lambda_{max}^{Acetonitrile}$ 229nm (ϵ=13,000).

IR:

(film) 3470(OH) and 1675cm^{-1} (C=O).

^{1}H NMR:

($CDCl_3$) 6.29(1H, t, *J*=1.5Hz, H-2); 2.32(1H, d, *J*=18.8, H-4), 2.60(1H, d, *J*=18.8Hz, H-4); 1.73(1H, dd, *J*=12.0, 2.5Hz, H-7); 1.87(1H, dd, *J*=12.0, 2.5Hz, H-7); 2.20(1H, dd, *J*=19.0, 2.5Hz, H-8); 1.63(1H, dd, *J*=19.0, 2.5Hz, H-8); 5.75(1H, br s, H-10); 4.49(1H, dd, *J*=17.0, 1.5Hz, H-13); 4.56(1H, dd, *J*=17.0, 1.5Hz, H-13); 1.50(3H, s, CH_3-14); 1.17(3H, s, CH_3-15); and 1.93ppm (3H, s, CH_3-16).

^{13}C NMR:

(CDCl$_3$) 129.6, C-2; 207.0, C-3; 50.6, C-4; 53.3, C-5; 47.1, C-6; 30.9, C-7; 28.3, C-8; 160.1, C-9; 126.4, C-10; 202.5, C-11; 186.3, C-12; 61.6, C-13; 23.8, C-14; 18.2, C-15; and 29.0ppm; C-16.

Mass Spectrum:

HREIMS: 248.141*m/e* (M^+); calcd for $C_{15}H_{20}O_3$, 248.154; LREIMS: 248(M^+, 1%), 181(14), 131(31), 124(26), and 69*m/e* (100).

References

D. R. Sanson, D. G. Corley, C. L. Barnes, S. Searles, E. O. Schlemper, M. S. Tempesta, and G. E. Rottinghaus; New Mycotoxins from *Fusarium sambucinum*; J. Org. Chem., Vol. 54, pp. 4313-4318(1989).

M. E. Savard and B. A. Blackwell; A Compilation of Spectral Characteristics of Secondary Metabolites from *Fusarium* Fungi; In Mycotoxins in Grain; Compounds Other Than Aflatoxin; J. D. Miller and H. L. Trenholm, eds., Eagan Press, St. Paul, pp. 59-257 (1994).

Common/Systematic Name
FS-4

Molecular Formula/Molecular Weight
$C_{15}H_{22}O_3$; MW = 250.15689

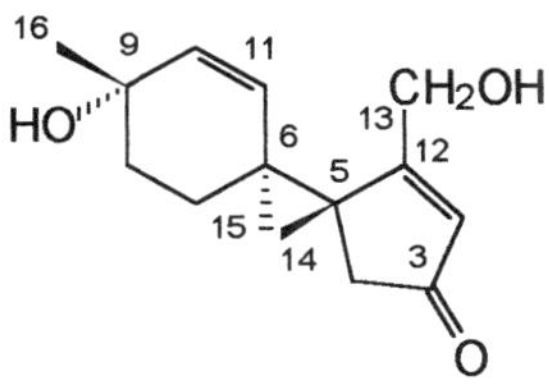

General Characteristics
Isolated as a colorless glass.

Fungal Source
Fusarium sambucinum.

Isolation/Purification
Fungal cultures were extracted with chloroform-acetone (85:15, v/v), allowed to sit over-night, filtered and the solid residue re-extracted with acetone. The acetone extract was combined with the chloroform-acetone extract, concentrated under vacuum and the non-polar materials removed by hexane drip. The solvent was decanted, concentrated and chromatographed by flash chromatography with toluene, toluene-acetone 4:1, 2:1, 1:1 (v/v), acetone, and acetone-methanol, 1:1 (v/v). The toluene-acetone (1:1, v/v) fraction was further purified by preparative reversed-phased HPLC with water-acetonitrile (5:1, v/v) as mobile phase. This resulted in purified FS-4.

Spectral Data

UV:
$\lambda_{max}^{Acetonitrile}$ 198nm (ϵ = 10,400 π - π^* transition).

IR:
(film) 3450(OH) and 1690cm^{-1} (C=O).

^{1}H NMR:
($CDCl_3$) 6.27(1H, t, *J*=1.5Hz, H-2); 2.15(1H, d, *J*=19.0, H-4), 2.73(1H, d, *J*=19.0Hz, H-4); 1.40(1H, m, H-7); 1.70(1H, m, H-7); 1.70(1H, m, H-8); 1.85(1H, m, H-8); 5.25(1H, d, *J*=10.0Hz, H-10); 5.61(1H, dd, *J*=10.0, 1.5Hz, H-11); 4.69(1H, d, *J*=17.0, H-13); 4.35(1H, d, *J*=17.0, H-13); 1.29(3H, s, CH_3-14); 0.98(3H, s, CH_3-15); and 1.25ppm (3H, s, CH_3-16).

^{13}C NMR:

(CDCl$_3$) 128.1, C-2; 205.0, C-3; 49.0, C-4; 28.2, C-7; 32.5, C-8; 133.6, C-10; 130.9, C-11; 183.0, C-12; 62.0, C-13; 19.2, C-14; 18.0, C-15; and 29.0ppm (C-16).

Mass Spectrum:

EIMS: 235(4%, M^+ - Me), 125(86), 108(100), and 81*m/e* (83); exact mass for $C_8H_{13}O$ (M^+ - $C_7H_9O_2$) calcd. 125.097; found 125.096*m/e*; $C_7H_9O_2$ (M^+ - $C_8H_{13}O$) calcd 125.060, found 125.059; C_8H_{11} ($C_8H_{13}O$ - H_2O) calcd. 107.086, found 107.086.

References

D. R. Sanson, D. G. Corley, C. L. Barnes, S. Searles, E. O. Schlemper, M. S. Tempesta, and G. E. Rottinghaus; New Mycotoxins from *Fusarium sambucinum*; J. Org. Chem., Vol. 54, pp. 4313-4318(1989).

M. E. Savard and B. A. Blackwell; A Compilation of Spectral Characteristics of Secondary Metabolites from *Fusarium* Fungi; In Mycotoxins in Grain; Compounds Other Than Aflatoxin; J. D. Miller and H. L. Trenholm, eds., Eagan Press, St. Paul, pp. 59-257 (1994).

Common/Systematic Name

3-Ketoapotrichothecene

Molecular Formula/Molecular Weight

$C_{15}H_{22}O_3$; MW = 250.15689

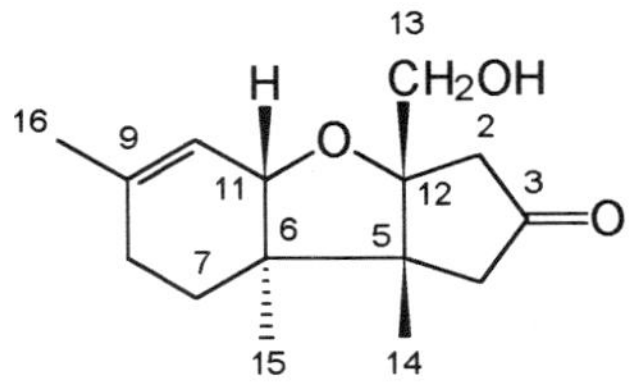

General Characteristics

Colorless glass.

Fungal Source

Fusarium sambucinum.

Isolation/Purification

Fungal cultures were extracted with chloroform-acetone (85:15, v/v), allowed to sit over night, filtered and the solid residue re-extracted with acetone. The acetone extract was combined with the chloroform-acetone extract, concentrated under vacuum and the non-polar materials removed by hexane drip. The solvent was decanted, concentrated and chromatographed by flash chromatography with toluene, toluene-acetone 4:1, 2:1, 1:1 (v/v), acetone, and acetone-methanol, 1:1 (v/v). The toluene-acetone (2:1, v/v) fraction was further purified by preparative normal-phase TLC which resulted in purified 3-ketoapotrichothecene.

Spectral Data

UV:

$\lambda_{max}^{Acetonitrile}$ 197nm (ϵ=8,600 π to π^* transition).

IR:

(film) 3420(OH) and 1737cm^{-1} (C=O).

^{1}H NMR:

($CDCl_3$) 2.60(1H, dd, *J*=20.0, 2.2Hz, H-2); 2.79(1H, dd, *J*=20.0, 1.4Hz, H-2); 2.14(1H, dd, *J*=19.2, 1.4Hz, H-4), 2.68(1H, dd, *J*=19.2, 2.2Hz, H-4); 1.48(1H, m, H-7); 1.63(1H, m, H-7); 2.05, 2.15(2H, m, H-8); 5.55(1H, m, H-10); 4.23(1H, m, H-11); 3.53(1H, d, *J*=11.3Hz, H-13); 3.83(1H, d, *J*=11.3Hz, H-13); 1.16(3H, s, CH_3-14); 0.76(3H, s, CH_3-15); and 1.68ppm (3H, s, CH_3-16).

^{13}C NMR:

(CDCl$_3$) 49.6, C-2; 215.5, C-3; 49.6, C-4; 51.3, C-5; 46.2, C-6; 28.8, C-7; 26.8, C-8; 135.7, C-9; 210.4, C-10; 80.1, C-11; 90.8, C-12; 65.0, C-13; 19.2, C-14; 15.3, C-15; and 22.6ppm (C-16).

Mass Spectrum:

HREIMS: 250.158*m/e* (M^+); calcd for $C_{15}H_{22}O_3$, 250.156. LREIMS: 250(M^+ ,15%), 235(38), 124(45), 107(50), and 43*m/e* (100).

References

D. R. Sanson, D. G. Corley, C. L. Barnes, S. Searles, E. O. Schlemper, M. S. Tempesta, and G. E. Rottinghaus; New Mycotoxins from *Fusarium sambucinum*; J. Org. Chem., Vol. 54, pp. 4313-4318(1989).

M. E. Savard and B. A. Blackwell; A Compilation of Spectral Characteristics of Secondary Metabolites from *Fusarium* Fungi; In Mycotoxins in Grain; Compounds Other Than Aflatoxin; J. D. Miller and H. L. Trenholm, eds., Eagan Press, St. Paul, pp. 59-257 (1994).

Common/Systematic Name

3α-Hydroxyapotrichothecene

3α,13-Dihydroxy-11-epiapotrichothec-9-ene

Molecular Formula/Molecular Weight

$C_{15}H_{24}O_3$; MW = 252.17254

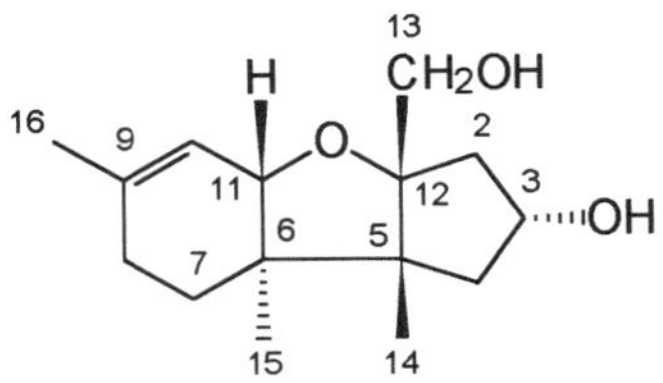

General Characteristics

Crystals from 2-propanol-hexane; mp., 167-169°C; $[\alpha]_D$ - 33.2° (in EtOH).

Fungal Source

Fusarium sambucinum, F. graminearum (ATCC 28114), *F. crookwellense, F. culmorum,* and *F. sporotrichioides.*

Isolation/Purification

Fungal cultures were extracted with chloroform-acetone (85:15, v/v), allowed to sit over night, filtered and the solid residue re-extracted with acetone. The acetone extract was combined with the chloroform-acetone extract, concentrated under vacuum and the non-polar materials removed by hexane drip. The solvent was decanted, concentrated and chromatographed by flash chromatography with toluene, toluene-acetone 4:1, 2:1, 1:1 (v/v), acetone, and acetone-methanol, 1:1 (v/v). The toluene-acetone (1:1, v/v) fraction was further purified by reversed-phase TLC using methanol-water, 7:3 (v/v), which resulted in purified 3α-hydroxyapotrichothecene. Alternatively, the crude extract from *F. graminearum* was chromatographed on Florisil; after removal of 3-acetyldeoxynivalenol, an oil remained which was chromatographed by medium-pressure liquid chromatography using LiChroprep silica gel column eluted with the following: 10% ethyl acetate-hexane; 20% ethyl acetate-hexane; 30% ethyl acetate-hexane; and ethyl acetate. The later fractions eluting with ethyl acetate contained the 3α and 3β-isomers; these were separated by preparative HPLC using a CSC-S nitrile column with a 6% 2-propanol-hexane mobile phase and a flow rate of 4 ml/minute.

Spectral Data

UV:

$\lambda_{max}^{Acetonitrile}$ 196nm (ε=7,200 π to π* transition).

IR:
(film) 3400cm^{-1} (OH).

^{1}H NMR:
($CDCl_3$) 1.74(1H, m, H-2); 2.62(1H, ddd, *J*=1.7, 6.1, 12.3Hz, H-2); 4.30(1H, b m, H-3), 1.64(1H, m, H-4); 2.15(1H, dd, *J*=10.3, 13.0Hz, H-4); 1.40(1H, dddd, *J*=2.0, 4.0, 5.8, 13.0Hz, H-7); 1.58(1H, m, H-7); 2.02(1H, m, H-8); 1.62(1H, b m, H-8); 5.55(1H, b sptet, H-10); 4.18(1H, b sptet, H-11); 3.18(1H, b t, *J*=11.1Hz, H-13); 3.77(1H, dd, *J*=8.0, 11.1Hz, H-13); 1.02(3H, s, CH_3-14); 0.95(3H, s, CH_3-15); and 1.50ppm (3H, q, *J*=1.4Hz, CH_3-16).

^{13}C NMR:
($CDCl_3$) 44.4, C-2; 72.8, C-3; 43.5, C-4; 52.5, C-5; 44.7, C-6; 27.8, C-7; 29.3, C-8; 135.5, C-9; 21.4, C-10; 81.3, C-11; 92.5, C-12; 63.3, C-13; 19.2, C-14; 17.9, C-15; and 22.6ppm (C-16).

Mass Spectrum:
HREIMS: 252.173*m/e* (M^+); calcd for $C_{15}H_{24}O_3$, 252.186. LREIMS: 252(M^+, 28%), 237(17), 140(100), and 124*m/e* (51).

References

R. Greenhalgh, D. A. Fielder, L. A. Morrison, J-P Charland, B. A. Blackwell, M. E. Savard, and J. W. Apsimon; Secondary Metabolites of *Fusarium* species: Apotrichothecene Derivatives; J. Agric. food Chem., Vol. 37, pp. 699-705(1989).

D. R. Sanson, D. G. Corley, C. L. Barnes, S. Searles, E. O. Schlemper, M. S. Tempesta, and G. E. Rottinghaus; New Mycotoxins from *Fusarium sambucinum*; J. Org. Chem., Vol. 54, pp. 4313-4318(1989).

M. E. Savard and B. A. Blackwell; A Compilation of Spectral Characteristics of Secondary Metabolites from *Fusarium* Fungi; In Mycotoxins in Grain; Compounds Other Than Aflatoxin; J. D. Miller and H. L. Trenholm, eds., Eagan Press, St. Paul, pp. 59-257 (1994).

Common/Systematic Name

3β-Hydroxyapotrichothecene

Molecular Formula/Molecular Weight

$C_{15}H_{24}O_3$; MW = 252.17254

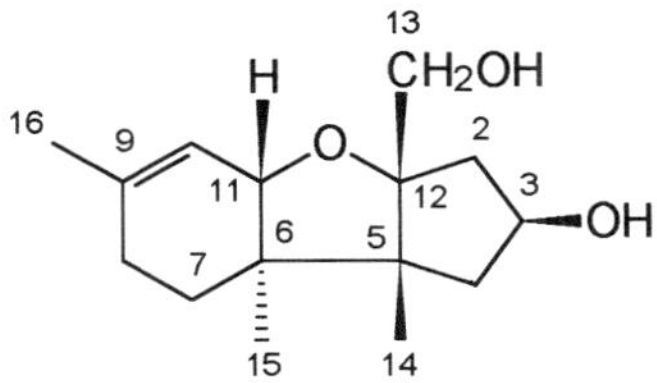

General Characteristics

Colorless glass.

Fungal Source

Fusarium sambucinum.

Isolation/Purification

Fungal cultures were extracted with chloroform-acetone (85:15, v/v), allowed to sit over night, filtered and the solid residue re-extracted with acetone. The acetone extract was combined with the chloroform-acetone extract, concentrated under vacuum and the non-polar materials removed by hexane drip. The solvent was decanted, concentrated and chromatographed by flash chromatography with toluene, toluene-acetone 4:1, 2:1, 1:1 (v/v), acetone, and acetone-methanol, 1:1 (v/v). The toluene-acetone (1:1, v/v) fraction was further purified by reversed-phase TLC using methanol-water, 7:3 (v/v), which resulted in purified 3β-hydroxyapotrichothecene.

Spectral Data

UV:

$\lambda_{max}^{Acetonitrile}$ 196nm (ε=7,800 π to π* transition).

IR:

(film) 3420 and 1048cm^{-1} (-C-O-C-).

^{1}H NMR:

($CDCl_3$) 1.38(1H, m, H-2); 2.45(1H, ddd, *J*=1.3, 5.8, 6.4Hz, H-2); 4.51(1H, b m, H-3), 2.10(1H, H-4); 2.23(1H, H-4); 1.36(1H, m, H-7); 1.57(1H, m, H-7); 1.99(2H, m, H-8); 5.50(1H, H-10); 4.11(1H, H-11); 3.56(1H, d, *J*=11.4Hz, H-13); 3.78(1H, d, *J*=11.4Hz, H-13); 1.07(3H, s, CH_3-14); 0.52(3H, s, CH_3-15); and 1.63ppm (3H, b s, CH_3-16).

^{13}C NMR:

($CDCl_3$) 47.0, C-2; 74.2, C-3; 45.7, C-4; not observed, C-5; not observed, C-6; 27.5, C-7; 29.3, C-8; not observed, C-9; 122.5, C-10; 81.3, C-11; not observed, C-12; 65.5, C-13; 20.0, C-14; 16.5, C-15; and 22.5ppm (C-16).

Mass Spectrum:

HREIMS: 252.181*m/e* (M^+); calcd for $C_{15}H_{24}O_3$, 252.186. LREIMS: 252(M^+, 15%), 237(15), 124(38), 107(92), and 83*m/e* (100).

Reference

D. R. Sanson, D. G. Corley, C. L. Barnes, S. Searles, E. O. Schlemper, M. S. Tempesta, and G. E. Rottinghaus; New Mycotoxins from *Fusarium sambucinum*; J. Org. Chem., Vol. 54, pp. 4313-4318(1989).

Macrocyclic Trichothecenes and Related Metabolites

16

Trichodermadiene
Trichodermadienediol A
Trichodermadienediol B
12,13-Deoxytrichodermadiene
Verrol
Trichoverrol A
(C6'*R*,C7'*R*)-Isotrichoverrol A
(2'*E*,C6'*R*,C7'*R*)-Isotrichoverrol A
Trichoverrol B
(C6'*R*,C7'*S*)-Isotrichoverrol B
(2'*E*,C6'*R*,C7'*S*)-Isotrichoverrol B
Trichoverrin A
(2'*E*,4'*Z*)-Isotrichoverrin A
(C6'*R*,C7'*R*)-Isotrichoverrin A
9β,10β-Epoxyisotrichoverrin A
8α-Hydroxyisotrichoverrin A
Trichoverrin B
(C6'*R*,C7'*R*)-Isotrichoverrin B
(2'*E*,4'*Z*)-Isotrichoverrin B
9β,10β-Epoxyisotrichoverrin B
(2'*E*)-12,13-Deoxyisotrichoverrin B
(9'*E*)-Roridin L-2
Roridin L-2
Verrucarin A
Verrucarin A β-D-glucoside
2'-Dehydroverrucarin A
Verrucarin B
Verrucarin J
Verrucarin K
Verrucarin L
Verrucarin L Acetate
Roridin A
Roridin A 13β-D-glucoside
8α-Butoyloxyroridin A
8α-Crotonyloxyroridin A
Isororidin A
Roridin D
Roridin D β-D-glucoside
Roridin E
Roridin E β-D-glucoside
Isororidin E
Epiroridin E
Epiisororidin E
7β,8β-Epoxyisororidin E

Roridin K Acetate
Roridin H (Verrucarin H)
Roridin J
7β,8β-Epoxyroridin H
7β,8β,2',3'-Diepoxyisororidin H
Satratoxin F
Satratoxin G
Isosatratoxin F
Isosatratoxin G
Satratoxin H
S-Isosatratoxin H
12'-Hydroxy-2'-isoverrucarin J (PD 113,325)
M-Isosatratoxin H (PD 113,326)
Vertisporin

Common/Systematic Name

Trichodermadiene

Molecular Formula/Molecular Weight

$C_{23}H_{30}O_5$; MW = 386.20932

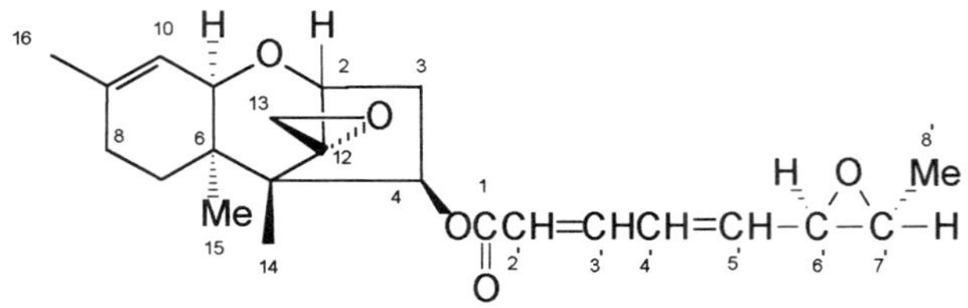

General Characteristics

Crystallization from ether gave needles; mp., 145-146°; $[\alpha]_D^{27}$ +17.7°(*c*=3.2, in $CHCl_3$).

Fungal Source

Myrothecium verrucaria (ATCC 24571).

Isolation/Purification

Trichodermadiene was isolated by a methanol extraction of the mycelium of a fermentation of *Myrothecium verrucaria*. Chromatography on silica gel gave a series of the less polar trichothecenes (roridin H and verrucarins B and J) and a previously uncharacterized trichothecene which had an R_f value higher than any heretofore reported macrocyclic trichothecene. Crystallization from ether gave needles.

Biological Activity

Trichodermadiene showed a T/C = 143 at 26mg/kg *in vivo* against p388 mouse leukemia (PS).

Spectral Data

UV:

λ_{max}^{EtOH} 264nm (log ϵ = 4.41).

IR:

($CHCl_3$) 1700, 1640, and 1600cm^{-1}.

^{1}H NMR:

($CDCl_3$) 3.83(1H, d, *J*=5.0Hz, H-2); 2.1(1H, m, H-3β); 2.66(1H, dd, *J*=7.5, 15.0Hz, H-3α); 5.7(1H.dd, *J*=4.0, 7.5Hz, H-4); 5.43(1H, d, *J*=5.5Hz, H-10); 3.64(1H, d, *J*=5.5Hz, H-11); 2.97(2H, J_{AB}=4.0Hz, H-13); 0.74(3H, s, H-14); 1.0(3H, s, H-15); 1.72(3H, s, H-16); 5.7(1H, d, *J*=11.0Hz, H-2'); 6.57(1H, t, *J*=11.0Hz, H-3'); 7.83(1H, dd, *J*=11, 15.5Hz, H-4'); 5.7(1H, dd, *J*=8, 15.5Hz, H-5'); 3.21(1H, dd, *J*=2.0, 8.0Hz,

H-6'); 2.97(1H. dq, *J*= 2.0, 5Hz, H-7'); and 1.36ppm (1H, d, *J*= 5.0Hz, H-7').

^{13}C NMR:

($CDCl_3$) 79.2 d, C-2; 36.9 t, C-3; 75.0 d, C-4; 49.2 s, C-5; 40.5 s, C-6; 24.6 t, C-7; 28.1 t, C-8; 140.0 s, C-9; 118.9 d, C-10; 70.6 d, C-11; 65.5 s, C-12; 47.8 t, C-13; 6.0 q, C-14; 16.1 q, C-15; 23.2 q, C-16; 165.8 s, C-1'; 118.4 d, C-2'; 143.1 d, C-3'; 130.3 d, C-4'; 140.4 d, C-5'; 58.8 d, C-6'; 56.8 d, C-7'; and 17.5ppm q, C-8'.

Mass Data:

EIMS: 386*m/e* (M^+); anal. calcd for $C_{23}H_{30}O_5$: C, 71.48; H, 7.82%; found: C, 71.38, H, 8.07%.

Reference

B. B. Jarvis, J.O. Midiwo, G. P. Stahly, G. Pavanasasivam, and E.P. Mazzola; Trichodermadiene: A New Trichothecene; Tetrahedron Letters, Vol. 21, pp. 787-788(1980).

Common/Systematic Name

Trichodermadienediol A

Molecular Formula/Molecular Weight

$C_{23}H_{32}O_6$; MW = 404.21989

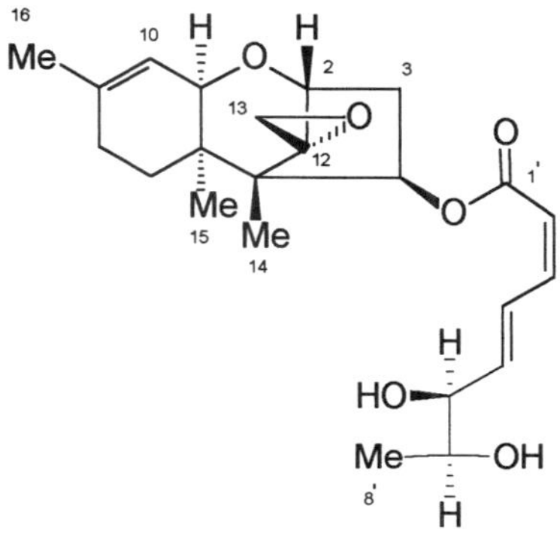

General Characteristics

Crystallization from dichloromethane-hexane; mp., 184-185°; $[\alpha]_D^{28}$ +26.3° (*c*=0.39, in $CHCl_3$).

Fungal Source

Myrothecium verrucaria (ATCC 24571).

Isolation/Purification

The fungal culture broth was passed through XAD-2 resin; the resin was eluted with methanol yielding an aqueous methanol fraction that was concentrated to yield an aqueous concentrate. A portion of the aqueous concentrate was extracted with ethyl acetate. The organic extract was washed with water and saturated salt solution and dried. Removal of the solvent by rotary evaporation yielded a dark brown gum. HPLC analysis indicated that the principal trichothecenes present were verrucarin J, verrucarin B, verrucarin A, isororidin E, roridin E, roridin A, trichodermadienediols A and B, trichoverrols A and B, and trichoverrins A and B in the order of increasing retention time on a silica column (ethyl acetate-hexane eluent). The gum was subjected to flash chromatography (silica gel) with increasing amounts of methanol in dichloromethane to yield four fractions: I (eluted with 0-1% methanol in methylene chloride), II (eluted with 1-5% methanol in methylene chloride), III (eluted with 5-7.5% methanol in methylene chloride), and IV (eluted with methanol). Fraction II was subjected to partition chromatography. The sample was applied to a column of Celite impregnated with 83% aqueous methanol and eluted with 1-5% dichloromethane in petroleum ether to give a fraction rich in the trichothecenes. This was chromatographed to yield an oil, R_f 0.15-0.20 (silica gel, 3% methanol in methylene chloride). This material was subjected to HPLC (1-4% methanol-methylene chloride gradient) followed by HPLC with 70% ethyl acetate in hexane to yield trichodermadienediol A and trichodermadienediol B.

Spectral Data

UV:
λ_{max}^{MeOH} 260nm (log ϵ=4.53).

^{1}H NMR:
($CDCl_3$) 0.76(3H, s, 14-H); 0.98(3H, s, 15-H); 1.13(3H, d, *J*=6Hz, 8'-H); 1.74(3H, s, 16-H); 2.60(1H, dd, *J*=8 and 15Hz, 3α-H); 3.03(2H, AB, *J*=4Hz, 13-H); 3.66(1H, d, *J*=5 Hz, 11-H); 3.87(1H, d, *J*=5Hz, 2-H); 4.06(1H, m, 6'-H); 5.44(1H, d, *J*=5Hz, 10-H); 5.73(1H, d, *J*=11Hz, 2'-H); 6.09(1H, dd, *J*=6, 16Hz, 5'-H); 6.64(1H, dd, *J*=11Hz, 3'-H); and 7.65ppm (1H, dd, J =11.0, 16Hz, 4'-H.

^{13}C NMR:
($CDCl_3$) 79.1 d, C-2; 37.0 t, C-3; 75.0 d, C-4; 49.3 s, C-5; 40.5 s, C-6; 24.5 t, C-7; 28.1 t, C-8; 140.2 s, C-9; 118.7 d, C-10; 70.6 d, C-11; 66.1 s, C-12; 48.1 t, C-13; 6.2 q, C-14; 16.1 q, C-15; 23.2 q, C-16; 166.0 s, C-1'; 118.7 d, C-2'; 143.4 d, C-3'; 127.9 d, C-4'; 141.9 d, C-5'; 76.6 d, C-6'; 70.6 d, C-7'; and 18.9ppm q, C-8'.

Mass Spectrum:
HRCIMS (methane gas reagent): 405.2263*m/e* (M^+ + H, calcd 405.2277); diacetate, 489.2455*m/e* (M^+ + H, calcd 489.2488).

Reference

B. B. Jarvis, G. P. Stahly, G. Pavanasasivam, J. O. Midiwo, T. Desilva, C. E. Holmlund, E.P. Mazzola and R. F. Geoghegan; Isolation and Characterization of the Trichoverroids and New Roridins and Verrucarins, J. Org. Chem.,Vol. 47, pp. 1117-1124(1982).

Common/Systematic Name

Trichodermadienediol B

Molecular Formula/Molecular Weight

$C_{23}H_{32}O_6$; MW = 404.21989

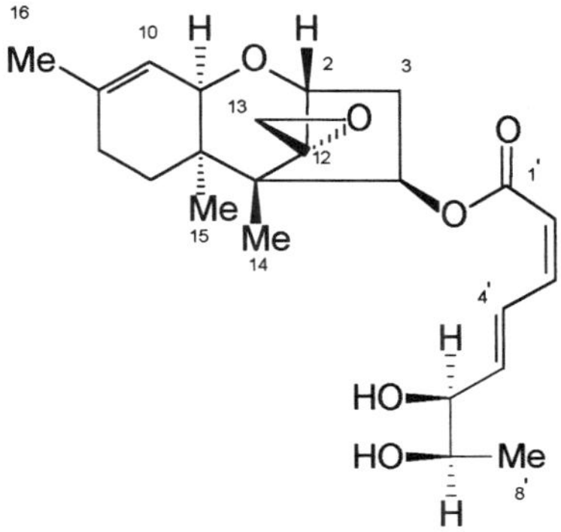

General Characteristics

Isolated as an oil; $[\alpha]_D^{28}$ - 15.8° (*c*=0.80, in $CHCl_3$).

Fungal Source

Myrothecium verrucaria (ATCC 24571).

Isolation/Purification

The fungal culture broth was passed through XAD-2 resin; the resin was eluted with methanol yielding an aqueous methanol fraction that was concentrated to yield an aqueous concentrate. A portion of the aqueous concentrate was extracted with ethyl acetate. The organic extract was washed with water and saturated salt solution and dried. Removal of the solvent by rotary evaporation yielded a dark brown gum. HPLC analysis indicated that the principal trichothecenes present were verrucarin J, verrucarin B, verrucarin A, isororidin E, roridin E, roridin A, trichodermadienediols A and B, trichoverrols A and B, and trichoverrins A and B in the order of increasing retention time on a silica column (ethyl acetate-hexane eluent). The gum was subjected to flash chromatography (silica gel) with increasing amounts of methanol in dichloromethane to yield four fractions: I (eluted with 0-1% methanol-methylene chloride), II (eluted with 1-5% methanol-methylene chloride), III (eluted with 5-7.5% methanol-methylene chloride), and IV (eluted with methanol). Fraction II was subjected to partition chromatography. The sample was applied to a column of Celite impregnated with 83% aqueous methanol and eluted with 1-5% dichloromethane in petroleum ether to give a fraction rich in the trichothecenes. This was chromatographed to yield an oil, R_f, 0.15-0.20 (silica gel, 3% methanol-methylene chloride). This material was subjected to HPLC (1-4% methanol-methylene chloride gradient) followed by HPLC with 70% ethyl acetate in hexane to yield trichodermadienediol A and trichodermadienediol B.

Spectral Data

UV:

λ_{max}^{MeOH} 260nm (log ϵ=4.55).

^{1}H NMR:

(CDCl$_3$) 0.74(3H, s, 14-H); 0.98(3H, s, 15-H); 1.16(3H, d, *J*=6Hz, 8'-H); 1.73(3H, s, 16-H); 2.62(1H, dd, *J*=8,15Hz, 3α-H); 3.04(2H, AB, *J*=4Hz, 13-H); 3.66(1H, d, *J*=5Hz, 11-H); 3.88(1H, d, *J*=5Hz, 2-H); 4.30(1H, m, 6'-H); 5.44(1H, d, *J*=5Hz, 10-H); 5.72(1H, d, *J*=11Hz, 2'-H); 6.16(1H, dd, *J*=6, 16Hz, 5'-H); 6.66(1H, dd, *J*'s=11Hz, 3'-H); and 7.64ppm (1H, dd, *J*=11, 16Hz, 4'-H); trichodermadienediol B diacetate, 0.74(3H, s, 14-H); 0.98(3H, s, 15-H); 1.23(3H, d, *J*=6Hz, 8'-H); 1.74(3H, s, 16-H); 2.06 and 2.12(3H each, s, acetates); 2.60(1H, dd, *J*=8, 15Hz, 3α-H); 3.00(2H, AB, *J*=4Hz, 13-H); 3.64(1H, d, *J*=5Hz, 11-H); 3.86(1H, d, *J*=5 Hz, 2-H); 5.16(1H, dq, *J*=4, 6Hz, 7'-H); 6.60(1H, dd, *J*'s=11Hz, 3'-H); and 7.68ppm (1H, dd, *J*=11, 16Hz, 4'-H).

^{13}C NMR:

(CDCl$_3$) 79.1 d, C-2; 36.9 t, C-3; 74.9 d, C-4; 49.2 s, C-5; 40.5 s, C-6; 24.5 t, C-7; 28.0 t, C-8; 140.3 s, C-9; 118.6 d, C-10; 70.6 d, C-11; 66.1 s, C-12; 48.1 t, C-13; 6.1 q, C-14; 16.0 q, C-15; 23.2 q, C-16; 166.0 s, C-1'; 118.2 d, C-2'; 143.7 d, C-3'; 128.0 d, C-4'; 141.3 d, C-5'; 75.6 d, C-6'; 70.3 d, C-7'; and 17.7ppm q, C-8'.

Mass Spectrum:

HRCIMS (methane gas reagent): 405.2252*m/e* (M$^+$ + H, calcd 405.2277); diacetate, 489.2436*m/e* (M$^+$ + H, calcd 489.2488).

Reference

B. B. Jarvis, G. P. Stahly, G. Pavanasasivam, J. O. Midiwo, T. Desilva, C. E. Holmlund, E. P. Mazzola, and R. F. Geoghegan; Isolation and Characterization of the Trichoverroids and New Roridins and Verrucarins; J. Org. Chem.,Vol. 47, pp. 1117-1124(1982).

Common/Systematic Name

12,13-Deoxytrichodermadiene

Molecular Formula/Molecular Weight

$C_{23}H_{30}O_4$; MW = 370.21441

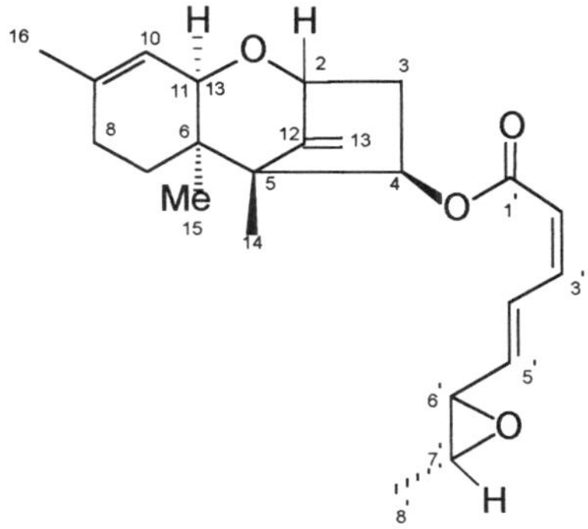

General Characteristics

Isolated as an oil; $[\alpha]_D^{25}$ - 5.6° (*c*=0.95, in $CHCl_3$).

Fungal Source

Myrothecium verrucaria (ATCC 24571).

Isolation/Purification

The fungal culture broth was passed through XAD-2 resin; the resin was eluted with methanol yielding an aqueous methanol fraction that was concentrated to yield an aqueous concentrate. A portion of the aqueous concentrate was extracted with ethyl acetate. The organic extract was washed with water and saturated salt solution and dried. Removal of the solvent by rotary evaporation yielded a dark brown gum. The gum was subjected to flash chromatography (silica gel) with increasing amounts of methanol in dichloromethane to yield four fractions: I (eluted with 0-1% methanol-methylene chloride), II (eluted with 1-5% methanol-methylene chloride), III (eluted with 5-7.5% methanol-methylene chloride), and IV (eluted with methanol). Fraction I was passed through a silica gel flash column and eluted with dichloromethane to yield several fractions. The first fraction was subjected to preparative TLC (20% hexane in methylene chloride) on 2-mm silica gel plates to yield an oil. Further purification was done on a Magnum-9 column (silica gel) under gradient conditions (90-100% methylene chloride in hexane) to give 12,13-deoxytrichodermadiene as an oil.

Spectral Data

UV:

λ_{max}^{MeOH} 265nm (log ϵ=3.42).

^{1}H NMR:

($CDCl_3$) 0.98(3H, s, 14-H); 0.98(3H, s, 15-H); 1.40(3H, d, *J*=5Hz, 8'-H); 1.72(3H, br s, 16-H); 2.00(1H, m, H-3β); 2.62(1H, dd, *J*=7 and 15Hz, 3α-H); 4.75, 5.16(1H each, s, 13-H); 3.68(1H, d, *J*=5 Hz, 11-H); 4.47(1H, d, *J*=5Hz, 2-H); 3.21(1H, dd, *J*=2.0, 8.0Hz, 6'-H); 5.40(1H, d, *J*=5Hz, 10-H); 5.80(1H, d, *J*=11Hz, 2'-H); 5.70(1H, dd, *J*=8, 15Hz, 5'-H); 6.60(1H, t, *J*=11Hz, 3'-H); 7.75(1H, dd, *J*=11.0, 15Hz, 4'-H); 5.70(1H, dd, *J*=8, 15Hz, 5'-H); 3.21(1H, dd, *J*=2, 8Hz, 6'-H); and 3.01ppm (1H, dq, *J*=2, 5Hz, 7'-H).

^{13}C NMR:

($CDCl_3$) 75.7, C-2; 38.0, C-3; 75.1, C-4; 52.1, C-5; 40.4, C-6; 23.6, C-7; 28.1, C-8; 139.8, C-9; 119.0, C-10; 70.6, C-11; 152.7, C-12; 104.9, C-13; 10.2, C-14; 16.2, C-15; 23.3, C-16; 169.4, C-1'; 118.3, C-2'; 143.2, C-3'; 129.9, C-4'; 140.3, C-5'; 58.8, C-6'; 57.0, C-7'; and 17.5ppm, C-8'.

Mass Spectrum:

HRCIMS (methane gas reagent), 371.2216*m/e* (M^+ + H, calcd 371.2222).

Reference

B. B. Jarvis, V. M. Vrudhula, J. O. Mikiwo, and E. P. Mazzola; New Trichoverroids from *Myrothecium verrucaria*: Verrol and 12,13-Deoxytrichodermadiene; J. Org. Chem., Vol. 48, pp. 2576-2578 (1983).

Common/Systematic Name
Verrol

Molecular Formula/Molecular Weight
$C_{21}H_{30}O_6$; MW = 378.20424

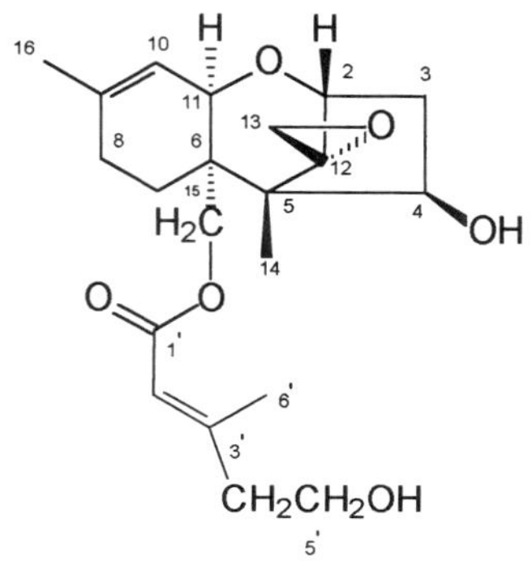

General Characteristics
Isolated as an oil.

Fungal Source
Myrothecium verrucaria (ATCC 24571).

Isolation/Purification
The fungal culture broth was passed through XAD-2 resin; the resin was eluted with methanol yielding an aqueous methanol fraction that was concentrated to yield an aqueous concentrate. A portion of the aqueous concentrate was extracted with ethyl acetate. The organic extract was washed with water and saturated salt solution and dried. Removal of the solvent by rotary evaporation yielded a dark brown gum. HPLC analysis indicated that the principal trichothecenes present were verrucarin J, verrucarin B, verrucarin A, isororidin E, roridin E, roridin A, trichodermadienediols A and B, trichoverrols A and B, and trichoverrins A and B in the order of increasing retention time on a silica column (ethyl acetate-hexane eluent). The gum was subjected to flash chromatography (silica gel) with increasing amounts of methanol in dichloromethane to yield four fractions: I (eluted with 0-1% methanol-methylene chloride), II (eluted with 1-5% methanol-methylene chloride), III (eluted with 5-7.5% methanol-methylene chloride), and IV (eluted with methanol). Fraction III of the crude extract was subjected to flash chromatography (silica gel, 0-8% methanol in methylene chloride) to yield three major fractions rich in roridin A, verrol, and trichoverrins, respectively. The verrol containing fraction was subjected to flash chromatography again under the conditions described above to yield a fraction which was mostly verrol and trichoverrols. This was further purified by column chromatography on silica (10-25% 2-propanol in hexane) to yield verrol as an oil.

Spectral Data

^{1}H NMR:

(CDCl$_3$) 0.87(3H, s, 14-H); 1.70(3H, br s, 16-H); 2.60(1H, dd, *J*=7.5, 15.7Hz, 3α-H); 2.00(1H, m, 3β-H); 2.96(2H, AB, *J*=3.9Hz, 13-H); 5.42(1H, d, *J*=5.4Hz, 10-H); 5.73(1H, q, *J*=1.2Hz, 2'-H); 2.42(1H, t, *J*=6.1, 4'-H); 3.82(1H, d, *J*=5.1Hz, 2-H); 1.9(2H, m, 7-H); 2.0(2H, m, 8-H); 3.64(1H, d, *J*=5.4Hz, 11-H); 2.96(2H, AB, *J*=3.9Hz, 13-H); 4.05(2H, AB, *J*=12.4Hz, 15-H); 3.80(2H, t, *J*=6.1Hz, 5'-H); and 2.21ppm (3H, d, *J* =1.2Hz, 6'-H).

^{13}C NMR:

(CDCl$_3$) 78.8, C-2; 39.9, C-3; 74.5, C-4; 49.2, C-5; 42.8, C-6; 21.4, C-7; 28.1, C-8; 140.7, C-9; 118.6, C-10; 66.7, C-11; 65.6, C-12; 47.6, C-13; 7.1, C-14; 62.9, C-15; 23.1, C-16; 166.0, C-1'; 117.2, C-2'; 157.3, C-3'; 43.9, C-4'; 60.3, C-5'; and 18.8ppm, C-6'.

Mass Spectrum:

HRCIMS (methane gas reagent): 379.2112*m/e* (M^+ + H, calcd 379.2120).

Reference

B. B. Jarvis, V. M. Vrudhula, J. O. Mikiwo, and E. P. Mazzola; New Trichoverroids from *Myrothecium verrucaria*: Verrol and 12,13-Deoxytrichodermadiene; J. Org. Chem., Vol. 48, pp. 2576-2578(1983).

Common/Systematic Name

Trichoverrol A

Molecular Formula/Molecular Weight

$C_{23}H_{32}O_7$; MW = 420.21480

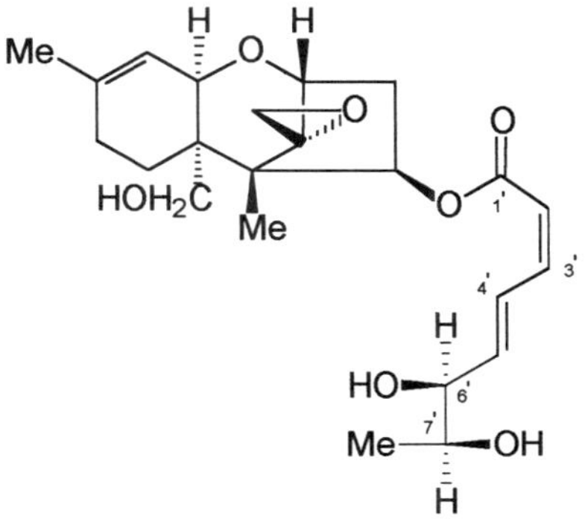

General Characteristics

Crystals from ethyl acetate-petroleum ether; mp., 177-179°; $[\alpha]_D^{28}$ +37.7° (*c*=0.45, in $CHCl_3$).

Fungal Source

Myrothecium verrucaria (ATCC 24571).

Isolation/Purification

The fungal culture broth was passed through XAD-2 resin; the resin was eluted with methanol yielding an aqueous methanol fraction that was concentrated to yield an aqueous concentrate. A portion of the aqueous concentrate was extracted with ethyl acetate. The organic extract was washed with water and saturated salt solution and dried. Removal of the solvent by rotary evaporation yielded a dark brown gum. HPLC analysis indicated that the principal trichothecenes present were verrucarin J, verrucarin B, verrucarin A, isororidin E, roridin E, roridin A, trichodermadienediols A and B, trichoverrols A and B, and trichoverrins A and B in the order of increasing retention time on a silica column (ethyl acetate-hexane eluent). The gum was subjected to flash chromatography (silica gel) with increasing amounts of methanol in dichloromethane to yield four fractions: I (eluted with 0-1% methanol-methylene chloride), II (eluted with 1-5% methanol-methylene chloride), III (eluted with 5-7.5% methanol-methylene chloride), and IV (eluted with methanol). Fraction III of the crude extract was subjected to partition chromatography. The sample was applied to a column of Celite impregnated with 83% aqueous methanol and eluted with 15% dichloromethane in petroleum ether to give a gum. Flash chromatography (90% ethyl acetate-petroleum ether) yielded two major fractions, III-A (R_f, 0.35 in 90% ethyl acetate-petroleum ether) and III-B (R_f, 0.30 in 90% ethyl acetate-petroleum ether). After filtration through TLC grade silica gel, each of these fractions was purified by HPLC (1-6% methanol-methylene chloride, gradient, 30 min) to give trichoverrol A and trichoverrol B from fraction III-A and trichoverrin A and trichoverrin B from fraction III-B.

Spectral Data

UV:
λ_{max}^{MeOH} 260nm (log ϵ=4.56).

^{1}H NMR:
($CDCl_3$) 0.84(3H, s, 14-H); 1.19(3H, d, *J*=6Hz, 8'-H); 1.72(3H, s, 16-H); 2.46(1H, dd, *J*=8, 15Hz, 3α-H); 3.00(2H, AB, *J*=4Hz, 13-H); 5.49(1H, d, *J*=5Hz, 10-H); 5.73(1H, d, *J*=11Hz, 2'-H); 6.66(1H, dd, *J*s=11Hz, 3'-H); 7.62(1H, dd, *J*=11, 16Hz, 4'-H).

^{13}C NMR:
($CDCl_3$) 79.0d, C-2; 36.3 t, C-3; 75.5 d, C-4; 49.1 s, C-5; 44.4 s, C-6; 21.3 t, C-7; 28.2 t, C-8; 140.6 s, C-9; 118.8 d, C-10; 66.9 d, C-11; 66.1 s, C-12; 48.3 t, C-13; 6.8 q, C-14; 62.7 t, C-15; 23.3 q, C-16; 166.9 s, C-1'; 118.2 d, C-2'; 144.2 d, C-3'; 127.8 d, C-4'; 142.5 d, C-5'; 76.5 d, C-6'; 70.7 d, C-7'; and 19.0ppm q, C-8'.

Mass Spectrum:
HRCIMS (methane gas reagent): 421.2226*m/e* (M^+ + H, calcd 421.2226).

Reference

B. B. Jarvis, G. P. Stahly, G. Pavanasasivam, J. O. Midiwo, T. Desilva, C. E. Holmlund, E. P. Mazzola and R. F. Geoghegan; Isolation and Characterization of the Trichoverroids and New Roridins and Verrucarins; J. Org. Chem., Vol. 47, pp. 1117-1124(1982).

Common/Systematic Name

(C6'*R*,C7'*R*)-Isotrichoverrol A

Molecular Formula/Molecular Weight

$C_{23}H_{32}O_7$; MW = 420.21480

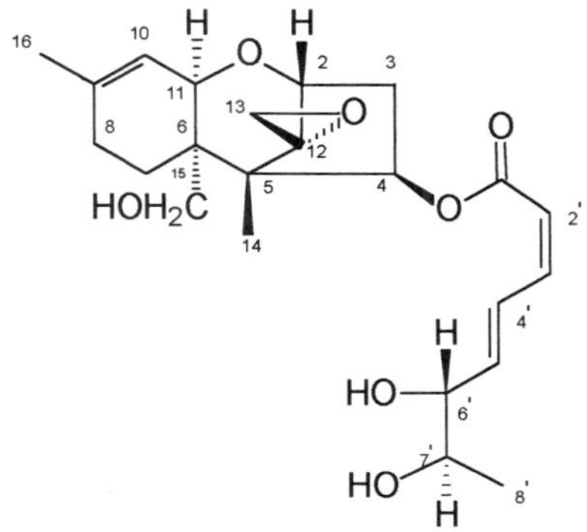

General Characteristics

Isotrichoverrol A was recrystallized from methylene chloride-hexane to give crystals; mp., 180-183°C; $[\alpha]_D^{20}$ +54.0° (*c*=1.65, in $CHCl_3$).

Fungal Source

*Myrothecium verrucaria (*ATCC 20540).

Isolation/Purification

The fermentation procedures with *Myrothecium verrucaria (*ATCC 20540) were carried out in a manner similar to those described previously (Jarvis *et al.*, 1982). Samples 1-4 (S1, S2, S3, and S4) from this isolate were the lower R_f fractions from silica gel chromatography (methanol in methylene chloride), given in the order of increasing polarity. To sample 1, which contained some solid material, was added cold ethyl acetate. The solid was collected and recrystallized from methylene chloride-hexane to give (C6'*R*,C7'*R*)-isotrichoverrol A.

Spectral Data

^{1}H NMR:

($CDCl_3$) 0.81(3, s, H-14); 1.19(3H, d, *J*=6.3 Hz, H-8'); 1.54(1H, brd, *J*=7.6Hz, H-7A); 1.70(3H, s, H-16); 1.98(3H, m, H-7B, H-8); 2.08(1H, ddd, *J*=4.0, 5.1, 15.4Hz, H-3β), 2.49(1H, dd, *J*=8.0, 15.4Hz, H-3α); 2.83(1H, d, *J*=4.0Hz, H-13A); 3.14(1H, d, *J*=4.0Hz, H-13B); 3.63(1H, d, *J*=12.3Hz, H-15A); 3.67(1H, dq, *J*=6.3, 6.3Hz, H-7'); 3.80(1H, d, *J*=12.3Hz, H-15B); 3.83(1H, d, *J*=5.1Hz, H-2'); 3.88(1H, br d, *J*=5.0Hz, H-11); 4.03(1H, m, H-6'); 5.47(1H, br d, *J*=5.0Hz, H-10); 5.70(1H, d, *J*=11.5Hz, H-2'); 6.06(1H, dd, *J*=5.7, 15.5Hz, H-5'); 6.08(1H, m, H-4); 6.61(1H, dd, *J*=11.3, 11.5Hz, H-3'); and 7.59ppm (1H, dd, *J*=11.3, 15.5Hz, H-4').

^{13}C NMR:
($CDCl_3$) 79.0d, C-2; 36.3 t, C-3; 75.5 d, C-4; 49.1 s, C-5; 44.4 s, C-6; 21.3 t, C-7; 28.2 t, C-8; 140.6 s, C-9; 118.8 d, C-10; 66.9 d, C-11; 66.1 s, C-12; 48.3 t, C-13; 6.8 q, C-14; 62.7 t, C-15; 23.3 q, C-16; 166.9 s, C-1'; 118.2 d, C-2'; 144.2 d, C-3'; 127.8 d, C-4'; 142.5 d, C-5'; 76.5 d, C-6'; 70.7 d, C-7'; and 19.0ppm q, C-8'.

Mass Spectrum:
HRCIMS: calcd for $C_{23}H_{33}O_7$ ($[M^+ + H]^+$) 421.2226; found 421.2211*m/e*.

References

B. B. Jarvis; Macrocyclic Trichothecenes; In Mycotoxins and Phytoalexins; R. P. Sharma and D. K. Salunkhe, eds.; CRC Press, Boca Raton, Florida, pp. 361-421(1991).

B. B. Jarvis, G. P. Stahly, G. Pavanasasivam, J. O. Midiwo, T. Desilva, C. E. Holmlund, E.P. Mazzola and R. F. Geoghegan; Isolation and Characterization of the Trichoverroids and New Roridins and Verrucarins, J. Org. Chem.,Vol. 47, pp. 1117-1124(1982).

B. B. Jarvis, S. Wang, and H. L. Ammon; Trichoverroid Stereoisomers; J. Nat. Prod., Vol. 59, pp. 254-261(1996).

Common/Systematic Name

(2'*E*,C6'*R*,C7'*R*)-Isotrichoverrol A

Molecular Formula/Molecular Weight

$C_{23}H_{32}O_7$; MW = 420.21480

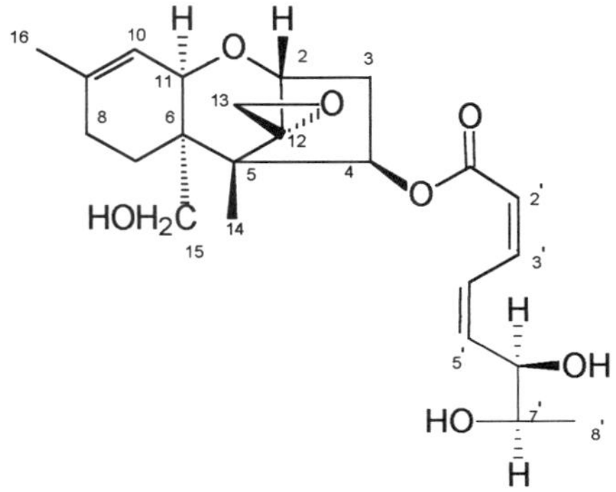

General Characteristics

Isolated as an oil.

Fungal Source

*Myrothecium verrucaria (*ATCC 20540).

Isolation/Purification

The fermentation procedures with *Myrothecium verrucaria (*ATCC 20540) were carried out in a manner similar to those described previously (Jarvis *et al*., 1982). Samples 1-4 (S1, S2, S3, and S4) from this isolate were the lower R_f fractions from silica gel chromatography (methanol-methylene chloride), given in the order of increasing polarity. To sample 1, which contained some solid material, was added cold ethyl acetate. The solid was collected and recrystallized from methylene chloride-hexane to give isotrichoverrol A. The remaining portion of S1 was subjected to semipreparative CCC (V_c=355ml) with a solvent system of methanol-water-chloroform-hexane (3:2:3:1.2, v/v/v/v), flow rate was 2.4ml/min (ca. 400mg/injection, total 10 injections) to give isotrichoverrol A and isotrichoverrol B. Another fraction from this CCC was subjected to CCC (semipreparative column) with a solvent system of methylene chloride-carbon tetrachloride-methanol-water (2:3:3:2, v/v/v/v) (ca. 400mg/injection). The major fraction of this sample was eluted with little retention from the column, and there were no detectable trichothecenes in this fraction, according to TLC analysis. Seven additional fractions were collected: S1F1a, S1F1b, S1F1c, S1F1d, S1F1e, S1F1f, and S1F1g. Fraction S1F2 contained mainly trichoverrols according to TLC analysis. The sample was subjected to preparative CCC with a solvent system of chloroform-hexane-methanol-water (3:1:3:2, v/v/v/v) and a flow rate of 3.2ml/min to give six fractions: S1F2a, S1F2b, S1F2c, S1F2d, S1F2e, and S1F2f. S1F2e was further chromatographed on CCC with a solvent system of of chloroform-hexane-methanol-water (3:1:3:2, v/v/v) and a flow rate of 2.0ml/min. The chromatogram appears as a single peak; however, the eluent was collected into two parts, A and B. Fraction A was subjected to CCC (analytical column) with a solvent system of methylene chloride-carbon tetrachloride-methanol-water (3:5:2:6:4, v/v/v/v/v) and a flow rate of 1 ml/min (ca. 40mg/injection) to give (2'*E*,C6'*R*,C7'*R*)-isotrichoverrol A and isotrichoverrol B as oils.

Spectral Data

UV:

λ_{max}^{MeOH} 262nm (log ϵ=4.36).

IR:

($CHCl_3$) 3600, 3470(OH), 1703(C=O), 1644(C=C), and 1620cm^{-1} (C=C).

^{1}H NMR:

($CDCl_3$) 0.80(3H, s, H-14); 1.19(3H, d, *J*=6.3Hz, H-8'); 1.70(3H, s, H-16); 2.47(1H, dd, *J*=8.1, 15.3Hz, H-3α),(1H, d, *J*=4.0Hz, H-13A); 3.12(1H, d, *J*=4.0Hz, H-13B); 3.64(1H, d, *J*=12.5Hz, H-15A); 3.67(1H, dd, *J*~6.3Hz, H-7'); 3.80(1H, d, *J*=12.5Hz, H-15B); 3.83(1H, d, *J*=5.0Hz, H-2); 3.92(1H, d, *J*=5.2Hz, H-11); 3.97(1H, dd, *J*=6.1, 6.3Hz, H-6'); 5.48(1H, bd, *J*=5.2Hz, H-10); 5.94(1H, d, *J*=15.4Hz, H-2'); 6.10(1H, dd, *J*=6.1, 15.4Hz, H-5'); 6.12(1H, dd, *J*=3.7, 8.2Hz, H-4); 6.45(1H, dd, *J*=11.3, 15.4Hz, H-4'); and 7.29ppm(1H, dd, *J*=11.3, 15.4Hz, H-3').

^{13}C NMR:

($CDCl_3$) 6.4, C-14; 19.1, C-8'; 21.2, C-7; 23.3, C-16; 28.0, C-8; 35.9, C-3; 44.3, C-6; 48.2, C-13; 48.9, C-5; 62.9, C-15; 65.6, C-12; 66.8, C-11; 70.6, C-7'; 75.6, C-4; 76.5, C-6'; 79.0, C-2; 118.7, C-10; 121.6, C-2'; 129.6, C-4'; 140.4, C-9; 141.5, C5'; 144.4, C-3'; and 167.7ppm, C-1'.

Mass Spectrum:

HREIMS: calcd for $C_{23}H_{32}O_7$ (M^+), 420.2148; found, 420.2164*m/e*.

References

B. B. Jarvis; Macrocyclic Trichothecenes; In Mycotoxins and Phytoalexins; R. P. Sharma and D. K. Salunkhe, eds.; CRC Press, Boca Raton, Florida, pp. 361-421(1991).

B. B. Jarvis, G. P. Stahly, G. Pavanasasivam, J. O. Midiwo, T. DeSilva, C. E. Holmlund, E. P. Mazzola, and R. F. Geoghegan, Jr.; Isolation and Characterization of the Trichoverroids and New Roridins and Verrucarins; J. Org. Chem., Vol. 47, pp. 1117-1124(1982).

B. B. Jarvis, S. Wang, and H. L. Ammon; Trichoverroid Stereoisomers; J. Nat. Prod., Vol. 59, pp. 254-261(1996).

Common/Systematic Name
Trichoverrol B

Molecular Formula/Molecular Weight
$C_{23}H_{32}O_7$; MW = 420.21480

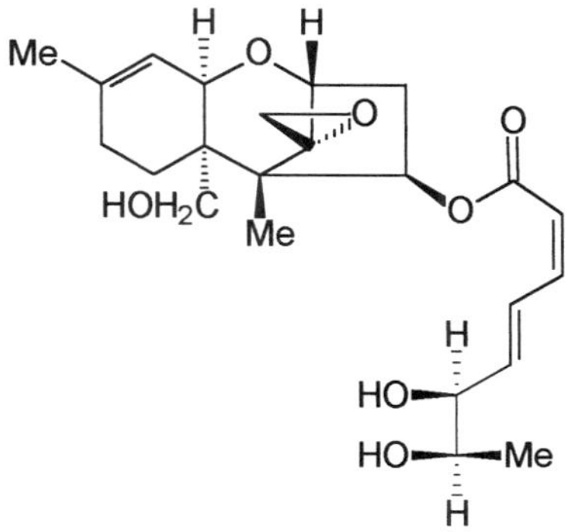

General Characteristics
Isolated as an oil; $[\alpha]_D^{28}$ -3.3° (c=0.39, in $CHCl_3$).

Fungal Source
Myrothecium verrucaria (ATCC 24571).

Isolation/Purification
The fungal culture broth was passed through XAD-2 resin; the resin was eluted with methanol yielding an aqueous methanol fraction that was concentrated to yield an aqueous concentrate. A portion of the aqueous concentrate was extracted with ethyl acetate. The organic extract was washed with water and saturated salt solution and dried. Removal of the solvent by rotary evaporation yielded a dark brown gum. HPLC analysis indicated that the principal trichothecenes present were verrucarin J, verrucarin B, verrucarin A, isororidin E, roridin E, roridin A, trichodermadienediols A and B, trichoverrols A and B, and trichoverrins A and B in the order of increasing retention time on a silica column (ethyl acetate/hexane eluent). The gum was subjected to flash chromatography (silica gel) with increasing amounts of methanol in dichloromethane to yield four fractions: I (eluted with 0-1% methanol-methylene chloride), II (eluted with 1-5% methanol-methylene chloride), III (eluted with 5-7.5% methanol-methylene chloride), and IV (eluted with methanol). Fraction III of the crude extract was subjected to partition chromatography. The sample was applied to a column of Celite impregnated with 83% aqueous methanol and eluted with 15% dichloromethane in petroleum ether to give a gum. Flash chromatography (90% ethyl acetate-petroleum ether) yielded two major fractions, III-A (R_f, 0.35 in 90% ethyl acetate-petroleum ether) and III-B (R_f, 0.30 in 90% ethyl acetate-petroleum ether). After filtration through TLC grade silica gel, each of these fractions was purified by HPLC (1-6% methanol-methylene chloride, gradient, 30 min) to give trichoverrol A and trichoverrol B from fraction III-A and trichoverrin A and trichoverrin B from fraction III-B.

Spectral Data

UV:

λ_{max}^{MeOH} 260nm (log ϵ=4.53).

^{1}H NMR:

($CDCl_3$) 0.84(3H, s, 14-H); 1.16(3H, d, *J*=6Hz, 8'-H); 1.74(3H, 8, 16-H); 2.47(1H, dd, *J*=8, 15Hz, 3α-H); 3.07(2H, AB, *J*=4Hz, 13-H); 4.18 (1H, m, 6'-H); 5.50(1H, d, *J*=5Hz, 10-H); 5.74(1H, d, *J*=11Hz, 2'-H); 6.67(1H, dd, *J*=11, 11Hz, 3'-H); 7.61(1H, dd, *J*=11, 16Hz, 4'-H).

^{13}C NMR:

($CDCl_3$) 79.0 d, C-2; 36.2 t, C-3; 75.5 d, C-4; 49.1 s, C-5; 44.4 s, C-6; 21.2 t, C-7; 28.12 t, C-8; 140.6 s, C-9; 118.8 d, C-10; 66.9 d, C-11; 66.0 s, C-12; 48.3 t, C-13; 6.8 q, C-14; 62.6 t, C-15; 23.2 q, C-16; 167.0 s, C-1'; 117.9 d, C-2'; 144.3 d, C-3'; 128.0 d, C-4'; 141.6 d, C-5'; 75.5 d, C-6'; 70.3 d, C-7'; and 17.8ppm q, C-8'.

Mass Spectrum:

HRCIMS (methane gas reagent): 421.2223*m/e* (M^+ + H, calcd 421.2226).

Reference

B. B. Jarvis, G. P. Stahly, G. Pavanasasivam, J. O. Midiwo, T. Desilva, C. E. Holmlund, E. P. Mazzola and R. F. Geoghegan; Isolation and Characterization of the Trichoverroids and New Roridins and Verrucarins; J. Org. Chem.,Vol. 47, pp. 1117-1124(1982).

Common/Systematic Name
(C6'*R*,C7'*S*)-Isotrichoverrol B

Molecular Formula/Molecular Weight
$C_{23}H_{32}O_7$; MW = 420.21480

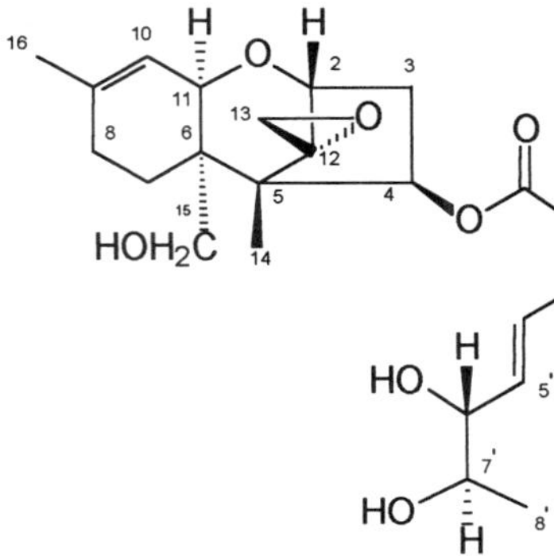

General Characteristics
Isotrichoverrol B was isolated as an oil; $[\alpha]_D^{20}$ - 4.0° (*c*=1.50, in $CHCl_3$).

Fungal Source
*Myrothecium verrucaria (*ATCC 20540).

Isolation/Purification
The fermentation procedures with *Myrothecium verrucaria (*ATCC 20540) were carried out in a manner similar to those described previously (Jarvis *et al.*, 1982). Samples 1-4 (S1, S2, S3, and S4) from this isolate were the lower R_f fractions from silica gel chromatography (methanol-methylene chloride), given in the order of increasing polarity. To sample 1, which contained some solid material, was added cold ethyl acetate. The solid was collected and recrystallized from methylene chloride-hexane to give isotrichoverrol A. The remaining portion of S1 was subjected to semipreparative high speed countercurrent chromatography (V_c=355ml) with a solvent system of methanol-water-chloroform-hexane (3:2:3:1.2, v/v/v/v); flow rate was 2.4ml/min (ca. 400mg/injection, total 10 injections) to give isotrichoverrol A and isotrichoverrol B.

Spectral Data

^{1}H NMR:
($CDCl_3$) 0.80(3H, s, H-14); 1.12(3H, d, *J*=6.4Hz, H-8'); 1.57(1H, m, H-7A); 1.70(3H, s, H-16); 1.98(3H, m, H-7B, H-8); 2.08(1H, ddd, *J* =4.0, 5.2, 15.4Hz, H-3β); 2.49(1H, dd, *J*=7.8, 15.4Hz, H-3α); 2.82(1H, d, *J*=3.9Hz, H-13A); 3.12(1H, d, *J*=3.9Hz, H-13B); 3.61(1H, d, *J*=12.3Hz, H-15A); 3.81(1H, d, *J*=12.3Hz, H-15B); 3.83(1H, d, *J*=5.2Hz, H-2); 3.86(1H, br d, *J*=5.1Hz, H-11); 3.90(1H, dq, *J*=3.5, 6.5Hz, H-7'); 4.25(1H, m, H-6'); 5.45(1H, br d, *J*=5.1Hz, H-10); 5.70(1H, d,

J=11.4Hz, H-2'); 6.09(1H, m, H-4); 6.11(1H, dd, *J*=6.0, 15.4Hz, H-5'); 6.63(1H, dd, *J*=11.3, 11.4Hz, H-3'); and 7.55ppm (1H, dd, *J*=11.3, 15.4Hz, H-4').

^{13}C NMR:

The ^{13}C NMR data are identical to those reported earlier for (C6'S,C7'R)-trichoverrol B.

Mass Spectrum:

HRCIMS: calcd for $C_{23}H_{33}O_7$; $[M^+ + H]^+$, 421.2226; found, 421.2206*m/e*.

References

B. B. Jarvis; Macrocyclic Trichothecenes; In Mycotoxins and Phytoalexins; R. P. Sharma and D. K. Salunkhe, eds.; CRC Press, Boca Raton, Florida, pp. 361-421(1991).

B. B. Jarvis, G. P. Stahly, G. Pavanasasivam, J. O. Midiwo, T. Desilva, C. E. Holmlund, E.P. Mazzola and R. F. Geoghegan; Isolation and Characterization of the Trichoverroids and New Roridins and Verrucarins, J. Org. Chem.,Vol. 47, pp. 1117-1124(1982).

B. B. Jarvis, S. Wang, and H. L. Ammon; Trichoverroid Stereoisomers; J. Nat. Prod., Vol. 59, pp. 254-261(1996).

Common/Systematic Name

(2'*E*,C6'*R*,C7'*S*)-Isotrichoverrol B

Molecular Formula/Molecular Weight

$C_{23}H_{32}O_7$; MW = 420.21480

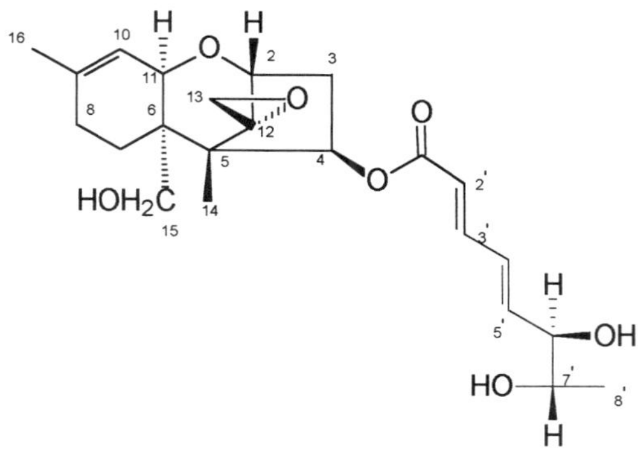

General Characteristics

Isolated as an oil.

Fungal Source

*Myrothecium verrucaria (*ATCC 20540).

Isolation/Purification

The fermentation procedures with *Myrothecium verrucaria (*ATCC 20540) were carried out in a manner similar to those described previously (Jarvis *et al.*, 1982). Samples 1-4 (S1, S2, S3, and S4) from this isolate were the lower R_f fractions from silica gel chromatography (methanol-methylene chloride), given in the order of increasing polarity. To sample 1, which contained some solid material, was added cold ethyl acetate. The solid was collected and recrystallized from methylene chloride-hexane to give isotrichoverrol A. The remaining portion of S1 was subjected to semipreparative CCC (V_c=355ml) with a solvent system of methanol-water-chloroform-hexane (3:2:3:1.2, v/v/v/v); flow rate was 2.4ml/min (ca. 400mg/injection, total 10 injections) to give isotrichoverrol A and isotrichoverrol B. Another fraction from this CCC was subjected to CCC (semipreparative column) with a solvent system of methylene chloride-carbon tetrachloride-methanol-water (2:3:3:2, v/v/v/v; ca. 400mg/injection). The major fraction of this sample was eluted with little retention from the column, and there were no detectable trichothecenes in this fraction, according to TLC analysis. Seven additional fractions were collected: S1F1a, S1F1b, S1F1c, S1F1d, S1F1e, S1F1f, and S1F1g. Fraction S1F2 contained mainly trichoverrols according to TLC analysis. The sample was subjected to preparative CCC with a solvent system of chloroform-hexane-methanol-water (3:1:3:2, v/v/v/v) and a flow rate of 3.2ml/min to give six fractions: S1F2a, S1F2b, S1F2c, S1F2d, S1F2e, and S1F2f. S1F2f was subjected to CCC (analytical column) with a solvent system of methylene chloride-carbon tetrachloride-methanol-water (2:3:3:2, v/v/v/v) and a flow rate of 1 ml/min to give a mixture of (2'*E*)-isotrichoverrol B and another unknown trichoverroid. This mixture was chromatographed on CCC (analytical column) with a solvent system of methylene chloride-carbon tetrachloride-hexane-methanol-water (3:5:2:6:4, v/v/v/v/v) and a flow rate of 1ml/min to give pure (2'*E*)-isotrichoverrol B, as an oil.

Spectral Data

UV:
λ_{max}^{MeOH} 262nm (log ϵ = 4.44).

IR:
($CHCl_3$) 3600, 3470(OH), 1705(C=O), 1645(C=C), and 1621cm^{-1} (C=C).

^{1}H NMR:
($CDCl_3$) 0.79(3H, s, H-14); 1.12(3H, d, *J*=6.5 Hz, H-8'); 1.69(3H, s, H-16); 2.47(1H, dd, *J*=8.0, 15.3Hz, H-3α); 2.80(1H, d, *J*=4.0Hz, H-13A); 3.11(1H, d, *J*=4.0Hz, H-13B); 3.63(1H, d, *J*=12.2Hz, H-15A); 3.80(1H, d, *J*=12.2Hz, H-15B); 3.82(1H, 3, *J*=5.1Hz, H-2); 3.88-3.93(2H, m, H11 and H-7'); 4.21(1H, m, H-6'); 5.47(1H, bd, *J*=4.5Hz, H-10); 5.93(1H, d, *J*=15.3Hz, H-2'); 6.10(1H, dd, *J*=3.6, 8.2Hz, H-4); 6.13(1H, dd, *J*=5.9, 15.9Hz, H-5'); 6.42(1H, dd, *J*=10.9, 15.9Hz, H-4'); and 7.29ppm (1H, dd, *J*=10.9, 15.3Hz, H-3').

^{13}C NMR:
($CDCl_3$) 6.4, C-14; 17.6, C-8'; 21.2, C-7; 23.2, C-16; 28.0, C-8; 35.9, C-3; 44.3, C-6; 48.1, C-13; 48.9, C-5; 62.8, C-15; 65.6, C-12; 66.8, C-11; 70.1, C-7'; 75.3, C-6'; 75.6, C-4; 79.0, C-2; 118.8, C-10; 121.5, C-2'; 129.6, C4'; 140.5, C-5'; 140.5, C-9; 144.5, C3'; and 167.7ppm, C-1'.

Mass Spectrum:
HREIMS: calcd for $C_{23}H_{32}O_7$ (M^+), 420.2148; found, 420.2188*m/e*.

References

B. B. Jarvis; Macrocyclic Trichothecenes; In Mycotoxins and Phytoalexins; R. P. Sharma and D. K. Salunkhe, eds.; CRC Press, Boca Raton, Florida, pp. 361-421(1991).

B. B. Jarvis, G. P. Stahly, G. Pavanasasivam, J. O. Midiwo, T. DeSilva, C. E. Holmlund, E. P. Mazzola, and R. F. Geoghegan, Jr.; Isolation and Characterization of the Trichoverroids and New Roridins and Verrucarins; J. Org. Chem., Vol. 47, pp. 1117-1124(1982).

B. B. Jarvis, S. Wang, and H. L. Ammon; Trichoverroid Stereoisomers; J. Nat. Prod., Vol. 59, pp. 254-261(1996).

Common/Systematic Name

Trichoverrin A

Molecular Formula/Molecular Weight

$C_{28}H_{38}O_9$; MW = 518.25158

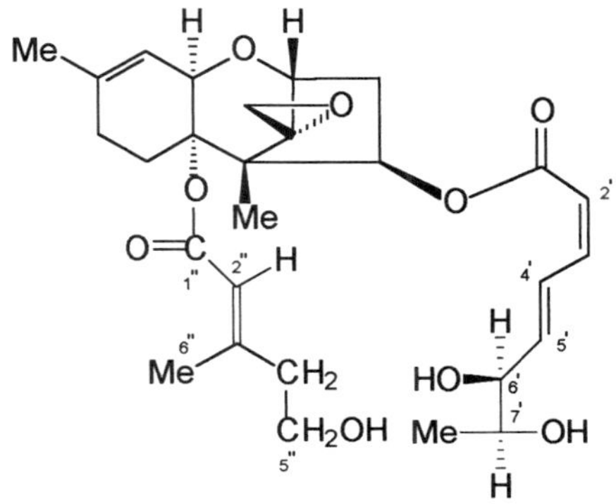

General Characteristics

Crystals from ethyl acetate-petroleum ether; mp., 78-79°; $[\alpha]_D^{28}$ -21.5° (c=0.39, in $CHCl_3$).

Fungal Source

Myrothecium verrucaria (ATCC 24571).

Isolation/Purification

The fungal culture broth was passed through XAD-2 resin; the resin was eluted with methanol yielding an aqueous methanol fraction that was concentrated to yield an aqueous concentrate. A portion of the aqueous concentrate was extracted with ethyl acetate. The organic extract was washed with water and saturated salt solution and dried. Removal of the solvent by rotary evaporation yielded a dark brown gum. HPLC analysis indicated that the principal trichothecenes present were verrucarin J, verrucarin B, verrucarin A, isororidin E, roridin E, roridin A, trichodermadienediols A and B, trichoverrols A and B, and trichoverrins A and B in the order of increasing retention time on a silica column (ethyl acetate-hexane eluent). The gum was subjected to flash chromatography (silica gel) with increasing amounts of methanol in dichloromethane to yield four fractions: I (eluted with 0-1% methanol-methylene chloride), II (eluted with 1-5% methanol-methylene chloride), III (eluted with 5-7.5% methanol-methylene chloride), and IV (eluted with methanol). Fraction III of the crude extract was subjected to partition chromatography. The sample was applied to a column of Celite impregnated with 83% aqueous methanol and eluted with 15% dichloromethane in petroleum ether to give a gum. Flash chromatography (90% ethyl acetate-petroleum ether) yielded two major fractions, III-A (R_f, 0.35 in 90% ethyl acetate-petroleum ether) and III-B (R_f, 0.30 in 90% ethyl acetate-petroleum ether). After filtration through TLC grade silica gel, each of these fractions was purified by HPLC (1-6% methanol-methylene chloride, gradient, 30 min) to give trichoverrol A and trichoverrol B from fraction III-A and trichoverrin A and trichoverrin

B from fraction III-B.

Spectral Data

UV:

λ_{max}^{MeOH} 260nm (log ε=4.60).

^{1}H NMR:

($CDCl_3$) 0.82(3H, s, 14-H); 1.21(3H, d, *J*=6Hz, 8'-H); 1.74(3;H, s, 16-H); 2.53(1;H, dd, *J*=8, 15Hz, 3α-H); 3.04(2H, AB, *J*=4Hz, 13-H); 4.18(2H, s, 15-H); 5.52(1H, d, *J*=5Hz, 10-H); 5.75(1H, d, *J*=11Hz, 2'-H); 5.90(1H, s, 2'-H); 6.67(1H, dd, *J*'s=11Hz, 3'-H); and 7.63ppm (1H, dd, *J*=11, 16Hz, 4'-H).

^{13}C NMR:

($CDCl_3$) 79.1 d, C-2; 36.9 t, C-3; 75.1 td, C-4; 48.6 s, C-5; 42.9 s, C-6; 21.9 t, C-7; 27.9 t, C-8; 140.5 s, C-9; 118.5 d, C-10; 66.7 d, C-11; 65.8 s, C-12; 48.2 t, C-13; 6.7 q, C-14; 63.5 t, C-15; 23.2 q, C-16; 166.0 s, C-1'; 118.1 d, C-2'; 144.1 d, C-3'; 127.5 d, C-4'; 142.4 d, C-5'; 76.5 d, C-6'; 70.5 d, C-7'; 18.9 q, C-8'; 166.0 s, C-1"; 116.9 d, C-2"; 157.3 s, C-3"; 43.6 t, C-4"; 59.7 t, C-5"; and 19.1ppm q, C-6".

Mass Spectrum:

HRCIMS (methane gas reagent): 533.2754*m/e* (M^+ + H, calcd 533.2754).

Reference

B. B. Jarvis, G. P. Stahly, G. Pavanasasivam, J. O. Midiwo, T. Desilva, C. E. Holmlund, E. P. Mazzola and R. F. Geoghegan; Isolation and Characterization of the Trichoverroids and New Roridins and Verrucarins; J. Org. Chem., Vol. 47, pp. 1117-1124(1982).

Common/Systematic Name

(2'*E*,4'*Z*)-Isotrichoverrin A

Molecular Formula/Molecular Weight

$C_{29}H_{40}O_9$; MW = 532.26723

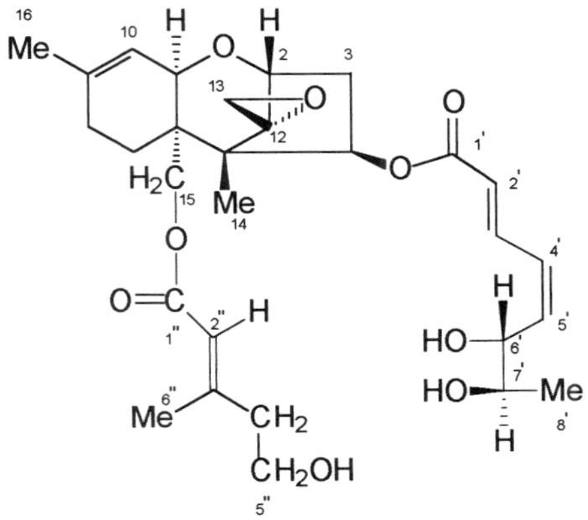

General Characteristics

Isolated as an amorphous solid.

Fungal Source

*Myrothecium verrucaria (*ATCC 20540).

Isolation/Purification

The fermentation procedures with *Myrothecium verrucaria (*ATCC 20540) were carried out in a manner similar to those described previously (Jarvis *et al.*, 1982). Samples 1-4 (S1, S2, S3, and S4) from this isolate were the lower R_f fractions from silica gel chromatography (methanol-methylene chloride), given in the order of increasing polarity. To sample 1, which contained some solid material, was added cold ethyl acetate. The solid was collected and recrystallized from methylene chloride-hexane to give isotrichoverrol A. The remaining portion of S1 was subjected to semipreparative CCC (V_c=355ml) with a solvent system of methanol-water-chloroform-hexane (3:2:3:1.2, v/v/v/v); flow rate was 2.4ml/min (ca. 400mg/injection, total 10 injections) to give isotrichoverrol A and isotrichoverrol B. Another fraction from this CCC was subjected to CCC (semipreparative column) with a solvent system of methylene chloride-carbon tetrachloride-methanol-water (2:3:3:2, v/v/v/v; ca. 400mg/injection). The major fraction of this sample was eluted with little retention from the column, and there were no detectable trichothecenes in this fraction, according to TLC analysis. Seven additional fractions were collected: S1F1a, S1F1b, S1F1c, S1F1d, S1F1e, S1F1f, and S1F1g. S1F1e was subjected to C_{18} reversed-phase TLC (70% methanol in 0.5 M aqueous NaCl) to give (2'*E*,4'*Z*)-isotrichoverrin A.

Spectral Data

UV:
λ_{max}^{MeOH} 261nm (log ϵ=4.49).

IR:
($CHCl_3$) 3600(OH), 1710(C=O), and 1652cm-^{1} (C=C).

^{1}H NMR:
($CDCl_3$) 0.78(3H, s, H-14); 1.12(3H, d, *J*=6.3Hz, 8'-H); 1.69(3H, s, 16-H); 2.17(3H, d, *J*=1.0Hz, 6"-H); 2.40(2H, m, H-4"); 2.55(1H, dd, *J*=7.9, 16.0Hz, H-3α); 2.81(1H, d, *J*=4Hz, H-13A); 3.13(1H, d, *J*=4.0Hz, H-13B); 3.66(1H, dq, J values ~ 6.6Hz, H-7'); 3.83(1H, d, *J*=5.3Hz, H-2); 3.94(1H, bd, *J*=4.8Hz, H-11); 4.10(2H, s, H-15); 4.37(1H, dd, *J*=6.7, 8.1Hz, H-6'); 5.46(1H, bd, *J*=4.8Hz, H-10); 5.79(1 H, dd, *J*=8.3, 10.7Hz, H-5'); 5.81(1H, d, *J*=1.0Hz, H-2"); 5.95(1H, d, *J*=15.2Hz, H-2'); 6.13(1H, dd, *J*=3.4, 7.9Hz, H-4); 6.24(1H, dd, *J*=10.7, 11.9Hz, H-4'); and 7.64ppm(1H, dd, *J*=11.9, 15.2Hz, H-3').

^{13}C NMR:
($CDCl_3$) 6.6, C-14; 18.6, C-8'; 19.0, C-6"; 21.9, C-7; 23.2, C-16; 27.8, C-8; 36.7, C-3; 43.0, C-6; 43.7, C-4"; 48.1, C-13; 48.6, C-5; 59.7, C-5"; 63.5, C-15; 65.5, C-12; 66.8, C-11; 70.7, C-7'; 72.4, C-6'; 75.7, C-4; 79.1, C-2; 117.1, C-2"; 118.5, C-10; 123.1, C-2'; 129.2, C4'; 138.6, C-5'; 139.8, C-3'; 140.5, C-9; 157.0, C-3"; 165.9, C-1"; and 166.9ppm, C-1'.

Mass Spectrum:
HRCIMS: calcd for $C_{29}H_{41}O_9$ (M^+ + 1), 533.2751; found, 533.2772*m/e*.

References

B. B. Jarvis; Macrocyclic Trichothecenes; In Mycotoxins and Phytoalexins; R. P. Sharma and D. K. Salunkhe, eds.; CRC Press, Boca Raton, Florida, pp. 361-421(1991).

B. B. Jarvis, G. P. Stahly, G. Pavanasasivam, J. O. Midiwo, T. DeSilva, C. E. Holmlund, E. P. Mazzola, and R. F. Geoghegan, Jr.; J. Org. Chem., Vol. 47, pp. 1117-1124(1982).

B. B. Jarvis, S. Wang, and H. L. Ammon; Trichoverroid Stereoisomers; J. Nat. Prod., Vol. 59, pp. 254-261(1996).

Common/Systematic Name

(*C6'R,C7'R*)-Isotrichoverrin A

Molecular Formula/Molecular Weight

$C_{29}H_{40}O_9$; MW = 532.26723

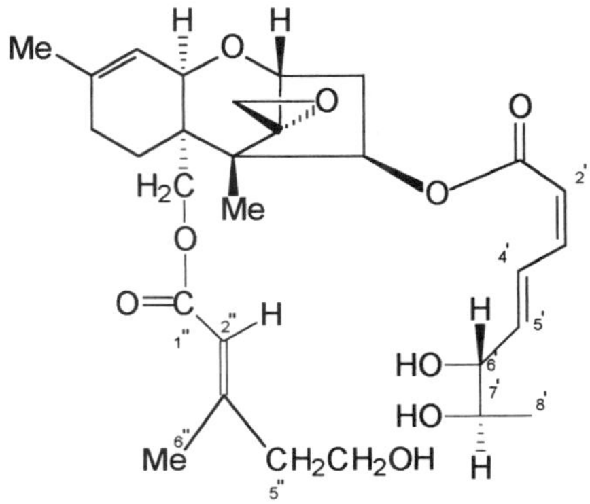

General Characteristics

Isolated as an amorphous solid; $[\alpha]_D^{20}$ + 5.6° (*c*=2.10, in $CHCl_3$).

Fungal Source

*Myrothecium verrucaria (*ATCC 20540).

Isolation/Purification

The fermentation procedures with *Myrothecium verrucaria* (ATCC 20540) were carried out in a manner similar to those described previously (Jarvis *et al*., 1982). Samples 1-4 (S1, S2, S3, and S4) from this isolate were the lower R_f fractions from silica gel chromatography (methanol-methylene chloride), given in the order of increasing polarity. Sample 2 (S2) contained mainly trichoverrins according to TLC analysis. This sample was chromatographed on CCC (semipreparative column, V_c=355ml) with a solvent system of chloroform-hexane-methanol-water (3:1:3:2, v/v/v/v) and a flow rate of 3.2ml/min (ca. 400mg/injection). Like fractions were combined to give seven fractions: S2F1, S2F2, S2F3, S2F4, S2F5, S2F6, and S2F7. A portion of S2F2 was subjected to CCC (semipreparative column) with a solvent system of methylene chloride-carbon tetrachloride-methanol-water (2:3:3:2, v/v/v/v) and a flow rate of 2.8ml/min. The components of the mobile phase (organic layer, methylene chloride-carbon tetrachloride) were varied from 2:3 to 5:2 (v/v), starting at t = 120 min and going to t = 160 min. Like portions were combined to give seven fractions: I, (*C6'R,C7'R*)-isotrichoverrin A; II, (*C6'R,C7'S*)-isotrichoverrin B; III, a mixture of isotrichoverrin B and trichoverrin C); IV, V, VI, 2'*E*-isotrichoverrin A; VII, 2'*E*-isotrichoverrin B.

Spectral Data

^{1}H NMR:
(CDCl$_3$) 0.79(3H, s, H-14); 1.19(3H, d, *J*=6.3Hz, H-14'); 1.70(3H, s, H-16); 2.17(3H, d, *J*=1.0Hz, H-6"); 2.40(2H, m, H-4"); 2.56(1H, dd, *J*=7.6, 15.5Hz, H-3α); 2.82(1H, d, *J*=4.0Hz, H-13A); 3.14(1H, d, *J*=4.0Hz, H-13B); 3.66(1H, dq, *J*=6.3, 6.3Hz, H-7'); 3.80(2H, m, H-5"); 3.84(1H, d, *J*=5.4Hz, H-2); 3.98(1H, d, *J*=4.7Hz, H-11); 4.03(1H, m, H-6'); 4.07(1H, d, *J*=12.5Hz, H-15A); 4.14(1H, d, *J*=12.5Hz, H-15B); 5.46(1H, d, *J*=4.7Hz, H-10); 5.67(1H, d, *J*=11.3Hz, H-2'); 5.85(1H, d, *J*=1.0Hz, H-2"); 6.07(1H, dd, *J*=4.7, 15.5Hz, H-5'); 6.20(1H, dd, *J*=7.6, 15.5Hz, H-4); 6.59(1H, dd, *J*=11.3, 11.3Hz, H-3'); and 7.54ppm(1H, dd, *J*=11.3, 15.5Hz, H-4').

^{13}C NMR:
(CDCl$_3$) 6.7, C-14; 18.9, C-8'; 19.1, C-6"; 21.9, C-7; 23.2, C-16; 27.9, C-8; 36.9, C-3; 42.9, C-6; 43.6, C-4"; 48.2, C-13; 48.6, C-5; 59.7, C-5"; 63.4, C-15; 65.8, C-12; 66.6, C-11; 70.6, C-7'; 75.0, C-4; 76.1, C-6'; 79.1, C-2; 117.0, C-2"; 118.2, C-2'; 118.5, C-10; 127.1, C-4'; 140.4, C-9; 142.1, C-5'; 143.7, C-3'; 157.0, C-3"; 165.9, C-1"; and 166.0ppm, C-1'.

Mass Spectrum:
HRCIMS: calcd for $C_{29}H_{41}O_9$ $(M + H)^+$, 533.2751; found, 533.2759***m/e***.

References

B. B. Jarvis; Macrocyclic Trichothecenes; In Mycotoxins and Phytoalexins; R. P. Sharma and D. K. Salunkhe, eds.; CRC Press, Boca Raton, Florida, pp. 361-421(1991).

B. B. Jarvis, G. P. Stahly, G. Pavanasasivam, J. O. Midiwo, T. DeSilva, C. E. Holmlund, E. P. Mazzola, and R. F. Geoghegan, Jr.; Isolation and Characterization of the Trichoverroids and New Roridins and Verrucarins; J. Org. Chem., Vol. 47, pp. 1117-1124(1982).

B. B. Jarvis, S. Wang, and H. L. Ammon; Trichoverroid Stereoisomers; J. Nat. Prod., Vol. 59, pp. 254-261(1996).

Common/Systematic Name

9β,10β-Epoxyisotrichoverrin A

Molecular Formula/Molecular Weight

$C_{29}H_{40}O_{10}$; MW = 548.26215

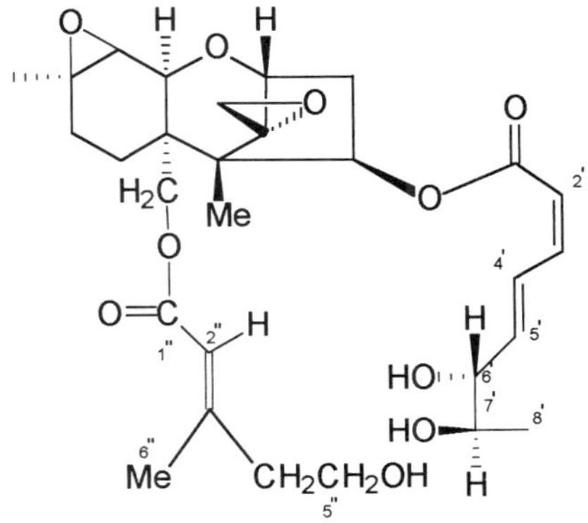

General Characteristics

Isolated as an oil; $[\alpha]_D^{20}$ - 16° (*c*=0.12, in $CHCl_3$).

Fungal Source

*Myrothecium verrucaria (*ATCC 20540).

Isolation/Purification

The fermentation procedures with *Myrothecium verrucaria (*ATCC 20540) were carried out in a manner similar to those described previously (Jarvis *et al.*, 1982). Samples 1-4 (S1, S2, S3, and S4) from this isolate were the lower R_f fractions from silica gel chromatography (methanol-methylene chloride), given in the order of increasing polarity. Sample 3 (S3) from *M. verrucaria* isolate ATCC 20540, which was more polar than those that contained trichoverrols (S1) and trichoverrins (S2), was partitioned between chloroform and methanol-water mixture (50%). The organic fraction was subjected to preparative TLC (Chromatotron, 2 mm, silica gel) with methanol-methylene chloride (3-10%). The most polar fraction was subjected to high speed countercurrent distribution (CCC) with a solvent system of chloroform-hexane-methanol-water (12:8:15:5, v/v/v/v) at a flow rate of 1.8ml/min to give 9β,10β-epoxyisotrichoverrin A and 9β,10β-epoxyisotrichoverrin B.

Spectral Data

^{1}H NMR:
(CDCl$_3$) 0.72(3H, s, H-14); 1.20(3H, d, *J*=6.5Hz, H-8'); 1.34(3H, s, H-16); 1.60-2.00(5H, m, H-7, H-8, H-3β); 2.20(3H, d, *J*=0.9Hz, H-6"); 2.41(2H, t, *J*= 6.0Hz, H-4"); 2.53(1H, dd, *J*=7.9, 15.5Hz, H-3α); 2.78(1H, d, *J*=4.0Hz, H-13A); 3.11(1H, d, *J*=5.5Hz, H-10); 3.19(1H, d, *J*=4.0Hz, H-13B); 3.67(1H, dq *J*=6.5, 6.5Hz, H-7'); 3.81(2H, m, H-5"); 3.89(1H, br d, *J*=5.5Hz, H-11);3.93(1H, d, *J*=5.1Hz, H-2); 4.03(1H, m, H-6'); 4.04(1H, d, *J*=12.5Hz, H-15A); 4.15(1H, d, *J*=12.5Hz, H-15B); 5.68(1H, d, *J*=11.3Hz, H-2'; 5.82(1H, d, *J*=0.9Hz, H-2"); 6.03(1H, dd, *J*=3.5, 7.5Hz, H-4); 6.08(1H, dd, *J*=5.8, 15.4Hz, H-5'); 6.60(1H, dd, *J*=11.3, 11.3Hz, H-3'); and 7.55ppm (1H, dd, *J*=11.3, 15.4Hz, H-4').

^{13}C NMR:
(CDCl$_3$) 6.8, C-14; 18.9, C-8'; 19.2, C-6"; 19.4, C-7; 22.4, C-16; 26.5, C-8; 26.5, C-8; 36.6, C-3; 42.6, C-6; 43.6, C-4"; 48.0, C-13; 48.5, C-5; 57.3, C-10; 57.5, C-9; 59.7, C-5"; 63.1, C-15; 65.2, C-12; 66.9, C-11; 70.6, C-7'; 74.8, C-4; 76.2, C-6'; 78.7, C-2; 116.5, C-2"; 118.1, C-2'; 127.5, C-4'; 142.2, C-5'; 143.9, C-3'; 158.1, C-3"; 165.8, C-1'; and 166.0ppm, C-1".

Mass Spectrum:
HRCIMS: calcd for $C_{29}H_{41}O_{10}$ $(M + H)^+$, 549.2700; found, 549.2732*m/e*.

References

B. B. Jarvis; Macrocyclic Trichothecenes; In Mycotoxins and Phytoalexins; R. P. Sharma and D. K. Salunkhe, eds.; CRC Press, Boca Raton, Florida, pp. 361-421(1991).

B. B. Jarvis, G. P. Stahly, G. Pavanasasivam, J. O. Midiwo, T. DeSilva, C. E. Holmlund, E. P. Mazzola, and R. F. Geoghegan, Jr.; Isolation and Characterization of the Trichoverroids and New Roridins and Verrucarins; J. Org. Chem., Vol. 47, pp. 1117-1124(1982).

B. B. Jarvis, S. Wang, and H. L. Ammon; Trichoverroid Stereoisomers; J. Nat. Prod., Vol. 59, pp. 254-261(1996).

Common/Systematic Name

8α-Hydroxyisotrichoverrin A

Molecular Formula/Molecular Weight

$C_{29}H_{40}O_{10}$; MW = 548.26215

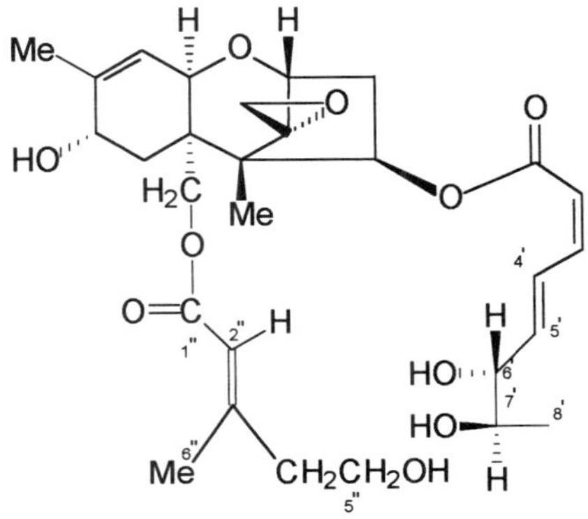

General Characteristics

Isolated as an oil; $[\alpha]_D^{20}$ - 22.0° (*c*=0.37, in $CHCl_3$).

Fungal Source

*Myrothecium verrucaria (*ATCC 20540).

Isolation/Purification

The fermentation procedures with *Myrothecium verrucaria (*ATCC 20540) were carried out in a manner similar to those described previously (Jarvis *et al.*, 1982). Samples 1-4 (S1, S2, S3, and S4) from this isolate were the lower R_f fractions from silica gel chromatography (methanol-methylene chloride), given in the order of increasing polarity. Sample 4 (S4) was triturated with methanol. The soluble portion was concentrated and dissolved in 50% aqueous methanol solution, and the solution was washed with carbon tetrachloride-hexane, chloroform-hexane (7:3, v/v), and chloroform. The aqueous phase was concentrated by rotary evaporation and extracted with chloroform. The chloroform extract was subjected to high-speed countercurrent distribution (CCC) with a solvent system of chloroform-hexane-methanol-water (7:3:5:5, v/v/v/v) to give 16-hydroxyisotrichodermadienediols A and B and 8α-hydroxyisotrichoverrin A.

Spectral Data

^{1}H NMR:

($CDCl_3$) 0.81(3H, s, H-14); 1.19(3H, d, *J*=6.3Hz, H-14'); 1.69(1H, br d, *J*=14.4Hz, H-7β); 1.84(3H, s, H-16); 2.02(1H, m, H-3β); 2.17(3H, s, H-6"); 2.32(1H, dd, *J*=6.5, 14.4Hz, H-7α); 2.39(2H, m, H-4"); 2.58(1H, dd, *J*=7.8, 15.5Hz, H-3α); 2.85(1H, d, *J*=4.0Hz, H-13A); 3.14(1H, d, *J*=4.0Hz, H-13B); 3.66(1H, dq, *J*=6.3, 6.3Hz, H-7'); 3.78(2H, m, H-5"); 3.83(1H, d, *J*=5.3Hz, H-2); 4.03(1H, br d, *J*=5.7Hz, H-11); 4.09(1H, m, H-6'); 4.11(1H, br d, *J*=6.5Hz, H-8); 4.24(1H, d, *J*=13.0Hz, H-15A); 4.39(1H, d, *J*=13.0Hz, H-15B); 5.58(1H, br d, *J*=5.7Hz, H-10); 5.68(1H, d, *J*=11.3Hz, H-2'); 5.85(1H, s, H-2"); 6.07(1H, dd, *J*=5.1, 15.5Hz, H-5'); 6.30(1H, dd, *J*=3.1, 7.8Hz, H-4); 6.60(1H, dd, *J*=11.3, 11.3Hz, H-3'); and 7.53ppm (1H, dd, *J*=11.3, 15.5Hz, H-4').

^{13}C NMR:

($CDCl_3$) 6.6, C-14; 18.9, C-8'; 19.2, C-6"; 20.4, C-16; 31.3, C-7; 36.8, C-3; 42.9, C-6; 43.5, C-4"; 48.3, C-13; 48.5, C-5; 59.6, C-5"; 64.6, C-15; 65.8, C-12; 66.5, C-8; 66.8, C-11; 70.5, C-7'; 74.8, C-4; 76.4, C-6'; 79.0, C-2; 116.9, C-2"; 118.1, C-2'; 120.9, C-10; 127.3, C-4'; 139.8, C-9; 142.2, C-5'; 144.0, C-3'; 157.2, C-3"; 165.2, C-1'; and 166.0ppm, C-1".

Mass Spectrum:

HRCIMS: calcd for $C_{29}H_{41}O_{10}$ $(M + H)^+$, 549.2700; found, 549.2710*m/e*.

References

B. B. Jarvis; Macrocyclic Trichothecenes; In Mycotoxins and Phytoalexins; R. P. Sharma and D. K. Salunkhe, eds.; CRC Press, Boca Raton, Florida, pp. 361-421(1991).

B. B. Jarvis, G. P. Stahly, G. Pavanasasivam, J. O. Midiwo, T. DeSilva, C. E. Holmlund, E. P. Mazzola, and R. F. Geoghegan, Jr.; Isolation and Characterization of the Trichoverroids and New Roridins and Verrucarins; J. Org. Chem., Vol. 47, pp. 1117-1124(1982).

B. B. Jarvis, S. Wang, and H. L. Ammon; Trichoverroid Stereoisomers; J. Nat. Prod.,Vol. 59, pp. 254-261(1996).

Common/Systematic Name

Trichoverrin B

Molecular Formula/Molecular Weight

$C_{29}H_{40}O_9$; MW = 532.26723

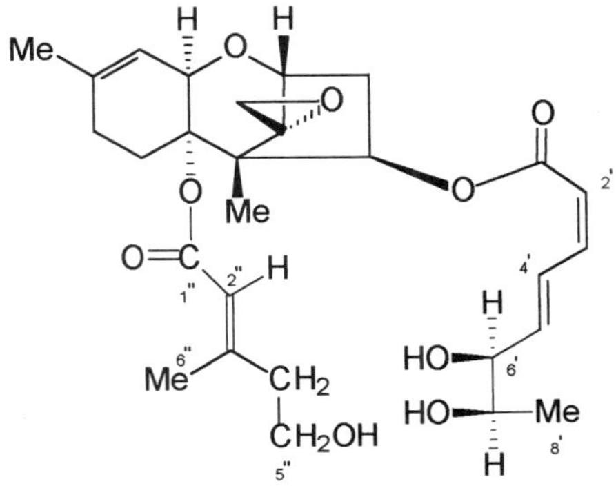

General Characteristics

Isolated as an oil; $[\alpha]_D^{28}$ -32.2° (c=0.57, in $CHCl_3$).

Fungal Source

Myrothecium verrucaria (ATCC 24571).

Isolation/Purification

The fungal culture broth was passed through XAD-2 resin; the resin was eluted with methanol yielding an aqueous methanol fraction that was concentrated to yield an aqueous concentrate. A portion of the aqueous concentrate was extracted with ethyl acetate. The organic extract was washed with water and saturated salt solution and dried. Removal of the solvent by rotary evaporation yielded a dark brown gum. HPLC analysis indicated that the principal trichothecenes present were verrucarin J, verrucarin B, verrucarin A, isororidin E, roridin E, roridin A, trichodermadienediols A and B, trichoverrols A and B, and trichoverrins A and B in the order of increasing retention time on a silica column (ethyl acetate-hexane eluent). The gum was subjected to flash chromatography (silica gel) with increasing amounts of methanol in dichloromethane to yield four fractions: I (eluted with 0-1% methanol-methylene chloride), II (eluted with 1-5% methanol-methylene chloride), III (eluted with 5-7.5% methanol-methylene chloride), and IV (eluted with methanol). Fraction III of the crude extract was subjected to partition chromatography. The sample was applied to a column of Celite impregnated with 83% aqueous methanol and eluted with 15% dichloromethane in petroleum ether to give a gum. Flash chromatography (90% ethyl acetate-petroleum ether) yielded two major fractions, III-A (R_f, 0.35 in 90% ethyl acetate-petroleum ether) and III-B (R_f, 0.30 in 90% ethyl acetate-petroleum ether). After filtration through TLC grade silica gel, each of these fractions was purified by HPLC (1-6% methanol-methylene chloride, gradient, 30 min) to give trichoverrol A and trichoverrol B from fraction III-A and trichoverrin A and trichoverrin

B from fraction III-B.

Spectral Data

UV:

λ_{max}^{MeOH} 260nm (log ϵ=4.53).

^{1}H NMR:

($CDCl_3$) 0.82(3H, s, 14-H); 1.15(3H, d, *J*=6Hz, 8'-H); 1.70(3H s, 16-H); 2.48(1H, dd, *J*=8, 15Hz, 3α-H); 3.04(2H, AB, *J*=4Hz, 13-H); 4.18(2H, s, 15-H); 5.51(1H, d, *J*=5Hz, 10-H); 5.73(1H, d, *J*=11Hz, 2'-H); 5.93(1H, 8, H-2'); 6.68(1H, dd, *J*'s=11Hz, H-3'); and 7.58ppm (1H, dd, *J*=11, 16Hz, 4'-H).

^{13}C NMR:

($CDCl_3$) 79.2 d, C-2; 36.9 t, C-3; 75.1 d, C-4; 48.6 s, C-5; 42.9 s, C-6; 21.9 t, C-7; 27.9 t, C-8; 140.5 s, C-9; 118.6 d, C-10; 66.7 d, C-11; 65.8 s, C-12; 48.3 t, C-13; 6.7 q, C-14; 63.5 t, C-15; 23.2 q, C-16; 166.1 s, C-1'; 117.9 d, C-2'; 144.1 d, C-3'; 127.6 d, C-4'; 141.4 d, C-5'; 75.4 d, C-6'; 70.3 d, C-7'; 17.9 q, C-8'; 166.0 s, C-1"; 116.9 d, C-2"; 157.2 s, C-3"; 43.6 t, C-4"; 59.7 t, C- 5"; and 19.2ppm q, C-6".

Mass Spectrum:

HRCIMS (methane gas reagent): 533.2722*m/e* (M^+ + H, calcd 533.2754).

Reference

B. B. Jarvis, G. P. Stahly, G. Pavanasasivam, J. O. Midiwo, T. Desilva, C. E. Holmlund, E. P. Mazzola and R. F. Geoghegan; Isolation and Characterization of the Trichoverroids and New Roridins and Verrucarins; J. Org. Chem., Vol. 47, pp. 1117-1124(1982).

Common/Systematic Name
(C6'*R*,C7'*S*)-Isotrichoverrin B

Molecular Formula/Molecular Weight
$C_{29}H_{40}O_9$; MW = 532.26723

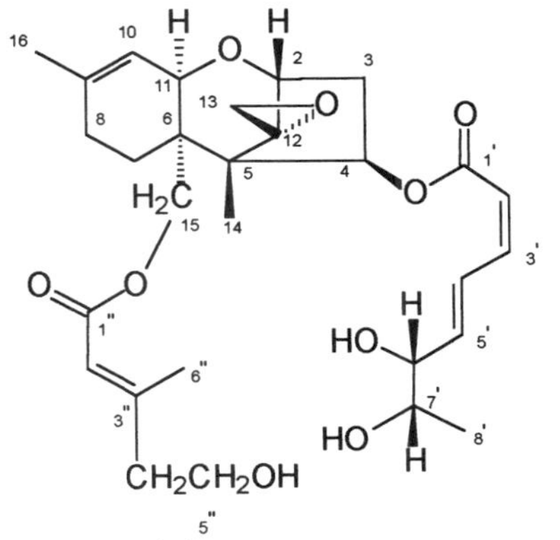

General Characteristics
Isolated as an oil; $[\alpha]_D^{20}$ - 25.0° (*c*=2.20, in $CHCl_3$).

Fungal Source
*Myrothecium verrucaria (*ATCC 20540).

Isolation/Purification
The fermentation procedures with *Myrothecium verrucaria (*ATCC 20540) were carried out in a manner similar to those described previously (Jarvis *et al*., 1982). Samples 1-4 (S1, S2, S3, and S4) from this isolate were the lower R_f fractions from silica gel chromatography (methanol-methylene chloride), given in the order of increasing polarity. Sample 2 (S2) contained mainly trichoverrins according to TLC analysis. This sample was chromatographed on CCC (semipreparative column, V_c=355ml) with a solvent system of chloroform-hexane-methanol-water (3:1:3:2, v/v/v/v) and a flow rate of 3.2ml/min (ca. 400mg/injection). Like fractions were combined to give seven fractions: S2F1, S2F2, S2F3, S2F4, S2F5, S2F6, and S2F7. A portion of S2F2 was subjected to CCC (semipreparative column) with a solvent system of of methylene chloride-carbon tetrachloride-methanol-water (2:3:3:2, v/v/v/v) and a flow rate of 2.8ml/min. The components of the mobile phase (organic layer, CH_2Cl_2/ CCl_4) were varied from 2:3 to 5:2 (v/v), starting at t = 120 min and going to t = 160 min. Like portions were combined to give seven fractions: I, (*C6'R,C7'R*)-isotrichoverrin A, II, (*C6'R,C7'S*)-isotrichoverrin B, III, a mixture of isotrichoverrin B and trichoverrin C), IV, V, VI, 2'*E*-isotrichoverrin A, VII, 2'*E*-isotrichoverrin B.

Spectral Data

^{1}H NMR:
(CDCl$_3$) 0.78(3H, s, H-14); 1.12(3H, d, *J*=6.5Hz, H-14'); 1.69(3H, s, H-16); 2.16(3H, d, *J*=1.1Hz, H-6"); 2.39(2H, t, *J*=6.0Hz, H-4"); 2.55(1H, dd, *J*=7.7, 15.5Hz, H-3α); 2.82(1H, d, *J*= 4.0Hz, H-13A); 3.14(1H, d, *J*=4.0Hz, H-13B); 3.75(1H, dt, *J*=6.0; 11.5Hz, H-5"A); 3.83(1H, dt, *J*=6.0, 11.5Hz, H-5"B); 3.84(1H, d, *J*=5.1Hz, H-2); 3.89(1H, dq, *J*=3.6, 6.5Hz, H-7'); 3.97(1H, d, *J*=5.4Hz, H-11); 4.10(2H, s, H-15); 4.23(1H, m, H-6'); 5.46(1H, d, *J*=5.4Hz, H-10); 5.66(1H, d, *J*=11.3Hz, H-2'); 5.83(1H, d, *J*=1.0Hz, H-6"); 6.11(1H, dd, *J*=5.2, 15.5Hz, H-5'); 6.19(1H, dd, *J*=3.3, 7.7Hz, H-4); 6.60(1H, dd, *J*= 11.3, 11.3Hz, H-3'); and 7.52ppm(1H, dd, *J*=11.3, 15.5Hz, H-4').

^{13}C NMR:
(CDCl$_3$) 6.7, C-14; 17.9, C-8'; 19.2, C-6"; 21.9, C-7; 23.2, C-16; 27.9, C-8; 36.9, C-3; 42.9, C-6; 43.6, C-4"; 48.2, C-13; 48.6, C-5; 59.7, C-5"; 63.4, C-15; 65.8, C-12; 66.6, C-11; 70.2, C-7'; 75.0, C-4; 75.4, C-6'; 79.1, C-2; 116.9, C-2"; 118.0, C-2'; 118.5, C-10; 127.6, C-4'; 140.4, C9; 141.1, C-5'; 143.9, C-3'; 157.0, C-3"; 165.9, C-1"; and 166.0ppm, C-1'.

Mass Spectrum:
HRCIMS: calcd for $C_{29}H_{41}O_9$ $(M + H)^+$, 533.2751; found, 533.2786*m/e*.

References

B. B. Jarvis; Macrocyclic Trichothecenes; In Mycotoxins and Phytoalexins; R. P. Sharma and D. K. Salunkhe, eds.; CRC Press, Boca Raton, Florida, pp. 361-421(1991).

B. B. Jarvis, G. P. Stahly, G. Pavanasasivam, J. O. Midiwo, T. DeSilva, C. E. Holmlund, E. P. Mazzola, and R. F. Geoghegan, Jr.; Isolation and Characterization of the Trichoverroids and New Roridins and Verrucarins; J. Org. Chem., Vol. 47, pp. 1117-1124(1982).

B. B. Jarvis, S. Wang, and H. L. Ammon; Trichoverroid Stereoisomers; J. Nat. Prod., Vol. 59, pp. 254-261(1996).

Common/Systematic Name

(2'*E*,4'*Z*)-Isotrichoverrin B

Molecular Formula/Molecular Weight

$C_{29}H_{40}O_9$; MW = 532.26723

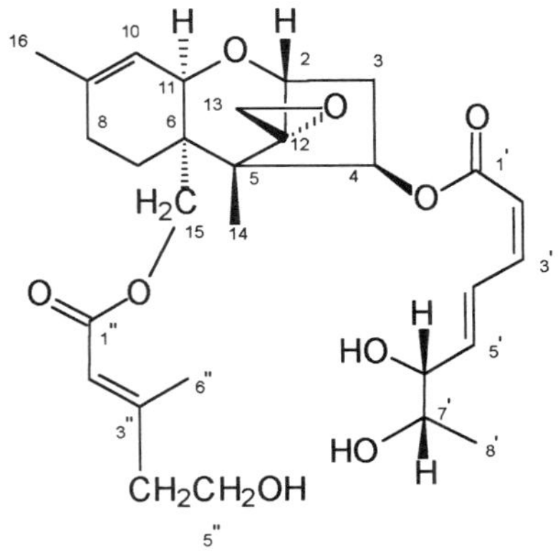

General Characteristics

Isolated as an amorphous solid.

Fungal Source

*Myrothecium verrucaria (*ATCC 20540).

Isolation/Purification

The fermentation procedures with *Myrothecium verrucaria (*ATCC 20540) were carried out in a manner similar to those described previously (Jarvis *et al.*, 1982). Samples 1-4 (S1, S2, S3, and S4) from this isolate were the lower R_f fractions from silica gel chromatography (methanol-methylene chloride), given in the order of increasing polarity. Sample 2 (S2) contained mainly trichoverrins according to TLC analysis. This sample was chromatographed on semipreparative countercurrent chromatography (CCC; V_c=355ml) with a solvent system of chloroform-hexane-methanol-water (3:1:3:2, v/v/v/v) and a flow rate of 3.2ml/min (ca. 400mg/injection). Like fractions were combined to give seven fractions: S2F1, S2F2, S2F3, S2F4, S2F5, S2F6, and S2F7. A portion of S2F2 was subjected to semi-preparative CCC with a solvent system of methylene chloride-carbon tetrachloride-methanol-water (2:3:3:2, v/v/v/v) and a flow rate of 2.8ml/min. The components of the mobile phase (organic layer, methylene chloride-carbon tetrachloride) were varied from 2:3 to 5:2 (v/v), starting at t = 120 min and going to t = 160 min. Like portions were combined to give seven fractions: I, (C6'*R*,C7'*R*)-isotrichoverrin A, II, (C6'*R*,C7'*S*)-isotrichoverrin B, III, a mixture of isotrichoverrin B and trichoverrin C, IV, V, VI, (2'*E*)-isotrichoverrin A), VII, (2'*E*)-isotrichoverrin B). Fractions IV and V were subjected to CCC (semi-preparative column) separately with the solvent system of methylene chloride-carbon tetrachloride-methanol-water (2:3:3:2, v/v/v/v) and a flow rate of 1.8ml/min to yield fractions rich in (*2'E,4'Z*)-isotrichoverrin B. These fractions were combined and purified on TLC (silica gel, 5% methanol in methylene chloride, developed three times) to give pure (2'*E*,4'*Z*) isotrichoverrin B.

Spectral Data

UV:

λ_{max}^{MeOH} 262nm (log ϵ=4.38).

IR:

($CHCl_3$) 3600(OH), 3470(OH), 1710(C=O), and 1646cm^{-1} (C=C).

^{1}H NMR:

($CDCl_3$) 0.77(3H, s, H-14); 1.11(3H, d, *J*=6.4Hz, H-8'); 1.69(3H, s, H-16); 2.17(3H, s, H-6"); 2.40(2H, t, *J*=5.7Hz, H-4"); 2.55(1H, dd, *J*=7.8, 15.5Hz, H-3α), 2.81(1H, d, *J*=4.0Hz, H-13A); 3.13(1H, d, *J*=4.0Hz, H-13B); 3.75-3.92(3H, m, H-7', H-5"); 3.83(1H, d, *J*=5.1Hz, H-2); 3.95(1H, bd, *J* =4.8Hz, H-11); 4.11(2H, s, H-15); 4.60(1H, dd, *J*=3.3, 8.6Hz, H-6'); 5.46(1H, bd, *J*=4.8Hz, H-10); 5.83(1H, s, H-2"); 5.88(1H, dd, *J*=8.6,11.0Hz, H-5'); 5.94(1H, d, *J*=15.1Hz, H-2'); 6.16(1H, dd, *J*=3.5, 7.8Hz, H-4); 6.26(1H, dd, *J*=11.0, 11.8Hz, H-4'); and 7.59ppm(1H, dd, *J*=11.8, 15.1Hz, H-3').

^{13}C NMR:

($CDCl_3$) 6.6, C-14; 17.3, C-8'; 19.0, C-6"; 21.9, C-7; 23.2, C-16; 27.9, C-8; 36.7, C-3; 42.9, C-6; 43.7, C-4"; 48.1, C-13; 48.7, C-5; 59.7, C-5"; 63.5, C-15; 65.5, C-12; 66.8, C-11; 70.4, C-7'; 71.6, C-6'; 75.6, C-4; 79.1, C-2; 117.2, C-2"; 118.5, C-10; 122.7, C-2'; 128.9, C-4; 138.1, C-5'; 139.9, C-3'; 140.5, C-9; 156.9, C-3"; 165.9, C-1"; and 167.0ppm, C-1'.

Mass Spectrum:

HRCIMS: calcd for $C_{29}H_{41}O_9$, $(M + H)^+$, 533.2751; found, 533.2768*m/e*.

References

B. B. Jarvis; Macrocyclic Trichothecenes; In Mycotoxins and Phytoalexins; R. P. Sharma and D. K. Salunkhe, eds.; CRC Press, Boca Raton, Florida, pp. 361-421(1991).

B. B. Jarvis, G. P. Stahly, G. Pavanasasivam, J. O. Midiwo, T. DeSilva, C. E. Holmlund, E. P. Mazzola, and R. F. Geoghegan, Jr.; Isolation and Characterization of the Trichoverroids and New Roridins and Verrucarins; J. Org. Chem., Vol. 47, pp. 1117-1124(1982).

B. B. Jarvis, S. Wang, and H. L. Ammon; Trichoverroid Stereoisomers; J. Nat. Prod.,Vol. 59, pp. 254-261(1996).

Common/Systematic Name

9β,10β-Epoxyisotrichoverrin B

Molecular Formula/Molecular Weight

$C_{29}H_{40}O_{10}$; MW = 548.26723

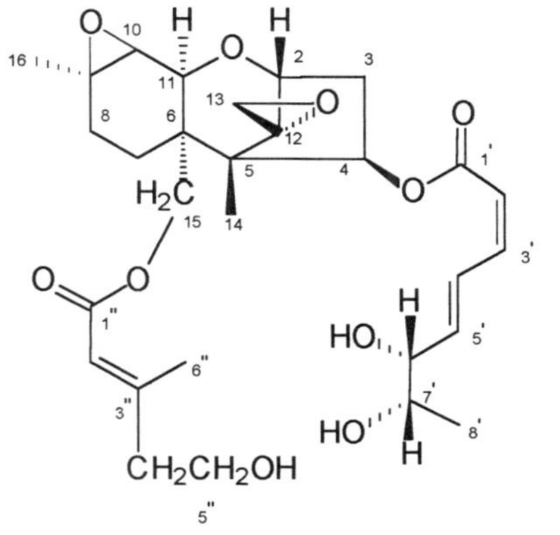

General Characteristics

Isolated as an oil; $[\alpha]_D^{20}$ - 21.0° (*c*= 0.13, in $CHCl_3$).

Fungal Source

*Myrothecium verrucaria (*ATCC 20540).

Isolation/Purification

The fermentation procedures with *Myrothecium verrucaria (*ATCC 20540) were carried out in a manner similar to those described previously (Jarvis *et al.*, 1982). Samples 1-4 (S1, S2, S3, and S4) from this isolate were the lower R_f fractions from silica gel chromatography (methanol-methylene chloride), given in the order of increasing polarity. Sample 3 (S3) from *M. verrucaria* isolate ATCC 20540, which was more polar than those that contained trichoverrols (S1) and trichoverrins (S2), was partitioned between chloroform and methanol-water mixture (50%). The organic fraction was subjected to preparative TLC (Chromatotron, 2mm, silica gel) with methanol-methylene chloride (3-10%). The most polar fraction was subjected to high speed countercurrent distribution (CCC) with a solvent system of chloroform-hexane-methanol-water (12:8:15:5, v/v/v/v) at a flow rate of 1.8ml/min to give 9β,10β-epoxyisotrichoverrin A and 9β,10β-epoxyisotrichoverrin B.

Spectral Data

^1H NMR:

($CDCl_3$) 0.74(3H, s, H-14); 1.13(3H, d, *J*=6.4Hz, H-8'); 1.34(3H, s, H-16); 1.70-2.03(5H, m, H-3β, H-7, H-8); 2.20(3H, d, *J*=0.9Hz, H-6"); 2.41(2H, t, *J*=6.1Hz, H-

4"); 2.53(1H, dd, J=7.9, 15.5Hz, H-3α); 2.78(1H, d, J=4.0Hz, H-13A); 3.10(1H, d, J=5.6Hz, H-10); 3.19(1H, d, J=4.0Hz, H-13B); 3.81(2 H, m, H-5"); 3.90(2H, m, H-11, H-7'); 3.93(1H, d, J=5.2Hz, H-2); 4.04(1H, d, J=12.6Hz, H-15A); 4.15(1H, d, J=12.6Hz, H-15B); 5.67(1H, d, J=11.3Hz, H-2'); 5.81(1H, d, J=0.9Hz, H-2"); 6.03(1H, dd, J=3.4, 7.9Hz, H-4); 6.12(1H, dd, J=5.3, 15.5Hz, H-5'); 6.62(1H, dd, J=11.3, 11.3Hz, H-3'); and 7.53ppm (1H, dd, J=11.3, 15.5Hz, H-4').

^{13}C NMR:
(CDCl$_3$) 6.7, C-14; 17.9, C-8'; 19.2, C-6"; 19.4, C-7; 22.3, C-16; 26.4, C-8; 36.6, C-3; 42.6, C-6; 43.6, C4"; 48.0, C-13; 48.5, C-5; 57.3, C-10; 57.5, C-9; 59.7, C-5"; 63.1, C-15; 65.2, C-12; 66.7, C-11; 70.2, C-7'; 74.7, C-4; 75.4, C-6'; 78.7, C-2; 116.5, C-2"; 118.0, C-2'; 127.7, C-4'; 142.1, C-5'; 143.9, C-3'; 158.4, C-3"; 165.8, C1'; and 165.9ppm, C-1".

Mass Spectrum:
HRCIMS: calcd for $C_{29}H_{41}O_{10}$ $(M + H)^+$, 549.2700; found, 549.2754*m/e*.

References

B. B. Jarvis; Macrocyclic Trichothecenes; In Mycotoxins and Phytoalexins; R. P. Sharma and D. K. Salunkhe, eds.; CRC Press, Boca Raton, Florida, pp. 361-421(1991).

B. B. Jarvis, G. P. Stahly, G. Pavanasasivam, J. O. Midiwo, T. DeSilva, C. E. Holmlund, E. P. Mazzola, and R. F. Geoghegan, Jr.; Isolation and Characterization of the Trichoverroids and New Roridins and Verrucarins; J. Org. Chem., Vol. 47, pp. 1117-1124(1982).

B. B. Jarvis, S. Wang, and H. L. Ammon; Trichoverroid Stereoisomers; J. Nat. Prod., Vol. 59, pp. 254-261(1996).

Common/Systematic Name

(2'*E*)-12,13-Deoxyisotrichoverrin B

Molecular Formula/Molecular Weight

$C_{29}H_{40}O_8$; MW = 516.27230

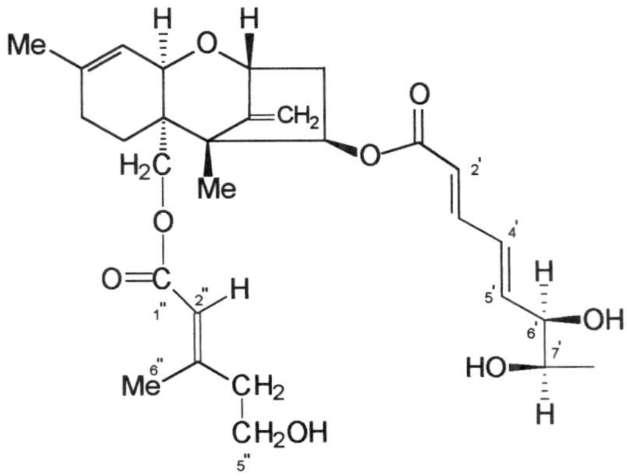

General Characteristics

Isolated as an oil.

Fungal Source

*Myrothecium verrucaria (*ATCC 20540).

Isolation/Purification

The fermentation procedures with *Myrothecium verrucaria (*ATCC 20540) were carried out in a manner similar to those described previously (Jarvis *et al.*, 1982). Samples 1-4 (S1, S2, S3, and S4) from this isolate were the lower R_f fractions from silica gel chromatography (methanol-methylene chloride), given in the order of increasing polarity. To sample 1, which contained some solid material, was added cold ethyl acetate. The solid was collected and recrystallized from methylene chloride-hexane to give isotrichoverrol A. The remaining portion of S1 was subjected to semipreparative CCC (V_c=355ml) with a solvent system of methanol-water-chloroform-hexane (3:2:3:1.2, v/v/v/); flow rate was 2.4ml/min (ca. 400mg/injection, total 10 injections) to give isotrichoverrol A and isotrichoverrol B. Another fraction from this CCC was subjected to CCC (semipreparative column) with a solvent system of methylene chloride-carbon tetrachloride-methanol-water (2:3:3:2, v/v/v/v; ca. 400mg/injection). The major fraction of this sample was eluted with little retention from the column, and there were no detectable trichothecenes in this fraction, according to TLC analysis. Seven additional fractions were collected: S1F1a, S1F1b, S1F1c, S1F1d, S1F1e, S1F1f, and S1F1g. S1F1f was subjected to reversed-phase TLC on C_8 (55% methanol in water) to give (2'*E*)12,13-deoxyisotrichoverrin B as an oil.

Spectral Data

UV:
λ_{max}^{MeOH} 260nm (log ε=4.44).

IR:
($CHCl_3$) 1707(C=O) and 1652cm^{-1} (C=C).

^1H NMR:
($CDCl_3$) 1.02(3H, s, H-14); 1.12(3H, d, *J*=6.5Hz, H-8'); 1.66(3H, s, H-16); 2.18(3H, d, *J*=1.0Hz, H-6"); 2.39(2H, t, *J*=5.6Hz, H-4"); 2.57(1H, dd, *J*=7.7, 15.5Hz, H-3α); 3.76-3.90(3H, m, H-7', H-5"); 3.96(1H, bd, *J*=5.7Hz, H-11); 4.11(2H, s, H-15); 4.18(1H, m, H-6'); 4.42(1H, d, *J*=5.1Hz, H-2); 4.71(1H, s, H-13A); 5.13(1H, s, H-13B); 5.41(1H, bd, *J*=5.7Hz, H-10); 5.83(1H, d, *J*=15.4Hz, H-2'); 5.84(1H, d, *J*=1.1Hz, H-2"); 6.06(1H, dd, *J*=3.0, 7.7Hz, H-4); 6.11(1H, dd, *J*=5.9, 15.6Hz, H-5'); 6.39(1H, dd, *J*=10.9, 15.6Hz, H-4'); and 7.21ppm(1H, dd, *J*=10.9, 15.4 Hz, H-3').

^{13}C NMR:
($CDCl_3$) 11.1, C-14; 17.6, C-8'; 19.0, C-6"; 20.9, C-7; 23.2, C-16; 28.0, C-8; 37.9, C-3; 42.8, C-6; 43.8, C-4"; 51.6, C-5; 59.8, C-5"; 63.7, C-15; 66.6, C-11; 70.2, C-7'; 75.4, C4; 75.6, C-6'; 78.8, C-2; 105.4, C-13; 117.3, C-2"; 118.8, C-10; 121.8, C-2'; 129.8, C-4'; 140.2, C-5'; 140.1, C-9; 143.9, C-3'; 152.3, C-12; 156.7, C-3"; 166.2, C-1"; and 166.5ppm, C-1'.

Mass Spectrum:
HRCIMS: calcd for $C_{29}H_{41}O_9$, (M^++ 1), 517.2801; found, 517.2849*m/e*.

References

B. B. Jarvis; Macrocyclic Trichothecenes; In Mycotoxins and Phytoalexins; R. P. Sharma and D. K. Salunkhe, eds.; CRC Press, Boca Raton, Florida, pp. 361-421(1991).

B. B. Jarvis, G. P. Stahly, G. Pavanasasivam, J. O. Midiwo, T. DeSilva, C. E. Holmlund, E. P. Mazzola, and R. F. Geoghegan, Jr.; Isolation and Characterization of the Trichoverroids and New Roridins and Verrucarins; J. Org. Chem., Vol. 47, pp. 1117-1124(1982).

B. B. Jarvis, S. Wang, and H. L. Ammon; Trichoverroid Stereoisomers; J. Nat. Prod., Vol. 59, pp. 254-261(1996).

Common/Systematic Name

(9'*E*)-Roridin L-2

Molecular Formula/Molecular Weight

$C_{29}H_{38}O_9$; MW = 530.25158

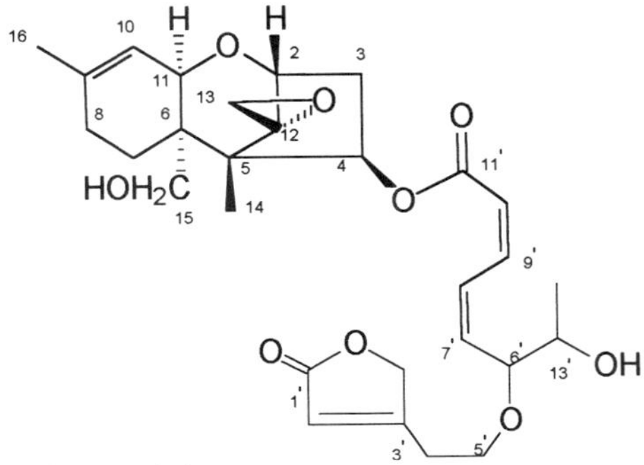

General Characteristics

Isolated as an oil.

Fungal Source

*Myrothecium verrucaria (*ATCC 20540).

Isolation/Purification

The fermentation procedures with *Myrothecium verrucaria (*ATCC 20540) were carried out in a manner similar to those described previously (Jarvis *et al*., 1982). Samples 1-4 (S1, S2, S3, and S4) from this isolate were the lower R_f fractions from silica gel chromatography (methanol-methylene chloride), given in the order of increasing polarity. To sample 1, which contained some solid material, was added cold ethyl acetate. The solid was collected and recrystallized from methylene chloride-hexane to give isotrichoverrol A. The remaining portion of S1 was subjected to semipreparative high-speed countercurrent chromatography (CCC, V_c=355ml) with a solvent system of methanol-water-chloroform-hexane (3:2:3:1.2, v/v/v/v); flow rate was 2.4ml/min (ca. 400 mg/injection, total 10 injections) to give isotrichoverrol A and isotrichoverrol B. Another fraction from this CCC was subjected to CCC (semipreparative column) with a solvent system of methylene chloride-carbon tetrachloride-methanol-water (2:3:3:2, v/v/v/v) (ca. 400mg/injection). The major fraction of this sample was eluted with little retention from the column, and there were no detectable trichothecenes in this fraction, according to TLC analysis. Seven additional fractions were collected: S1F1a, S1F1b, S1F1c, S1F1d, S1F1e, S1F1f, and S1F1g. S1F1d was subjected to reversed-phase TLC on C_8 plates (60% methanol in water) to give isotrichoverrin A and (9'*E*)-roridin L-2.

Spectral Data

^{1}H NMR:

(CDCl$_3$) 0.81(3H, s, H-14); 1.11(3H, d, *J*=6.3Hz, H-14'); 1.71(3H, s, H-16); 2.49(1H, dd, *J*=7.9, 15.5Hz, H-3α); 2.70(2H, t, *J* =6.0Hz, H-4'); 2.81(1H, d, *J*=4.0Hz, H-13A), 3.13(1H, d, *J*=4.0Hz, H-13B); 3.83(1H, d, *J*=5.1Hz, H-2); 3.92(1H, bd, *J*=5.7Hz, H-11); 4.77(2H, d, *J*=1.5Hz, H-12'); 5.48(1H, bd, *J*=5.7Hz, H-10); 5.90(1H, d, *J*=1.5Hz, H-2'); 5.90(1H, dd, *J*=8.2, 15.3Hz, H-7'); 5.97(1H, d, *J*=15.4Hz, H-10'); 6.12(1H, dd, *J*=3.6, 7.9Hz, H-4); 6.36(1H, dd, *J*=11.0, 15.3Hz, H-8'); and 7.27ppm (1H, dd, *J*=11.0, 15.4Hz, H-9').

^{13}C NMR:

(CDCl$_3$) 6.6, C-14; 18.4, C-14'; 19.0, C-12'; 23.2, C-16; 28.0, C-8; 29.3, C-4'; 31.3, C-7; 35.9, C-3; 44.2, C-6; 48.2, C-13; 49.0, C-5; 63.0, C-15; 65.6, C-12; 66.2, C-5'; 66.8, C-11; 71.4, C-13'; 75.8, C-4; 79.0, C-2; 85.9, C-6'; 116.7, C-2'; 118.8, C-10; 122.6, C-10'; 132.4, C-8'; 138.6, C-7'; 140.5, C-9; 143.4, C9'; 166.8, C-11'; 167.4, C-3'; and 173.2ppm, C-1'.

Mass Spectrum:

HREIMS: calcd for $C_{29}H_{38}O_9$ (M^+), 530.2516; found, 530.2516*m/e*.

References

B. B. Jarvis; Macrocyclic Trichothecenes; In Mycotoxins and Phytoalexins; R. P. Sharma and D. K. Salunkhe, eds.; CRC Press, Boca Raton, Florida, pp. 361-421(1991).

B. B. Jarvis, G. P. Stahly, G. Pavanasasivam, J. O. Midiwo, T. DeSilva, C. E. Holmlund, E. P. Mazzola, and R. F. Geoghegan, Jr.; Isolation and Characterization of the Trichoverroids and New Roridins and Verrucarins; J. Org. Chem., Vol. 47, pp. 1117-1124(1982).

B. B. Jarvis, S. Wang, and H. L. Ammon; Trichoverroid Stereoisomers; J. Nat. Prod.,Vol. 59, pp. 254-261(1996).

Common/Systematic Name
Roridin L-2

Molecular Formula/Molecular Weight
$C_{29}H_{38}O_9$; MW = 530.25158

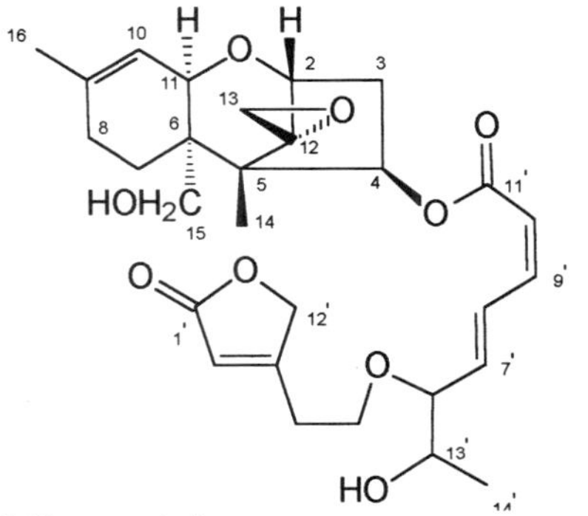

General Characteristics
Isolated as a white, homogeneous solid; mp., 93-97°C; $[\alpha]_D$ + 83.6° (*c*= 1.0, in $CHCl_3$).

Fungal Source
Myrothecium roridum.

Isolation/Purification
Fermented beer was extracted with ethyl acetate, concentrated, and chromatographed by silica gel high performance liquid chromatography eluted with methylene chloride-ethyl acetate, 50:50 (v/v) and by C_{18}-reversed phase chromatography eluted with methanol-water, 50:50 (v/v).

Spectral Data

UV:
λ_{max}^{MeOH} 259nm (ϵ=24,650).

IR:
(CCl_4) 3500, 3500, 1785, 1750, 1710, 1640, and 1600cm^{-1}.

^{1}H NMR:
($CDCl_3$) 0.84(3H, s, H-14); 1.14(3H, d, *J*=6.0Hz, H-14'); 1.72(3H, s, H-16); 2.50(1H, dd, *J*=8.0, 15.5Hz, H-3α); 2.0(1H, m, H-3β); 2.70(2H, m, H-4'); 2.81(1H, d, *J*=4.0Hz, H-13A); 3.13(1H, d, *J*=4.0Hz, H-13B); 3.70(1H, m, H-2); 3.70(1H, m, H-11); 4.78(1H, dd, *J*=1.5, 17.5Hz, H-12'A); 4.84(1H, dd, *J*=1.5Hz, 17.5Hz, H-12'B); 5.48(1H, d, *J*=5.0 Hz, H-10); 5.92(1H, br, *J*=1.3Hz, H-2'); 5.86(1H, dd, *J*=7.0, 15.5Hz, H-7'); 5.78(1H, d, *J*=11.5Hz, H-10'); 6.10(1H, dd, *J*=3.5, 8.0Hz, H-4);

7.61(1H, dd, J=11.5, 15.5Hz, H-8'); and 6.61ppm (1H, t, J=11.5Hz, H-9').

^{13}C NMR:

($CDCl_3$) 6.7, C-14; 18.5, C-14'; 73.6, C-12'; 23.3, C-16; 28.1, C-8; 29.3, C-4'; 21.2, C-7; 36.3, C-3; 44.3, C-6; 6.7, C-13; 48.9, C-5; 62.7, C-15; 65.7, C-12; 66.4, C-5'; 66.9, C-11; 69.8, C-13'; 75.5, C-4; 79.0, C-2; 85.4, C-6'; 116.7, C-2'; 118.9, C-10; 118.8, C-10'; 130.6, C-8'; 139.1, C-7'; 140.6, C-9; 143.5, C9'; 166.5, C-11'; 167.8, C-3'; and 174.2ppm (C-1').

Mass Spectrum:

EIMS: 530*m/e* (M^+).

References

R. J. Bloem, T. A. Smitka, R. H. Bunge, J. C. French, and E. P. Mazzola; Roridin L-2, A New Trichothecene; Tet. Lett., Vol. 24, pp. 249-252(1983).

B. B. Jarvis; Macrocyclic Trichothecenes; In Mycotoxins and Phytoalexins; R. P. Sharma and D. K. Salunkhe, eds.; CRC Press, Boca Raton, Florida, pp. 361-421(1991).

Common/Systematic Name

Verrucarin A

Molecular Formula/Molecular Weight

$C_{27}H_{34}O_9$; MW = 502.22028

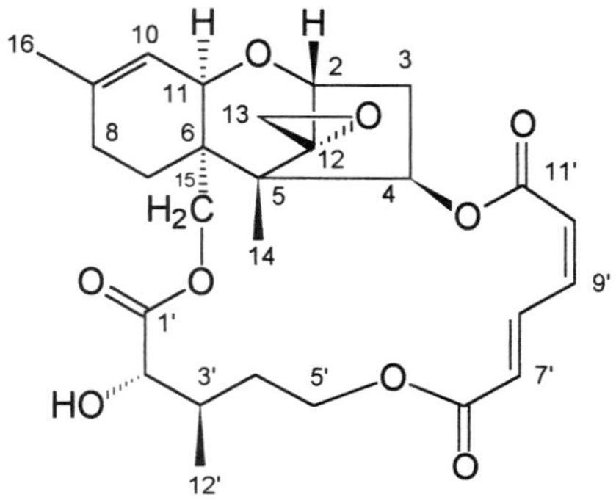

General Characteristics

Crystals; mp., >360° (dec.); $[\alpha]_D^{22}$ +206° (c=1.012, in dioxane); +260° (in $CHCl_3$).

Fungal Source

Myrothecium verrucaria and *M. roridum.*

Biological Activity

Rats given verrucarin A developed creatinuria; *in vitro* it inhibited ATP-creatine phosphotransferase. It caused severe edema in body cavities. Major clinical signs in several different experimental animals were diarrhea, hematuria, vomiting, anorexia, loss of weight, ataxia, and thirst. At relatively low dosages, it caused leukocytosis followed by severe leukopenia. The LD_{50} values in mice were 1.5mg/kg (IV) and 0.5mg/kg (IP). It caused dermal toxicity: necrosis of epidermis with suppuration and extensive necrosis of dermal tissue with damage extending into subcuticulis. ID_{50} of protein synthesis in rabbit reticulocytes was 10-15μg/ml.

Spectral Data

UV:

λ_{max}^{EtOH} 260nm (ϵ=17,700).

^1H NMR:

($CDCl_3$) 5.83(H-4); 5.46(H-10); 2.97(H-13a); 0.87(H-14); 1.79(H-16); 4.20(H-2'); 6.06(H-7'); 8.08(H-8'); 6.70(H-9'); 6.17(H-10'); and 0.89ppm (H-12').

^{13}C NMR:

($CDCl_3$) 78.6, C-2; 34.6, C-3; 75.3, C-4; 49.2, C-5; 43.9, C-6; 19.7, C-7; 27.2, C-8; 140.7, C-9; 117.7, C-10; 66.6, C-11; 64.9, C-12; 47.4, C-13; 7.0, C-14; 63.1, C-15; 22.6, C-16; 174.3, C-1'; 73.8, C-2'; 32.9, C-3'; 31.9, C-4'; 60.8, C-5'; 165.8, C-6'; 127.2, C-7'; 138.6, C-8'; 138.6, C-9'; 125.5, C-10'; 165.1, C-11'; and 9.8ppm, C-12'.

TLC Data

A. Adsorbent: silica gel G; solvent system, chloroform-methanol, 98:2 v/v; R_f, 0.70; detection, H_2SO_4 spraying and heating at 110°C for 5 minutes. B. Adsorbent: alumina; solvent system, chloroform-methanol, 98:2 v/v; R_f, 0.28; detection, H_2SO_4 spraying and heating at 110°C for 5 minutes.

References

R. J. Cole and R. H. Cox; Handbook of Toxic Fungal Metabolites; Academic Press, New York, pp. 247-248(1981).

J. Gutzwiller and Ch. Tamm; Uber die Struktur von Verrucarin A; Helvetica Chimica Acta, Vol. 48, pp. 157-176(1965).

B. B. Jarvis; Macrocyclic Trichothecenes; In Mycotoxins and Phytoalexins; R. P. Sharma and D. K. Salunkhe, eds.; CRC Press, Boca Raton, Florida, pp. 361-421(1991).

Common/Systematic Name

Verrucarin A β-D-glucoside

Molecular Formula/Molecular Weight

$C_{33}H_{44}O_{14}$; MW = 664.27311

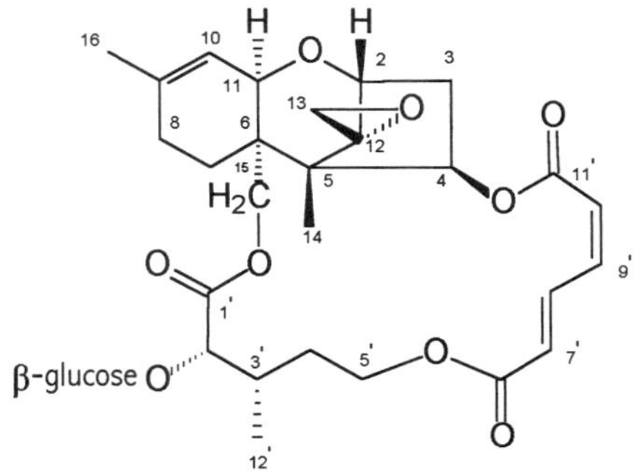

General Characteristics

Amorphous solid; $[\alpha]_D$ + 98° (*c*=0.63, in $CHCl_3$).

Fungal Source

Baccharis coridifolia.

Isolation/Purification

The crude extract (10% methanol-chloroform) of female *B. coridifolia* plant was partitioned (hexane-10% water in methanol) and the aqueous methanol, after solvent removal,was chromatographed (silica gel) with ethyl ether-hexane, ethyl ether-hexane, and methanol-methylene chloride. The 20% methanol-methylene chloride was subjected to further flash chromatography, preparative TLC (Chromatotron), and finally preparative C_{18} reversed phase HPLC to give verrucarin A β-D-glucoside.

Biological Activity

Cytotoxic: IC_{60} ca. 100 ng/ml.

Spectral Data

IR:

(CH_2Cl_2) 3440, 1720, 1660, 1640, 1595, 1270, 1195, and 1080cm^{-1}.

^{1}H NMR:

($CDCl_3$) 7.99(1H, dd, *J*=12.0, 15.5Hz, H-8'); 6.65(1H, dd, *J*=12.0, 15.5Hz, H- 8'); 6.65(1H, dd, *J*=11.1, 12.0Hz, H-9'); 6.14(1H, d, *J*=11.1Hz, H-10'); 6.02(1H, d, *J*=15.5Hz, H-7'); 5.77(1H, dd, *J*=3.9, 8.1Hz, H-4); 5.42(1H, br d, *J*=5.0Hz, H-10); 4.75 and 4.20(1H each, AB, *J*=12.1Hz, H-15); 4.46(1H, ddd, *J*=H-5'B); 4.20(1H, d,

J=2.0Hz, H-2'); 4.12(1H, d, J=7.6Hz, H-1"); 3.97(1H, ddd, J=11.7, 11.7, 3.5Hz, H-5'A); 3.90(1H, dd, J=3.6, 11.8Hz, H-6"B); 3.84(1H, d, J=5.1Hz, H-2); 3.79(1H, d, J=5.1, 11.8Hz, H-6"A); 3.54-3.57(3H, m, H-11, H-3", H-4"); 3.40(1H, dd, J=7.6, 9.2Hz, H-2"); 3.36(1H, ddd, J=3.6, 5.1, 7.8Hz, H-5"); 3.11 and 2.78(1H each, AB, J=3.9Hz, H-13); 2.46(1H, dd, J=8.1, 15.4Hz, H-3α); 2.44(1H, m, H-3'); 2.20(1H, ddd, J=3.9, 5.1, 15.4Hz, H-3β); 1.99(1H, m, H- 8B); 1.80-1.90(4H, m, H-4', H-7B, H-8A); 1.75(3H, s, H-16); 1.69(1H, m, H-7A); 0.94(3H, d, J=5.9Hz, H-12'); and 0.82ppm (3H, s, H-14).

^{13}C NMR:

($CDCl_3$) 78.9(C-2), 34.9(C-3), 75.6(C-4), 49.5(C-5), 44.1(C-6), 20.1(C-7), 27.5(C-8), 141.0(C-9), 118.0(C-10), 66.8(C-11), 65.2(C-12), 47.8(C-13), 7.4(C-14), 63.6(C-15), 23.4(C-16), 172.4(C-1'), 80.6(C-2'), 32.4(C-3'), 32.1(C-4'), 61.0(C-5'), 166.1(C-6'), 127.3(C-7'), 138.8(C-8'), 138.7(C-9'), 125.9(C-10'), 165.4(C-11'), 11.2(C-12'), 102.6(C-1"), 73.6(C-2"), 76.5(C-3"), 70.0(C-4"), 75.7(C-5"), and 62.3ppm (C-6").

TLC Data

Adsorbent: Silica gel; solvent system: 10% methanol-methylene chloride; R_f, 0.38.

Reference

B. B. Jarvis, S. Wang, C. Cox, M. M. Rao, V. Philip, M. S. Varaschin, and C. S. Barros; Brazilian *Baccharis* toxins: Livestock Poisoning and the Isolation of Macrocyclic Trichothecene Glucosides; Natural Toxins, Vol. 4, pp. 58-71(1996).

Common/Systematic Name
2'-Dehydroverrucarin A

Molecular Formula/Molecular Weight
$C_{27}H_{32}O_9$; MW = 500.20463

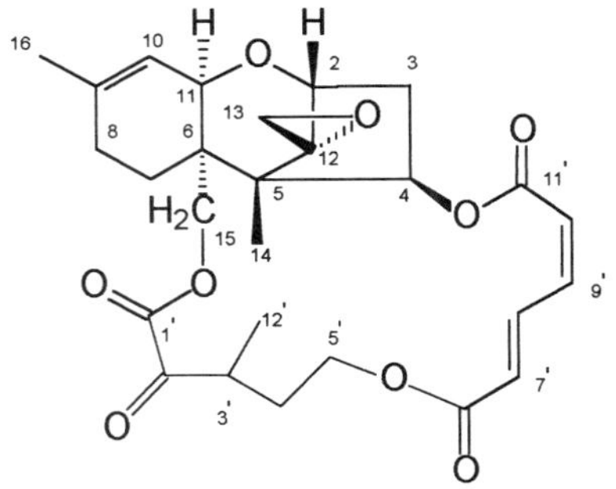

General Characteristics
Needles from acetone-ethyl ether; mp., 233-240°C; $[\alpha]_D^{25}$ + 118° (in $CHCl_3$).

Fungal Source
Myrothecium roridum.

Biological Activity
Antibiotic activity similar to that of verrucarin A.

Spectral Data

UV:
λ_{max}^{EtOH} 262nm (ε=23,400).

IR:
(KBr) 1710, 1725, 1590, and 1630cm^{-1}.

Reference
B. B. Jarvis; Macrocyclic Trichothecenes; In Mycotoxins and Phytoalexins; R. P. Sharma and D. K. Salunkhe, eds.; CRC Press, Boca Raton, Florida, pp. 361-421(1991).

Common/Systematic Name
Verrucarin B

Molecular Formula/Molecular Weight
$C_{27}H_{32}O_9$; MW = 500.20463

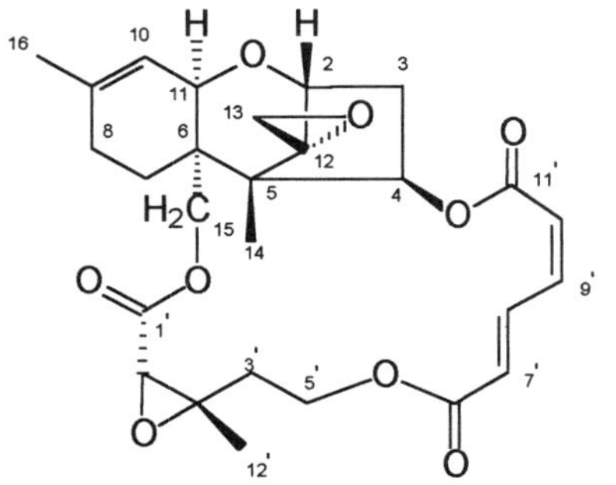

Fungal Source
Myrothecium verrucaria and *M. roridum.*

General Characteristics
Crystals; mp., >330°C; $[\alpha]_D$ + 94° (in $CHCl_3$); + 101° (in dioxane); + 147° (in benzene).

Biological Activity
Typical trichothecene type activity: dermal toxicity, antifungal, cytostatic, and acute toxicity to vertebrate animals. The LD_{50} in mice dosed IV was 7.0mg/kg. The ED_{50} for cytostatic activity *in vitro* against Ehrlich ascites tumor cells was 0.003μg/ml.

Spectral Data

UV:
λ_{max}^{EtOH} 258.5nm (ϵ=23,400).

^{1}H NMR:
($CDCl_3$) 5.90(H-4); 5.47(H-10); 3.00(H-13a); 0.88(H-14); 1.74(H-16); 3.41(H-2'); 6.10(H-7'); 7.98(H-8'); 6.69(H-9'); 6.19(H-10'); and 1.56ppm (H-12').

^{13}C NMR:
($CDCl_3$) 78.7,C-2; 34.8, C-3; 75.4, C-4; 49.0, C-5; 43.6, C-6; 19.8, C-7; 27.4, C-8; 140.4, C-9; 118.0, C-10; 66.9, C-11; 64.9, C-12; 47.5, C-13; 7.3, C-14; 63.6,C-15; 22.8, C-16; 167.4, C-1'; 58.0, C-2'; 61.1, C-3'; 36.9, C-4'; 60.4, C-5'; 165.8, C-6'; 127.2, C-7'; 138.0, C-8'; 138.0, C-9'; 125.6, C-10'; 164.8; C11', and 15.8ppm, C-12'.

TLC Data

Absorbent: Kieselgel G; solvent, ethyl ether (two consecutive runs); R_f, 0.37; detection, iodine vapors.

References

R. J. Cole and R. H. Cox; Handbook of Toxic Fungal Metabolites; Academic Press, New York, pp. 253-254(1981).

B. B. Jarvis; Macrocyclic Trichothecenes; In Mycotoxins and Phytoalexins; R. P. Sharma and D. K. Salunkhe, eds.; CRC Press, Boca Raton, Florida, pp. 361-421(1991).

Common/Systematic Name

Verrucarin J

Molecular Formula/Molecular Weight

$C_{27}H_{32}O_8$; MW = 484.20972

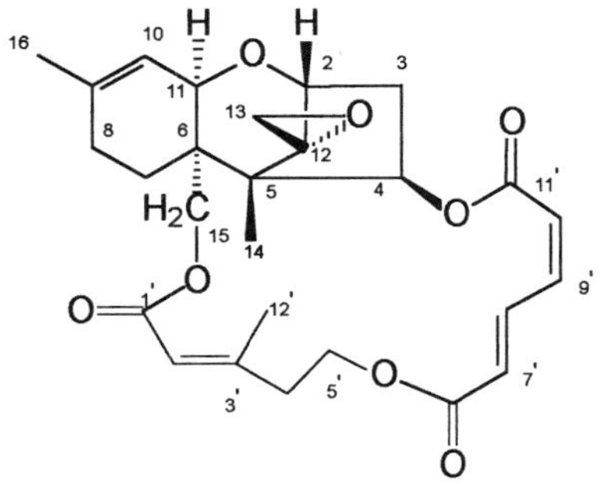

Fungal Source

Myrothecium verrucaria.

General Characteristics

Colored needles from chloroform-ether; acetone-ether; mp., >315°C (dec.); $[\alpha]_D^{22}$ +22° (*c*=1.011, in $CHCl_3$); $[\alpha]_D^{23}$ + 41° (*c*=0.784, in benzene).

Biological Activity

Antibiotic activity similar to that of verrucarin A.

Spectral Data

UV:

λ_{max}^{EtOH} 196(ε=15,500), 219(19,900), and 262nm (14,500).

IR:

(CH_2Cl_2) 2810, 1710, 1650, 1630, 1588, 1352, 1221, 1180, 1147, 1070-1088, 1042, 995, 968, 877, and 820cm^{-1}.

^{1}H NMR:

($CDCl_3$) 5.90(H-4); 5.47(H-10); 2.98(H-13a); 0.83(H-14); 4.30(H-15a); 1.72(H-16); 3.50(H-2'); 2.50(H-4'a); 3.82(H-5'); 6.05(H-7'); 8.12(H-8'); 6.60(H-9'); 6.10(H-10'); and 2.28ppm (H-12').

TLC Data

Adsorbent: Kieselgel G; solvent was ethyl ether (two consecutive runs); R_f, 0.42; detection by iodine vapors.

References

R. J. Cole and R. H. Cox; Handbook of Toxic Fungal Metabolites; Academic Press, New York, pp. 259 (1981).

B. B. Jarvis; Macrocyclic Trichothecenes; In Mycotoxins and Phytoalexins; R. P. Sharma and D. K. Salunkhe, eds.; CRC Press, Boca Raton, Florida, pp. 361-421(1991).

Common/Systematic Name

Verrucarin K

12,13-Deoxyverrucarin A

Molecular Formula/Molecular Weight

$C_{27}H_{34}O_8$; MW = 486.22537

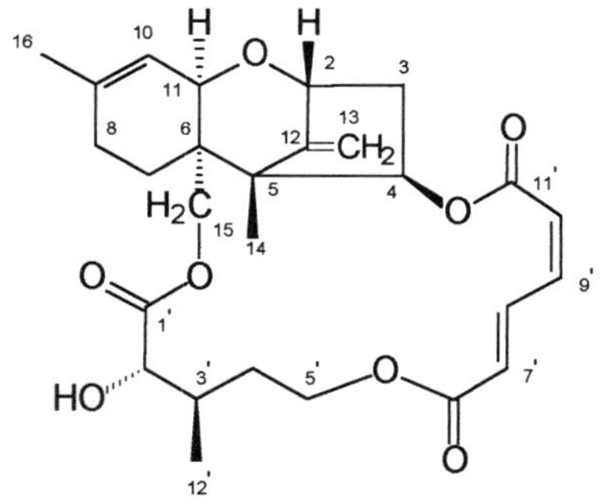

Fungal Source

Myrothecium verrucaria.

General Characteristics

Crystals from dichloromethane-ether; mp., >320°C (dec.); $[\alpha]_D^{23}$ +218° (*c*=0.58, in $CHCl_3$). Monoacetyl derivative, colorless needles from acetone-ether-petroleum ether; mp., 199-202°C; $[\alpha]_D^{23}$ + 143° (*c*=0.83, in $CHCl_3$).

Spectral Data

UV:

λ_{max}^{EtOH} 259nm (ϵ=15,500).

IR:

1710, 3550, 1630, and 1585cm^{-1}.

^{1}H NMR:

($CDCl_3$) 5.81(H-4); 5.39(H-10); 4.71(H-13a); 5.18(H-13b); 1.09(H-14); 3.66(H-15); 1.70(H-16); 6.05(H-7'); 8.05(H-8'); 6.67(H-9'); 6.08(H-10'); and 0.89ppm (H-12').

^{13}C NMR:

($CDCl_3$) 78.5, C-2; 35.9, C-3; 75.5, C-4; 52.0, C-5; 44.2, C-6; 18.7, C-7; 27.4, C-8; 140.5, C-9; 118.2, C-10; 66.5, C-11; 151.6, C-12; 106.3, C-13; 12.1, C-14; 63.5, C-15; 23.2, C-16; 174.5, C-1'; 74.0, C-2'; 61.1, C-3'; 32.1, C-4'; 61.1, C-5'; 165.9, C-6'; 127.4, C-7'; 138.7, C-8'; 138.7, C-9'; 125.6, C-10'; 165.3, C-11'; and 10.0ppm, C-12'.

References

R. J. Cole and R. H. Cox; Handbook of Toxic Fungal Metabolites; Academic Press, New York, pp. 260(1981).

B. B. Jarvis; Macrocyclic Trichothecenes; In Mycotoxins and Phytoalexins; R. P. Sharma and D. K. Salunkhe, eds.; CRC Press, Boca Raton, Florida, pp. 361-421(1991).

Common/Systematic Name

Verrucarin L

Molecular Formula/Molecular Weight

$C_{27}H_{32}O_9$; MW = 500.20463

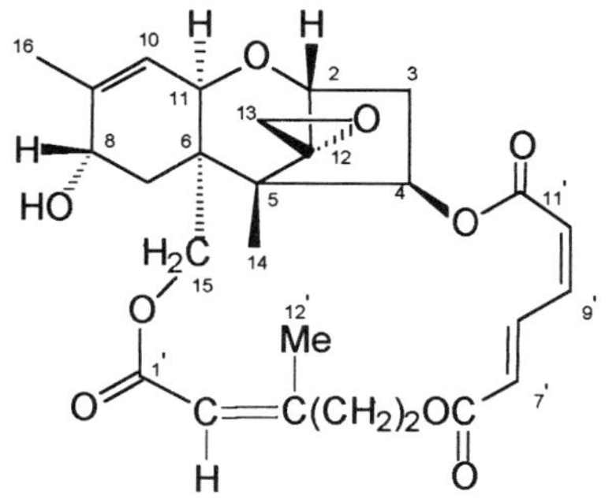

General Characteristics

Crystals from dichloromethane-hexane, mp., 230-235°C; $[\alpha]_D^{27}$ + 15.0° (c= 0.92 in chloroform). Acetate derivative, crystals from dichloromethane-ether, m.p. 132-135°C; $[\alpha]_D^{27}$ + 29.7° (*c*=0.52, in $CHCl_3$).

Isolation/Purification

Spores of *Myrothecium verrucaria* grown on N-Z amine agar were added to Czapek-Dox media and allowed to grow at 28°C in a shake culture. After 2 days, the solution was divided into three equal portions and added to three separate Fernback flasks containing 1L of production media. After 3 days of growth, the mycelium in each flask was separately centrifuged, washed, and resuspended in 1L of sterile water. Trichoverrin A and trichoverrin B were added separately to flasks one and two; flask three was used as the control. After 7 days, the mycelium was removed and extracted with ethyl acetate. The mycelium extract was subjected to partition chromatography on 500g Celite impregnated with 250ml of 18% water in methanol. The column was eluted with petroleum ether followed by increasing amounts of dichloromethane in petroleum ether up to 40% dichloromethane in petroleum ether. Fractions were combined on the basis of TLC analysis to give a total of eight fractions: A, B, C, D, E, F, G, and H (methanol wash). Flash chromatography of fraction G (3% MeOH in CH_2Cl_2) gave a fraction rich in roridin A, which upon crystallization from dichloromethane-hexane yielded roridin A. The mother liquor was subjected to HPLC (2% methanol-methylene chloride) to give verrucarin L which elutes just before roridin A.

Fungal Source

Myrothecium verrucaria (ATCC 24571).

Spectral Data

UV:
λ_{max}^{EtOH} 262nm (log ϵ= 4.42).

^{1}H NMR:
(CDCl$_3$) 0.86(3H, s, 14-H); 1.87(3H, s, 16-H); 2.26(3H, d, *J* =1Hz, 12'-H); 2.99(2H, AB, *J*=4Hz, 13-H); 3.80(1H, d, *J*=5Hz, 11-H); 4.45(2H AB, *J*=12 Hz, 15-H); 5.2(1H, m, 8-H); 5.58 (1H, d, *J* =5Hz 10-H); 6.00 (1H, d, *J* =16Hz, 7'-H); 6.12 (1H, d, *J*=11Hz, 10'-H); 6.65(1H, dd, *J*'s=11Hz, 9'-H); and 8.10ppm (1 H, dd, *J*=11, 16Hz, 8'-H). Verrucarin L acetate, 0.86(3H, s, 14-H); 1.80(3H, s, 16-H); 1.94(acetate); 2.27(3H, d, *J*=1Hz, 12'-H); 2.97(2H, AB, *J*=4Hz, 13-H); 3.75(1H, d, *J*=5Hz, 11-H); 4.40(2H, AB, *J*=12 Hz, 15-H); 5.70(1H, d, *J*= 5.0Hz, 10-H); 5.96(1H, d, *J*=16Hz, 7'-H); 6.07(1H, d, *J*=11Hz, 10'-H); 6.61(1H, dd, *J*'s=11Hz, 9'-H); and 8.01ppm (1H, dd, *J*=11, 16Hz, 8'-H).

^{13}C NMR:
(CDCl$_3$) 79.0 d, C-2; 35.3 t, C-3; 75.1 d, C-4; 48.8 s, C-5; 42.5 s, C-6; 30.1 t, C-7; 66.8 d, C-8; 139.7 s, C-9; 120.9 d, C-10; 67.2 d, C-11; 65.5 s, C-12; 48.1 t, C-13; 6.9 q, C-14; 65.0 t, C-15; 20.6 q, C-16; 165.7 s, C-1'; 118.2 d, C-2'; 156.6 C-3'; 40.3 t, C-4'; 60.5 t, C-5'; 165.5 s, C-6'; 127.2 d, C-7'; 139.3 d, C-8'; 139.3 d, C-9'; 125.6 d, C-10'; 165.7 s, C-11'; and 17.3ppm q, C-12'.

Mass Spectrum:
HRCIMS (methane gas reagent), 501.2112*m/e* (M^+ + H, calcd 501.2124). Verrucarin L acetate (chemical ionization, methane gas reagent), 543.2217*m/e* (M^+ + H; calcd for 543.2230).

Reference

B. B. Jarvis, G. P. Stahly, G. Pavanasasivam, J. O. Midiwo, T. Desilva, C. E. Holmlund, E.P. Mazzola and R. F. Geoghegan; Isolation and Characterization of the Trichoverroids and New Roridins and Verrucarins; J. Org. Chem., Vol. 47, pp. 1117-1124(1982).

Common/Systematic Name

Verrucarin L Acetate

Molecular Formula/Molecular Weight

$C_{29}H_{34}O_{10}$; MW = 542.21520

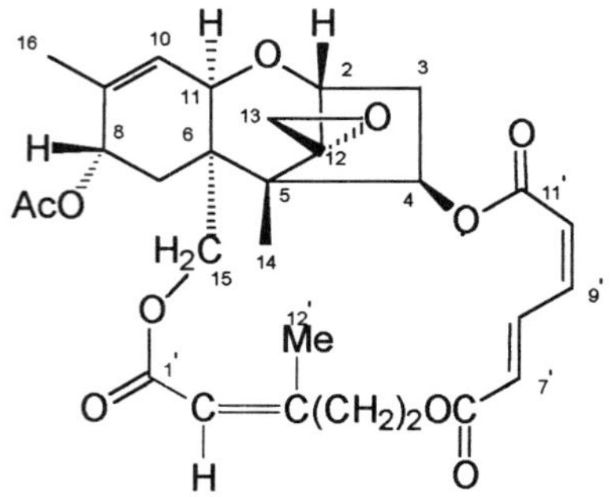

General Characteristics

Crystals from ether-hexane, mp., 132-135°C; $[\alpha]_D^{27}$ + 29.7° (c= 0.52 in $CHCl_3$).

Isolation/Purification

Spores of *Myrothecium verrucaria* grown on N-Z amine agar were added to Czapek-Dox media and allowed to grow at 28°C in a shake culture. After 2 days, the solution was divided into three equal portions and added to three separate Fernback flasks containing 1L of production media. After 3 days of growth, the mycelium in each flask was separately centrifuged, washed, and resuspended in 1L of sterile water. Trichoverrin A and trichoverrin B were added separately to flasks one and two; flask three was used as the control. After 7 days, the mycelium was removed and extracted with ethyl acetate. The mycelium extract was subjected to partition chromatography on 500g Celite impregnated with 250ml of 18% water in methanol. The column was eluted with petroleum ether followed by increasing amounts of dichloromethane in petroleum ether up to 40% dichloromethane in petroleum ether. Fractions were combined on the basis of TLC analysis to give a total of eight fractions: A, B, C, D, E, F, G, and H (methanol wash). Fraction E was subjected to MPLC using 30-40% ethyl acetate in hexane to give verrucarin B, verrucarin L acetate, and a mixture of verrucarin A and roridin J.

Fungal Source

Myrothecium verrucaria (ATCC 24571).

Spectral Data

UV:

λ_{max}^{EtOH} 261nm (log ϵ= 4.28).

^{1}H NMR:

(CDCl$_3$) 0.86(3H, s, 14-H); 1.80(3H, s, 16-H); 194 (acetate); 2.27(3H, d, *J*=1Hz, 12'-H); 2.97(2H, AB, *J*=4 Hz, 13-H); 3.75(1H, d, *J* =5Hz 11-H); 4.40(2H, AB, *J*=12Hz, 15-H); 5.70(1H, d, *J*=5.0Hz, 10'-H); 5.96(1H, d, *J*=16Hz, 7'-H); 6.07(1H, d, *J*=11Hz, 10'-H); 6.61(1H, dd, *J*'s=11Hz, 9'-H); and 8.01ppm (1H, dd, *J*=11, 16Hz, 8'-H).

^{13}C NMR:

(CDCl$_3$) 79.0 d, C-2; 34.9 t, C-3; 74.1 d, C-4; 49.0 s, C-5; 42.2 s, C-6; 26.5 t, C-7; 68.8 d, C-8; 136.5 s, C-9; 123.9 d, C-10; 67.0 d, C-11; 65.3 s, C-12; 47.9 t, C-13; 7.0 q, C-14; 64.5 t, C-15; 21.0 q, C-16; 165.5 s, C-1'; 117.8 d, C-2'; 156.9 C-3'; 40.2 t, C-4'; 60.4 t, C-5'; 165.4 s, C-6'; 127.8 d, C-7'; 138.8 d, C-8'; 139.9 d, C-9'; 125.2 d, C-10'; 165.8 s, C-11'; and 17.1 q, C-12'; 170.9, s, CH$_3$<u>C</u>=O; and 20.4ppm q, CH$_3$C=O.

Mass Spectrum:

HRCIMS (methane gas reagent), 543.2217*m/e* (M$^+$ + H, calcd 543.2230).

Reference

B. B. Jarvis, G. P. Stahly, G. Pavanasasivam, J. O. Midiwo, T. Desilva, C. E. Holmlund, E.P. Mazzola and R. F. Geoghegan; Isolation and Characterization of the Trichoverroids and New Roridins and Verrucarins; J. Org. Chem., Vol. 47, pp. 1117-1124(1982).

Common/Systematic Name

Roridin A

Molecular Formula/Molecular Weight

$C_{29}H_{40}O_9$; MW = 532.26723

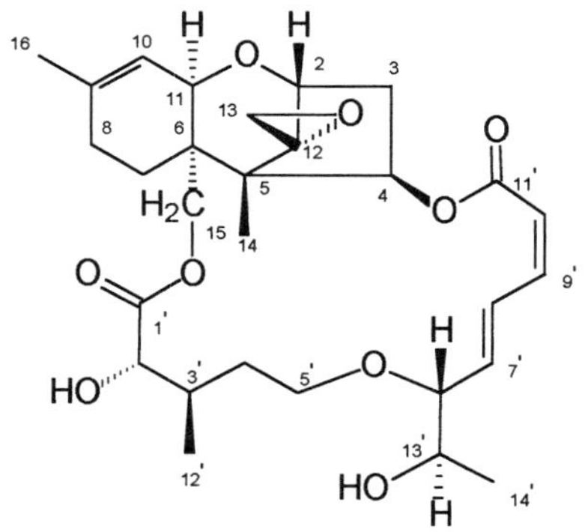

General Characteristics

Crystals from ether; mp., 198-204°C; $[\alpha]_D^{22}$ +130° (*c*=1.36, in $CHCl_3$); $[\alpha]_D^{22}$ + 192° (*c*=1.38 in dioxane); di-*O*-acetylroridin A, needles from ether-petroleum ether; mp., 165-166°C; $[\alpha]_D^{22}$ +168.5° (*c*=1.108, in $CHCl_3$).

Fungal Source

Myrothecium verrucaria and *M. roridum*.

Biological Activity

The LD_{50} value of roridin A in mice dosed IV was 1mg/kg. In mouse tumor cells, it caused 50% inhibition of cell growth at 1ng/ml.

Spectral Data

UV:

λ_{max}^{EtOH} 263nm (ϵ=18,600).

IR:

(Kbr) 3546, 3472, 1742, 1709, 1704, 1701, 1637, 1631, and 1597cm^{-1}.

^{1}H NMR:

($CDCl_3$) 5.85(1H, H-4); 5.44(1H, H-10); 2.96(1H, H-13a); 0.80(3H, H-14); 4.44(1H, H-15a); 1.74(3H, H-16); 4.09(1H, H-2'); 6.00(1H, H-7'); 7.68(1H, H-8'); 6.66(1H, H-9'0; 5.78(1H, H-10'); 1.08(3H, H-12'); and 1.17ppm (3H, H-14').

^{13}C NMR:

(CDCl$_3$) 78.8, C-2; 34.6, C-3; 74.2, C-4; 49.1, C-5; 43.6, C-6; 20.0, C-7; 27.5, C-8; 140.4, C-9; 118.2, C-10; 66.9, C-11; 64.9, C-12; 47.4, C-13; 7.2, C-14; 64.2, C-15; 22.9, C-16; 174.5, C-1'; 75.3, C-2'; 36.7, C-3'; 33.0, C-4'; 69.5, C-5'; 83.7, C-6'; 139.0, C-7'; 126.0, C-8'; 143.6, C-9'; 117.2, C-10'; 166.3, C-11'; 14.4, C-12'; 70.4, C-13'; and 18.0ppm C-14'.

TLC Data

A. Adsorbent: silica gel G; solvent: chloroform-methanol, 98:2 v/v; R_f, 0.70; detection: H_2SO_4 spraying and heating at 110°C for 5 minutes; B. Adsorbent: alumina; solvent: chloroform-methanol, 98:2 v/v; R_f, 0.18; detection: H_2SO_4 spraying and heating at 110°C for 5 minutes.

References

B. B. Jarvis; Macrocyclic Trichothecenes; In Mycotoxins and Phytoalexins; R. P. Sharma and D. K. Salunkhe, eds.; CRC Press, Boca Raton, Florida, pp. 361-421(1991).

R. J. Cole and R. H. Cox; Handbook of Toxic Fungal Metabolites; Academic Press, New York, pp. 230-231(1981).

Common/Systematic Name

Roridin A 13' β-D-glucoside

Molecular Formula/Molecular Weight

$C_{35}H_{50}O_{14}$; MW = 694.32006

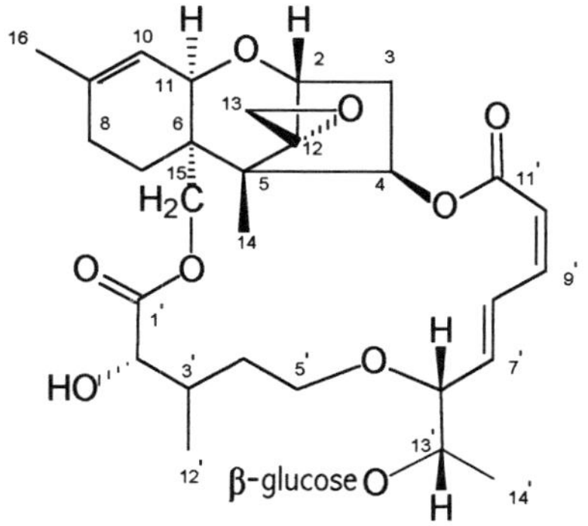

General Characteristics

Amorphous solid; $[\alpha]_D$ + 90° (c=1.6, in $CHCl_3$).

Fungal Source

Female *Baccharis coridifolia*.

Isolation/Purification

The crude extract (10% methanol-chloroform) of female *B. coridifolia* plant was partitioned (hexane-10% water in methanol) and the aqueous methanol, after solvent removal was chromatographed (silica gel) with ethyl ether-hexane, ethyl ether-hexane, and methanol-methylene chloride. The first methanol fraction from the chromatography of the crude extract of the plant (see verrucain A glucoside isolation) was slurried with 70% methanol-water and filtered through a pad of C-18 silica (*ca.* 10 g, 40μm), washed with 70% methanol-water. The filtrate was concentrated by rotary evaporation to give a gum. The gum was subjected to CCC (semi-preparative column, Vc = 355ml) with a solvent system of methanol-water-chloroform-hexane (6:4:7:3, v/v/v/v) and the lower organic phase as the mobile phase to give five fractions A, B, C, D, E. Fraction E from a reversed phase filtration chromatography was subjected to C_{18} reversed phase semipreparative HPLC (250 x 10 mm, 63% methanol-water, 4.0mL/min) to yield roridin A β-glucoside.

Biological Activity

Cytotoxic: IC_{90} ca. 1ng/ml.

Spectral Data

IR:
(CH_3Cl) 3406, 1732, 1718, 1637, 1600, 1181, and 1081cm^{-1}.

^{1}H NMR:
(pyridine-d_5) 7.92(1H, dd, J=11.5, 15.7Hz, H-8'); 6.58(1H, dd, J=11.1, 11.5Hz, H-9'); 6.41(1H, dd, J=2.5, 15.7Hz, H-7'); 6.03(1H, dd, J=4.0, 8.1Hz, H-4); 5.81(1H, d, J=11.1Hz, H-10'); 5.49(1H, br d, J=4.3Hz, H-10); 4.96(1H, d, J=7.7Hz, H-1"); 4.66 and 4.60(1H each, AB, J=12.2Hz, H-15); 4.57(1H, m, H-6"B); 4.55(1H, m, H-6'); 4.51(1H, d, J=3.5Hz, H-2'); 4.40(1H, dd, J=5.4, 11.8Hz, H-6"A); 4.37(1H, dq, J=6.2, 6.2Hz, H-13'); 4.27(1H, dd, J=8.7, 8.9Hz, H-4"); 4.25(1H, dd, J=8.5, 8.9Hz, H-3"); 4.03(1H, dd, J=7.7, 8.5Hz, H-2"); 3.97(1H, m, H-5"); 3.93(1H, d, J=4.9Hz, H-2); 3.70(1H, d, J=4.9Hz, H-11); 3.55(1H, m, H-5'B); 3.48(1H, m, H-5'A); 3.10 and 2.86(1H each, AB, J=4.1Hz, H-13); 2.51(1H, m, H-3'); 2.43(1H, dd, J=8.1, 15.2Hz, H-3α); 2.26(1H, ddd, J=4.0, 4.9, 15.2Hz, H-3β); 2.00(1H, m, H-4'); 1.90(2H, m, H-4', H-7B); 1.83(1H, m, H-8B); 1.77(2H, m, H-7A, H-8A); 1.53(3H, s, H-16); 1.42(3H, d, J=6.6Hz, H-12'); 1.192(3H, d, J=6.2Hz, H-14'); and 1.08ppm(3H, s, H-14).

^{13}C NMR:
(pyridine-d_5) 79.1, C-2; 35.3, C-3; 75.3, C-4; 49.8, C-5; 44.2, C-6; 20.5, C-7; 27.8, C-8; 139.6, C-9; 119.7, C-10; 67.3, C-11; 65.8, C-12; 47.7, C-13; 7.6, C-14; 63.6, C-15; 23.1, C-16; 175.0, C-1'; 76.2, C-2'; 36.8, C-3'; 34.7, C-4'; 69.5, C-5'; 80.9, C-6'; 141.6, C-7'; 126.5, C-8'; 144.3, C-9'; 117.0, C-10'; 166.9, C-11'; 14.7, C-12'; 76.6, C-13'; 14.8, C-14' 104.1, C-1"; 75.2, C-2"; 78.6, C-3"; 71.6, C-4"; 78.6, C-5"; and 62.8ppm, C-6".

TLC Data
Adsorbent: Silica gel; solvent system: 10% methanol-methylene chloride; R_f, 0.20.

Reference
B. B. Jarvis, S. Wang, C. Cox, M. M. Rao, V. Philip, M. S. Varaschin, and C. S. Barros; Brazilian *Baccharis* toxins: Livestock Poisoning and the Isolation of Macrocyclic Trichothecene Glucosides; Natural Toxins, Vol. 4, pp. 58-71(1996).

Common/Systematic Name

8α-Butoyloxyroridin A; YM-47525

Molecular Formula/Molecular Weight

$C_{33}H_{46}O_{11}$; MW = 618.30401

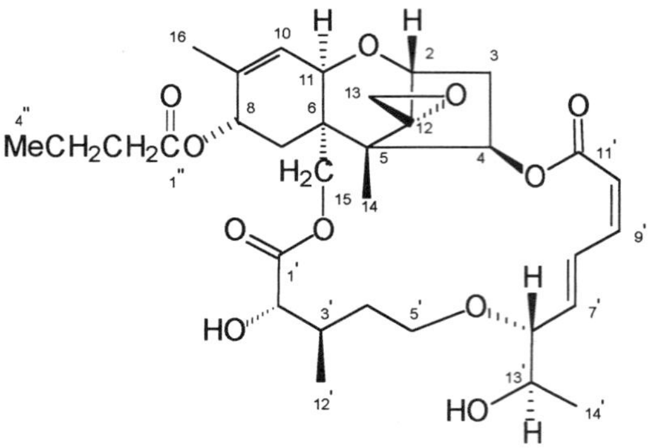

General Characteristics

Crystalline solid; $[\alpha]_D = +152.4°$ (c=0.84, in MeOH).

Fungal Source

Unidentified fungal species (likely a deuteromycete in the Agonomycetes) isolated from a deadwood sample of *Acer* sp.

Isolation/Purification

The filtrate from a submerged culture was extracted at pH 3 (ethyl acetate) and the extract subjected to silica gel chromatography (methanol in chloroform). The active fraction was crystallized from hexane and the solid subjected to reversed phase HPLC (water-acetonitrile) to give 6.5mg of 8α-crotonyloxyroridin A and 10.6mg of 8α-butoyloxyroridin A.

Biological Activity

Inhibited growth of *Candida albicans* at 6.25mg/mL.

Spectral Data

UV:

λ_{max}^{MeOH} 262nm (ϵ=18,100).

IR:

($CHCl_3$) 3450, 2970, 1720, 1640, 1600, and 1440cm^{-1}.

^{1}H NMR:

(CDCl$_3$) 0.80(3H, s, H-14); 0.93(3H, t, *J*=7.6Hz, H-4"); 1.10(3H, d, *J*=6.8Hz, H-12'); 1.19(3H, d, *J*=6.1Hz, H-14'); 1.60(1H, tq, *J*=7.6 and 7.6Hz, H-3"); 1.74(2H, m, H-4'); 1.74(3H, br s, H-16); 1.99 br dq, *J*=2.7 and 6.8Hz, H-3'); 2.11(1H, br d, *J*=14.0Hz, H-7B); 2.14(1H, t, *J*=7.6Hz, H-2"); 2.21(1H, dd, *J*=5.5 and 14.0Hz, H-7A); 2.22(1H, ddd, *J*=4.8, 8.2*, and 15.5Hz, H-3β); 2.47(1H, dd, *J*=8.2 and 15.5Hz, H-3α); 2.81 and 3.09(1H each, AB, *J*=3.6Hz, H-13); 3.54(2H, t, *J*=5.8Hz, H-5'); 3.60(1H, br q, *J*=6.1Hz, H-13'); 3.64(1H, br d, *J*=3.4Hz, H-6'); 3.69(1H, d, *J*=5.5Hz, H-11); 3.84(1H, d, *J*=4.8Hz, H-2); 4.02(1H, dd, *J*=2.7 and 7.6Hz, H-2'); 4.36 and 4.58(1H each, AB, *J*=12.2Hz, H-15); 5.28(1H, br d, *J*=5.5Hz, H-8); 5.67(1H, br d, *J*=5.5Hz, H-10); 5.77(1H, d, *J*=11.6Hz, H-10'); 5.78(1H, dd, *J*=8.2 and 8.2Hz*, H-4); 5.98(1H, dd, *J*=3.4, 15.9Hz, H-7'); 6.64(1H, dd, *J*=11.6 and 11.6Hz, H-9'); and 7.63(1H, dd, *J*=11.6, 15.9Hz, H-8').

* As reported, but value should be closer to 5Hz.

^{13}C NMR:

(CDCl$_3$) 78.8, C-2; 34.8, C-3; 73.7, C-4; 49.3, C-5; 42.3, C-6; 26.2, C-7; 67.8, C-8; 136.7, C-9; 123.5, C-10; 66.6, C-11; 65.1, C-12; 47.6, C-13; 7.4, C-14; 65.5, C-15; 20.4, C-16; 174.3, C-1'; 75.5, C-2'; 37.4, C-3'; 33.5, C-4'; 70.2, C-5'; 84.0, C-6', 139.4, C-7'; 126.0, C-8'; 144.1, C-9'; 117.3, C-10'; 166.3, C-11'; 14.5, C-12'; 70.8, C-13'; 18.2, C-14'; 173.5, C-1"; 36.0, C-2"; 18.5, C-3"; and 13.6ppm, C-4".

Reference

T. Sugawara, A. Tanaka, K. Nagai, K. Suzuki, and G. Okada; New Members of the Trichothecene Family; J. Antibiotics, Vol. 50, pp. 778-780(1997).

Common/Systematic Name
8α-Crotonyloxyroridin A
YM-47524

Molecular Formula/Molecular Weight
$C_{33}H_{46}O_{11}$; MW = 618.30401

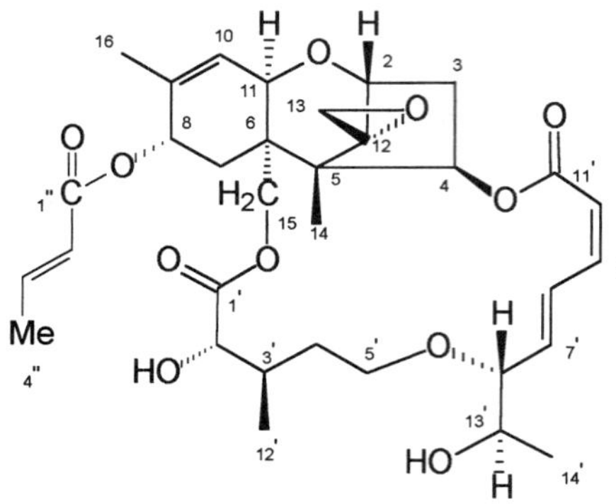

General Characteristics
Crystalline solid; $[\alpha]_D$ +100.5° (*c*=0.58, in MeOH).

Fungal Source
Unidentified fungal species (likely a deuteromycete in the Agonomycetes) isolated from a deadwood sample of *Acer* sp.

Isolation/Purification
The filtrate from a submerged culture was extracted at pH 3 (ethyl acetate) and the extract subjected to silica gel chromatography (methanol in chloroform). The active fraction was crystallized from hexane and the solid subjected to reversed phase HPLC (water-acetonitrile) to give 6.5mg of 8α-crotonyloxyroridin A and 10.6mg of 8α-butoyloxyroridin A.

Biological Activity
Inhibited growth of *Candida albicans* at 6.25mg/mL.

Spectral Data

UV:
λ_{max}^{MeOH} 207(ϵ = 18,100) and 262nm (17,300).

IR:
($CHCl_3$) 3500, 2980, 1710, 1640, 1600, and 1440cm^{-1}.

^{1}H NMR:

($CDCl_3$) 0.79(3H, s, H-14); 1.08(3H, d, *J*=7.3Hz, H-12'); 1.19(3H, d, *J*=6.1Hz, H-14'); 1.7(2H, m, H-4'); 1.76(3H, br s, H-16); 1.88(3H, dd, *J*=6.7 and 1.3Hz, H-4"); 2.19(2H, br s, H-7); 2.23(1H, ddd, *J*=4.9, 4.9, and 15.8Hz, H-3β); 2.47(1H, dd, *J*= 7.9 and 15.8Hz, H-3α); 2.82 and 3.09(1H each, AB, *J*=3.9Hz, H-13); 3.5(2H, m, H- 5'); 3.59(1H, br q, *J*=6.1Hz, H-13'); 3.63(1H, br d, *J*=3.0Hz, H-6'); 3.71(1H, d, *J*= 5.5Hz, H-11); 3.84(1H, d, *J*=4.9Hz, H-2); 3.91(1H, dd, *J*=2.4 and 7.3Hz, H-2'); 4.40 and 4.57(1H each, AB, *J*=12.2Hz, H-15); 5.25(1H, br s, H-8); 5.67(1H, dd, *J*= 1.3 and 15.3Hz, H-2"); 5.70(1H, br d, *J*=5.5Hz, H-10); 5.77(1H, d, *J*=11.3Hz, H- 10'); 5.78(1H, dd, *J*=4.9, 7.9Hz, H-4); 5.98(1H, dd, *J*=3.0, 15.2Hz, H-7'); 6.64(1H, dd, *J*=11.3 and 11.6Hz, H-9'); 6.94(1H, dq, *J*=6.7 and 15.3Hz, H-3"); and 7.62ppm (1H, dd, *J*=11.6, 15.2Hz, H-8').

^{13}C NMR:

($CDCl_3$) 78.8, C-2; 34.8, C-3; 73.7, C-4; 49.3, C-5; 42.4, C-6; 26.2, C-7; 68.0, C-8; 136.8, C-9; 123.5, C-10; 66.6, C-11; 65.0, C-12; 47.6, C-13; 7.5, C-14; 65.6, C-15; 20.5, C-16; 174.6, C-1'; 75.7, C-2'; 37.6, C-3'; 33.2, C-4'; 70.3, C-5'; 84.0, C-6'; 139.3, C-7'; 125.9, C-8'; 144.0, C-9'; 117.4, C-10'; 166.3, C-11'; 14.6, C-12'; 70.8, C-13'; 18.2, C-14'; 166.1, C-1"; 121.8, C-2"; 146.7, C-3"; and 18.1ppm, C-4".

Reference

T. Sugawara, A. Tanaka, K. Nagai, K. Suzuki, and G. Okada; New Members of the Trichothecene Family; J. Antibiotics, Vol. 50, pp. 778-780(1997).

Common/Systematic Name

Isororidin A

Molecular Formula/Molecular Weight

$C_{29}H_{40}O_9$; MW = 532.26723

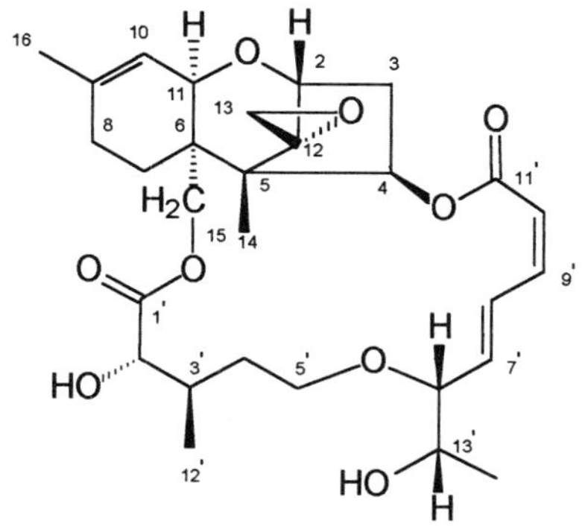

General Characteristics

Clear spherical crystals from methylene chloride-hexane; mp., 183-185°C $[\alpha]_D^{25}$ +6.7° (*c*=3.3, in $CHCl_3$).

Fungal Source

Myrothecium verrucaria (ATCC 24571).

Isolation/Purification

Partition chromatography of the mycelial extract gave a fraction rich in roridin A. This fraction was subjected to flash chromatography on silica gel eluting with 3% methanol in methylene chloride to give three principal fractions: A, B, and C, in the order of elution. Fraction A was composed of roridin D and roridin K acetate. Fraction C was composed mostly of trichothecenes of lower R_f than that of roridin A. Fraction B was crystallized from methylene chloride-hexane to give roridin A. The mother liquor was subjected to preparative HPLC (2% methanol-methylene chloride) to give verrucarin L, roridin A, and isororidin A in their order of elution.

Spectral Data

^{1}H NMR:

($CDCl_3$) 0.83(3H, s, H-14); 1.09(3H, d, *J*=7Hz, H-12'); 1.16(3H, d, *J*=7Hz, H-14'); 1.75(3H, s, H-16); 2.48(1H, dd, *J*=8 and 15Hz, H-3α); 2.96(2H, AB, *J*=4Hz, H-13); 3.60(1H, d, *J*=5Hz, H-11); 3.86(1H, d, *J*=5Hz, H-2); 4.11(1H, dd, *J*=3 and 6Hz, H-2'); 4.44(2H, s br, H-15); 5.41(1H, d, *J*=5Hz, H-10); 5.80(1H, m, H-4); 5.80(1H, d, *J*=11Hz, H-10'); 6.00(1H, dd, *J*=2 and 15.5Hz, H-7'); 6.66(1H, dd, *J*'s=11Hz, H-9'); and 7.64ppm (1H, dd, *J*=11 and 15.5Hz, H-8').

^{13}C NMR:

($CDCl_3$) 7.5, q, C-14; 14.4, q, C-12'; 17.9, q, C-14'; 20.3, t, C-7; 23.3, q, C-16; 27.7, t, C-8; 33.3, t, C-4'; 34.9, t, C-3; 37.0, d, C-3'; 43.8, s, C-6; 47.8, t, C-13; 49.4, s, C-5; 64.4, t, C-15; 65.3, s, C-12; 67.2, d, C-11; 69.4, t, C-5'; 70.0, d, C-13'; 74.4, d, C-4; 75.5, d, C-2'; 79.1, d, C-2; 82.6, d, C-6'; 117.3, d, C-10'; 118.3, d, C-10; 126.4, d, C-8'; 139.0, d, C-7'; 140.9, s, C-9; 143.9, d, C-9'; 166.6, s, C-11'; and 174.9ppm, s, C-1'.

References

B. B. Jarvis; Macrocyclic Trichothecenes; In Mycotoxins and Phytoalexins; R. P. Sharma and D. K. Salunkhe, eds.; CRC Press, Boca Raton, Florida, pp. 361-421(1991).

B. W. Jarvis, J. O. Midiwo, J. L. Flippen-Anderson, and E. P. Mazzola; Stereochemistry of the Roridins; J. Nat. Prod., Vol. 45, pp. 440-448(1982).

Common/Systematic Name
Roridin D

Molecular Formula/Molecular Weight
$C_{29}H_{38}O_9$; MW = 530.25158

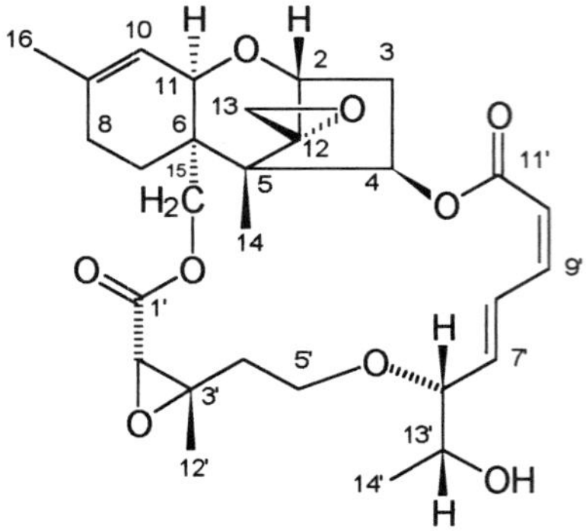

General Characteristics
Needles from acetone-ether; mp., 232-235°C; $[\alpha]_D^{23}$ +29°(c= 2.71, in $CHCl_3$).

Fungal Source
Myrothecium verrucaria and *M. roridum*.

Biological Activity
Antibiotic activity.

Spectral Data

UV:
λ_{max}^{EtOH} 260(ϵ=21,400).

IR:
(KBr) 3540-3440, 2970, 1747, 1711, 1641, 1601, 1420, 1190, 1105, 1083, 968, 818, 753, and 660cm^{-1}.

^{13}C NMR:
($CDCl_3$) 78.8, C-2; 34.9, C-3; 74.3, C-4; 49.0, C-5; 43.1, C-6; 20.4, C-7; 27.4, C-8; 140.1, C-9; 118.4, C-10; 66.9, C-11; 65.1, C-12; 47.4, C-13; 6.8, C-14; 64.3, C-15; 22.9, C-16; 167.8, C-1'; 57.9, C-2'; 62.9, C-3'; 39.4, C-4'; 67.3, C-5'; 85.3, C-6'; 138.1, C-7'; 126.2, C-8'; 142.9, C-9'; 117.8, C-10'; 166.1, C-11'; 17.2, C-12'; 70.5, C-13'; and 17.9ppm, C-14'.

TLC Data

Absorbent: Kieselgel G; solvent system, ethyl ether (two consecutive runs); R_f, 0.18; Detection, iodine vapors.

References

B, Bohner, E. Fetz, E. Harri, H. P. Sigg, and C. Tamm; Helv. Chim. Acta., Vol. 48, pp. 1079(1965).

R. J. Cole and R. H. Cox; Handbook of Toxic Fungal Metabolites; Academic Press, New York, pp. 237-238(1981).

B. B. Jarvis; Macrocyclic Trichothecenes; In Mycotoxins and Phytoalexins; R. P. Sharma and D. K. Salunkhe, eds.; CRC Press, Boca Raton, Florida, pp. 361-421(1991).

Common/Systematic Name

Roridin D β-D-glucoside

Molecular Formula/Molecular Weight

$C_{35}H_{48}O_{14}$; MW = 692

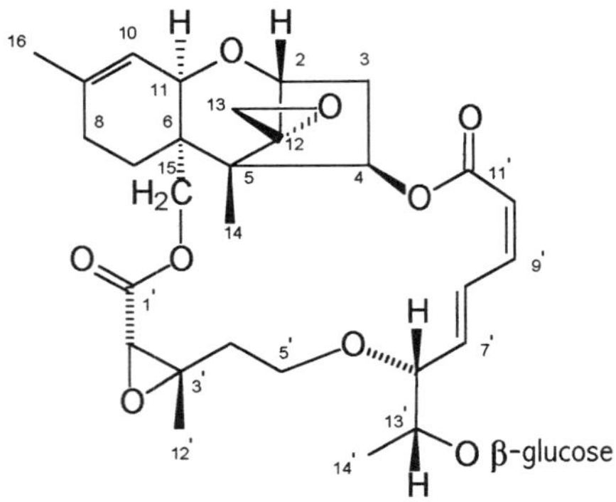

General Characteristics

Amorphous solid; $[\alpha]_D$ + 27° (*c*=0.80, in $CHCl_3$).

Fungal Source

Female *Baccharis coridifolia*..

Isolation/Purification

The first methanol fraction from the chromatography of the crude extract of the plant (see verrucain A glucoside isolation) was slurried with 70% methanol-water and filtered through a pad of C-18 silica (*ca.* 10 g, 40 μm), washed with 70% methanol-water. The filtrate was concentrated by rotary evaporation to give a gum. The gum was subjected to CCC (semi-preparative column, Vc = 355 ml) with a solvent system of methanol-water-chloroform-hexane (6:4:7:3 v/v/v/v) and the lower organic phase as the mobile phase to give five fractions A, B, C, D, E. Fraction C was subjected to PTLC (Chromatotron, silica gel, 2 mm) with 3-10% methanol-methylene chloride to give three portions CI, CII and CIII. Roridin D glucoside was isolated by semipreparative HPLC (silica gel, 250 x10 mm, 6% methanol-methylene chloride, 4.0 mL/min) from all three of these fractions.

Biological Activity

Cytotoxic: IC_{85} ca. 1 ng/ml.

Spectral Data

IR:

(CH_2Cl_2) 3418, 1750, 1718, 1650, 1600, 1181, and 1081cm^{-1}.

^{1}H NMR:

(pyridine-d5) 7.63 (1H, dd, *J*= 11.9, 15.4Hz, H-8'); 6.50 (1H, dd, *J*= 11.2, 11.9Hz, H-9'); 6.38 (1H, dd, *J*= 2.3, 15.4Hz, H-7'); 6.00 (1H, dd, *J*= 3.9, 7.9Hz, H-4); 5.79 (1H, d, *J*= 11.2Hz, H-10'); 5.49 (1H, br d, *J*= 4.1Hz, H-10); 4.99 (1H, d, *J*= 7.7Hz, H-1"); 4.71 and 4.40 (1H each, AB, *J*= 12.4Hz, H-15); 4.58 (1H, m, H-6"B); 4.56 (1H, m, H-6'); 4.37 (1H, m, H-6"A); 4.35 (1H, dq, *J*= 6.2, 6.2Hz, H-13'); 4.26 (1H, dd, *J*= 8.0, 7.7Hz, H-4"); 4.24 (1H, dd, *J*= 8.6, 7.7Hz, H-3"); 4.04 (1H, dd, *J*= 7.7, 8.6Hz, H-2"); 4.00 (1H, m, H-5"); 3.95 (1H, d, *J*= 4.9Hz, H-2); 3.73 (1H, d, *J*= 4.7Hz, H-11); 3.82 (1H, dd, *J*= 10.0, 10.3Hz H-5'B); 3.73 (1H, d, *J*= 4.7Hz, H-11); 3.62 (1H, s, H-2'); 3.26 (1H, m, H-5'A); 3.12 and 2.89 (1H each, AB, *J*= 4.0Hz, H-13); 2.47 (1H, dd, *J*= 8.3, 15.3Hz, H-3α); 2.42 (1H, dd, *J*= 10.0, 15.0Hz, H-4'B); 2.26 (1H, ddd, *J*= 3.9, 4.9, 15.3Hz, H-3β); 1.88-1.95 (4H, m, H-7, H-8); 1.90 (3H, s, H-12'); 1.57 (3H, s, H-16); 1.37 (1H, dd, *J*= 3.9, 15.0Hz, H4'A); 1.20 (3H, d, *J*= 6.2Hz, H-14'); and 1.07ppm (3H, s, H-14).

^{13}C NMR:

($CDCl_3$) 79.1, C-2; 35.3, C-3; 75.3, C-4; 49.8, C-5; 43.7, C-6; 20.6, C-7; 27.7, C-8; 139.5, C-9; 119.8, C-10; 67.2, C-11; 65.8, C-12; 47.7, C-13; 7.4, C-14; 64.7, C-15; 23.1, C-16; 168.7, C-1'; 58.6, C-2'; 63.8, C-3'; 40.6, C-4'; 68.4, C-5'; 82.6, C-6'; 141.4, C-7'; 125.9, C-8'; 143.9, C-9'; 117.2, C-10'; 169.9, C-11'; 17.6, C-12'; 77.4, C-13'; 17.9ppm, C-14'.

TLC Data

Adsorbent: Silica gel; solvent system: 10% methanol-methylene chloride; R_f, 0.26; detection with iodine vapors.

Reference

B. B. Jarvis, S. Wang, C. Cox, M. M. Rao, V. Philip, M. S. Varaschin, and C. S. Barros; Brazilian *Baccharis* toxins: Livestock Poisoning and the Isolation of Macrocyclic Trichothecene Glucosides; Natural Toxins, Vol. 4, pp. 58-71 (1996).

Common/Systematic Name

Roridin E

Molecular Formula/Molecular Weight

$C_{29}H_{38}O_8$; MW = 514.25667

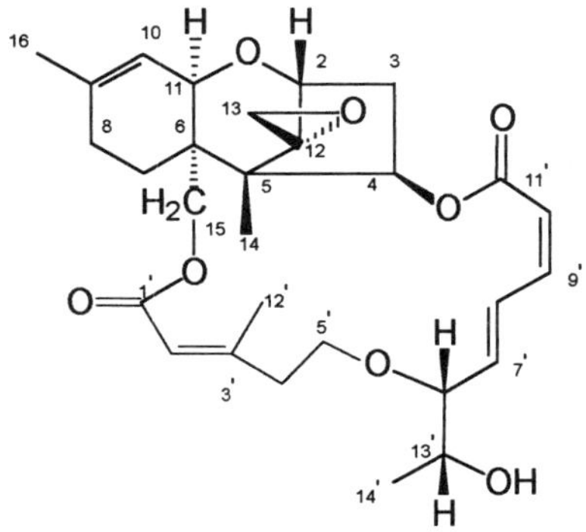

General Characteristics

Colored needles from ether-pentane; mp., 177-178°C or 211-212°C; needles from ether, 220-221°C; $[\alpha]_D^{23}$ -27° (*c*=1.3, in $CHCl_3$); $[\alpha]_D^{25}$ -21° (*c*=1.852, in $CHCl_3$).

Fungal Source

Myrothecium verrucaria and *M. roridum*.

Biological Activity

Antibiotic activity.

Spectral Data

UV:

λ_{max}^{EtOH} 195(ε=15,800), 223(25,100), and 263nm (19,900).

IR:

(CH_2Cl_2) 3570, 3050, 2975, 1712, 1647, 1603, 1365, 1220, 1180, 1148, 1142, 1096, 1090, 1080, 966, and 814cm^{-1}.

^{1}H NMR:

($CDCl_3$) 3.82, (1H, d, *J*= 5.0Hz, H-2); 2.04, (1H, ddd, *J*= 4.2, 5.0, 15.5Hz, H-3β; 2.53, (1H, dd, *J*= 8.2, 15.0Hz, H-3α); 6.20, (1H, dd, *J*= 4.0, 8.2Hz, H-4); 5.47 (1H, br d, *J*= 5.0Hz, H-10); 3.89 (1H, d, *J*= 5.0Hz, H-11); 2.81 and 3.12(1H each, AB, *J*= 4.1Hz, H-13); 0.79 (3H, s, H-14); 3.93 and 4.32 (1H each, AB, *J*= 12.5Hz, H-15); 1.71 (3H, br s, H-16); 5.95(1H, q, *J*= 1.5Hz, H-2'); 3.70 (1H, m, H-6'); 5.89 (1H, dd, *J*= 2.0, 16.0Hz, H-7'); 7.51(1H, dd, *J*= 11.2, 16.0Hz, H-8'); 6.56 (1H, dd, *J*= 11.0,

11.2Hz, H-9'); 5.73 (1H, d, *J*= 11.0Hz, H-10'); 2.25 (3H, d, *J*= 1.5Hz, H-12'); 3.70 (1H, m, H-13'; and 1.19ppm (3H, d, *J*= 6.0Hz, H-14').

^{13}C NMR:

($CDCl_3$) 79.3, C-2; 35.8, C-3; 74.2, C-4; 48.4, C-5; 42.8, C-6; 21.6, C-7; 27.7, C-8; 140.0, C-9; 117.8, C-10; 67.2, C-11; 65.6, C-12; 48.1, C-13; 6.7, C-14; 63.7, C-15; 23.2, C-16; 165.8, C-1'; 119.0, C-2'; 159.0, C-3'; 41.3, C-4'; 69.8, C-5'; 83.8, C-6'; 138.1, C-7'; 126.6, C-8'; 143.7, C-9'; 117.2, C-10'; 166.4, C-11'; 20.2, C-12'; 70.5, C-13'; 18.3, C-14'.

TLC Data

Adsorbent: Kieselgel G; solvent system: ethyl ether (two consecutive runs); R_f, 0.24; detection with iodine vapors.

References

B. Bohner, E. Fetz, E. Harri, H. P. Sigg, and C. Tamm; Helv. Chim. Acta.; Vol. 48, pp. 1079(1965).

R. J. Cole and R. H. Cox; Handbook of Toxic Fungal Metabolites; Academic Press, New York, pp. 237-238(1981).

B. B. Jarvis; Macrocyclic Trichothecenes; In Mycotoxins and Phytoalexins; R. P. Sharma and D. K. Salunkhe, eds.; CRC Press, Boca Raton, Florida, pp. 361-421(1991).

M. Matsumoto; Structures of Isororidin E, Epoxyisororidin E, Epoxyroridin H, and Diepoxyroridin H, New Metabolites Isolated from a Species of *Cylindrocarpon*; J. Sci. Hinoshima; University serial A; Vol. 43, pp. 107-118 (1979).

Common/Systematic Name

Roridin E β-D-glucoside

Molecular Formula/Molecular Weight

$C_{35}H_{48}O_{13}$; MW = 676.30949

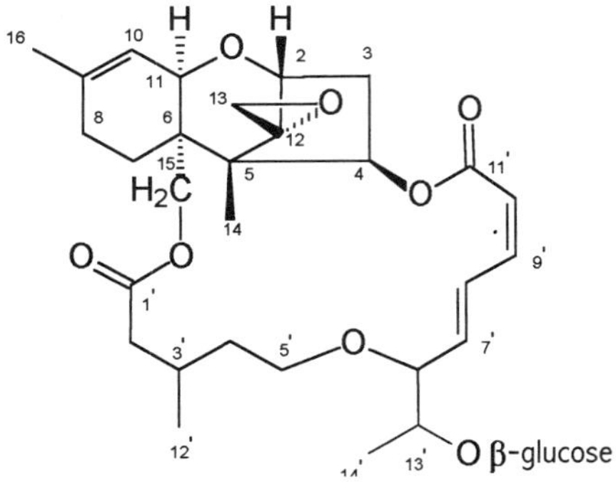

General Characteristics

Amorphous solid; $[\alpha]_D$+ 37° (*c*=2.0, in $CHCl_3$).

Fungal Source

Female *Baccharis coridifolia.*

Isolation/Purification

The first methanol fraction from the chromatography of the crude extract of the plant (see verrucain A glucoside isolation) was slurried with 70% methanol-water and filtered through a pad of C_{18} silica (*ca.* 10 g, 40 μm), washed with 70% methanol-water. The filtrate was concentrated by rotary evaporation to give a gum. The gum was subjected to CCC (semi-preparative column, Vc = 355 ml) with a solvent system of methanol-water-chloroform-hexane (6:4:7:3 v/v/v/v) and the lower organic phase as the mobile phase to give five fractions A, B, C, D, E. Fraction B was subjected to C_{18} reversed phase HPLC (250 x 10 mm, 68% methanol-water, 4.0 mL/min) to yield roridin E β-glucoside.

Biological Activity

Cytotoxic: IC_{85} ca. 1 ng/ml.

Spectral Data

IR:

(CH_2Cl_2) 3412, 1706, 1643, 1600, 1181, and 1081cm^{-1}.

^{1}H NMR:

(CDCl$_3$) 7.39(1H, dd, *J*=12.0, 15.0Hz, H-8'); 6.59(1H, dd, *J*=11.2, 12.0Hz, H-9'); 6.08(1H, dd, *J*=3.9, 7.6Hz, H-4); 5.98(1H, dd, *J*=2.7, 15.0Hz, H-7'); 5.86(1H, s, H-2'); 5.69(1H, d, *J*=11.2 Hz, H-10'); 5.44(1H, d, *J*=4.4Hz, H-10); 4.38(1H, d, *J*=7.4Hz, H-1"); 4.31 and 3.90(1H each, AB, *J*=12.4Hz, H-15); 4.10(1H, m, H-6'); 3.98(1H, dq, *J* =5.5, 6.0Hz, H-13'); 3.80-3.83(3H, m, H-6", H-11); 3.80(1H, d, *J*=5.2Hz, H-2); 3.70(1H, m, H-5'B); 3.56(1H, dd, *J*=8.6, 9.4Hz, H-4"); 3.51(1H, dd,*J*=8.0, 9.4Hz, H-3"); 3.48(1H, m, H-5'A); 3.33(1H, dd, *J*=7.4, 8.0Hz, H-2"); 3.28(1H, bd, *J*=8.6Hz, H-5"); 3.09 and 2.78(1H each, AB, *J*=3.7Hz, H-13); 2.48(1H, dd, *J*=7.6, 15.0Hz, H-3'); 2.43(2H, m, H-4'); 2.21(3H, s, H-12'); 2.04(1H, ddd, *J*=4.0, 5.0, 15.0Hz, H-3ß); 1.98(4H, m, H-7, H-8); 1.68(3H, s, H-16); 1.08(3H, d, *J*=6.0Hz, H-14'); and 0.76ppm(3H, s, H-14). (pyridine-*d*5) 7.71(1H, dd, *J*=11.8, 15.5Hz, H-8'); 6.49(1H, dd, *J*=11.1, 11.8Hz, H-9'); 6.34(1H, dd, *J*=2.8, 15.5Hz, H-7');6.23(1H, dd, *J*=4.0, 8.0Hz, H-4); 6.02(1H, s, H-2'); 5.74(1H, d, *J*=11.1Hz, H-10'); 5.51(1H, br d, *J*=5.0Hz, H-10); 4.96(1H, d, *J*=7.8Hz, H-1"); 4.75 and 4.09(1H each, AB, *J*=12.5Hz, H-15); 4.57(1H, dd, *J*=2.2, 11.8Hz, H-6"B); 4.40(1H, dq, *J*=6.3, 6.3Hz, H-13'); 4.37(1H, m, H-6"A); 4.26(2H, m, H-3", H-4"); 4.03(1H, dd, *J*=7.8, 8.0Hz, H-2"); 3.99(1H, m, H-5"); 3.92(1H, d, *J*=5.0Hz, H-2); 3.83(1H, br d, *J*=5.0Hz, H-11); 3.48(1H, m, H-5'B); 3.38(1H, m, H-5'A); 3.10 and 2.85(1H each, AB, *J*=4.0Hz, H-13); 2.47(1H, dd, *J*=8.0, 15.0Hz, H-3α); 2.41(3H, s, H-12'); 2.31(2H, m, H-4'); 2.19(1H, ddd, *J*=4.0, 5.0, 15.0Hz, H-3β); 1.92-1.99(3H, m, H-7B, H-8); 1.79(1H, br d, *J*=7.5Hz, H-7A); 1.56(3H, s, H-16); 1.12(3H, d, *J*=6.3Hz, H-14'); and 1.05ppm (3h, s, H-14).

^{13}C NMR:

(CDCl$_3$) 79.2, C-2; 35.6, C-3; 74.3, C-4; 48.5, C-5; 42.8, C-6; 21.3, C-7; 27.6, C-8; 140.2, C-9; 117.2, C-10; 67.2, C-11; 65.6, C-12; 48.1, C-13; 6.8, C-14; 63.6, C-15; 23.3, C-16; 166.5, C-1'; 118.8, C-2'; 159.0, C-3'; 41.4, C-4'; 69.0, C-5'; 80.4, C-6'; 138.6, C-7'; 126.9, C-8'; 143.9, C-9'; 117.2, C-10'; 166.2, C-11'; 19.5, C-12'; 76.7, C-13'; 15.0, C-14' 101.8, C-1"; 73.2, C-2"; 76.2, C-3'; 69.7, C-4"; 75.5, C-5"; and 61.7ppm, C-6".

<u>TLC Data</u>

Adsorbent: Silica gel; solvent system: 10% methanol-methylene chloride; R_f, 0.26; detection with iodine vapors.

<u>Reference</u>

B. B. Jarvis, S. Wang, C. Cox, M. M. Rao, V. Philip, M. S. Varaschin, and C. S. Barros; Brazilian *Baccharis* toxins: Livestock Poisoning and the Isolation of Macrocyclic Trichothecene Glucosides; Natural Toxins, Vol. 4, pp. 58-71(1996).

Common/Systematic Name

Isororidin E

Molecular Formula/Molecular Weight

$C_{29}H_{38}O_8$; MW = 514.25667

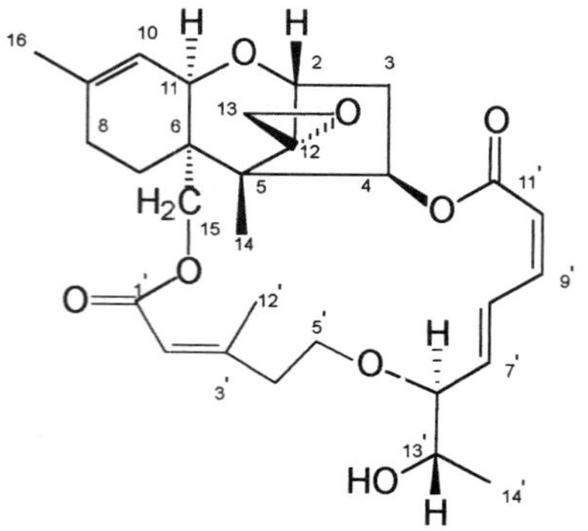

General Characteristics

Colorless prisms from ethyl acetate; mp., 200-202°C; $[\alpha]_D$ - 65.1° (in $CHCl_3$).

Fungal Source

Cylindrocarpon spp.

Spectral Data

UV:

λ_{max}^{EtOH} 223(ϵ=24,000) and 262nm (16,000).

IR:

(CH_3Cl) 3757, 1713, 1644, and 1598cm^{-1}.

^{1}H NMR:

3.84(H-2); 2.03(H-3a); 2.58(H-3b); 6.35(H-4); 5.50(H-10); 4.09(H-11); 2.83(H-13a); 3.15(H-13b); 0.80(H-14); 4.06(H-15a); 4.16(H-15b); 1.71(H-16); 5.83(H-2'); 3.74(H-6'); 5.71(H-7'); 7.55(H-8'); 6.60(H-9'); 5.82(H-10'); 2.22(H-12'); 3.70(H-13'); and 1.17ppm (H-14').

^{13}C NMR:

(CD_3Cl) 79.2, C-2; 36.6, C-3; 75.3, C-4; 48.5, C-5; 42.6, C-6; 22.7, C-7; 27.7, C-8; 140.1, C-9; 118.9, C-10; 66.7, C-11; 65.7, C-12; 47.7, C-13; 6.4, C-14; 64.5, C-15; 23.2, C-16; 166.3, C-1'; 119.5, C-2'; 158.0, C-3'; 40.0, C-4'; 67.0, C-5'; 83.2, C-6'; 135.3, C-7'; 131.0, C-8'; 142.0, C-9'; 117.1, C-10'; 166.3, C-11'; 19.8, C-12'; 67.6, C-13'; and 18.5ppm, C-14'.

References

R. J. Cole and R. H. Cox; Handbook of Toxic Fungal Metabolites; Academic Press, New York, pp. 242 (1981).

B. B. Jarvis; Macrocyclic Trichothecenes; In Mycotoxins and Phytoalexins; R. P. Sharma and D. K. Salunkhe, eds.; CRC Press, Boca Raton, Florida, pp. 361-421(1991).

M. Matsumoto, H. Minato, K. Tori, and M.Ueyama; Structures of Isororidin E, Epoxyisororidin E, and Epoxy- and Diepoxyroridin H, New Metabolites Isolated from *Cylindrocarpon* Species Determined by Carbon-13 and Hydrogen-1 NMR Spectroscopy. Revision of C-2':C-3' Double Bond Configuration of the Roridin Group; Tet. Lett.; pp. 4093-4096(1977).

Common/Systematic Name

Epiroridin E

Molecular Formula/Molecular Weight

$C_{29}H_{38}O_8$; MW = 514.25667

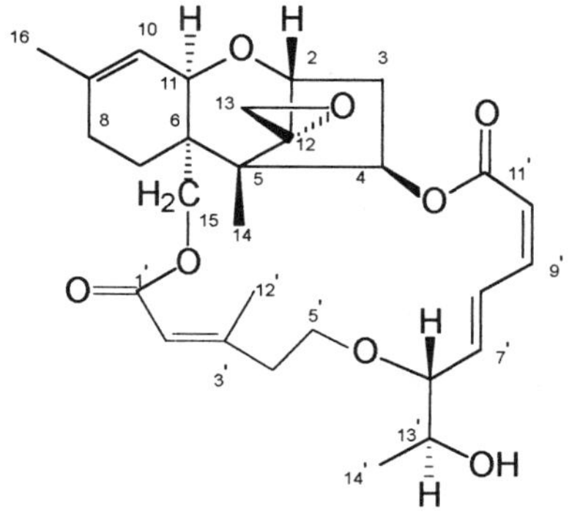

General Characteristics

Amorphous solid; $[\alpha]_D^{30} = +0.70°$ (c=1.8, in chloroform).

Fungal Source

Myrothecium verrucaria (ATCC 24571).

Isolation/Purification

A chromatography fraction from an earlier fermentation of *M. verrucaria* ATCC 24571 [Jarvis *et al.*; J. Org. Chem.; Vol. 47,pp. 1117-1124 (1982)] was subjected to CCC (V_c = 850ml) with a solvent system of carbon tetrachloride-methanol-water (5:3:2, v/v/v), the lower organic phase was the mobile phase and the flow rate was 3.3ml/min, to give verrucarin A (23mg), roridin D (11mg), a fraction rich in roridin E (400mg), and roridin A (67mg). The roridin E fraction was subjected to CCC (V_c 355mL) with a solvent system of carbon tetrachloride-hexane-methanol-water (4:1:3:2, v/v/v/v), the lower organic phase was the mobile phase, and the flow rate was 1.8ml/min, to give 310mg of a mixture of roridin E and isororidin E and a later fraction of pure epiroridin E (50mg).

Spectral Data

IR:

($CHCl_3$) 2491,1713, 1652, and 1601cm^{-1}.

^{1}H NMR:

($CDCl_3$) 0.76(3H, s, H-14); 1.13(3H, d, J=6.0Hz, H-14'); 1.67(3H, s, H-16); 1.92~2.20(5H, m, H-7, H-8, H-3β); 2.24(3; H, s, H-12'); 2.42~2.54(3H, m, H-4', H-3α); 2.83(1H, d, J=4.0Hz, H-13B); 3.15(1H, d, J=4.0Hz, H-13A); 3.50(1H, dt,

J=15.0, 6.0Hz, H-5B); 3.69(1H, dt, *J*=15.0, 6.0Hz, H-5A); 3.87(1H, d, *J*=5.0Hz, H-2); 3.79-3.90(2H, m, H-6', H-13'); 3.89(1H, d, *J*=12.0Hz, H-15B); 3.91(1H, d, *J*=5.0Hz, H-11); 4.31(1H, d, *J*=12.0Hz, H-15A); 5.44(1H, d, *J*=5.0Hz, H-10); 5.70(1H, d, *J*=11.0Hz, H-10'); 5.86(1H, dd, *J*=3.0, 15.0Hz, H-7'); 5.98(1H, s, H-2'); 6.15(1H, dd, *J*=4.0, 8.0Hz, H-4); 6.54(1H, dd, *J*=11.0Hz, H-9'); and 7.45ppm (1H, dd, *J*=11.0, 15.0Hz, H-8').

^{13}C NMR:

($CDCl_3$) 6.7, C-14; 17.8, C-14'; 19.8, C-12'; 21.5, C-7; 23.2, C-16; 27.2, C-8; 35.7, C-3; 41.4, C-4'; 42.7, C-6; 48.1, C-13; 48.4, C-5; 63.6, C-15; 65.6, C-12; 67.2, C-11; 69.1, C-13'; 69.5, C-5'; 74.2, C-4; 79.2, C-2; 82.5, C-6'; 117.2, C-10'; 117.6, C-10; 118.9, C-2'; 126.8, C-8'; 137.8, C-7'; 140.8, C-9; 143.6, C-9'; 159.0, C-3'; 165.9, C-1'; and 166.4ppm, C-11'.

Reference

B. B. Jarvis and S. Wang; Stereochemistry of the Roridins. Diastereomers of Roridin E; J. Nat. Prod., Vol. 62, pp. 1284-1289(1999).

Common/Systematic Name
Epiisororidin E

Molecular Formula/Molecular Weight
$C_{29}H_{38}O_8$; MW = 514.25667

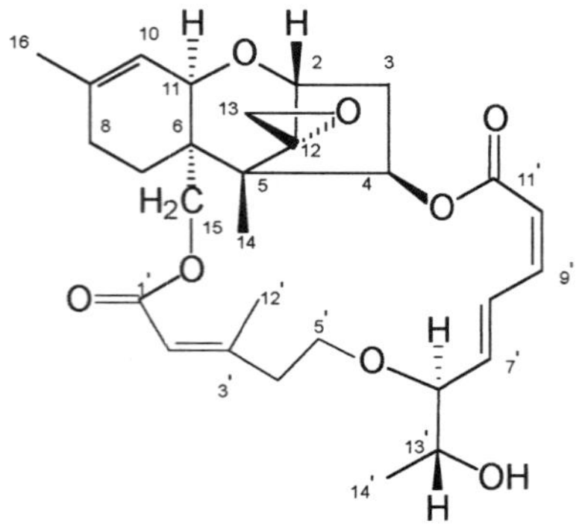

General Characteristics
Amorphous solid; $[\alpha]_D^{30}$ = -29.2° (*c*=1.5, in $CHCl_3$).

Fungal Source
Myrothecium verrucaria (ATCC 24571).

Isolation/Purification
Extraction of a submerged culture of *M. verrucaria* [see Jarvis, B. B., Armstrong, C. A., Zeng, M. J.; Antibiotics; Vol. 43, pp. 1502-1504 (1990)] with organic solvent gave 7.5g of crude extract after solvent removal. A series of chromatographies (silica gel and CCC) gave 353mg of a mixture of roridin E and isororidin E, 17mg of mixture of roridin E, isororidin E and epiisororidin E and 20mg of pure epiisororidin E. The roridin E diastereomers can be separated by RP-HPLC on a phenyl column (Phenomenex, 4.6 x 250mm) with 40% acetonitrile in water at a flow rate of 1.2ml/min. The observed retention times under these conditions were: roridin E (27.7 min), isororidin E (23.3 min), epiroridin E (26.1 min), and epiisororidin E (22.1 min).

Spectral Data

IR:
($CHCl_3$) 3486,1713, 1647, and 1599cm^{-1}.

^{1}H NMR:
($CDCl_3$) 0.77(3H, s, H-14); 1.12(3H, d, *J*=6.5Hz, H-14'); 1.68(3H, s, H-16); 1.96-2.13(5H, m, H-3β, H-7, H-8); 2.21(3H, d, *J*=1.2Hz, H-12'); 2.29(1H, m, H-4'B); 2.50-2.56(2H, m, H-3α, H-4'A); 2.81(1H, d, *J*=4.0Hz, H-13B); 3.13(1H, d, *J*=4.0Hz, H-

13A); 3.56(1H, ddd, *J*=5.0, 7.4, 10.1 Hz, H-5'B); 3.73(1H, ddd, *J*=7.4, 7.5, 10.1Hz, H-5'A); 3.83(1H, d, *J*=5.0Hz, H-2); 3.89(1H, m, H-6'); 3.98(1H, dq, *J*=3.0, 6.5Hz, H-13'); 4.01(1H, d, *J*=12.5Hz, H-15B); 4.03(1H, d, *J*=5.5Hz, H-11); 4.17(1H, d, *J*=12.5Hz, H-15A); 5.47(1H, d, *J* = 5.5Hz, H-10); 5.80(1H, d, *J*=11.0Hz, H-10'); 5.82(1H, d, *J*=1.2Hz, H-2'); 5.87(1H, dd, *J*=6.1, 15.6Hz, H-7'); 6.29(1H, dd, *J*=4.1, 8.0Hz, H-4); 6.60(1H, dd, *J*=11.0, 11.0Hz, H-9'); and 7.54ppm (1H, dd, *J* = 11.0, 15.6Hz, H-8').

^{13}C NMR:

6.5, C-14; 17.9, C-14'; 19.2, C-12'; 22.3, C-7; 23.2, C-16; 27.7, C-8; 36.4, C-3; 40.3, C-4'; 42.6, C-6; 47.8, C-5; 48.4, C-13; 64.3, C-15; 66.3, C-5'; 66.6, C-12; 67.0, C-11; 68.5, C-13'; 75.0, C-4; 79.2, C-2; 81.9, C-6'; 117.2, C-10'; 117.6, C-10; 119.0, C-2'; 131.0, C-8'; 134.7, C-7'; 140.2, C-9; 142.3, C-9'; 157.9, C-3'; 166.3, C-1'; and 166.5ppm, C-11'.

Reference

B. B. Jarvis and S. Wang; Stereochemistry of the Roridins. Diastereomers of Roridin E; J. Nat. Prod., Vol. 62, pp. 1284-1289(1999).

Common/Systematic Name

7β,8β-Epoxyisororidin E

Molecular Formula/Molecular Weight

$C_{29}H_{36}O_9$; MW = 528.23593

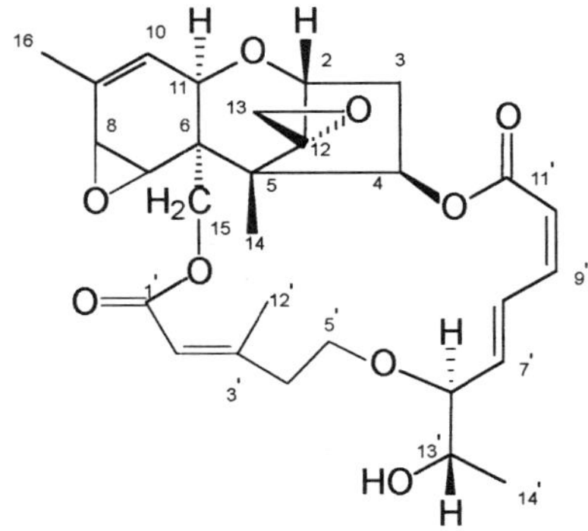

General Characteristics

Colorless prisms from acetone; mp., 216-219°C; $[\alpha]_D^{24}$ - 69.9° (*c*= 0.438 in $CHCl_3$).

Fungal Source

Cylindrocarpon spp.

Spectral Data

UV:

λ_{max}^{EtOH} 221(ϵ=26,300) and 262nm (16,700).

IR:

(CH_3Cl) 3567, 1712, 1644, and 1598cm^{-1}.

^{1}H NMR:

($CDCl_3$) 3.90(1H, d, *J*= 4.7Hz, H-2); 2.06(1H, ddd, J= 4,3, 4.7, 15.0Hz, H-3β); 2.55(1H, dd, *J*= 8.1, 15.0Hz, H-3α); 6.30(1H, dd, *J*= 4.3, 8.1Hz, H-4); 3.34(1H, dd, *J*= 3.2, 4.0Hz, H-7); 3.17(1H, dd, *J*= 2.1, 4.0Hz, H-8); 5.75(1H, ddd, *J*= 1.5, 2.1, 7.0Hz, H-10); 4.21(1H, dd, *J*= 3.2, 7.0Hz, H-11); 2.99 and 3.21(1H each, AB, *J*= 3.4Hz, H-13); 1.02(3H, s, H-14); 3.79 and 4.07(1H each, AB, *J*= 12.5Hz, H-15); 2.00(3H, d, *J*= 1.5Hz, H-16); 5.80(1H, q, *J*= 1.0Hz, H-2'); 3.75(1H, m, H-6'); 5.77(1H, dd, *J*= 5.0, 15.9Hz, H-7'); 7.54(1H, dd, *J*= 11.0, 15.9Hz, H-8'); 6.62(1H, dd, *J*= 11.0, 11.1Hz, H-9'); 5.83(1H, d, *J*= 11.1Hz, H-10'); 2.24(3H, d, *J*= 1.0Hz, H-12'); 3.70(1H, m, H-13'); and 1.16ppm (3H, d, *J*= 6.0Hz, H-14').

^{13}C NMR:
($CDCl_3$) 79.2, C-2; 36.6, C-3; 74.6, C-4; 47.0, C-5; 44.0, C-6; 50.8, C-7; 56.1, C-8; 138.2, C-9; 123.0, C-10; 66.7, C-11; 65.7, C-12; 48.3, C-13; 7.2, C-14; 62.9, C-15; 21.9, C-16; 165.9, C-1'; 119.1, C-2'; 159.0, C-3'; 40.1, C-4'; 67.0, C-5'; 83.3, C-6'; 135.5, C-7'; 130.5, C-8'; 142.4, C-9'; 116.7, C-10'; 166.2, C-11'; 20.0, C-12'; 69.7, C-13'; and 18.5ppm, C-14'.

References

R. J. Cole and R. H. Cox; Handbook of Toxic Fungal Metabolites; Academic Press, New York, pp. 243(1981).

B. B. Jarvis; Macrocyclic Trichothecenes; In Mycotoxins and Phytoalexins; R. P. Sharma and D. K. Salunkhe, eds.; CRC Press, Boca Raton, Florida, pp. 361-421(1991).

M. Matsumoto, H. Minato, K. Tori,and M. Ueyama; Structures of Isororidin E, Epoxyisororidin E, and Epoxy- and Diepoxyroridin H, New Metabolites Isolated from *Cylindrocarpon* Species Determined by Carbon-13 and Hydrogen-1 NMR Spectroscopy. Revision of C-2': C-3' Double Bond Configuration of the Roridin Group; Tet. Lett.; pp. 4093-4096(1977).

Common/Systematic Name

Roridin K acetate

Molecular Formula/Molecular Weight

$C_{31}H_{40}O_{10}$; MW = 572.26215

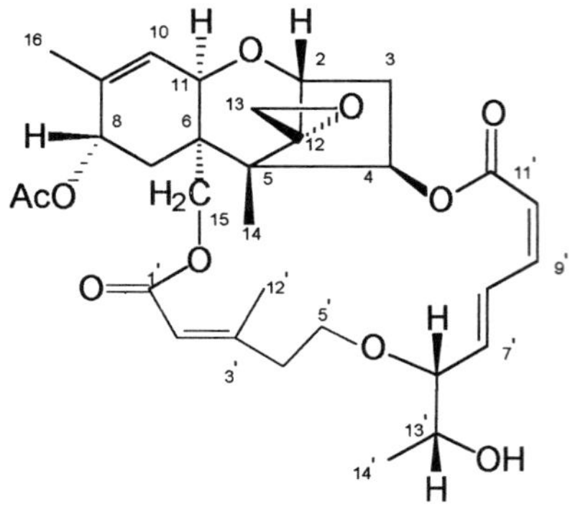

General Characteristics

Crystals from dichloromethane-hexane, mp., 255-257°C; $[\alpha]_D^{25}$ + 2.1° (*c*= 5.6 in $CHCl_3$).

Isolation/Purification

Spores of *Myrothecium verrucaria* grown on N-Z amine agar were added to Czapek-Dox media and allowed to grow at 28°C in a shake culture. After 2 days, the solution was divided into three equal portions and added to three separate Fernback flasks containing 1L of production media. After 3 days of growth, the mycelium in each flask was separately centrifuged, washed, and resuspended in 1L of sterile water. Trichoverrin A and trichoverrin B were added separately to flasks one and two; flask three was used as the control. After 7 days, the mycelium was removed and extracted with ethyl acetate. The mycelium extract was subjected to partition chromatography on 500g Celite impregnated with 250ml of 18% water in methanol. The column was eluted with petroleum ether followed by increasing amounts of dichloromethane in petroleum ether up to 40% dichloromethane in petroleum ether. Fractions were combined on the basis of TLC analysis to give a total of eight fractions: A, B, C, D, E, F, G, and H (methanol wash). Fraction F was subjected to MPLC (30-60% ethyl acetate in hexane) to yield a fraction composed principally of a mixture of roridin E and isororidin E in a ratio of ca. 1:4, v/v. The following fraction was subjected to HPLC (20% ethyl acetate in hexane) to give roridin D and roridin K acetate.

Fungal Source

Myrothecium verrucaria (ATCC 24571).

Spectral Data

UV:

λ_{max}^{EtOH} 263nm (log ϵ= 4.21).

^{1}H NMR:

(CDCl$_3$) 0.78(3H, s, 14-H); 1.19(3H, d, *J*= 6.0Hz, 14'-H); 1.76(3H, s, 16-H); 1.19(acetate); 2.30(3H, d, *J*=1.2Hz, 12'-H); 2.52(1H, dd, *J*=7, 15Hz, 3α-H); 2.97(2H, *J*=4Hz, 13-H); 3.84(1H, d, *J*=5Hz, 2-H); 3.90(1H, d, *J*=5Hz, 11-H); 4.31(2H AB, *J*=12Hz, 15-H); 5.75(1H, d, *J*=11Hz, 10'-H); 5.78(1H, d, *J*=16Hz, 7'-H); 6.10(1H, dd, *J*=4, 8Hz, 4-H); 6.57(1H, dd, *J*'s=11Hz, 9'-H); and 7.47ppm (1H, dd, *J*=11, 16Hz, 8'-H).

^{13}C NMR:

(CDCl$_3$) 79.1 d, C-2; 35.5 t, C-3; 73.8 d, C-4; 48.6 s, C-5; 42.2 s, C-6; 27.4 t, C-7; 68.8 d, C-8; 136.4 s, C-9; 124.0 d, C-10; 67.0 d, C-11; 65.4 s; C-12; 48.0 t, C-13; 6.8 q, C-14; 64.7 t, C-15; 21.1 q, C-16; 165.9 s, C-1'; 117.6 d, C-2'; 159.7 s, C-3'; 41.2 t, C-4'; 70.3 t, C-5'; 84.1 d, C-6'; 138.5 d, C-7'; 126.5 d, C-8'; 143.0 d, C-9'; 116.7 d, C-10'; 166.2 s, C-11'; 20.2 q, C-12'; 70.7 d, C-13'; 18.3 q, C-14'; 170.8 s, $\underline{C}OCH_3$; and 20.7ppm q, $CO\underline{C}H_3$.

Mass Spectrum:

HRCIMS (methane gas reagent): 573.2692*m/e* (M^+ + H, calcd 573.2700).

Reference

B. B. Jarvis, G. P. Stahly, G. Pavanasasivam, J. O. Midiwo, T. Desilva, C. E. Holmlund, E.P. Mazzola and R. F. Geoghegan; Isolation and Characterization of the Trichoverroids and New Roridins and Verrucarins; J. Org. Chem., Vol. 47, pp. 1117-1124(1982).

Common/Systematic Name

Roridin H; Verrucarin H

Molecular Formula/Molecular Weight

$C_{29}H_{36}O_8$; MW = 512.24102

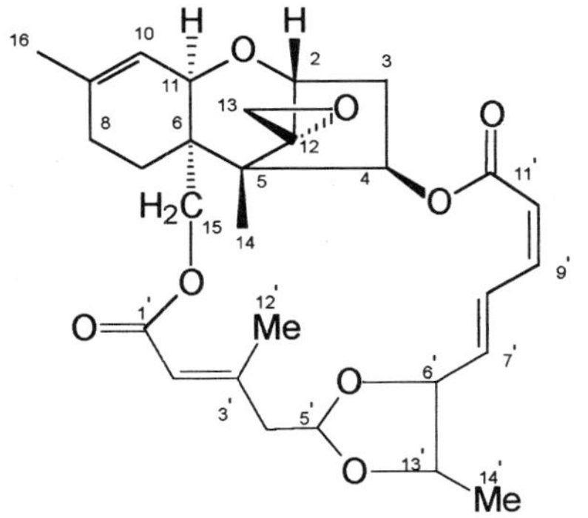

General Characteristics

Crystals from acetone-ether, mp >325°C (dec.); $[\alpha]_D^{23}$ +31° (*c*=1.16, in $CHCl_3$); $[\alpha]_D^{23}$ + 40.3° (*c*=1.065, in benzene); $[\alpha]_D^{23}$ +31.5° (*c*=0.855, in dioxane).

Fungal Source

Myrothecium verrucaria.

Biological Activity

Antibiotic activity.

Spectral Data

UV:

195(ϵ=15,800), 224 (24,500), and 260nm (18,200).

IR:

(CH_2CH_2) 2970, 2910, 1710, 1645, 1600, 1380, 1355, 1220, 1175, 1115, 1101, 1087, 1071, 1033, 1005, 992, 971, and 832cm^{-1}.

^{1}H NMR:

($CDCl_3$) 3.80(1H, d, H-2); 5.90(H-4); 5.42(1H, d, *J*=4.0Hz, H-10); 3.64(H-11); 2.96(2H, AB, *J*=4.0Hz, H-13); 0.85(H-14); 4.15(2H, AB, *J*=12.0Hz, H-15); 1.69(H-16); 5.67(H-2'); 2.74(1H, m, H-4'); 5.58(1H, *J*= 3.5, 8.0Hz, H-5'); 4.03(1H, m, H-6'); 5.90(1H, m, H-7'); 7.68(1H, dd, *J*=11.0, 15.5Hz, H-8'); 6.55(1H, t, *J*=11.0Hz, H-9'); 5.79(1H, d, *J*=11.0Hz, H-10'); 2.27(3H, d, *J*=1.5Hz, H-12'); 3.65(1H, m, H-13'); and 1.32ppm(3H, d, *J*=6.0Hz, H-14').

^{13}C NMR:
($CDCl_3$) 79.0,C-2; 34.8,C-3; 74.0, C-4; 48.9,C-5; 43.2, C-6; 20.5, C-7; 27.6, C-8; 139.9, C-9; 118.6, C-10; 67.6, C-11; 65.3, C-12; 47.3, C-13; 7.0, C-14; 63.0, C-15; 22.9, C-16; 166.0, C-1'; 119.0, C-2'; 154.4, C-3'; 47.7, C-4'; 100.8, C-5'; 81.9, C-6'; 134.6, C-7'; 126.2, C-8'; 142.5, C-9'; 118.9, C-10'; 166.0, C-11'; 18.2, C-12'; 76.8, C-13'; and 16.3ppm, C-14'.

TLC Data

Absorbent: Kieselgel G; solvent, ethyl ether (two consecutive runs); R_f, 0.51; detection: iodine vapors.

References

R. J. Cole and R. H. Cox; Handbook of Toxic Fungal Metabolites; Academic Press, New York, pp. 239-240(1981).

B. B. Jarvis; Macrocyclic Trichothecenes; In Mycotoxins and Phytoalexins; R. P. Sharma and D. K. Salunkhe, eds.; CRC Press, Boca Raton, Florida, pp. 361-421(1991).

M. Matsumoto; Structures of Isororidin E, Epoxyisororidin E, Epoxyroridin H, and Diepoxyroridin H, New Metabolites Isolated from a Species of *Cylindrocarpon*; J. Sci. Hinoshima, University serial A, Vol. 43, pp.107-118 (1979).

Common/Systematic Name

Roridin J

Molecular Formula/Molecular Weight

$C_{29}H_{36}O_9$; MW = 528.23593

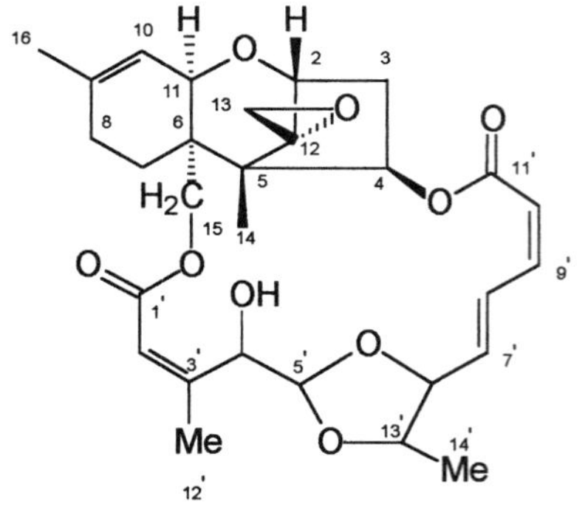

General Characteristics

Crystals from dichloromethane-hexane; mp., 281-285°C; $[\alpha]_D^{28}$ + 21.8° (in $CHCl_3$). Acetate derivative, crystals from dichloromethane-ether; mp., 230-235°C; $[\alpha]_D^{28}$ - 40.6° (in $CHCl_3$).

Fungal Source

Myrothecium verrucaria (ATCC 24571).

Isolation/Purification

The metabolite was isolated by a combination of column chromatographies (adsorption and partition) and recrystallizations from an ethyl acetate extract of the fermentation broth. Roridin J is closely related to roridin H, but can be separated by careful chromatography using alumina with hexane-methylene chloride as eluant.

Biological Activity

Exhibited substantial *in vivo* activity against P388 mouse leukemia (PS). It was toxic at 10mg/kg and exhibited the following T/C activities (dose level) in PS: 158 (5mg/kg), 149 (2.5mg/kg), 140 (1.25mg/kg), and 125 (0.62mg/kg).

Spectral Data

UV:

λ_{max}^{EtOH} 261nm (log ϵ=4.28).

IR:
(KBr) 3535(OH), 1715(C=O), 1645, and 1595cm^{-1} (diene); acetate, 1745 and 1715(C=O's), 1655, 1605cm^{-1} (diene).

^{1}H NMR:
($CDCl_3$) 3.85(1H, d, *J*=5.0Hz, H-2); 2.1(1H, m, H-3β); 2.48(1H, dd, *J*=8.0, 15Hz, H-3α); 6.0(1H, dd, *J*=4.0, 8.0Hz, H-4); 2.0(2H, m, H-7); 2.0(2H, m, H-8); 5.44(1H, d, *J*=5.0Hz, H-10); 3.63(1H, d, *J*=5.0Hz, H-11); 2.97(2H, AB, *J*=4.0Hz, H-13); 0.87(3H, H-14); 4.21(2H, AB, *J*=2.0Hz, H-15); 1.74(3H, H-16); 5.84(1H, d, *J*=1, 2Hz, H-2'); 3.85(1H, d, *J*=7.0Hz, H-4'); 5.24(1H, d, *J*=7.0Hz, H-5'); 3.87(1H, H-6'); 5.8(1H, d, *J*=15, 5.0Hz, H-7'); 7.70(1H, dd, *J*=11.5, 15.5Hz, H-8'); 6.54(1H, t, *J*=11.5Hz, H-9'); 5.9(1H, d, *J*=1.5Hz, H-10'); 2.28(3H, d, *J*=1, 2.0Hz, H-12'); 3.70(1H, q, *J*=6.0Hz, H-13'); and 1.36ppm (3H, d, *J*=6.0Hz, H-14').

^{13}C NMR:
($CDCl_3$) 79.2, d, C-2; 34.7, t, C-3; 73.9, d, C-4; 49.2, C-5; 43.3, C-6; 20.4, t, C-7; 27.6, t, C-8; 140.4, C-9; 118.6, d, C-10; 67.9, d, C-11; 65.6, C-12; 47.9, t, C-13; 7.4, q, C-14; 63.4, t, C-15; 23.3, q, C-16; 165.9, C-1'; 119.8, d, C-2'; 155.4, C-3'; 79.8, d, C-4'; 103.4, d, C-5'; 82.3, d, C-6'; 134.5, d, C-7'; 126.1, d, C-8'; 143.1, d, C-9'; 118.9, d, C-10'; 166.2, C-11'; 13.1, q, C-12'; 76.5, d, C-13' and 16.0ppm, q, C-14'.

Mass Spectrum:
EIMS: 528*m/e* (M^+).

<u>Reference</u>

B. B. Jarvis, G. P. Stahly, and G. Pavanasasivam, E. P. Mazzola; Structure of Roridin J. A New Macrocyclic Trichothecene from *Myrothecium verrucaria*; Journal of Antibiotics; Vol. 33, pp. 256-258(1980).

Common/Systematic Name

7β,8β-Epoxyroridin H

Molecular Formula/Molecular Weight

$C_{29}H_{34}O_9$; MW = 526.22028

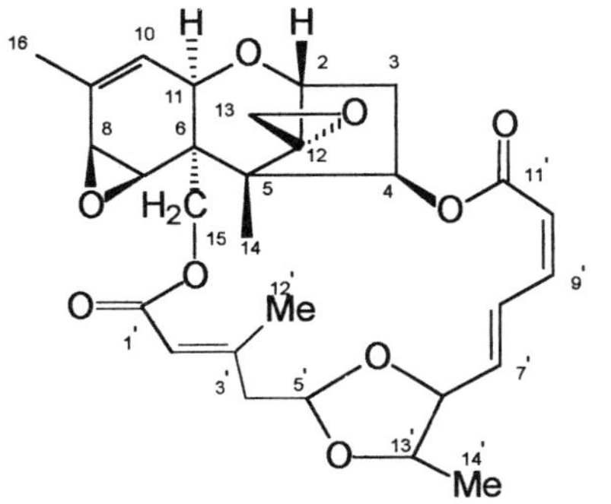

General Characteristics

Colorless, amorphous powder.

Fungal Source

Cylindrocarpon spp.

Spectral Data

IR:

($CHCl_3$) 1717, 1646, and 1601cm^{-1}.

^{1}H NMR:

($CDCl_3$) 5.91 (1H, d, *J*= 4.5Hz, H-2); 2.15, (1H, ddd, *J*= 4.0, 4.5, 14.0Hz, H-3β; 2.40 (1H, dd, *J*= 8.0, 14.0Hz, H-3α); 5.87 (1H, dd, *J*= 4.0, 8.0Hz, H-4); 3.75 (1H, dd, *J*= 3.0, 4.0Hz, H-7); 3.17 (1H, dd, *J*= 2.1, 4.0Hz, H-8); 5.69 (1H, m, H-10); 4.08 (1H, m, H-11); 2.98 and 3.18(1H each, AB, *J*= 3.6Hz, H-13); 1.12 (3H, s, H-14); 3.41 and 4.43 (1H each, AB, *J*= 12.3Hz, H-15); 1.98 (3H, d, *J*= 1.4Hz, H-16); 5.69(1H, q, *J*= 1.0Hz, H-2'); 2.32 and 2.41 (1H each, m, H-4'); 5.54 (1H, dd, J= 3.4, 8.4Hz, H-5'); 4.06 (1H, ddd, *J*= 2.0, 2.3, 8.0Hz, H-6'); 5.95 (1H, dd, *J*= 2.3, 15.4Hz, H-7'); 7.76(1H, ddd, *J*= 2.0, 11.4, 15.4Hz, H-8'); 6.58 (1H, dd, *J*= 11.1, 11.4Hz, H-9'); 5.79 (1H, d, *J*= 11.1Hz, H-10'); 2.28 (3H, d, *J*= 1.0Hz, H-12'); and 1.34ppm (3H, d, *J*= 5.9Hz, H-14').

^{13}C NMR:
($CDCl_3$) 79.3, C-2; 35.0, C-3; 73.6, C-4; 48.2, C-5; 44.2, C-6; 50.9, C-7; 57.2, C-8; 138.0, C-9; 123.0, C-10; 67.9, C-11; 65.5, C-12; 47.9, C-13; 8.2, C-14; 65.8, C-15; 22.0, C-16; 165.9, C-1'; 118.7, C-2'; 155.6, C-3'; 47.7, C-4'; 101.0, C-5'; 82.0, C-6'; 135.4, C-7'; 126.2, C-8'; 143.4, C-9'; 118.4, C-10'; 165.9, C-11'; 18.4, C-12'; 77.1, C-13'; and 16.5ppm, C-14'.

References

R. J. Cole and R. H. Cox; Handbook of Toxic Fungal Metabolites; Academic Press, New York, pp. 244(1981).

B. B. Jarvis; Macrocyclic Trichothecenes; In Mycotoxins and Phytoalexins; R. P. Sharma and D. K. Salunkhe, eds.; CRC Press, Boca Raton, Florida, pp. 361-421(1991).

M. Matsumoto; Structures of Isororidin E, Epoxyisororidin E, Epoxyroridin H, and Diepoxyroridin H, New Metabolites Isolated from a Species of *Cylindrocarpon*; J. Sci. Hinoshima, University serial A, Vol. 43, pp. 107-118 (1979).

Common/Systematic Name

7β,8β,2',3'-Diepoxyisororidin H

Molecular Formula/Molecular Weight

$C_{29}H_{34}O_{10}$; MW = 542.21520

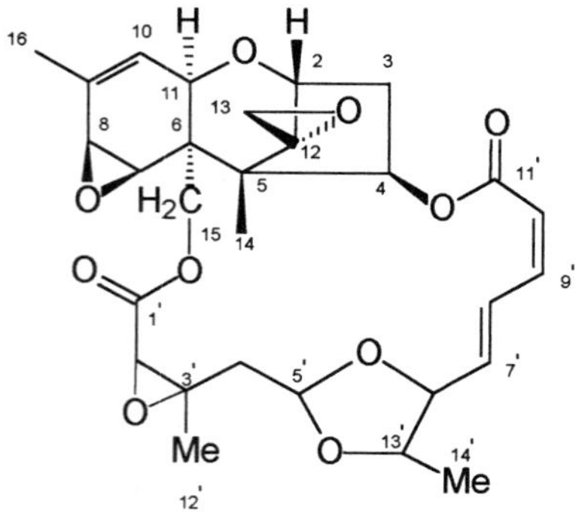

General Characteristics

Colorless prisms from ethyl acetate, mp 291-293°C (dec.).

Fungal Source

Cylindrocarpon spp.

Spectral Data

IR:

($CHCl_3$) 1755, 1710, 1645, and 1601cm^{-1}.

^{1}H NMR:

($CDCl_3$) 3.90 (1H, d, *J*= 4.5Hz, H-2); 2.26 (1H, ddd, *J*= 4.5, 5.0, 15.0Hz, H-3β; 2.45 (1H, dd, *J*= 8.0, 15.0Hz, H-3α); 5.89 (1H, dd, *J*= 5.0, 8.0Hz, H-4); 3.62 (1H, dd, *J*= 3.0, 3.9Hz, H-7); 3.18 (1H, dd, *J*= 1.9, 3.9Hz, H-8); 5.67 (1H, ddd, *J*= 1.5, 1.9, 6.3Hz, H-10); 3.75 (1H, dd, *J*= 3.0, 6.3Hz, H-11); 2.97 and 3.17(1H each, AB, *J*= 3.5Hz, H-13); 1.12 (3H, s, H-14); 4.44 (2H, s, H-15); 2.01 (3H, d, *J*= 1.5Hz, H-16); 3.29(1H, s, H-2'); 1.57 (1H, dd, *J*= 9.2, 14.0Hz, H-4'A); 2.32 (1H, dd, *J*= 2.7, 14.0Hz, H-4'B); 5.37 (1H, dd, *J*= 2.7, 9.2Hz, H-5'); 4.17 (1H, ddd, *J*= 1.8, 2.2, 8.0Hz, H-6'); 5.98 (1H, ddd, *J*= 2.2, 3.0, 15.5Hz, H-7'); 7.60(1H, ddd, *J*= 1.8, 11.3, 15.5Hz, H-8'); 6.62 (1H, dd, *J*= 11.3, 11.7Hz, H-9'); 5.88 (1H, d, *J*= 11.7Hz, H-10'); 1.60 (3H, s, H-12'); 3.70 (1H, m, H-13'); and 1.33ppm (3H, d, *J*= 6.0Hz, H-14').

^{13}C NMR:

($CDCl_3$) 79.2, C-2; 34.8, C-3; 73.9, C-4; 48.5, C-5; 44.7, C-6; 50.9, C-7; 56.3, C-8; 138.6, C-9; 122.4, C-10; 67.3, C-11; 65.3, C-12; 48.0, C-13; 8.5, C-14; 65.6, C-15; 22.0, C-16; 167.2, C-1'; 59.2, C-2'; 60.8, C-3'; 44.0, C-4'; 101.1, C-5'; 82.7, C-6'; 134.6, C-7'; 126.8, C-8'; 142.7, C-9'; 119.0, C-10'; 166.9, C-11'; 17.1, C-12'; 76.3, C-13'; and 15.8ppm, C-14'.

References

R. J. Cole and R. H. Cox; Handbook of Toxic Fungal Metabolites; Academic Press, New York, pp. 245 (1981).

B. B. Jarvis; Macrocyclic Trichothecenes; In Mycotoxins and Phytoalexins; R. P. Sharma and D. K. Salunkhe, eds.; CRC Press, Boca Raton, Florida, pp. 361-421(1991).

M. Matsumoto; Structures of Isororidin E, Epoxyisororidin E, Epoxyroridin H, and Diepoxyroridin H, New Metabolites Isolated from a Species of *Cylindrocarpon*; J. Sci. Hinoshima, University serial A, Vol. 43, pp.107-118 (1979).

Common/Systematic Name

Satratoxin F

Molecular Formula/Molecular Weight

$C_{29}H_{34}O_{10}$; MW = 542.21520

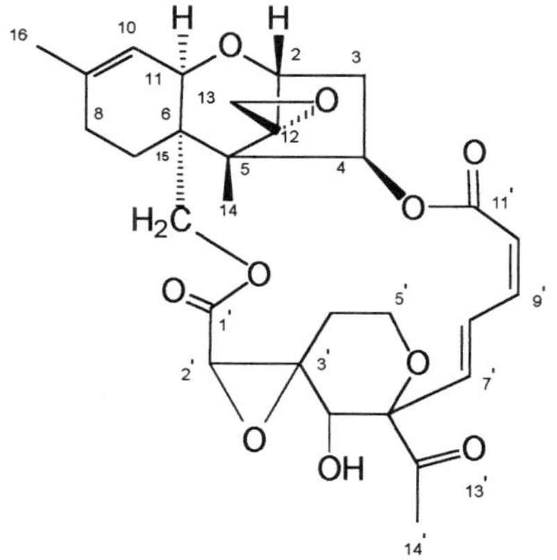

General Characteristics

Crystals; m.p., 140-143°C.

Fungal Source

Stachybotrys chartarum (*S. atra*) ATTC 26303.

Isolation/Purification

A fraction from the isolation of satratoxin H (see R. M. Eppley *et al.*; J. Org. Chem, Vol. 42, p. 240, 1977) was crystallized from $CHCl_3$-hexane.

Biological Activity

Cytotoxic.

Spectral Data

IR:

(CH_3Cl) 3460(OH), 1748(C=O), 1715, and 1183cm^{-1}.

^{1}H NMR:

($CDCl_3$) 0.83(3H, s, H-14); 1.73(3H, s, H-16); 2.0(5H, m, H-3β, H-7 and H-8); 2.5(1H, m, H-3α); 2.98(2H, center of AB system, *J*=4Hz, H- 13); 3.38(1H, s, H-2'); 3.59(1H, d, *J*=5Hz, H-11); 4.24(1H, s, H-12'); 3.85(1H, d, *J*=5Hz, H-2); 4.15(2H, m, H-5'); 3.88(2H, center of AB system, H- 15); 5.43(1H, d, *J*=5Hz, H-10); 5.60(1H, d, *J*=15.5Hz, H-7'); 5.9(1H, m, H- 4); 5.92(1H, d, *J*=10.5Hz, H-10'); 6.57(1H, dd, *J*=6 and 10.5Hz, H-9'); and 6.81ppm (1H, dd, *J*=6 and 15.5Hz, H-8').

^{13}C NMR:

79.2, C-2; 34.6, C-3; 74.3, C-4; 49.5, C-5; 43.2, C-6; 20.1, C-7; 27.5, C-8; 140.4, C-9; 118.6, C-10; 67.9, C-11; 65.3, C-12; 48.0, C-13; 8.0, C-14; 65.1, C-15; 23.3, C-16; 166.1, C-l'; 58.9, C-2'; 63.9, C-3'; 22.7, C4'; 61.2, C-5'; 87.1, C-6; 130.2, C-7'; 130.5, C-8'; 143.2, C-9'; 121.2, C-10'; 166.9, C-11'; 73.7, C-12'; 217.8, C-13'; and 29.7ppm, C-14'.

Reference

R. M. Eppley, E. P. Mazzola, M. E. Stack, and P. A. Dreifuss; Structures of Satratoxin F and Satratoxin G, Metabolites of *Stachybotrys atra*: Application of Proton and Carbon-13 Nuclear Magnetic Resonance Spectroscopy; J. Org. Chem., Vol. 45, pp. 2522-523(1980).

Common/Systematic Name
Satratoxin G

Molecular Formula/Molecular Weight
$C_{29}H_{36}O_{10}$; MW = 544.2309

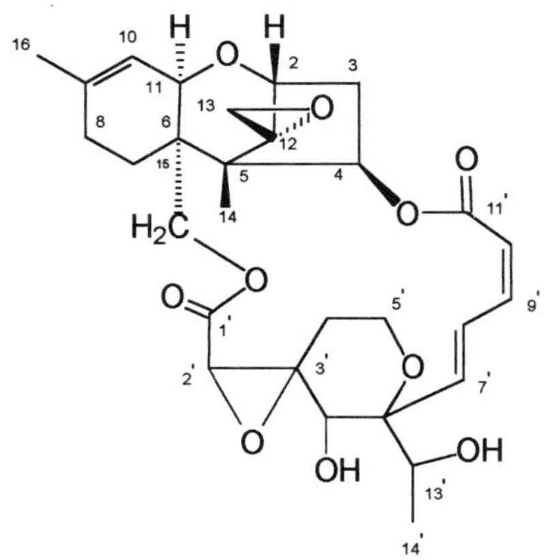

General Characteristics
Crystals; m.p., 132-136°C.

Fungal Source
Stachybotrys chartarum (*S. atra*) ATTC 26303.

Isolation/Purification
A fraction from the isolation of satratoxin H (see R. M. Eppley *et al.*; J. Org. Chem, Vol. 42, p. 240, 1977) was crystallized from $CHCl_3$-hexane.

Biological Activity
Cytotoxic.

Spectral Data

IR:
($CHCl_3$) 3450(OH), 1747(C=O), 1710, and 1185cm^{-1}.

^{1}H NMR:
($CDCl_3$) 0.87(1H, s, H-14); 1.12(3H, d, *J*=7Hz, H-14'); 1.74(3H, s, H-16); 2.0(5H, m, H-3β, H-7 and H-8); 2.5(1 H, m, H-3α); 2.5(2H, m, H-4'); 2.98(2H, center of AB system, *J*=4Hz, H-13); 3.61(1H, d, *J*=5Hz, H- 11); 3.43(1H, s, H-2'); 3.90(1H, d, *J*=5Hz, H-2); 3.9(2H, m, H-5'); 4.02(2H, center of AB system, *J*=12Hz, H-15); 4.35(1H, s, H-12'); 4.45(1H, q, *J*=7Hz, H-13'); 5.46(1H, d, *J*=5Hz, H-10); 5.90(1H, d,

J=16.5 Hz, H-7'); 5.93(1H, d, *J*=10.5Hz, H-10'); 6.0(1H, m, H-4); 6.68(1H, dd, *J*=7.5 and 10.5Hz, H-9'); and 7.00ppm (1H, dd, *J*=7.5 and 16.5Hz, H-8').

^{13}C NMR:

($CDCl_3$) 79.3, C-2; 34.4, C-3; 73.7, C-4; 49.3, C-5; 43.3, C-6; 20.2, C-7; 27.5, C-8; 140.3, C-9; 118.8, C-10; 67.1, C-11; 65.4, C-12; 48.1, C-13; 8.0, C-14; 64.9, C-15; 23.3, C-16; 166.9, C-1'; 61.0, C-2'; 65.4, C-3'; 22.7, C-4'; 60.3, C- 5'; 81.5, C-6'; 132.0, C-7'; 131.5, C-8'; 144.2, C-9' 120.0, C-10'; 166.9, C-11'; 72.6, C-12'; 70.1, C-13'; and 16.1ppm, C-14'.

Reference

R. M. Eppley, E. P. Mazzola, M. E. Stack, and P. A. Dreifuss; Structures of Satratoxin F and Satratoxin G, Metabolites of *Stachybotrys atra*: Application of Proton and Carbon-13 Nuclear Magnetic Resonance Spectroscopy; J. Org. Chem., Vol. 45, pp. 2522-523(1980).

Common/Systematic Name
Isosatratoxin F

Molecular Formula/Molecular Weight
$C_{29}H_{34}O_{10}$; MW = 542.21518

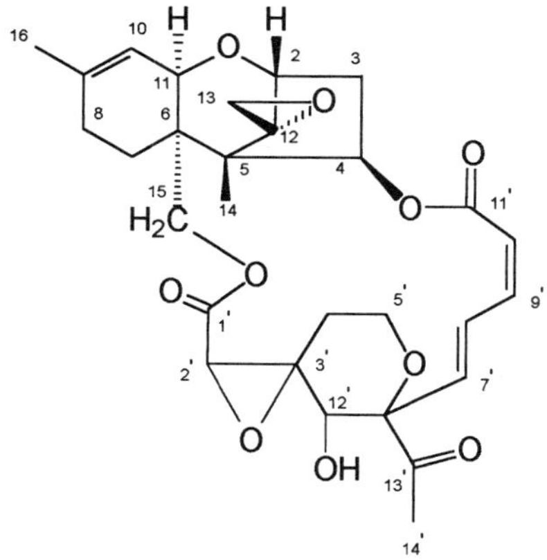

General Characteristics
Crystals; m.p., 153-155°C; $[\alpha]_D$ = + 46.4° (*c*=0.40, in acetone).

Fungal Source
Stachybotrys atra (*S. chartarum*) ATTC 26303.

Isolation/Purification
Methanol extraction of a culture of *S. atra* (JS5106) grown at room temperature for 30 days gave 7.5g of crude extract. This material was subjected to MPLC over silica gel. Elution with dichloromethane gave 520mg in the first fraction which was subjected to high speed countercurrent chromatography (methanol-water-carbon tetrachloride-hexane-methylene chloride, 6:4:8:1:1, v/v/v/v/v) to give five fractions. Fraction 4 was recrystallized from methylene chloride-hexane to give 20mg of isosatratoxin F.

Spectral Data

IR:
($CHCl_3$) 3478(OH), 1747(C=O), 1713, and 1188cm^{-1}.

^{1}H NMR:
($CDCl_3$) 0.80(3H, s, H-14); 1.70(3H, s, H-16); 1.80-2.00(4H, m, H-7 and H- 8); 2.20(ddd, 1H, *J*=4.7, 5.1, and 15.5Hz, H-3β), 2.50(1H, dd, *J*=8.0, 15.5Hz, H-3α); 2.80 and 3.12(1H each, AB, *J*= 4.0 Hz, H-13); 3.38(1H, s, H-2'); 3.54(1H, d, *J*=5.0Hz, H-11); 3.62(1H, s, H-12'); 3.83(1H, d, *J*=5.1Hz, H-2); 4.14(2H, m, H-5'); 4.20(2H, s, H-15); 5.39(1H, d, *J*=5.0Hz, H-10); 5.55(1H, dd, *J*=1.6 and 16.4Hz, H-7');

5.84(1H, dd, J=4.7 and 8.0Hz, H-4); 5.90(1H, dd, J=1.6 and 11.6Hz, H-10'); 6.54(1H, ddd, J=1.6, 5.7, and 11.6Hz, H-9'); and 6.72ppm (1H, ddd, J=1.6, 5.7, and 16.4Hz, H-8').

^{13}C NMR:

($CDCl_3$) 79.1, C-2; 34.4, C-3; 74.1, C-4; 49.4, C-5; 43.0, C-6; 20.0, C-7; 27.4, C-8; 140.5, C-9; 118.5, C-10; 67.7, C-11; 65.3, C-12; 47.9, C-13; 7.9, C-14; 65.0, C-15; 23.3, C-16; 166.0, C-1'; 58.8, C-2'; 63.8, C-3'; 22.5, C4'; 61.1, C- 5'; 87.0, C-6; 129.8, C-7'; 130.5, C-8'; 143.2, C-9'; 121.1, C-10'; 166.9, C-11'; 73.5, C-12'; 208.6, C-13'; and 27.4ppm, C-14'.

Reference

B. B. Jarvis, W. G. Sorenson, E.-L. Hintikka, M. Nikulin, Y. Zhou, J. Jiang, S. Wang, S. Hinkley, R. A. Etzel, and D. Dearborn; Studies of Toxin Production by Isolates of *Stachybotrys chartarum* and *Memnoniella echinata* Isolated During a Study of Pulmonary Hemosiderosis in Infants; Appl. Environ. Microbiol., Vol. 64, pp. 3620-3625(1998).

Common/Systematic Name

Isosatratoxin G

Molecular Formula/Molecular Weight

$C_{29}H_{36}O_{10}$; MW = 544.23085

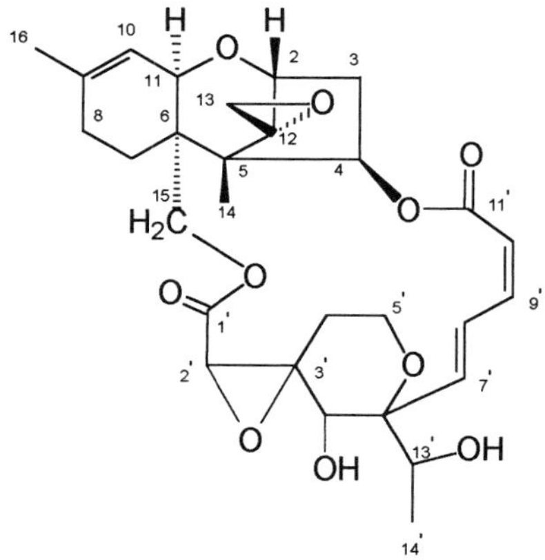

General Characteristics

Crystals; mp., 136-137°C.

Fungal Source

Stachybotrys chartarum.

Isolation/Purification

The black gummy crude extract derived from a rice culture of S. *chartarum* S-17 was triturated with hexane washes until no further color was extracted. The remaining black gum was partitioned between water and chloroform. The chloroform soluble portion was dried (Na_2SO_4) concentrated to dryness on the rotary evaporator to give a black gum. The gum was subjected to flash chromatography, over silica gel with a gradient of hexane-methanol-methylene chloride, and collected in 124 fractions. Fractions 83/84 (3% methanol-methylene chloride) were combined to give A; fractions 85-87 (3% methanol-methylene chloride) were combined to give B; fractions 88-89 (3% methanol-methylene chloride) and 90-99 (4% methanol-methylene chloride) were combined to give C; fractions 100-103 (5% methanol-methylene chloride) and fractions 104-110 (6% methanol-methylene chloride) were combined to give D; fractions 111-112 (6% methanol-methylene chloride) were combined to give E; fractions 113-115 (10% methanol-methylene chloride) were combined to give F; and fractions 116-119 were combined to give G. Fraction A was subjected to CCC (V_c = 850ml, methanol -water-carbon tetrachloride-methylene chloride-hexane(3: 2: 3.5:0.5:1 v/v/v/v/v) organic mobile phase at 3.2ml/min) to give 10 fractions (F1-F10). Fraction F5 was subjected to TLC (Chromatotron, 2 mm plate, 20% hexane in ethyl acetate) to give 2α-acetoxystachybotrylactone acetate. The stationary phase of this CCC was concentrated to dryness to give a gum which upon preparative TLC (Chromatotron, 2 mm plate, ~ 20% hexane in ethyl acetate) yielded fractions from which were isolated satratoxin G and isosatratoxin G.

Biological Activity

Cytotoxic.

Spectral Data

UV:

λ_{max}^{MeOH} 255nm.

IR:

(CH_3Cl) 3450(OH), 1745(C=O), and 1712cm^{-1} (C=O).

^{1}H NMR:

($CDCl_3$) 0.80(1H, s, H-14); 1.23(3H, d, *J*=6.5 Hz, H-14'); 1.70(3H, s, H-16); 1.84(2H, m, H-7); 2.03(2H, m, H-8); 2.17(1H, dt, *J*=5.0 and 15.2 Hz, H-3β; 2.44(1H, dd, *J*=8.5 and 15.2Hz, H-3α); 2.08(1H, dd, *J*=5.2 and 14.1Hz, H-4'A); 2.35(1 H, bd, *J*=14.1Hz, H-4'B); 2.81 and 3.12 (1H each, AB, *J*=4.0Hz, H-13); 3.55(1H, d, *J*=5.0 Hz, H-11); 3.74(1H, s, H-2'); 3.82(1H, d, *J*=5.0 Hz, H-2); 3.83(1H, m, H-5'B); 4.08(1H, dt, *J*=2.0 and 11.4Hz, H-5'B); 3.87(1H, q, *J*=6.5Hz, H-13'); 4.16 and 4.28(1H each, AB, *J*=12.5Hz, H-15); 4.30(1H, s, H-12'); 5.40(1H, d, *J*=5.0Hz, H-10); 5.80(1H, d, *J*=16.8Hz, H-7'); 5.90(1H, d, *J*=11.4Hz, H-10'); 5.90(1H, dd, *J*=5.0 and 8.5Hz, H-4); 6.65(1H, dd, *J*=6.8 and 11.4Hz, H-9'); and 6.88ppm (1H, dd, *J*=6.8 and 16.8Hz, H-8').

^{13}C NMR:

($CDCl_3$) 79.2, C-2; 34.5, C-3; 73.5, C-4; 49.5, C-5; 43.2, C-6; 20.0, C-7; 27.4, C-8; 140.5, C-9; 118.5, C-10; 67.8, C-11; 65.3, C-12; 48.0, C-13; 8.1, C-14; 64.7, C-15; 23.4, C-16; 166.5, C-1'; 54.2, C-2'; 65.0, C-3'; 27.4, C-4'; 60.9, C-5'; 81.5, C-6'; 130.9, C-7'; 130.1, C-8'; 144.0, C-9'; 120.3, C-10'; 168.5, C-11'; 68.7, C-12'; 73.0, C-13'; and 17.3ppm, C-14'.

Mass Spectrum:

HREIMS: 544.2301*m/e* for $C_{29}H_{36}O_{10}$; calcd., 544.2308.

References

B. B. Jarvis; Macrocyclic Trichothecenes; In Mycotoxins and Phytoalexins; R. P. Sharma and D. K. Salunkhe, eds.; CRC Press, Boca Raton, Florida, pp. 361-421(1991).

B. B. Jarvis, J. Salemme and A. Morais; *Stachybotrys* Toxins 1; Natural Toxins, Vol. 3, pp. 10-16(1995).

Common/Systematic Name
Satratoxin H

Molecular Formula/Molecular Weight
$C_{29}H_{36}O_9$; MW = 528.23593

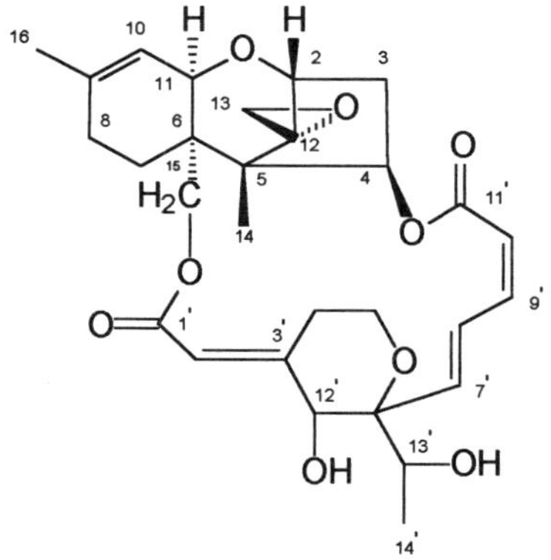

General Characteristics
Crystals; mp., 162-166°C.

Fungal Source
Stachybotrys atra.

Biological Activity
Toxic to brine shrimp and positive in rabbit skin tests. Details not reported.

Spectral Data

UV:
λ_{max}^{MeOH} 225(ε=14,700) and 255nm (10,400).

^{1}H NMR:
($CDCl_3$) 3.90(1H, m, H-2); 2.20(1H, ddd, *J*=4.0, 5.0, 15Hz, H-3β); 2.45(1H, dd, *J*=7.5, 15Hz, H-3α); 5.90(1H, m, H-4); 1.90(2H, m, H-7); 2.10(2H, m, H-8); 5.46(1H, d, *J*=5.0Hz, H-10); 3.62(1H, d, *J*=5.0Hz, H-11); 2.81 and 3.12(1H each, AB, *J*=4.0Hz, H-13); 3.12(1H, d, *J*=4.0Hz, H-13b); 0.83(3H, s, H-14); 2.88 and 4.56(1H each, AB, *J*=12.0Hz, H-15); 1.74(3H, s, H-16); 5.85(1H, d, *J*=2.0Hz, H-2'); 2.60(1H, m, H-4'a); 3.74(1H, dt, *J*=3.0, 10.0Hz, H-4'b); 3.90(2H, m, H-5'); 6.09(1H, d, *J*=17.5Hz, H-7'); 7.36(1H, dd, *J*=10.5, 17.5Hz, H-8'); 6.63(1H, t, *J*=10.5Hz, H-9'); 5.91(1H, d, *J*=10.5Hz, H-10'); 3.97 1H, s, H-12') 4.38(1H, q, *J*=7.0Hz, H-13'); and 1.16ppm (3H, d, *J*=7.0Hz, H-14').

^{13}C NMR:

(CDCl$_3$) 79.1, C-2; 34.4, C-3; 74.2, C-4; 49.0, C-5; 43.4, C-6; 20.4, C-7; 27.6, C-8; 140.2, C-9; 119.0, C-10; 68.2, C-11; 65.4, C-12; 48.0, C-13; 7.6, C-14; 64.2, C-15; 23.3, C-16; 166.2, C-1'; 119.0, C-2'; 155.1, C-3'; 25.3, C-4'; 60.4, C-5'; 81.4, C-6'; 134.2, C-7'; 132.2, C-8'; 143.0, C-9'; 120.4, C-10'; 167.0, C-11'; 73.7, C-12'; 69.7, C-13'; and 15.7ppm, C-14'.

TLC Data

Adsorbent: silica gel; solvent: isopropanol-chloroform, 2:98, v/v; R_f, not reported; detection method: not reported.

References

R. J. Cole and R. H. Cox; Handbook of Toxic Fungal Metabolites; Academic Press, New York, pp. 227-229(1981).

R. M. Eppley, E. P. Mazzola, R. J. Highet, and W. J. Bailey; Structure of Satratoxin H, a Metabolite of *Stachybotrys atra*. Application of Proton and Carbon-13 Nuclear Magnetic Resonance; J. Org. Chem., Vol. 42, pp. 240-243(1977).

B. B. Jarvis; Macrocyclic Trichothecenes; In Mycotoxins and Phytoalexins; R. P. Sharma and D. K. Salunkhe, eds.; CRC Press, Boca Raton, Florida, pp. 361-421(1991).

Common/Systematic Name

S-Isosatratoxin H

Molecular Formula/Molecular Weight

$C_{29}H_{36}O_9$; MW = 528.23593

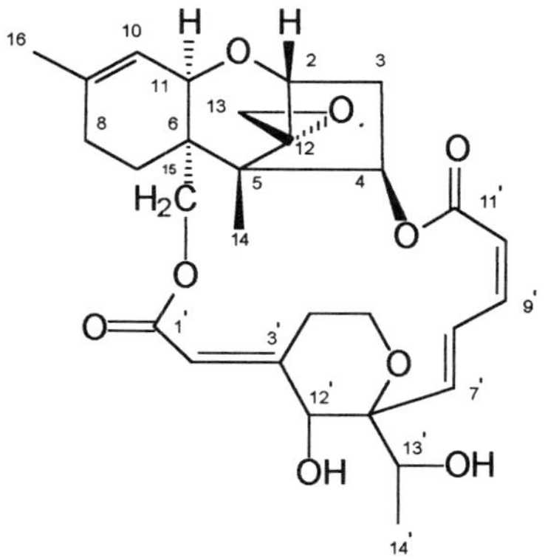

General Characteristics

Crystals, m.p., 180-183°C.

Fungal Source

Stachybotrys chartarum.

Isolation/Purification

In a manner similar to that described for extraction of *S. chartarum*, a rice culture of *S. chartarum* Egypt I gave a crude extract that was taken up in 10ml of methanol and filtered through a pad of C_{18} silica gel in a Büchner funnel. Elution with methanol gave, after solvent removal, a black gum. This material was dissolved in a small amount of methylene chloride and loaded onto a PEI silica gel column and eluted with methylene chloride-hexane(4:1, v/v), methylene chloride and 10% methanol in methylene chloride. A combination of preparative HPLC and TLC gave pure satratoxin H, *S*-isosatratoxin H, stachybotrylactone, and stachybotrylactam.

Biological Activity

Cytotoxic.

Spectral Data

UV:

λ_{max}^{MeOH} 228 and 255nm.

IR:
(CH_3Cl) 3440(OH) and 1712cm^{-1} (C=O).

^{1}H NMR:
($CDCl_3$) 0.80(1H, s, H-14); 1.35(3H, d, *J*=6.5 Hz, H-14'); 1.70(3H, s, H-16); 1.92(2H, m, H-7); 2.01(2H, m, H-8); 2.18(1H, dt, *J*=5.0 and 15.2Hz, H-3β); 2.45(1H, dd, *J*=8.0 and 15.2Hz, H-3α); 2.30(1H, m, H-4'A); 4.15(1H, bd, *J*=14.1Hz, H-4'B); 2.80 and 3.12(1H each, AB, *J*=4.0Hz, H-13); 3.57(1H, d, *J*=5.0Hz, H-11); 3.80(1H, d, *J*=5.0Hz, H-2); 3.83(2H, m, H-5'); 3.95(1H, q, *J*=6.5Hz, H-13'); 3.85 and 4.55(1H each, AB, *J*=12.5 Hz, H-15); 4.65(1H, s, H-12'); 5.41(1H, d, *J*=5.0Hz, H-10); 5.70(1H, d, *J*=17.0Hz, H-7'); 5.90(1H, d, *J*=11.4Hz, H-10'); 5.87(1H, dd, *J*=4.5 and 8.0Hz, H-4); 6.10(1H, s, H-2'); 6.52(1H, t, *J*=11.4Hz, H-9'); and 7.45ppm (1H, dd, *J*=11.4 and 17.0Hz, H-8').

^{13}C NMR:
($CDCl_3$) 79.2, C-2; 34.5, C-3; 74.1, C-4; 49.0, C-5; 43.4, C-6; 20.3, C-7; 27.7, C-8; 140.3, C-9; 119.0, C-10; 68.2, C-11; 65.5, C-12; 48.0, C-13; 7.5, C-14; 63.9, C-15; 23.3, C-16; 166.8, C-1'; 112.9, C-2'; 158.4, C-3'; 29.3, C-4'; 60.5, C-5'; 80.6, C-6'; 133.8, C-7'; 134.5, C-8'; 142.5, C-9'; 120.6, C-10'; 166.8, C-11'; 73.8, C-12'; 71.6, C-13'; and 17.3ppm, C-14'.

Mass Spectrum:
HREIMS: 528.2374m/e for $C_{29}H_{36}O_9$; calcd 528.2359.

References

B. B. Jarvis; Macrocyclic Trichothecenes; In Mycotoxins and Phytoalexins; R. P. Sharma and D. K. Salunkhe, eds.; CRC Press, Boca Raton, Florida, pp. 361-421(1991).

B. B. Jarvis, J. Salemme and A. Morais; *Stachybotrys* Toxins 1; Natural Toxins, Vol. 3, pp. 10-16(1995).

Common/Systematic Name

12'-Hydroxy-2'-isoverrucarin J
PD 113,325

Molecular Formula/Molecular Weight

$C_{27}H_{32}O_9$; MW = 500.20463

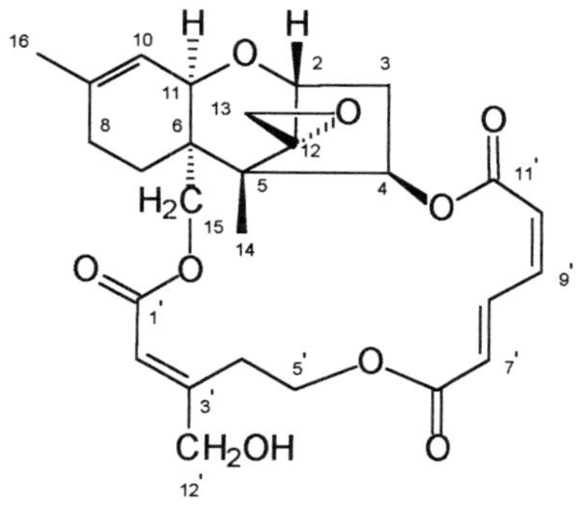

General Characteristics

Crystals; mp., >250°C.

Plant Source

Myrothecium roridum (ATCC 20605).

Isolation/Purification

A large scale submerged fermentation was extracted (ethyl acetate) and concentration of the organic layer gave 650g of gum. Large scale preparative HPLC of 118g of this gum over silica gel (Prep-500) gave 18 fractions. A portion (7.2g) from the 25% ethyl acetate-methylene chloride fraction (12g) was further chromatographed (MPLC, isopropanol-hexane) to give a fraction (1.37g) from which 568mg of 12'-hydroxy-2'-isoverrucarin J was crystallized (methylene chloride-cyclohexane).

Biological Activity

In vivo P388 mouse anti-leukemic activity: T/C x 100 at 5mg/kg = 129. Cytotoxic and skin irritant.

Spectral Data

UV:

λ_{max}^{MeOH} 217(ϵ = 23,500) and 262nm (18,900).

IR:

($CHCl_3$) 3640, 2980, 2920, 1745, 1660, 1270, 1210, and 1190cm^{-1}.

^{1}H NMR:

($CDCl_3$) 0.64(1H, s, H-14); 1.72(3H, s, H-16); 1.95(2H, m, H-7); ~2.05(2H, m H- 8); 2.19(1H, dt, *J*=6 and 17Hz, H-3β); 2.45(1H, dd, *J*=8 and 17Hz, H-3α); 2.3(1H, m, H-4'A); 4.14(1H, m, H-4'B); 2.83 and 3.14(1H each, AB, *J*=4Hz, H-13); 3.7(1H, d, *J*=5 Hz, H-11); 3.86(1H, d, *J*=6Hz, H-2); 4.20 and 4.27(1H each, AB, *J*=16Hz, H-12'); ~4.47(2H, m, H-5'); 3.7 and 5.07(1H each, AB, *J*=12Hz, H-15); 5.44(1H, dd, *J*=5 and 2Hz, H-10); 5.9(1H, d, *J*=16Hz, H-7'); 5.98(1H, dd, *J*=4 and 8Hz, H- 4); 6.10(1H, d, *J*=11Hz, H-10'); 6.1(1H, d, *J*=2 Hz, H-2'); 6.65(1H, t, *J*=11Hz, H- 9'); and 8.2ppm (1H, dd, *J*=11 and 16Hz, H-8').

^{13}C NMR:

79.2, C-2; 34.9, C-3; 75.2, C-4; 49.4, C-5; 43.7, C-6; 20.7, C-7; 26.9, C-8; 143.3, C-9; 118.3, C-10; 67.3, C-11; 65.2, C-12; 48.1, C-13; 7.0, C-14; 62.7, C-15; 23.2, C-16; 165.3, C-1'; 116.7, C-2'; 157.4, C-3'; 28.1, C-4'; 61.8, C-5'; 165.9, C-6'; 127.3, C-7'; 139.4, C-8'; 140.0, C-9'; 125.0, C-10'; 166.1, C-11'; and 64.4ppm, C-12'.

Reference

T. A. Smitka, R. H. Bunge, R. J. Bloem, and J. C. French; Two New Trichothecenes, PD 113,325 and PD 113,326; J. Antibiotics, Vol. 37, pp. 823-828(1984).

Common/Systematic Name

M-Isosatratoxin H; PD 113,326

Molecular Formula/Molecular Weight

$C_{29}H_{36}O_9$; MW = 528.23593

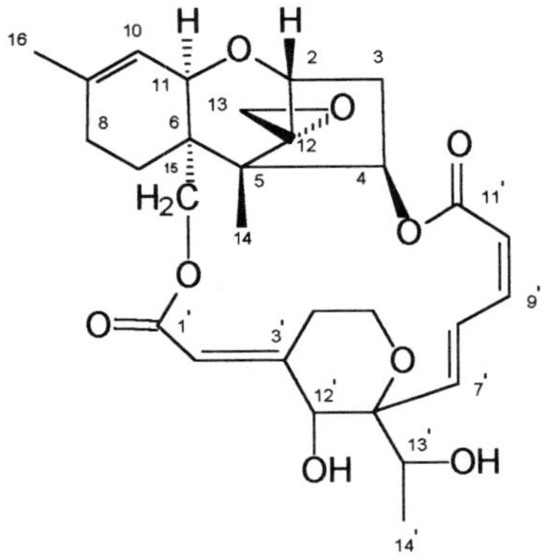

General Characteristics

Crystals mp., 168-171°C.

Fungal source

Myrothecium roridum (ATCC 20605).

Isolation/Purification

A large scale submerged fermentation of *M. roridum* was extracted with ethyl acetate. Concentration of the organic layer gave 650g of gum. Large scale preparative HPLC of 118g of this gum over silica gel (Prep-500, Waters Assoc.) gave 18 fractions. A portion (7.2g) from the 25% ethyl acetate-methylene chloride fraction was further chromatographed (MPLC, isopropanol-hexane) to give a fraction rich in *M*-isosatratoxin H. This fraction was further purified by reversed phase HPLC (C_{18}, water-acetonitrile) to give, after crystallization from methylene chloride-cyclohexane, 139mg of *M*-isosatratoxin H.

Biological Activity

In vivo P388 mouse anti-leukemic activity: T/C x 100 at 5mg/kg = 198. Cytotoxic and skin irritant.

Spectral Data

UV:

λ_{max}^{MeOH} 227(ϵ = 19,500) and 255nm (12,500).

IR:

($CHCl_3$) 3560, 3440, 2975, 2930, 1730, 1660, 1595, 1195, 1165, 1145, 1080, and 970cm^{-1}.

^{1}H NMR:

($CDCl_3$) 0.83(1H, s, H-14); 1.35(3H, d, *J*=7Hz, H-14'); 1.72(3H, s, H-16); 1.92(2H, m, H-7); ~2(2H, m H-8); 2.18(1H, dt, *J*=5 and 15Hz, H-3β); 2.45(1H, dd, *J*=8 and 15Hz, H-3α); 2.7(1H, m, H-4'A); 3.78(1H, m, H-4'B); 2.83 and 3.14(1H each, AB, *J*=4 z, H-13); 3.59(1H, d, *J*=5Hz, H-11); 3.9(1H, m, H-2); 3.9(2H, m, H-5'); 4.0(1H, q, *J*=6.5Hz, H-13'); 4.22(1H, s, H-12'); 4.54 and 5.10(1H each, AB, *J*=13Hz, H-15); 5.39(1H, d, *J*=17Hz, H-7'); 5.43(1H, d, *J*=5 Hz, H-10); 5.93(1H, d, *J*=12Hz, H-10'); 5.9(1H, m, H-4); 5.80(1H, d, *J*=2Hz, H-2'); 6.52(1H, dd, *J*=10 and 12Hz, H-9'); and 7.26ppm (1H, dd, *J*=10 and 17Hz, H-8').

^{13}C NMR:

79.1, C-2; 34.5, C-3; 74.2, C-4; 49.0, C-5; 43.4, C-6; 20.3, C-7; 27.6, C-8; 140.4, C-9; 118.9, C-10; 68.2, C-11; 65.5, C-12; 48.1, C-13; 7.5, C-14; 64.0, C-15; 23.3, C-16; 165.4, C-1'; 118.2, C-2'; 154.9, C-3'; 25.5, C-4'; 61.1, C-5'; 78.7, C-6'; 133.6, C-7'; 134.2, C-8'; 142.4, C-9'; 121.0, C-10'; 166.7, C-11'; 75.4, C-12'; 74.7, C-13'; and 15.8ppm, C-14'.

Reference

T. A. Smitka, R. H. Bunge, R. J. Bloem, and J. C. French; Two New Trichothecenes, PD 113,325 and PD 113,326; J. Antibiotics, Vol. 37, pp. 823-828(1984).

Common/Systematic Name
Vertisporin

Molecular Formula/Molecular Weight
$C_{29}H_{36}O_{10}$; MW = 544.23085

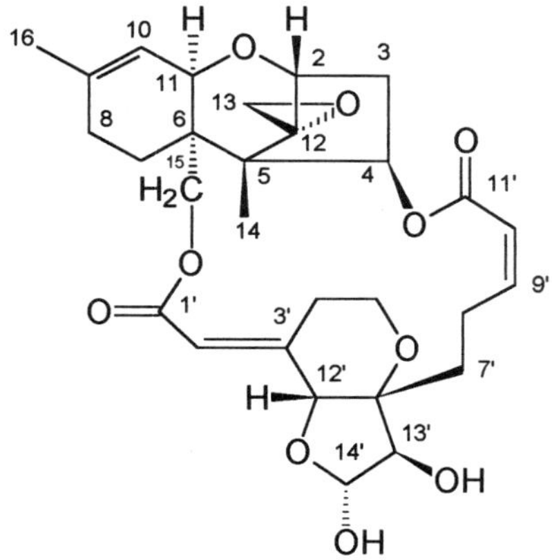

General Characteristics
A colorless amorphous powder; mp., 176-183°C; $[\alpha]_D^{26}$ + 62.5°; diacetate; mp., 145-155°C.

Fungal Source
Verticimonosporium diffractum.

Biological Activity
Cytotoxic and antibiotic activity: ED_{50} to HeLa cells was 0.001mg/ml; limited antifungal activity against *Trichophyton asteroides*.

Spectral Data

UV:
λ_{max}^{EtOH} 216nm (ϵ=19,500).

IR:
($CHCl_3$) 1723 and 1711cm^{-1}.

^1H NMR: (diacetate derivative)
(C_6D_6) 3.82(H-2); 5.80(H-4); 5.40(H-10); 3.57(H-11); 2.77(H-13a); 3.09(H-13b); 0.80(H-14); 3.97(H-15a); 4.24(H-15b); 1.70(H-16); 5.81(H-2'); 6.41(H-9'); 5.82(H-10'); 4.19(H-12'); 5.10(H-13'); and 6.61ppm (H-14').

^{13}C NMR:

($CDCl_3$) 79.0, C-2; 35.0, C-3; 74.0, C-4; 49.7, C-5; 43.2, C-6; 20.7, C-7; 27.7, C-8; 138.4, C-9; 119.9, C-10; 67.6, C-11; 65.3, C-12; 47.2, C-13; 8.0, C-14; 64.7, C-15; 23.0, C-16; 165.7, C-1'; 118.5, C-2'; 152.6, C-3'; 22.8, C-4'; 64.9, C-5'; 86.7, C-6'; 23.6, C-7'; 26.4, C-8'; 149.4, C-9'; 121.1, C-10'; 166.0, C-11'; 86.0, C-12'; 75.7, C-13'; and 97.5ppm, C-14'.

References

R. J. Cole and R. H. Cox; Handbook of Toxic Fungal Metabolites; Academic Press, New York, p. 241 (1981).

0

B. B. Jarvis; Macrocyclic Trichothecenes; In Mycotoxins and Phytoalexins; R. P. Sharma and D. K. Salunkhe, eds.; CRC Press, Boca Raton, Florida, pp. 361-421(1991).

H. Minato, T. Katayama, and K. Toni: Vertisporin, A New Antibiotic from *Verticimonosporim diffractum*; Tetrahedron Lett., Vol. 16, pp. 2579-2582 (1975)

17

Miotoxins

Miotoxin A
Miotoxin A 13' β-D-glucoside
Miotoxin B
Miotoxin C
Miotoxin D
Isomiotoxin D
Miotoxin E
Miotoxin F
Miotoxin G

Common/Systematic Name

Miotoxin A

Molecular Formula/Molecular Weight

$C_{29}H_{38}O_9$; MW = 530.25158

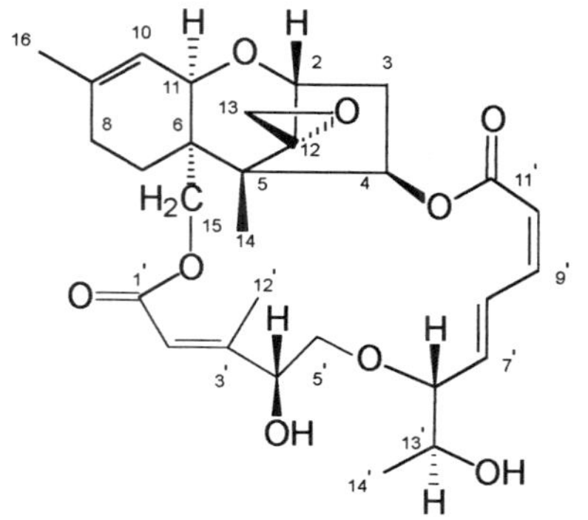

General Characteristics

Crystals mp., 159-161°C; $[\alpha]_D$ = +100.0° (*c*=1.40, in CH_2Cl_2). R_f=0.52 (CH_3-MeOH, 100:4) and 0.66 (ethyl acetate).

Plant Source

Baccharis coridifolia.

Isolation/Purification

Inflorescences and seeds of *B. coridifolia* were extracted with $CHCl_3$ and the extract flash chromatographed over silica gel. Repeated flash chromatography followed by PTLC led to the isolation of miotoxins A-D and *iso*-miotoxin D.

Spectral Data

UV:

λ_{max}^{EtOH} 220 and 263nm.

IR:

(KBr) 3410, 2960, 1710, 1635, 1220, and 1185cm^{-1}.

^{1}H NMR:

($CDCl_3$) 0.78(3H, s, H-14); 1.20(3H, d, *J*=6.0Hz, H-14'); 1.71(3H, s, H-16); 2.01(2H, m, H-7); 2.03(2H, m, H-8); 2.10(1H, ddd, no *J* values given, H-3β); 2.30(3H, d, *J*=1.5Hz, H-12'); 2.51(1H, d, *J*=8Hz, H-3α); 2.81, 3.13(1H each, AB pattern, *J*=4Hz, H-13); 3.72(1H, d, *J*=6.7Hz, H-5'); 3.74(1H, t, *J*=7Hz, H-6'); 3.84(1H, m, H-11); 4.32(1H, br s, H-4'); 3.84(1H, d, no *J* value given, H-2); 3.93, 4.38(1H each,

AB pattern, J=12Hz, H-15); 3.74(1H, t, J=7Hz, H-6'); 5.47(1H, d, J=5Hz, H-10); 5.75(1H, d, J=11Hz, H-10'); 5.88(1H, dd, J=3 and 16Hz, H-7'); 6.07(1H, d, J=1.5Hz H-2'); 6.11(1H, dd, J=4 and 8Hz, H-4); 6.55(1H, dd, $J_{8',9'}=J_{9',10'}$=11Hz, H- 9'); and 7.43ppm (1H, dd, J=11 and 16Hz, H-8').

^{13}C NMR:

($CDCl_3$) 79.1, C-2; 35.6, C-3; 74.4, C-4; 48.6, C-5; 42.8, C-6; 21.3, C-7; 27.7, C-8; 140.1, C-9; 118.9, C-10; 67.2, C-11; 65.5, C-12; 48.0, C-13; 6.7, C-14; 63.7, C-15; 23.2, C-16; 165.9, C-1'; 115.2, C-2'; 160.0, C-3'; 74.4, C-4'; 73.7, C-5'; 83.9, C-6'; 137.5, C-7'; 126.8, C-8'; 143.3, C-9'; 118.0, C-10'; 166.4, C-11'; 15.8, C-12'; 70.8, C-13'; and 18.6ppm C-14'.

Reference

G. G. Habermehl, L. Busam, and J. Stegemann; Miotoxin-A: A Novel Macrocyclic Trichothecene from the Brazilian Plant *Baccharis coridifolia*; Z. Naturforsch., Vol. 39c, pp.212-216(1983).

Common/Systematic Name

Miotoxin A 13' β-D-glucoside

Molecular Formula/Molecular Weight

$C_{35}H_{48}O_{14}$; MW = 692.30441

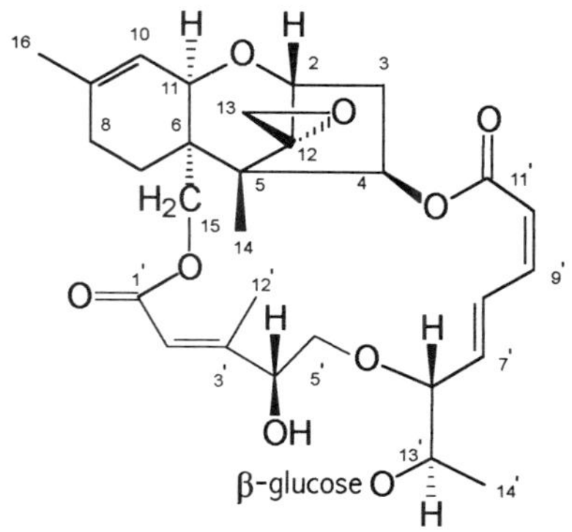

General Characteristics

An oil; $[\alpha]_D$ + 5° (*c*=1.13, in $CHCl_3$).

Plant Source

Female *Baccharis coridifolia*.

Isolation/Purification

Fraction D from a reversed phase filtration chromatography (see isolation of roridin E glucoside) was subjected to CCC (Vc = 355mL) with a solvent system of methanol-water-chloroform-carbon tetrachloride-hexane (6:4:6:1:3, v/v/v/v/v). The lower organic phase was the mobile phase and the flow rate was 1.8ml/min to yield roridin A glucoside and a fraction containing miotoxin A glucoside, which was further purified on C_{18} reversed phase HPLC (250 x 10mm, 60% methanol-water, 4.0mL/min) to give miotoxin A β-D-glucoside

Biological Activity

Cytotoxic: IC_{85} ca. 1 ng/ml.

Spectral Data

IR:

(KBr) 3431, 1712, 1650, 1600, 1181, and 1081cm^{-1}.

^{1}H NMR:

(pyridine-*d*5) 7.73(1H, dd, *J*=12.0, 15.6Hz, H-8'); 6.51(1H, dd, *J*=11.1, 12.0Hz, H-9'); 6.35(1H, dd, *J*=2.9, 15.6Hz, H-7'); 6.18(1H, s, H-2'); 6.10(1H, dd, *J*= 4.2, 8.1Hz, H-4);

5.76(1H, d, *J*=11.1Hz, H-10'); 5.48(1H, d, *J*=4.5Hz, H-10); 4.90 and 4.06(1H each, AB, *J*=12.5Hz, H-15); 4.89(1H, d, *J*=7.7Hz, H-1"); 4.62(1H, m, H-6'); 4.52(1H, m, H-6"B); 4.51(1H, m, H-4'); 4.39(1H, dq, *J*=6.3, 6.3Hz, H-13'); 4.37(1H, m, H-6"A); 4.26(1H, dd, *J*=8.5, 9.6Hz, H-4"); 4.23(1H, dd, *J*=8.5, 9.6Hz, H-3"); 4.01(1H, dd, *J*=7.7, 8.5Hz, H-2"); 3.95(2H, m, H-5'B, H-5"); 3.91(1H, d, *J*=5.1Hz, H-2); 3.76(1H, dd, *J*=4.3, 8.1Hz, H-5'A); 3.72(1H, d, *J*=5.0Hz, H-11); 3.08 and 2.84(1H each, AB, *J*=4.1Hz, H-13); 2.72(3H, s, H-12'); 2.42(1H, dd, *J*=8.1, 15.1Hz, H-3); 2.22(1H, ddd, *J*=4.2, 5.1, 15.1Hz, H-3); 1.86-1.93(4H, m, H-7, H-8); 1.56(3H, s, H-16); 1.11(3H, d, *J*=6.3Hz, H-14'); and 1.09ppm (3H, s, H-14).

^{13}C NMR:

(pyridine-*d*5) 79.2, C-2; 35.2, C-3; 74.9, C-4; 49.4, C-5; 43.6, C-6; 20.7, C-7; 27.7, C-8; 139.0, C-9; 120.1, C-10; 67.7, C-11; 66.0, C-12; 47.8, C-13; 7.5, C-14; 63.7, C-15; 23.1, C-16; 166.7, C-1'; 116.9, C-2'; 161.7, C-3'; 75.5, C-4'; 72.9, C-5'; 81.3, C-6'; 141.3, C-7'; 126.7, C-8'; 144.7, C-9'; 116.9, C-10'; 166.7, C-11'; 14.2, C-12'; 75.7, C-13'; 14.6, C-14'; 104.1, C-1"; 75.2, C-2"; 78.5, C-3"; 71.5, C-4"; 78.5, C-5"; and 62.7ppm, C-6".

Reference

B. B. Jarvis, S. Wang, C. Cox, M. M. Rao, V. Philip, M. S. Varaschin, and C. S. Barros; Brazilian *Baccharis* toxins: Livestock Poisoning and the Isolation of Macrocyclic Trichothecene Glucosides; Natural Toxins, Vol. 4, pp. 58-71(1996).

Common/Systematic Name
Miotoxin B

Molecular Formula/Molecular Weight
$C_{29}H_{38}O_9$; MW = 530.25158

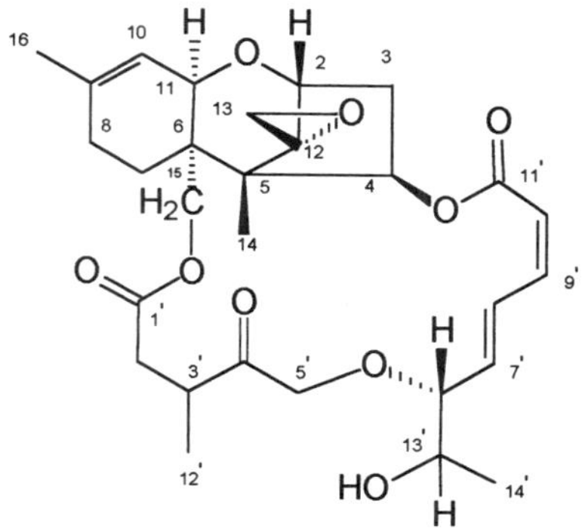

General Characteristics
Amorphous solid; R_f=0.45 (chloroform-methanol, 100:6) and 0.38 (ethyl acetate-hexane; 3:1, v/v).

Plant Source
Baccharis coridifolia.

Isolation/Purification
Inflorescences and seeds of *B. coridifolia* were extracted with $CHCl_3$ and the extract flash chromatographed over silica gel. Repeated flash chromatography followed by PTLC led to the isolation of miotoxins A-D and *iso*-miotoxin D.

Spectral Data

UV:
λ_{max}^{EtOH} 252nm (log ϵ=3.9).

IR:
(KBr) 3460, 2960, 1725, 1680, 1630, 1590cm^{-1}.

^{1}H NMR:
($CDCl_3$) 0.77(3H, s, H-14); 1.17(3H, d, *J*=6Hz, H-14'); 1.19(3H, d, *J*=7Hz, H-12'); 1.75(3H, s, H-16); 1.84(2H, m, H-7); 1.95(2H, m, H-8); 2.09(1H, dt, *J*=5 and 15Hz, H-3β); 2.31(1H, dd, *J*=5 and 17Hz, H-3α); 2.60, 2.98(1H each, d of AB, *J*=8 and 15Hz, H-2'); 2.83, 3.14(1H each, AB pattern, *J*=4Hz, H-13); 3.38(1H, m, H- 3'); 4.26(2H, AB, *J*=18Hz, H-5'); 3.79(2H, m, H-6' and H-13'); 3.70(1H, d, *J*=6Hz, H-11);

3.51(1H, d, J=5Hz, H-2); 3.73, 4.78(1H each, AB pattern, J=12Hz, H-15); 3.79(1H, m, H-6'); 5.44(1H, d, J=6Hz, H-10); 5.58(1H, dd, J=4.5 and 8Hz, H-4); 5.80(1H, d, J=11Hz, H-10'); 5.87(1H, dd, J=6 and 15Hz, H-7'); 6.61(1H, dd, $J_{8',9'}$=$J_{9',10'}$=11Hz, H-9'); and 7.52ppm (1H, m, H-8').

^{13}C NMR:

($CDCl_3$) 79.0, C-2; 36.5, C-3; 76.1, C-4; 48.9, C-5; 43.9, C-6; 20.6, C-7; 28.0, C-8; 141.0, C-9; 119.7, C-10; 67.3, C-11; 65.3, C-12; 48.0, C-13; 7.5, C-14; 63.0, C-15; 23.2, C-16; 172.1, C-1'; 37.1, C-2'; 38.1, C-3'; 211.1, C-4'; 73.2, C-5'; 85.1, C-6'; 136.2, C-7'; 129.8, C-8'; 141.5, C-9'; 118.3, C-10'; 166.5, C-11'; 18.7, C-12'; 70.2, C-13'; and 16.8ppm C-14'.

References

G. G. Habermehl, L. Busam, P. Heydel, D. Mebs, C. H. Tokarnia, J. Dobereiner, and M. Spraul; Macrocyclic Trichothecenes: Cause of Livestock Poisoning by the Brazilian Plant *Baccharis coridifolia*; Toxicon, Vol. 23, pp. 731-745(1985).

G. G. Habermehl and L. Busam; Miotoxins B and C, Two New Macrocyclic Trichothecenes from *Baccharis coridifolia* DC; Liebigs Ann. Chem., pp. 1746-1754(1984).

Common/Systematic Name

Miotoxin C

Molecular Formula/Molecular Weight

$C_{31}H_{42}O_{11}$; MW = 590.27271

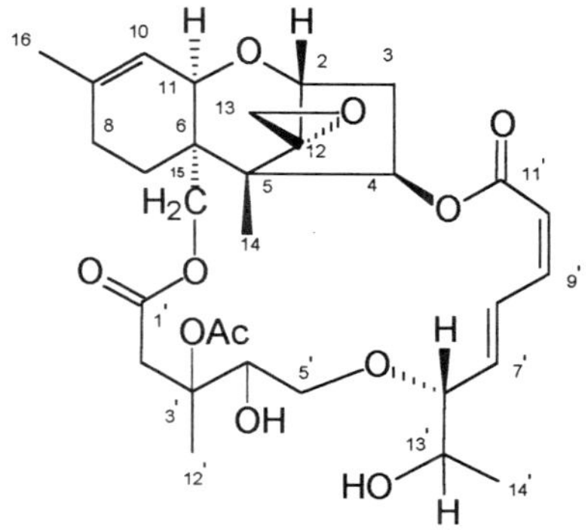

General Characteristics

Amorphous solid; R_f=0.45 (chloroform-methanol, 100:6) and 0.30 (ethyl acetate-hexane; 3:1, v/v).

Plant Source

Baccharis coridifolia.

Isolation/Purification

Inflorescences and seeds of *B. coridifolia* were extracted with $CHCl_3$ and the extract flash chromatographed over silica gel. Repeated flash chromatography followed by PTLC led to the isolation of miotoxins A-D and *iso*-miotoxin D.

Spectral Data

UV:

λ_{max}^{EtOH} 271nm (log ϵ=4.2).

IR:

(KBr) 3400, 2960, 1735, 1712, 1630, 1590cm^{-1}.

^{1}H NMR:

($CDCl_3$) 0.79(3H, s, H-14); 1.27(3H, d, *J*=6Hz, H-14'); 1.20(3H, s, H-12'); 1.76(3H, s, H-16); 1.85-2.12(4H, m, H-7 and H-8); 2.09(3H, s, acetate); 2.22(1H, dt, *J*=5 and 15Hz, H-3β); 2.49(1H, dd, *J*=8 and 17Hz, H-3α); 2.49, 2.67(1H each, AB, *J*=5Hz, H-2'); 2.86, 3.18(1H each, AB pattern, *J*=4Hz, H-13); 3.60(2H, m, H-5'); 4.05(1H, m, H-6'); 3.83(1H, br s, H-2); 3.90(1H, d, *J*=5Hz, H-11); 4.08, 4.55(1H each, AB pattern,

J=12Hz, H-15); 5.47(1H, d, *J*=5Hz, H-10); 5.88(1H, dd, *J*=4.5 and 8Hz, H-4); 5.86(1H, d, *J*=11Hz, H-10'); 5.91(1H, dd, *J*=3 and 16Hz, H-7'); 6.74(1H, dd, $J_{8',9'}=J_{9',10'}$=11Hz, H-9'); and 7.65ppm (1H, m, H-8').

^{13}C NMR:

($CDCl_3$) 79.0, C-2; 34.9, C-3; 74.4, C-4; 49.1, C-5; 43.4, C-6; 21.1, C-7; 27.7, C-8; 140.7, C-9; 118.4, C-10; 67.2, C-11; 65.2, C-12; 47.9, C-13; 7.1, C-14; 64.0, C-15; 23.2, C-16; 171.6, C-1'; 43.4, C-2'; 72.2, C-3'; 74.2, C-4'; 72.1, C-5'; 80.8, C-6'; 137.8, C-7'; 126.9, C-8'; 143.7, C-9'; 117.5, C-10'; 166.6, C-11'; 23.2, C-12'; 71.2, C-13'; 15.4, C-14'; 170.3(acetate C=O), and 20.5ppm (acetate Me).

References

G. G. Habermehl, L. Busam, P. Heydel, D. Mebs, C. H. Tokarnia, J. Dobereiner, and M. Spraul; Macrocyclic Trichothecenes: Cause of Livestock Poisoning by the Brazilian Plant *Baccharis coridifolia*; Toxicon, Vol. 23, pp. 731-745(1985).

G. G. Habermehl and L. Busam; Miotoxins B and C, Two New Macrocyclic Trichothecenes from *Baccharis coridifolia* DC; Liebigs Ann. Chem., pp. 1746-1754(1984).

Common/Systematic Name
Miotoxin D

Molecular Formula/Molecular Weight
$C_{29}H_{40}O_9$; MW = 532.26723

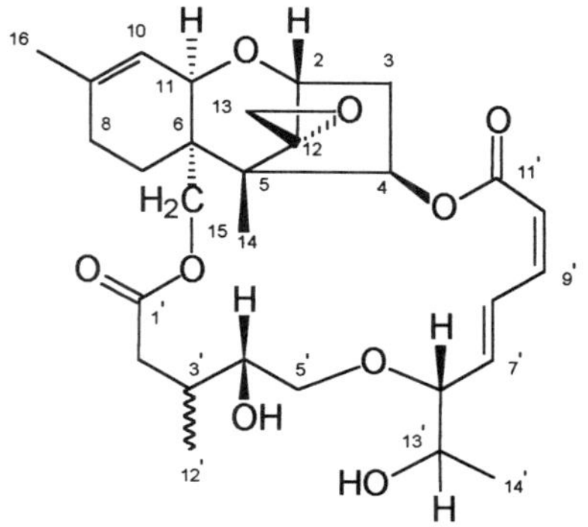

General Characteristics
Amorphous solid. R_f=0.56 (chloroform-methanol, 100:4) and 0.71 (ethyl acetate).

Plant Source
Baccharis coridifolia.

Isolation/Purification
Inflorescences and seeds of *B. coridifolia* were extracted with $CHCl_3$ and the extract flash chromatographed over silica gel. Repeated flash chromatography followed by PTLC led to the isolation of miotoxins A-D and *iso*-miotoxin D.

Spectral Data

IR:
(KBr) 3420, 1730, 1710, 1640, and 1600cm^{-1}.

^{1}H NMR:
($CDCl_3$) 0.77(3H, s, H-14); 0.98(3H, d, *J*=7Hz, H-12'); 1.20(3H, d, *J*=6Hz, H- 14'); 1.71(3H, s, H-16); 1.82-2.04(4H, m, H-7 and H-8); 2.16(1H, dt, *J*=5 and 15Hz, H-3β); 2.23-2.39(3H, m, H-2' and H-3'); 2.44(1H, dd, *J*=8 and 15Hz, H-3α); 2.81, 3.13(1H each, AB pattern, *J*=4Hz, H-13); 3.4-3.6(2H, m, H-5'); 3.70(1H, m, H-6'); 3.6(1H, m, H-11); 3.90, 3.84(1H, m, H-2); 3.90(1H, m, H-4'); 4.62(1H each, AB pattern, *J*=12Hz, H-15); 5.43(1H, dd, *J*=1.1 and 5Hz, H-10); 5.84(1H, dd, *J*=5.0, 8.0Hz, H-4); 5.77(1H, d, *J*=11Hz, H-10'); 6.0(1H, dd, *J*=3 and 16Hz, H-7'); 6.65(1H, dd, $J_{8',9'}=J_{9',10'}$=11Hz, H-9'); and 7.75ppm (1H, m, 8'-H).

^{13}C NMR:
($CDCl_3$) 79.2, C-2; 35.1, C-3; 74.5, C-4; 49.2, C-5; 43.5, C-6; 20.6, C-7; 27.9, C-8; 140.7, C-9; 118.6, C-10; 67.5, C-11; 65.4, C-12; 48.0, C-13; 7.2, C-14; 63.8, C-15; 23.3, C-16; 172.7, C-1'; 37.5, C-2'; 32.9, C-3'; 73.5, C-4'; 71.7, C-5'; 84.8, C-6'; 138.8, C-7'; 126.9, C-8'; 144.0, C-9'; 117.7, C-10'; 166.6, C-11'; 16.1, C-12'; 70.9, C-13'; and 18.5ppm C-14'.

References

G. G. Habermehl, L. Busam, P. Heydel, D. Mebs, C. H. Tokarnia, J. Dobereiner, and M. Spraul; Macrocyclic Trichothecenes: Cause of Livestock Poisoning by the Brazilian Plant *Baccharis coridifolia*; Toxicon, Vol. 23, pp. 731-745(1985).

G. G. Habermehl, L. Busam, and M. Spraul; Miotoxin D and *iso*-Miotoxin D, Two New Macrocyclic Trichothecene from *Baccharis coridifolia* DC; Liebigs Ann. Chem., pp. 633-639(1985).

Common/Systematic Name

Isomiotoxin D

Molecular Formula/Molecular Weight

$C_{29}H_{40}O_9$; MW = 532.26723

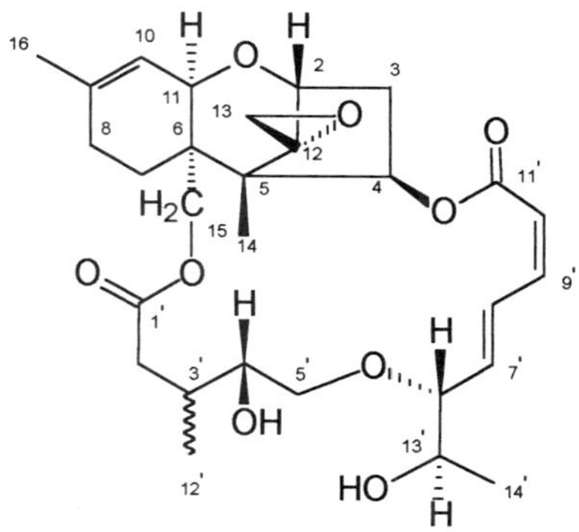

General Characteristics

Amorphous solid. R_f=0.56 (chloroform-methanol, 100:4) and 0.65 (ethyl acetate).

Plant Source

Baccharis coridifolia.

Isolation/Purification

Inflorescences and seeds of *B. coridifolia* were extracted with $CHCl_3$ and the extract flash chromatographed over silica gel. Repeated flash chromatography followed by PTLC led to the isolation of miotoxins A-D and isomiotoxin D.

Spectral Data

IR:

(KBr) 3460, 1725, 1710, 1640, and 1600cm^{-1}.

^{1}H NMR:

($CDCl_3$) 0.77(3H, s, H-14); 0.98(3H, d, *J*=7Hz, H-12'); 1.20(3H, d, *J*=6Hz, H- 14'); 1.71(3H, s, H-16); 1.84-2.04(4H, m, H-7 and H-8); 2.14-2.22(1H, m, H- 3β); 2.38-2.49(4H, m, H-3α, H-2', and H-3'); 2.81, 3.12(1H each, AB pattern, *J*=4Hz, H-13); 3.57-3.70(2H, m, H-5'); 3.57-3.70(1H, m, H-11); 3.90, 3.84(1H, m, H-2); 3.74-3.79(2H, m, H-4' and 6'); 4.62(1H each, AB pattern, *J*=12Hz, H-15); 5.42(1H, dd, *J*=1.2 and 5Hz, H-10); 5.80-5.82(1H, m, H-4); 5.79(1H, d, *J*=11Hz, H-10'); 6.04(1H, dd, *J*=3 and 16Hz, H-7'); 6.66(1H, dd, $J_{8',9'}$=$J_{9',10'}$=11Hz, H- 9'); and 7.81ppm (1H, m, H-8').

^{13}C NMR:
($CDCl_3$) 79.2, C-2; 35.0, C-3; 74.7, C-4; 49.3, C-5; 43.5, C-6; 20.6, C-7; 27.9, C-8; 140.8, C-9; 118.6, C-10; 67.5, C-11; 65.4, C-12; 47.9, C-13; 7.0, C-14; 63.6, C-15; 23.3, C-16; 172.7, C-1'; 38.3, C-2'; 32.4, C-3'; 73.0, C-4'; 74.7, C-5'; 86.0, C-6'; 139.5, C-7'; 126.7, C-8'; 143.8, C-9'; 117.9, C-10'; 166.8, C-11'; 14.7, C-12'; 71.0, C-13'; and 18.6ppm C-14'.

References

G. G. Habermehl, L. Busam, P. Heydel, D. Mebs, C. H. Tokarnia, J. Dobereiner, and M. Spraul; Macrocyclic Trichothecenes: Cause of Livestock Poisoning by the Brazilian Plant *Baccharis coridifolia*; Toxicon, Vol. 23, pp. 731-745(1985).

G. G. Habermehl, L. Busam, and M. Spraul; Miotoxin D and *iso*-Miotoxin D, Two New Macrocyclic Trichothecene from *Baccharis coridifolia* DC; Liebigs Ann. Chem., pp. 633-639(1985).

Common/Systematic Name
Miotoxin E

Molecular Formula/Molecular Weight
$C_{29}H_{38}O_{10}$; MW = 546.24650

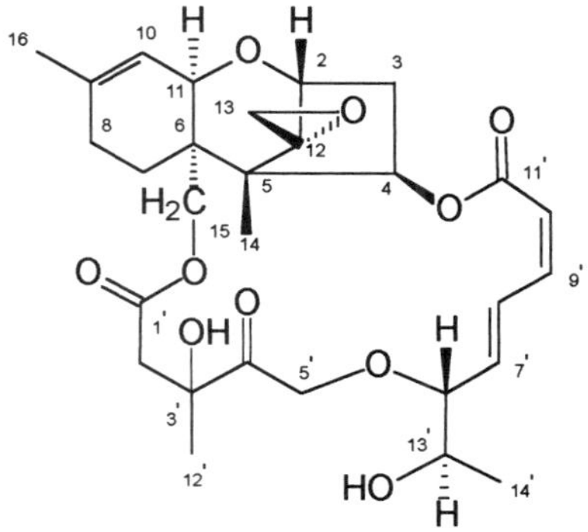

General Characteristics
An oil; $[\alpha]_D$ -25° (c=0.40, in $CHCl_3$).

Plant Source
Female *Baccharis coridifolia*.

Isolation/Purification
The 70-100% ethyl acetate in hexane and 10% methanol-methylene chloride fractions from the initial column chromatography of the crude extract (see description under verrucarin A β-glucoside) were subjected to flash chromatography (silica, 80g, methanol-methylene chloride) to yield various trichothecene-containing fractions which were combined, based on TLC analysis, and subjected to further chromatographic procedures including preparative TLC, filtration reversed phase chromatography, preparative HPLC, and countercurrent chromatography (CCC). From these operations were isolated miotoxins E, F, and G.

Spectral Data

IR:
($CHCl_3$) 3493, 1743,1706, 1637, 1600, 1175, 1081 cm^{-1}.

^1H NMR:
($CDCl_3$) 7.57(dd, 1H, J=11.5, 15.5Hz, H-8'), 6.60(dd, 1H, J=11.5, 11.5Hz, H-9'), 5.80(dd, 1H, J=5.7, 15.5Hz, H-7'), 5.76(d, 1H, J=11.5Hz, H-10'), 5.53(dd, 1H, J=4.5, 8.0Hz, H-4), 5.39(br d, 1H, J=5.0Hz, H-10), 5.09 and 3.47(AB, 1H each, J=12.3Hz, H-15), 4.72 and 4.42(AB, 1H each, J=18.4Hz, H-5'), 3.79(d, 1H, J=4.8Hz, H-2),

3.73(m, 2H, H-6', H-13'), 3.53(br d, 1H, *J*=5.0Hz, H-11), 3.11 and 2.80(AB, 1H each, *J*=4.0Hz, H-13), 2.94 and 2.59(AB, 1H each, *J*=17.6Hz, H-2'), 2.57(dd, 1H, *J*=8.0, 15.4Hz, H-3a), 2.07(ddd, 1H, *J*=4.5, 4.8, 15.4Hz, H-3b), 1.80-2.00(m, 4H, H-7, H-8), 1.71(s, 3H, H-16), 1.27(s, 3H, H-12')1.15(d, 3H, *J*=5.9Hz, H-14'), and 0.71ppm (s, 3H, H-14).

^{13}C NMR:

($CDCl_3$) 79.0, C-2; 36.7, C-3; 76.4, C-4; 48.8, C-5; 44.0, C-6; 20.5, C-7; 28.0, C-8; 141.3, C-9; 119.6, C-10; 67.2, C-11; 65.1, C-12; 48.0, C-13; 7.5, C-14; 63.6, C-15; 23.2, C-16; 172.3, C-1'; 43.0, C-2'; 77.0, C-3'; 211.0, C-4'; 69.2, C-5'; 85.7, C-6'; 135.9, C-7'; 130.7, C-8'; 141.6, C-9'; 118.0, C-10'; 166.4, C-11'; 26.0, C-12'; 70.2, C-13'; and 18.7ppm, C-14'.

Reference

B. B. Jarvis, S. Wang, C. Cox, M. M. Rao, V. Philip, M. S. Varaschin, and C. S. Barros; Brazilian *Baccharis* toxins: livestock poisoning and the isolation of macrocyclic trichothecene glucosides; *Natural Toxins*, Volume 4, pp. 58-71(1996).

Common/Systematic Name
Miotoxin F

Molecular Formula/Molecular Weight
$C_{29}H_{40}O_{10}$; MW = 548.26215

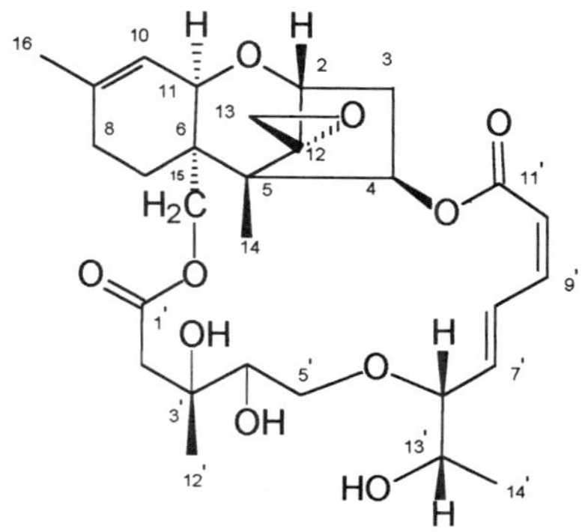

General Characteristics
An oil; $[\alpha]_D$ +29° (*c*=0.87, in $CHCl_3$).

Plant Source
Female *Baccharis coridifolia*.

Isolation/Purification
The 70-100% ethyl acetate in hexane and 10% methanol-methylene chloride fractions from the initial column chromatography of the crude extract (see description under verrucarin A β-glucoside) were subjected to flash chromatography (silica, 80g, methanol-methylene chloride) to yield various trichothecene-containing fractions which were combined, based on TLC analysis, and subjected to further chromatographic procedures including preparative TLC, filtration reversed phase chromatography, preparative HPLC, and countercurrent chromatography (CCC). From these operations were isolated miotoxins E, F, and G.

Spectral Data

IR:
($CHCl_3$) 3475, 1712, 1636, 1600, 1418, 1375, 1181, and 1081cm^{-1}.

^{1}H NMR:
($CDCl_3$) 7.78(dd, 1H, *J*=11.3, 15.6 Hz, H-8'); 6.66(dd, 1H, *J*=11.3, 11.3, H-9'); 5.98(dd, 1H, *J*=2.9, 15.6 Hz, H-7'); 5.81(dd, 1H, *J*=4.5, 8.1 Hz, H-4); 5.76(d, 1H, *J*=11.3 Hz, H-10'); 5.40(br d, 1H, *J*=4.8 Hz, H-10), 4.58 and 3.97(AB, 1H each, *J*=12.3 Hz, H-15); 4.08(dd, 1H, *J*=2.0, 9.5 Hz, H-4'), 3.83(d, 1H, *J*=5.0 Hz, H-2),

3.66(m, 1H, H-6'); 3.62(dq, 1H, J=6.0, 6.9 Hz, H-13'), 3.59(br d, 1H, J=4.8 Hz, H-11), 3.59(dd, 1H, J=2.0, 9.5 Hz, H-5'B); 3.48(dd, 1H, J=9.5, 9.5 Hz, H-5'A), 3.11 and 2.79(AB, 1H each, J=4.0 Hz, H-13), 2.65 and 2.44(AB, 1H each, J=15.7 Hz, H-2'), 2.41(dd, 1H, J=8.1, 15.4 Hz, H-3a), 2.15(ddd, 1H, J=4.5, 5.0, 15.4 Hz, H-3b), 1.80-2.00(m, 4H, H-7, H-8); 1.70(s, 3H, H-16); 1.19(d, 3H, J=6.0 Hz, H-14'); 1.12(s, 3H, H-12'); and 0.72ppm (s, 3H, H-14).

^{13}C NMR:

($CDCl_3$) 79.1, C-2; 34.9, C-3; 74.6, C-4; 49.1, C-5; 43.9, C-6; 20.6, C-7; 27.8, C-8; 140.8, C-9; 118.2, C-10; 67.3, C-11; 65.2, C-12; 48.0, C-13; 7.2, C-14; 64.4, C-15; 23.3, C-16; 171.9, C-1'; 43.9, C-2'; 72.4, C-3'; 74.4, C-4'; 70.9, C-5'; 85.3, C-6'; 138.8, C-7'; 126.2, C-8'; 144.1, C-9'; 117.5, C-10'; 166.8, C-11'; 22.7, C-12'; 71.4, C-13'; and 18.4ppm, C-14'.

Reference

B. B. Jarvis, S. Wang, C. Cox, M. M. Rao, V. Philip, M. S. Varaschin, and C. S. Barros; Brazilian *Baccharis* toxins: livestock poisoning and the isolation of macrocyclic trichothecene glucosides; Natural Toxins, Volume 4, pp. 58-71(1996).

Common/Systematic Name
Miotoxin G

Molecular Formula/Molecular Weight
$C_{29}H_{40}O_9$; MW = 532.26723

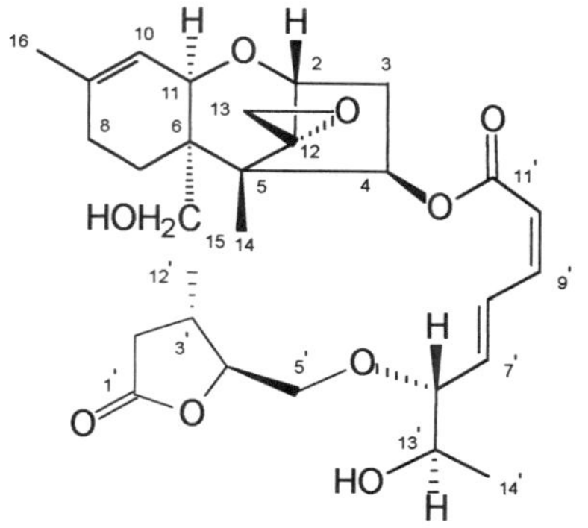

General Characteristics
An oil; $[\alpha]_D$ +31° (*c*=0.27, in $CHCl_3$).

Plant Source
Female *Baccharis coridifolia*.

Isolation/Purification
The 70-100% ethyl acetate in hexane and 10% methanol-methylene chloride fractions from the initial column chromatography of the crude extract (see description under verrucarin A β-glucoside) were subjected to flash chromatography (silica, 80g, methanol-methylene chloride) to yield various trichothecene-containing fractions which were combined, based on TLC analysis, and subjected to further chromatographic procedures including preparative TLC, filtration reversed phase chromatography, preparative HPLC, and countercurrent chromatography (CCC). From these operations were isolated miotoxins E, F, and G.

Spectral Data

IR:
($CHCl_3$) 3481, 1781, 1700, 1643, 1606, 1187, and 1081cm^{-1}.

^{1}H NMR:
($CDCl_3$) 7.59(dd, 1H, *J*=11.3, 15.5 Hz, H-8'); 6.60(dd, 1H, *J*=11.3,11.3 Hz, H-9'); 6.10(dd, 1H, *J*=3.8, 8.0 Hz, H-4); 5.83(dd, 1H, *J*=7.5, 15.5 Hz, H-7'); 5.77(d, 1H, *J*=11.3 Hz, H-10'); 5.47(br d, 1H, *J*=5.0 Hz, H-10); 4.16(ddd, 1H, *J*=3.3, 5.2, 6.8 Hz, H-4'); 3.89(br d, 1H, *J*=5.0 Hz, H-11); 3.83 and 3.65(AB, 1H each, *J*=12.5 Hz, H-15);

3.82(d, 1H, *J*=5.2 Hz, H-2); 3.72(dd, 1H, *J*=3.3, 11.0 Hz, H-5'B); 3.71(m, 1H, H-13'); 3.66(m, 1H, H-6'); 3.51(dd, 1H, *J*=5.2, 11.0 Hz, H-5'A); 3.11 and 2.80(AB, 1H each, *J*=4.0 Hz, H-13); 2.73(dd, 1H, *J*=8.5, 17.5 Hz, H-2'B); 2.48(dd, 1H, *J*=8.0, 15.3 Hz, H-3a); 2.43(m, 1H, H-3'); 2.17(dd, 1H, *J*=8.4, 17.5 Hz, H-2'A); 2.07(ddd, 1H, *J*=3.8, 5.2, 15.3 Hz, H-3b); 1.92-1.99(m, 3 H, H-7B, H-8); 1.70(s, 3H, H-16); 1.54(m, 1H, H-7A); 1.15(d, 3H, *J*=6.8 Hz, H-12'); 1.13(d, 3H, *J*=6.2 Hz, H-14'); and 0.81ppm (s, 3H, H-14).

^{13}C NMR:

($CDCl_3$) 79.0, C-2; 36.0, C-3; 75.4, C-4; 48.9, C-5; 44.2, C-6; 21.2, C-7; 28.0, C-8; 140.6, C-9; 118.7, C-10; 66.8, C-11; 65.6, C-12; 48.1, C-13; 6.8, C-14; 62.8, C-15; 23.3, C-16; 176.3, C-1'; 36.7, C-2'; 32.1, C-3'; 85.8, C-4'; 69.4, C-5'; 85.5, C-6'; 139.0, C-7'; 130.8, C-8'; 143.7, C-9'; 118.7, C-10'; 166.8, C-11'; 18.4, C-12'; 69.7, C-13'; and 18.2ppm, C-14'.

Reference

B. B. Jarvis, S. Wang, C. Cox, M. M. Rao, V. Philip, M. S. Varaschin, and C. S. Barros; Brazilian *Baccharis* Toxins: Livestock Poisoning and the Isolation of Macrocyclic Trichothecene Glucosides; Natural Toxins, Volume 4, pp. 58-71(1996).

18

Roritoxins

Roritoxin A
Roritoxin B
Roritoxin C
Roritoxin D

Common/Systematic Name
Roritoxin A

Molecular Formula/Molecular Weight
$C_{29}H_{34}O_{10}$; MW = 542.21520

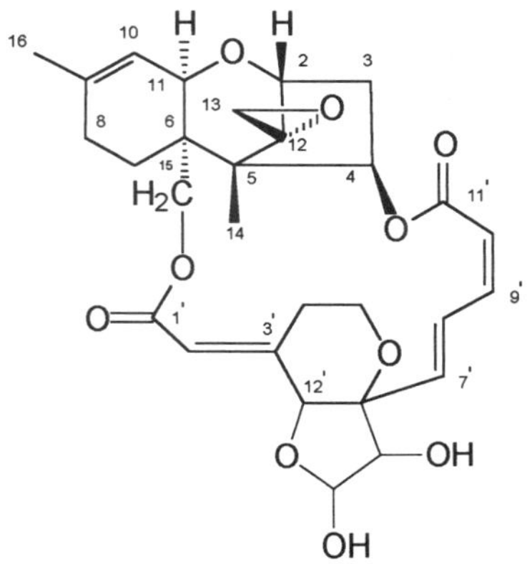

General Characteristics
Crystals; mp., 220-225°C; $[\alpha]_D^{25}$ + 16° (*c*= 0.51, in chloroform).

Fungal Source
Myrothecium roridum (CL-514; ATCC 20605).

Isolation/Purification
At the end of 3 weeks of rice fermentation with *M. roridum* the culture was extracted with methanol in a sonicator. The methanol extracts were combined, washed with hexane, and concentrated *in vacuo* to give an aqueous solution which was extracted with ethyl acetate. The ethyl acetate extract was dried and solvent was removed by rotary evaporation to give a brown gum. The crude extract was subjected to filtration chromatography (silica gel) with methanol in dichloromethane as the eluting solvent. Fractions obtained with 1-5% methanol in dichloromethane were combined to give a yellow material. This fraction was subjected to flash chromatography with a step gradient of isopropyl alcohol in dichloromethane as eluting solvent to obtain five fractions. Fractions 2, 3, and 4 obtained with 3-10% isopropyl alcohol were shown to contain trichothecenes by TLC analysis. These were subjected to further purification. Fraction 2 was triturated with dichloromethane and filtered. The white solid precipitate was recrystallized from methanol to give roritoxin D. The mother liquor from the recrystallization and the filtrate from the previous step were combined and purifed on the Chromatotron (eluting solvent 0-3% methanol in dichloromethane). An additional amount of roritoxin D was obtained, and fractions which were collected after the roritoxin D band were added to fraction 3 for further purification. Fraction 3 was triturated with dichloromethane and filtered. The

dichloromethane insoluble white solid obtained was recrystallized from methanol to yield crystals of a mixture of roritoxin C and D. The filtrate of the dichloromethane solution and the mother liquor of the recrystallization were combined and purified on the Chromatotron, (0-5% methanol in dichloromethane). The roritoxin C containing fraction was recrystallized from ethyl acetate to yield pure roritoxin C. The fractions which, by TLC, contained trichothecenes more polar than roritoxin C were combined with fraction 4. Fraction 4 was crystallized from 95% ethanol to yield roritoxin B. The mother liquor was purified on the Chromatotron (0-7% methanol in dichloromethane as eluting solvent). The roritoxin B containing fraction was recrystallized from ethyl acetate to give pure roritoxin B. Roritoxin A was isolated from a more polar fraction from this chromatography.

Biological Activity

The roritoxins were acutely cytotoxic against L1210 leukemia cells and they exhibited the following ID_{50}'s: roritoxin A, 0.0011μg/ml; roritoxin B, 0.0017μg/ml; roritoxin C, 0.0042μg/ml; and roritoxin D, 0.0021μg/ml. Roritoxin B was toxic at 80μg/kg in mice against P388 leukemia cells; roritixin B also exhibited toxicity (LD_{50} ca. 100μg/kg) when tested against B16 melanoma in mice.

Spectral Data

UV:
λ_{max}^{MeOH} 231 (log ε= 4.35) and 260nm (log ε= 4.70).

^{1}H NMR:
($CDCl_3$) 3.57(1H, *J*=5.1Hz, H-2); 2.46(1H, dd, *J*=8.4, 15.4Hz, H-3α); ~ 5.9(1H, H-4); ~ 1.9(1H, H-7); ~ 1.9(2H, H-8); 5.45(1H, *J*=4.8Hz, H-10); 3.85(1H, *J*=4.8Hz, H-11); 3.14(1H, *J*=3.9Hz, H-13A); 2.83(1H, *J*=3.9Hz, H-13B); 0.80(3H, s, H-14); 4.50(1H, *J*=12.4Hz, H-15A); ~ 3.9(1H, H-15B); 1.73(3H, s, H-16); ~5.9(1H, H-2'); 2.2(2H, H-4'); 3.9(2H, H-5'); 6.06(1H, *J*=16.6Hz, H-7'); 7.34(1H, *J*=10.6, 16.6Hz, H-8'); 6.60(1H, *J*=10.6, 10.6Hz, H-9'); 5.98(1H, *J*=10.6Hz, H-10'); 4.48(1H, s, H- 12'); ~ 5.9(1H, H-13'); and 5.22ppm (1H, *J*=5.0Hz, H-14').

^{13}C NMR:
($CDCl_3$) 79.2, C-2; 34.6, C-3; 74.4, C-4; 49.1, C-5; 43.5, C-6; 20.4, C-7; 27.7, C-8; 140.2, C-9; 119.0, C-10; 68.1, C-11; 65.4, C-12; 48.0, C-13; 7.5, C-14; 65.3, C-15; 23.2, C-16; 165.5, C-1'; 120.8, C-2'; 151.3, C-3'; 25.7, C-4'; 64.0, C-5'; 81.8, C-6'; 133.4, C-7'; 129.0, C-8'; 141.4, C-9'; 121.9, C-10'; 166.9, C-11'; 81.8, C-12'; 81.0, C-13'; and 96.7ppm, C-14'.

Mass Spectrum:
HREIMS: 542.2145*m/e* (M^+ calcd. 542.2151).

Reference

B. B. Jarvis and C. S. Yatawara; Roritoxins, New Macrocyclic Trichothecenes from *Myrothecium roridum*; J. Org. Chem., Vol. 51, pp. 2906-2910(1986).

Common/Systematic Name

Roritoxin B

Molecular Formula/Molecular Weight

$C_{29}H_{34}O_{11}$; MW = 558.21011

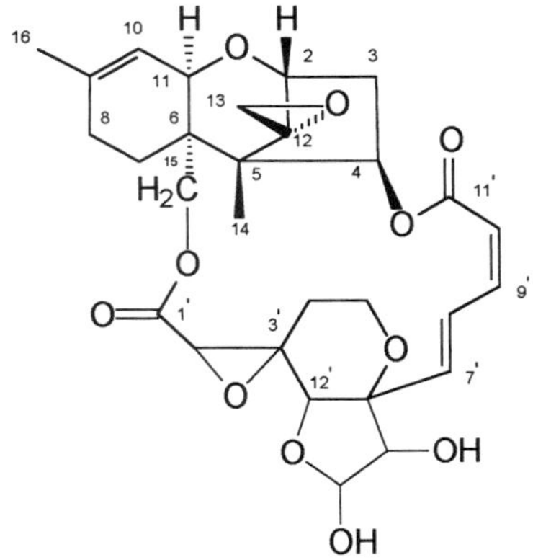

General Characteristics

Crystals, mp. 262-265°C (dec.); $[\alpha]_D^{25}$ + 2.6° (*c*=0.60, in chloroform).

Fungal Source

Myrothecium roridum (CL-514; ATCC 20605).

Isolation/Purification

See roritoxin A.

Biological Activity

See roritoxin A.

Spectral Data

UV:

λ_{max}^{MeOH} 254nm (log ε =4.99).

^{1}H NMR:

($CDCl_3$) 3.84(1H, *J*=4.8Hz, H-2); 2.45(1H, dd, *J*=8.5, 15.0Hz, H-3α); ~ 5.9(1H, H-4); ~ 1.9(1H, H-7); ~ 1.9(2H, H-8); 5.41(1H, *J*=5.5Hz, H-10); 3.57(1H, *J*=5.5Hz, H-11); 3.14(1H, *J*=3.9Hz, H-13A); 2.81(1H, *J*=3.9Hz, H-13B); 0.81(3H, s, H-14); 4.02(1H, *J*=12.0Hz, H-15A); 3.94(1H, *J*=12.0Hz, H-15B); 1.71(3H, s, H-16); 3.31(1H, s, H-2'); ~ 2.2(2H, H-4'); ~3.9(2H, H-5'); 5.87(1H, *J*=16.4Hz, H-7'); 7.01(1H, *J*=8.3, 16.4Hz, H-8'); 6.67(1H, *J*=8.3, 12.2Hz, H-9'); 5.96(1H, *J*=12.2Hz, H-10'); 4.25(1H, s, H-12'); 5.22(1H, *J*=5.0Hz, H-13'); and 5.93ppm (1H, *J*=5.0Hz, H-

14').

^{13}C NMR:
($CDCl_3$) 78.4, C-2; 33.9, C-3; 73.9, C-4; 48.7, C-5; 42.8, C-6; 19.2, C-7; 26.8, C-8; 138.8, C-9; 118.9, C-10; 66.6, C-11; 65.3, C-12; 47.3, C-13; 7.7, C-14; 64.2, C-15; 22.8, C-16; 167.3, C-1'; 56.4, C-2'; 62.0, C-3'; 22.8, C-4'; 60.1, C-5'; 82.2, C-6'; 131.2, C-7'; 129.7, C-8'; 143.3, C-9'; 120.1, C-10'; 166.5, C-11'; 81.9, C-12'; 78.1, C-13'; and 100.4ppm, C-14'.

Mass Spectrum:
HREIMS: 558.2106*m/e* (M^+ calcd. 558.2139).

Reference

B. B. Jarvis and C. S. Yatawara; Roritoxins, New Macrocyclic Trichothecenes from *Myrothecium roridum*; J. Org. Chem., Vol. 51, pp. 2906-2910(1986).

Common/Systematic Name
Roritoxin C

Molecular Formula/Molecular Weight
$C_{29}H_{32}O_{12}$; MW = 572.18938

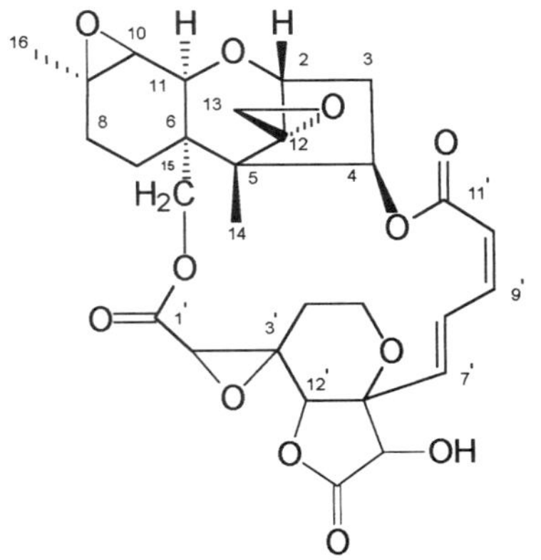

General Characteristics
Crystals; mp., 288-290°C (dec.); $[\alpha]_D^{25}$ + 8.9° (*c*= 0.40, in chloroform).

Fungal Source
Myrothecium roridum (CL-514; ATCC 20605).

Isolation/Purification
See roritoxin A.

Biological Activity
See roritoxin A.

Spectral Data

UV:
λ_{max}^{MeOH} 254nm (log ε = 4.97).

^{1}H NMR:
($CDCl_3$) 3.93(1H, *J*=4.8Hz, H-2); ~ 2.4(1H, H-3α); ~ 6.1(1H, H-4); ~ 1.9(1H, H-7); ~ 1.9(2H, H-8); 3.06(1H, *J*=5.0Hz, H-10); 3.56(1H, *J*=5.0Hz, H-11); 3.14(1H, *J*=3.8Hz, H-13A); 2.81(1H, *J*=3.8Hz, H-13B); 0.82(3H, s, H-14); 4.41(1H, *J*=12.6Hz, H-15A); 4.32(1H, *J*=12.6Hz, H-15B); 1.55(3H, s, H-16); 3.36(1H, s, H-2'); ~ 2.4(2H, H-4'); ~3.9(2H, H-5'); 5.82(1H, *J*=16.0Hz, H-7'); 7.10(1H, *J*=8.0, 16.0Hz, H-8'); 6.68(1H, *J*=8.0, 11.0Hz, H-9'); 5.97(1H, *J*=11.0Hz, H-10'); 4.24(1H, s, H-12'); and

5.40ppm (1H, s, H-13').

^{13}C NMR: (Roritoxin C Acetate)
($CDCl_3$) 78.8, C-2; 34.2, C-3; 73.1, C-4; 49.0, C-5; 42.9, C-6; 17.4, C-7; 26.2, C-8; 57.4, C-9; 57.7, C-10; 68.2, C-11; 64.8, C-12; 48.0, C-13; 8.0, C-14; 64.7, C-15; 22.2, C-16; 166.8, C-1'; 57.2, C-2'; 60.7, C-3'; 22.3, C-4'; 61.4, C-5'; 80.6, C-6'; 132.5, C-7'; 127.3, C-8'; 142.2, C-9'; 122.0, C-10'; 166.6, C-11'; 79.5, C-12'; 74.1, C-13'; 169.7, C-14'; 20.4, $\underline{C}H_3COO$-; and 168.6ppm, $CH_3\underline{C}OO$-.

Mass Spectrum:
HREIMS: 572.1955*m/e* (M^+ calcd. 572.1974).

Reference

B. B. Jarvis and C. S. Yatawara; Roritoxins, New Macrocyclic Trichothecenes from *Myrothecium roridum*; J. Org. Chem.; Vol. 51, pp. 2906-2910(1986).

Common/Systematic Name

Roritoxin D

Molecular Formula/Molecular Weight

$C_{29}H_{32}O_{11}$; MW = 556.19446

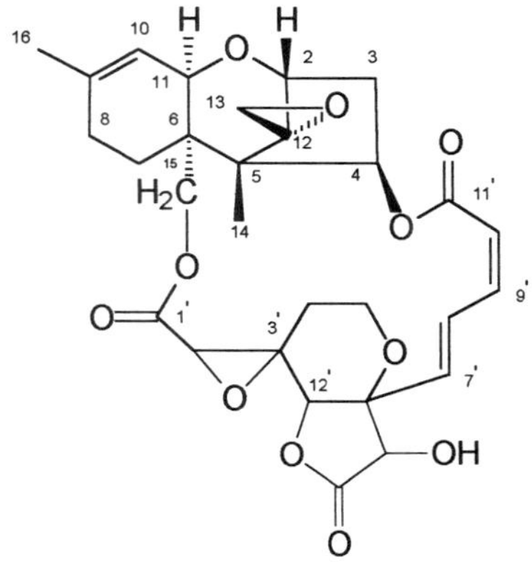

General Characteristics

Crystals; mp., 294-297°C (dec.); $[\alpha]_D^{25}$ + 30.0° (*c*= 0.10, in chloroform).

Fungal Source

Myrothecium roridum (CL-514; ATCC 20605).

Isolation/Purification

See roritoxin A.

Biological Activity

See roritoxin A.

Spectral Data

UV:

λ_{max}^{MeOH} 253nm (log ε = 4.98).

^{1}H NMR:

($CDCl_3$) 3.84(1H, *J*=4.6Hz, H-2); 2.45(1H, *J*=8.6, 15.2Hz, H-3α); ~5.8(1H, H- 4); ~2.0(1H, H-7); ~2.0(2H, H-8); 5.41(1H, *J*=5.0Hz, H-10); 3.57(1H, *J*=5.0Hz, H-11); 3.14(1H, *J*=3.9Hz, H-13A); 2.81(1H, *J*=3.9Hz, H-13B); 0.82(3H, s, H-14); 4.32(1H, *J*=12.5Hz, H-15A); 4.20(1H, *J*=12.5Hz, H-15B); 1.71(3H, s, H-16); 3.36(1H, s, H-2'); ~2.0(2H, H-4'); ~4.0(2H, H-5'); 5.88(1H, *J*=16.4Hz, H- 7'); 7.10(1H, *J*=8.2, 16.4Hz, H-8'); 6.67(1H, *J*=8.2, 11.1Hz, H-9'); 6.01(1H, *J*=11.1Hz, H-10'); 3.87(1H, s, H-12');

and 5.27ppm (1H, s, H-13').

^{13}C NMR: (Roritoxin D Acetate)
($CDCl_3$) 79.1, C-2; 34.3, C-3; 73.2, C-4; 49.3, C-5; 43.3, C-6; 20.4, C-7; 27.4, C-8; 140.5, C-9; 118.5, C-10; 67.8, C-11; 65.3, C-12; 48.0, C-13; 7.9, C-14; 65.2, C-15; 22.2, C-16; 166.7, C-1'; 57.3, C-2'; 60.4, C-3'; 23.3, C-4'; 61.3, C-5'; 80.5, C-6'; 132.5, C-7'; 127.0, C-8'; 142.0, C-9'; 122.1, C-10'; 166.4, C-11'; 79.4, C-12'; 74.0, C-13'; 169.6, C- 14'; 20.0, $\underline{C}H_3COO$-; and 168.8ppm, $CH_3\underline{C}OO$-.

Mass Spectrum:
HREIMS: 556.1940*m/e* (M^+ calcd. 556.1980).

Reference

B. B. Jarvis and C. S. Yatawara; Roritoxins, New Macrocyclic Trichothecenes from *Myrothecium roridum*; J. Org. Chem., Vol. 51, pp. 2906-2910(1986).

19

Myrotoxins and Mytoxins

- Myrotoxin A
- Myrotoxin B
- Myrotoxin C
- Myrotoxin C Hydrate
- Myrotoxin D
- Myrotoxin D Hydrate
- Mytoxin A
- Mytoxin B
- Mytoxin C

Common/Systematic Name

Myrotoxin A

Molecular formula / Molecular Weight

$C_{27}H_{32}O_9$; MW = 500.20463

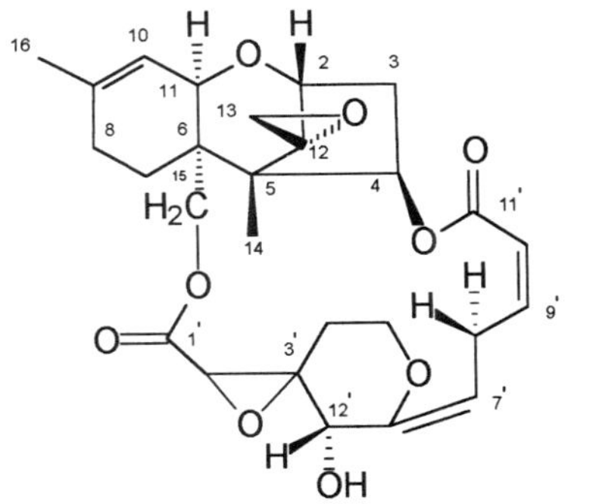

General Characteristics

Colorless solid; mp., 220-222°C; $[\alpha]_D$ +122.0 (c=0.50, in CH_2Cl_2).

Fungal Source

Myrothecium roridum (ATCC 60379).

Isolation/Purification

An aqueous shake culture of *Myrothecium roridum* (ATCC 60379) was filtered and supernatant extracted with ethyl acetate and the mycelium with acetone. The extracts were combined, concentrated, and subjected to filtration chromatography (silica gel, ethyl acetate-hexane) followed by MPLC (ethyl acetate-hexane through 10% $MeOH/CH_2Cl_2$). The 50% ethyl acetate-hexane fraction was subjected to MPLC (silica gel, 1-5% $MeOH/CH_2Cl_2$) followed by PTLC of a latter fraction (silica gel, 20-40% ethyl acetate/hexane followed by alumina, 20-60% ethyl acetate-hexane) giving myrotoxins A and B.

Biological Activity

Cytotoxic: $ID_{50} = 5 \times 10^{-4}$ μg/mL, L-1200 cells.

Spectral Data

IR:

(CH_2Cl_2) 3590(OH), 1760, and 1715cm^{-1} (C=O's).

^{1}H NMR:

($CDCl_3$) 0.80(3H, s, H-14); 1.73(3H, s, H-16); 1.90(2H, m, H-4'B); 2.0 - 2.1(4H, m,

H-7 and H-8); 2.17(1H, ddd, *J*=3.8, 5.0, 15.5Hz, H-3); 2.48(1H, dd, *J*=8.2, 15.5Hz, H-3); 2.60(1H, ddd, *J*=2.0, 9.0, 14.6Hz, H-8'B); 2.84(2H, m, H-4'A); 3.36(1H, s, H-2'); 3.63[1H, s(after D_2O exchange], H-12'); 3.69(1H, d, *J*=4.2Hz, H-11); 3.85(1H, d, *J*=5.0Hz, H-2); 2.79 and 3.13(1H each, AB, *J*=4.0Hz, H-13); 3.85 and 4.68(1H each, AB, *J*=12.0Hz, H-15); 4.00(1H, m, H-5'B); 4.12,(1H, dddd, *J*=1.5, 8.8, 9.8, 14.6Hz, H-8'A); 4.25(1H, m, H-5'A); 4.65(1H, dd, *J*=2.0, 9.8Hz, H-7'); 5.42(1H, d, *J*=4.2Hz, H-10); 5.85(1H, dd, *J*=3.8 and 8.2Hz, H-4); 5.93(1H, dd, *J*=1.5, 11.2Hz, H-10); and 6.59ppm (1H, ddd, *J*=8.8, 9.0, 11.2Hz, H-9').

^{13}C NMR:

($CDCl_3$) 79.1, C-2; 35.1, C-3; 74.8, C-4; 49.5, C-5; 43.2, C-6; 20.2, C-7; 27.4, C-8; 140.6, C-9; 118.5, C-10; 67.4, C-11; 65.4, C-12; 47.6, C-13; 7.8, C-14; 64.2, C-15; 23.3, C-16; 164.7, C-1'; 57.1, C-2'; 65.3, C-3'; 23.5, C-4'; 67.2, C-5'; 150.9, C-6'; 109.8, C-7'; 24.3, C-8'; 148.7, C-9'; 121.9, C-10'; 167.1, C-11'; and 72.1ppm, C-12'.

References

B. B. Jarvis, F. T. Comezoglu, Y.-W. Lee, J. L. Flippen-Anderson, R. D. Gilardi, and C. F. George; Novel Macrocyclic Trichothecenes from *Myrothecium roridum*; Bull. Soc.Chim. Belg., 95, pp. 681-697(1986).

B. B. Jarvis, Y.-W. Lee, F. T. Comezoglu, S. N. Comezoglu, and G. A. Bean; Myrotoxins: A New Class of Macrocyclic Trichothecenes; Tetrahedron Lett., Vol. 26, pp-4859-4862(1985).

Common/Systematic Name
Myrotoxin B

Molecular Formula/Molecular Weight
$C_{29}H_{34}O_{11}$; MW = 558.21011

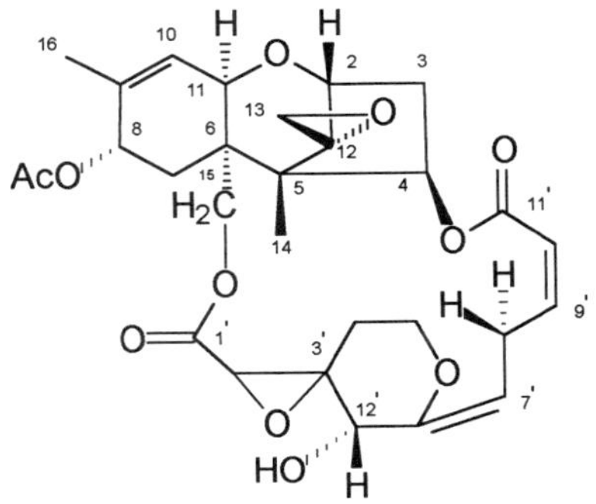

General Characteristics
Colorless solid; mp., 195-197°C; [α]D = +101.7° (c=0.60 in CH_2Cl_2).

Fungal Source
Myrothecium roridum (ATCC 60379 and ATCC 52485).

Isolation/Purification
An aqueous shake culture of *Myrothecium roridum* (ATCC 60379) was filtered and the supernatant extracted with ethyl acetate and the mycelium extracted with acetone. The extracts were combined, concentrated, and subjected to filtration chromatography (silica gel, ethyl acetate-hexane) followed by MPLC (ethyl acetate-hexane through 10% methanol-methylene chloride). The 50% ethyl acetate-hexane fraction was subjected to MPLC (silica gel, 1-5% methanol-methylene chloride) followed by PTLC of a latter fraction (silica gel, 20-40% ethyl acetate-hexane followed by alumina, 20-60% ethyl acetate-hexane) giving myrotoxins A and B.

Biological Activity
Immunotoxin, cytotoxic, LD_{50} in mice = 1.0mg/kg, inhibition of blastogenesis; LD_{50} = 1μg/rat intracerebrally.

Spectral Data

IR:
(CH_2Cl_2) 3600 (br, OH), 1710, 1730, and 1755cm^{-1} (C=O's).

^{1}H NMR:

($CDCl_3$) 0.79(3H, s, H-14); 1.76(3H, s, H-16); 1.89(2H, m, H-4'B); 2.1(2H, m, H-7); 2.17(1H, ddd, *J*=3.6, 5.2, and 15.7Hz, H-3β); 2.49(1H, dd, *J*=8.1 and 15.7Hz, H-3α); 2.61(1H, ddd, *J*=2.0, 9.0, and 14.6Hz, H-8'B); 2.86(2H, m, H- 4'A); 3.32(1H, s, H-2'); 3.63(1H, s(after D_2O exchange), H-12'); 3.68(1H, d, *J*=5.4Hz, H-11); 3.85(1H, d, *J*=5.2 Hz, H-2); 2.80 and 3.12(1H each, AB, *J*=4.0 Hz, H-13); 3.92 and 4.89(1H each, AB, *J*=12.0Hz, H-15); 3.98(1H, m, H-5'B); 4.11(1H, dddd, *J*=1.6, 8.7, 9.8, and 14.6Hz, H-8'A); 4.28(1H, m, H-5'A); 4.65(1H, dd, *J*=2.0 and 9.8Hz, H-7'); 5.28(1H, d, *J*=5.2Hz, H-8); 5.66(1H, d, *J*=5.4Hz, H-10); 5.83(1H, dd, *J*=3.6 and 8.1Hz, H-4); 5.92(1H, dd, *J*=1.6 and 11.2Hz, H-10'); 6.60ppm (1H, ddd, *J*=8.7, 9.0, and 11.2Hz, H-9').

^{13}C NMR:

($CDCl_3$) 78.9, C-2; 35.0, C-3; 74.8, C-4; 49.5, C-5; 42.0, C-6; 23.4, C-7; 68.1, C-8; 136.7, C-9; 164.5, C-1'; 56.7, C-2'; 65.2, C-3'; 23.2, C-4'; 67.1, C-5'; 150.9, C-6'; 109.7, C-7'; 26.7, C-8'; 149.0, C-9'; 121.9, C-10'; 166.8, C-11'; 72.1, C-12'; 20.5, acetate methyl; and 170.8ppm, acetate C=O.

References

B. B. Jarvis, F. T. Comezoglu, Y.-W. Lee, J. L. Flippen-Anderson, R. D. Gilardi, and C. F. George; Novel Macrocyclic Trichothecenes from *Myrothecium roridum*; Bull. Soc.Chim. Belg.,Vol. 95, pp. 681-697(1986).

B. B. Jarvis, Y.-W. Lee, F. T. Comezoglu, S. N. Comezoglu, and G. A. Bean; Myrotoxins: A New Class of Macrocyclic Trichothecenes; Tetrahedron Lett., Vol. 26, pp-4859-4862(1985).

Common/Systematic Name

Myrotoxin C

Molecular Formula/Molecular Weight

$C_{27}H_{32}O_9$; MW = 500.20463

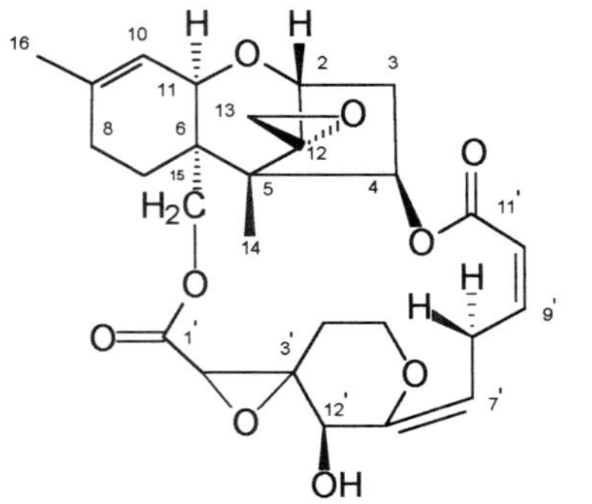

General Characteristics

Colorless solid; mp., 240°C (dec.); $[\alpha]_D$ = +124.5° (*c*=0.98, in CH_2Cl_2).

Fungal Source

Myrothecium roridum (ATCC 60379).

Isolation/Purification

An acetone extract of a rice culture of *Myrothecium roridum* (ATCC 60379) was concentrated and partitioned between aqueous $NaHCO_3$ and ethyl acetate; the ethyl acetate solubles were subjected to filtration chromatography (silical gel, ethyl acetate-hexane) followed by MPLC (ethyl acetate-hexane through 10% MeOH-CH_2Cl_2). The 50% ethyl acetate-hexane fraction was subjected to MPLC (silica gel, 1-5% MeOH-CH_2Cl_2) followed by PTLC of a latter fraction (silica gel, 20-40% ethyl acetate-hexane) to give myrotoxin C. A later MPLC fraction gave myrotoxin D upon PTLC (alumina, 20-60% ethyl acetate-hexane).

Biological Activity

Cytotoxic.

Spectral Data

IR:

(CH_2Cl_2) 3580, 2900, 1750, 1715, 1642, 1405, 1190, 1160, 1110, 1095, 1035, 992, 970, and 670 cm^{-1}.

^{1}H NMR:

($CDCl_3$) 0.81(3H, s, H-14); 1.73(3H, s, H-16); 1.8(1H, m, H-8B); 1.9(2H, m, H- 7); 2.0(2H, m, H-8A and H-4'B); 2.15(1H, ddd, *J*=3.9, 5.2, 15.5Hz, H-3A); 2.36(1H, dd, *J*=8.2, 15.5Hz, H-3); 2.57(1H, m, H-8'B); 2.80, 3.13(1H each, AB, *J*=4.1Hz, H-13); 3.57(1H, d, *J*=4.1Hz, H-11); 3.79(1H, s, H-2H); 3.84(1H, *J*=12.1Hz, H-15B); 3.85(1H, d, *J*=5.2Hz, H-2); 3.93(1H, ddd, *J*=2.4, 11.1, 13.1Hz, H-5'B); 4.15(1H, m, H-5'A); 4.20(1H, m, H-8'A); 4.43(1H, s after D_2O exchange, H-12'); 4.58(1H, d, *J*=12.1Hz, H-15A); 4.84(1H, ddd, *J*=1.8, 1.8, 10.0Hz, H-7'); 5.41(1H, d, *J*=4.1Hz, H-10); 5.86(1H, dd, *J*=3.9, 8.2Hz, H-4); 5.91(1H, dd, *J*=1.5, 11.2Hz, H-10'); 6.62ppm (1H, ddd, *J*=8.9, 8.9, 11.2, H-9').

^{13}C NMR:

($CDCl_3$) 79.1, C-2; 35.0, C-3; 72.5, C-4; 49.5, C-5; 43.1, C-6; 20.1, C-7; 27.4, C-8; 140.6, C-9; 118.4, C-10; 67.4, C-11; 65.3, C-12; 47.6, C-13; 7.7, C-14; 63.9, C-15; 23.2, C-16; 164.7, C-1'; 52.3, C-2'; 66.5, C-3'; 23.9, C-4'; 66.8, C-5'; 151.1, C-6'; 104.1, C-7'; 28.5, C-8'; 149.4, C-9'; 121.4, C-10'; 168.4, C-11'; and 67.8ppm C-12'.

Reference

B. B. Jarvis, F. T. Comezoglu, Y.-W. Lee, J. L. Flippen-Anderson, R. D. Gilardi, and C. F. George; Novel Macrocyclic Trichothecenes from *Myrothecium roridum*; Bull. Soc. Chim. Belg., Vol. 95, pp. 681-697(1986).

Common/Systematic Name
Myrotoxin C hydrate

Molecular Formula/Molecular Weight
$C_{27}H_{34}O_{10}$; MW = 518.21520

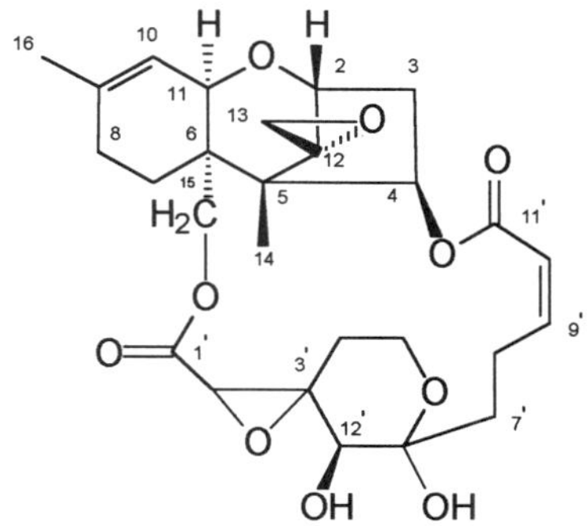

General Characteristics
Colorless solid; mp., 178-182°C; $[\alpha]_D$ = +29.5° (*c*=0.44, in CH_2Cl_2).

Fungal Source
Myrothecium roridum (ATCC 60379 and ATCC 52485).

Isolation/Purification
A fraction from a rice culture of *M. roridum* (ATCC 60379) rich in myrotoxins C and D was allowed to stand at room temperature in a mixture of acetone and chloroform. The solvent was removed, and the mixture subjected to MPLC (150g of 13-25μ silica gel, elution with 40-60% ethyl acetate-hexane) followed by PTLC (2mm alumina plate, elution with 40-70% ethyl acetate-hexane) to give 80mg of myrotoxin C hydrate and 60mg of myrotoxin D hydrate.

Spectral Data

IR:
(CH_2Cl_2) 3590(OH), 1750, and 1710cm^{-1} (C=O's).

^{1}H NMR:
($CDCl_3$) 0.82(3H, s, H-14); 1.71(3H, s, H-16); 1.6-2.4(10H, m, H-3β, H-7, H-8, H-4', H-7', H-8'A); 2.43(1H, dd, *J*=8.5 and 15.4Hz, H-3A); 3.00(1H, m, H-8'B); 2.80 and 3.12(1H each, AB, *J*=4.0Hz, H-13); 3.54(1H, d, *J*=5.4 Hz, H-11); 3.80(1H, s after D_2O exchange, H-12'); 3.83(1H, s, H-2'); 3.85(2H, m, H-5'); 3.85(1H, d, *J*=5.3Hz, H-2); 4.03 and 4.56(1H each, AB, *J*=12.3Hz, H-15); 5.40(1H, d, *J*=5.4Hz, H-10); 5.90(1H, dd, *J*=1.8 and 11.4Hz, H-10'); 5.93(1H, dd, *J*=4.5 and 8.5Hz, H-4); and 6.60ppm (1H, ddd, *J*=8.8, 8.8, and 11.4Hz, H-8').

^{13}C NMR:
($CDCl_3$) 8.0, C-14; 19.8, C-7'; 20.1, C-7; 23.2, C-16; 25.7, C- 4'; 27.4, C-8; 27.7, C-8'); 34.4, C-3; 43.2, C-6; 47.8, C-13; 49.8, C-5; 53.5, C-2'; 60.3, C-5'; 64.1, C-15; 64.3, C-3; 65.2, C-12; 67.3, C- 11; 72.8, C-4; 74.8, C-12'; 79.1, C-2; 100.6, C-6'; 118.3, C-10; 120.8, C-10'; 140.5, C-9; 150.9, C-9'; 166.5, C-1'; and 168.2ppm C-11'.

References

B. B. Jarvis, F. T. Comezoglu, S. Wang, and H. L. Ammon; Mycotoxins from a Plant Pathogenic Isolate of *Myrothecium roridum*; Mycotoxin Res., Vol. 7, pp. 73-78(1991).

F. T. Comezoglu; Trichothecenes: The Isolation of Myrotoxins and Mytoxins; Mechanistic Studies of Rearrangement and Biosynthesis; Ph.D. Thesis, University of Maryland, College Park, MD.

Common/Systematic Name
Myrotoxin D

Molecular formula / Molecular Weight
$C_{29}H_{34}O_{11}$; MW = 558.21011

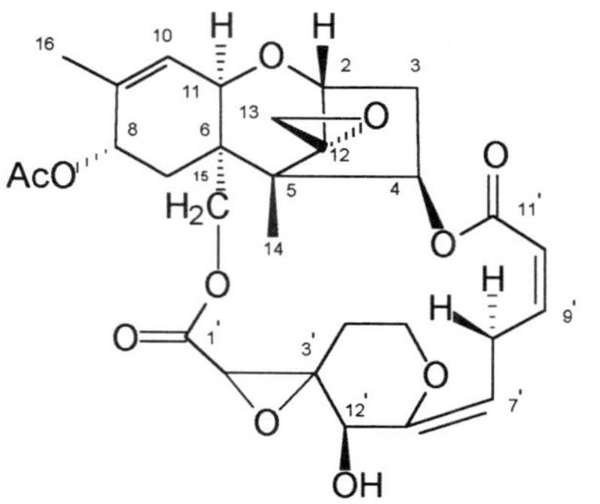

General Characteristics
Colorless solid; mp., 232-236°C; $[\alpha]_D$ = +106.0° (c=0.10, in $CHCl_3$).

Fungal Source
Myrothecium roridum (ATCC 60379).

Isolation/Purification
An acetone extract of a rice culture of *Myrothecium roridum* (ATCC 60379) was concentrated and partitioned between aqueous $NaHCO_3$ and ethyl acetate; the ethyl acetate solubles were subjected to filtration chromatography (silical gel, ethyl acetate-hexane) followed by MPLC (ethyl acetate-hexane through 10% methanol-methylene chloride). The 50% ethyl acetate-hexane fraction was subjected to MPLC (silica gel, 1-5% methanol-methylene chloride) followed by PTLC of a latter fraction (silica gel, 20-40% ethyl acetate-hexane) to give myrotoxin C. A later MPLC fraction gave myrotoxin D upon PTLC (alumina, 20-60% ethyl acetate-hexane).

Biological Activity
Cytotoxic.

Spectral Data

IR:
($CHCl_3$) 3580, 2900, 1750, 1710, 1640, 1370, 1160, 1115, 1095, 1000, and 975cm^{-1}.

^{1}H NMR:
($CDCl_3$) 0.78(3H, s, H-14); 1.73(3H, s, H-16); 1.95(3H, s, CH_3-acetate); 2.06(1H, m,

H-4'B); 2.07(1H, m, H-7B); 2.17(1H, m, H-7A); 2.15(1H, m, H-3β); 2.32(1H, m, H-4'A); 2.46(1H, dd, *J*=8.1 and 15.6Hz, H-3α); 2.55(1H, m, H-8'B); 2.79(1H, d, *J*=4.0Hz, H-13B); 3.08(1H, d, *J*=4.0Hz, H-13A); 3.65(1H, d, *J*=5.4Hz, H-11); 3.74(1H, s, H-2'); 3.82(1H, d, *J*=5.3Hz, H-2); 3.86, 4.87(1H each, AB, *J*=11.9Hz, H-15); 3.87(1H, m, H-5'B); 4.12(2H, m, H-5'A and H-8'A); 4.40(1H, s after D_2O exchange, H-12'); 4.80(1H, ddd, *J*=1.9, 1.9, and 9.9Hz, H-7'); 5.25(1H, d, *J*=5.0Hz, H-8); 5.63(1H, d, *J*=5.4Hz, H-10); 5.80(1H, dd, *J*=3.6 and 8.1Hz, H-4); 5.88(1H, dd, *J*=1.6 and 11.2Hz, H-10'); 6.60ppm (1H, ddd, *J*=8.8, 8.8, and 11.2Hz, H-9').

^{13}C NMR:

($CDCl_3$) 79.0, C-2; 35.0, C-3; 72.0, C-4; 49.5, C-5; 42.0, C-6; 24.0, C-7; 68.1, C-8; 136.8, C-9; 123.7, C-10; 66.8, C-11; 65.2, C-12; 47.5, C-13; 7.7, C-14; 65.9, C-15; 21.1, C-16; 164.6, C-1'; 51.9, C-2'; 66.9, C-3'; 26.8, C-4'; 66.9, C-5'; 151.2, C-6'; 104.2, C-7'; 28.2, C-8'; 149.7, C-9'; 121.5, C-10'; 166.2, C-11'; 67.9, C-12'; 20.5, acetate Me; and 170.8ppm, acetate C=O.

Reference

B. B. Jarvis, F. T. Comezoglu, Y.-W. Lee, J. L. Flippen-Anderson, R. D. Gilardi, and C. F. George; Novel Macrocyclic Trichothecenes from *Myrothecium roridum*; Bull. Soc. Chim. Belg., Vol. 95, pp. 681-697(1986).

Common/Systematic Name

Myrotoxin D hydrate

Molecular Formula/Molecular Weight

$C_{29}H_{36}O_{12}$; MW = 576.22068

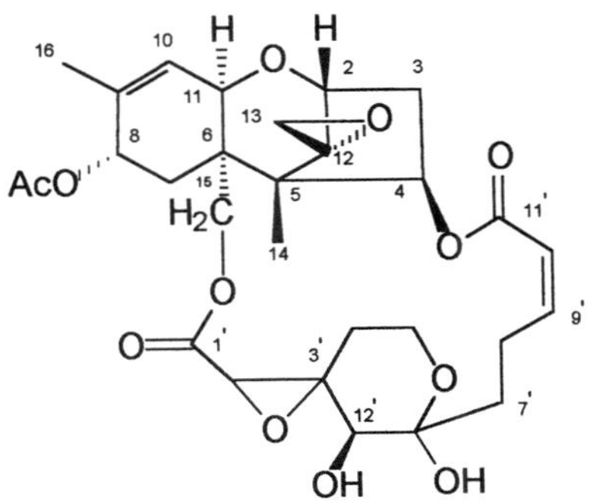

General Characteristics

Colorless solid; mp., 225-229°C; $[\alpha]_D$ = +31.5° (*c*=0.92, in CH_2Cl_2).

Fungal Source

Myrothecium roridum (ATCC 60379 and ATCC 52485).

Isolation/Purification

A fraction from a rice culture of *M. roridum* (ATCC 60379) rich in myrotoxins C and D was allowed to stand at room temperature in a mixture of acetone and chloroform. The solvent was removed, and the mixture subjected to MPLC (150g of 13-25μ silica gel, elution with 40-60% ethyl acetate-hexane) followed by PTLC (2mm alumina plate, elution with 40-70% ethyl acetate-hexane) to give 80mg of myrotoxin C hydrate and 60mg of myrotoxin D hydrate.

Spectral Data

IR:

(CH_2Cl_2) 3590 (OH), 1750, 1730, and 1710cm^{-1} (C=O's).

^{1}H NMR:

($CDCl_3$) 0.80(1H, s, H-14); 1.75(3H, s, H-16); 1.93(3H, s, acetate CH_3); 1.6-2.4(9H, m, H-3β, H-7, H-4', H-7', and H-8A); 2.45(1H, dd, *J*=8.3 and 15.3Hz, H-3α); 2.97(1H, m, H-8'B); 2.81, 3.10(1H each, AB, *J*=4.0Hz, H-13); 3.65(1H, d, *J*=5.4Hz, H-11); 3.80(1H, s after D_2O exchange, H-12'); 3.80(1H, s, H-2'); 3.85(1H, m, H-5'); 3.83(1H, d, *J*=5.3Hz, H-2); 4.09, 4.82(1H each, AB, *J*=12.3Hz, H-15); 5.30(1H, d, *J*=4.2Hz, H-8); 5.66(1H, d, *J*=5.4 Hz, H-10); 5.89(1H, dd, *J*=1.8 and 11.4Hz, H-10'); 5.93(1H, dd, *J*=4.5 and 8.3Hz, H-4); and 6.60ppm (1H, ddd, $J_{8.9,8.9}$=11.4Hz, H-9').

^{13}C NMR:

($CDCl_3$) 8.0, C- 14; 20.2, C-7'; 20.4, acetate CH_3; 20.9, C- 16; 25.8, C-7; 26.4, C-4'; 27.4, C-8'; 34.5, C-3; 42.0, C-6; 47.7, C-13; 49.8, C-5; 53.0, C-2'; 60.6, C-5'; 64.3, C-3'; 65.1, C-12; 66.0, C-15; 66.9, C-11; 68.2, C-8; 72.5, C-4; 75.4, C-12'; 79.1, C-2; 100.5, C-6'; 120.9, C-10'; 123.7, C-10; 136.7, C-9; 150.9, C-9'; 166.5, C-1'; 167.9, C-11'; and 170.7ppm, acetate C=O.

References

B. B. Jarvis, F. T Comezoglu, S. Wang, and H. L. Ammon; Mycotoxins from a Plant Pathogenic Isolate of *Myrothecium roridum*; Mycotoxin Res., Vol. 7, pp. 73-78(1991).

F. T Comezoglu; Trichothecenes: The Isolation of Myrotoxins and Mytoxins; Mechanistic Studies of Rearrangement and Biosynthesis; Ph.D. Thesis, University of Maryland, College Park, MD.

Common/Systematic Name

Mytoxin A

Molecular Formula/Molecular Weight

$C_{29}H_{36}O_{10}$; MW = 544.23085

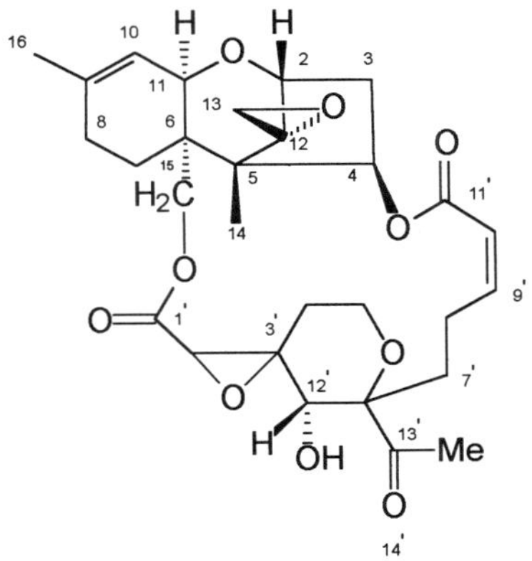

General Characteristics

Amorphous colorless solid; $[\alpha]_D$ +22.9° (c=0.96, in CH_2Cl_2).

Fungal Source

Myrothecium roridum (ATCC 60379).

Isolation/Purification

An aqueous shake culture of *Myrothecium roridum* was filtered and the supernatant extracted with ethyl acetate; the mycelium extracted with acetone. The two extracts were combined, concentrated, and subjected to filtration chromatography (silica gel, ethyl acetate-hexane) followed by MPLC (ethyl acetate-hexane through 10% methanol-methylene chloride). The 50% ethyl acetate-hexane fraction was subjected to MPLC (silica gel, 1-5% methanol-methylene chloride) followed by PTLC of a latter fraction (silica gel, 20-40% ethyl acetate-hexane followed by alumina, 20-60% ethyl acetate-hexane) to give mytoxins A and B. Mytoxin C was isolated by PTLC (silica gel, ethyl acetaate-hexane followed by silica gel, methanol-methylene chloride) of an earlier MPLC fraction.

Biological Activity

Cytotoxic.

Spectral Data

IR:
(CH_2Cl_2) 3580(OH), 1750, and 1710cm^{-1} (C=O).

^{1}H NMR:
($CDCl_3$) 0.79(3H, s, H-14); 1.58(1H, m, H-8'B); 1.67(1H, m, H-7'B); 1.67-2.00(6H, m, H-7, H-8, H-4B and H-7'B); 1.71(3H, s, H-16); 2.16(1H, ddd, *J*=4.5, 5.0, 15.4Hz, H-3α); 2.29(3H, s, H-14'); 2.33(1H, m, H-7'A); 2.56(1H,ddd, *J*=9.6, 9.6, and 14.1Hz, H-4'A); 2.79(1H, d, *J*=4.0Hz, H-13B); 3.02(1H, m, H-8'A); 3.12(1H, d, *J*=4.0Hz, H-13A); 3.23(1H, s(after D_2O exchange), H-12'); 3.42(1H, s, H-2'); 3.54(1H, d, *J*=5.1Hz, H-11); 3.84(1H, d, *J*=5.0Hz, H-2); 4.03(2H, d, *J*=9.6Hz, H- 5"s); 4.04(1H, d, *J*=12.3Hz, H-15B); 4.54(1H, d, *J*=12.3Hz, H-15A); 5.40(1H, d, *J*=5.1Hz, H-10); 5.85(1H, dd, *J*=1.8, 11.5Hz, H-10'); 5.92(1H, dd, *J*=4.5, 8.4Hz, H-4); and 6.44 ppm (1H, ddd, *J*=7.6, 9.1, 11.5Hz, H-9').

^{13}C NMR:
($CDCl_3$) 79.0, C-2; 34.4, C-3; 72.9, C-4; 49.6, C-5; 43.2, C-6; 19.9, C-7; 27.3, C-8; 140.5, C-9; 118.3, C-10; 67.3, C-11; 65.2, C-12; 47.8, C-13; 7.9, C-14; 64.4, C-15; 23.3, C-16; 166.4, C-l'; 58.7, C-2'; 63.9, C- 3'; 22.5, C-4'; 60.3, C-5'; 87.2, C-6'; 22.3, C-7'; 26.4, C-8'; 149.7, C-9'; 120.7, C-10'; 166.7, C-11'; 75.1, C-12'; 212.6, C-13'; and 28.6ppm, C-14'.

Mass Spectrum:
HRNICIMS: 544.2295*m/e* for $C_{29}H_{36}O_{10}$; calcd 544.2308.

Reference

B. B. Jarvis, F. T. Comezoglu, Y.-W. Lee, J. L. Flippen-Anderson, R. D. Gilardi, and C. F. George; Novel Macrocyclic Trichothecenes from *Myrothecium roridum*; Bull. Soc. Chim. Belg., Vol. 95, pp. 681-697(1986).

Common/Systematic Name
Mytoxin B

Molecular Formula/Molecular Weight
$C_{29}H_{36}O_9$; MW = 528.23593

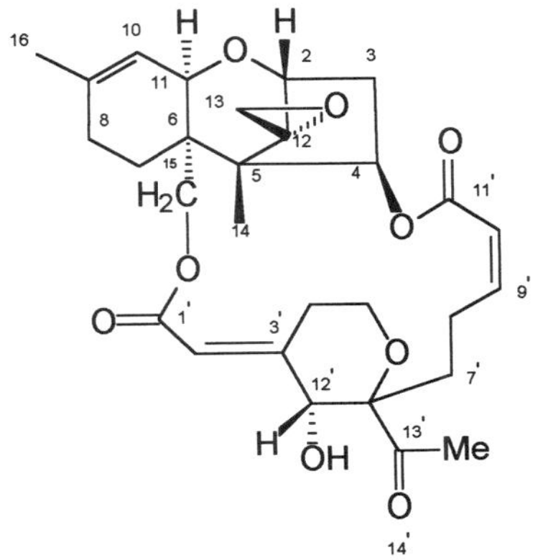

General Characteristics
Colorless solid; mp., 158-161°C; $[\alpha]_{D25}$ = +15.4° (*c*=0.78, in CH_2Cl_2).

Fungal Source
Myrothecium roridum.

Isolation/Purification
See mytoxin A.

Biological Activity
Cytotoxic.

Spectral Data

IR:
(CH_2Cl_2) 3600, 2925, 1720, 1655, 1640, 1355, 1230, 1180, 1165, 1085, 1055, 1030, 1000, 910, and 820cm^{-1}.

^{1}H NMR:
($CDCl_3$) 0.77(3H, s, H-14); 1.58(1H, ddd, *J*=3.3, 13.4, 13.4Hz, H-7'B); 1.70(3H, s, H-16); 1.73-2.02(5H, m, H-7, H-8 and H-8'B); 2.11(1H, ddd, *J*=3.6, 5.3, 15.6Hz, H-3β); 2.29(3H, s, H-14'); 2.30(1H, m, H-7'A); 2.45(1H, dd, *J*=8.1,15.6Hz, H-3α); 2.69(1H, m, H-4'B); 2.72(1H, m, H-8'A); 2.78, 3.10(1H each, AB, *J*=4.0Hz, H-13); 3.57(1H, d, *J*=4.0 Hz, H-11); 3.63(1H, d, *J*=13.6Hz, H-4'A); 3.82(1H, d, *J*=5.3Hz, H-2); 3.96, 4.21(1H each, AB, *J*=12.6Hz, H-15); 4.02(1H, s after D_2O exchange, H-12');

4.04(2H, dd, *J*=2.0, 8.1Hz, H-5'); 5.41(1H, d, *J*=4.0Hz, H-10); 5.75(1H, s, H-2'); 5.76(1H, dd, *J*=3.6, 8.1Hz, H-4); 5.80(1H, dd, *J*=2.0, 11.7Hz, H-10'); and 6.37ppm (1H, ddd, *J*=6.6, 9.1, 11.7Hz, H-9').

^{13}C NMR:

($CDCl_3$) 79.1, C-2; 35.0, C-3; 73.4, C-4; 49.5, C-5; 42.9, C-6; 20.6, C-7; 27.5, C-8; 140.3, C-9; 118.8, C-10; 67.7, C-11; 65.3, C-12; 47.6, C-13; 7.7, C-14; 64.3, C-15; 23.3, C-16; 165.9, C-1'; 117.3, C-2'; 154.3, C-3'; 25.7, C-4'; 63.2, C-5'; 87.7, C-6'; 22.0, C-7'; 27.9, C-8'; 148.7, C-9'; 121.3, C-10'; 166.3, C-11'; 77.3, C-12'; 213.1, C-13'; and 28.6ppm, C-14'.

Reference

B. B. Jarvis, F. T. Comezoglu, Y.-W. Lee, J. L. Flippen-Anderson, R. D. Gilardi, and C. F. George; Novel Macrocyclic Trichothecenes from *Myrothecium roridum*; Bull. Soc. Chim. Belg., Vol. 95, pp. 681-697(1986).

Common/Systematic Name
Mytoxin C

Molecular Formula/Molecular Weight
$C_{29}H_{36}O_{10}$; MW = 544.23085

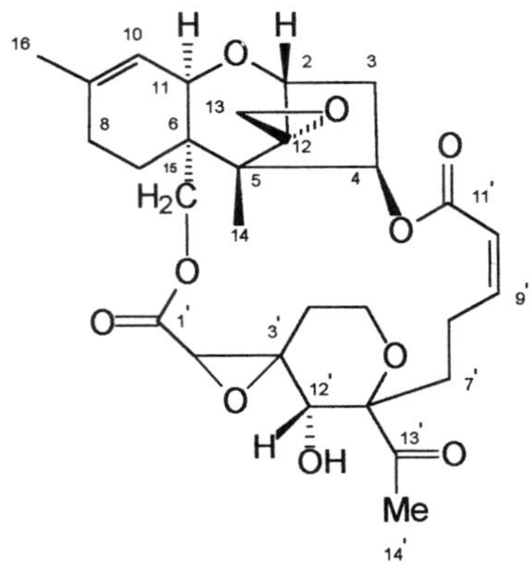

General Characteristics
Colorless solid; mp., 181-185°C; $[\alpha]_D$ = + 4.0° (c=0.83, in CH_2Cl_2).

Fungal Source
Myrothecium roridum (ATCC 60379).

Isolation/Purification
See mytoxin A.

Biological Activity
Cytotoxic.

Spectral Data

IR:
(CH_2Cl_2) 3510, 2900, 1750, 1710, 1650, 1360, 1200, 1170, 1100, 1090, 1040, 995, 960, 910, 860, 820, and 650cm^{-1}.

^{1}H NMR:
($CDCl_3$) 0.81(3H, s, H-14); 1.58(1H, m, H-8'B); 1.70(3H, s, H-16); 1.85(1H, m, H-7'B); 1.9-2.1(6H, m, H-7, H-8, and H-4'); 2.17(1H, ddd, J=4.5, 5.2, 15.3Hz, H-3A); 2.29(1H, m, H-7'A); 2.31(3H, s, H-14'); 2.42(1H, dd, J=8.4, 15.3Hz, H-3); 2.79, 3.11(1H each, AB, J=4.0, H-13); 3.07(1H, m, H-8A); 3.53(1H, d, J=5.2Hz, H-11); 3.82(1H, d, J=5.2Hz, H-2); 3.84(1H, s after D_2O exchange, H-12'); 3.86(1H, s, H- 2'); 3.91(1H, ddd, J=1.3, 5.2, 11.8Hz, H-5'B); 4.00(1H, ddd, J=2.1, 11.8, 11.8Hz, H-5'A);

4.02, 4.54(1H each, AB, *J*=12.3Hz, H-15); 5.39(1H, d, *J*=5.2Hz, H-10); 5.86(1H, dd, *J*=1.8, 11.4Hz, H-10'); 5.92(1H, dd, *J*=4.5, 8.4Hz, H-4); 6.47(1H, ddd, *J*=7.7, 9.0, 11.4Hz, H-9').

^{13}C NMR:

($CDCl_3$) 79.1, C-2; 34.5, C-3; 73.0, C-4; 49.7, C-5; 43.2, C-6; 19.8, C-7; 27.4, C-8; 140.6, C-9; 118.3, C-10; 67.4, C-11; 65.3, C-12; 47.8, C-13; 8.0, C-14; 64.1, C-15; 23.2, C-16; 166.5, C-1'; 53.7, C-2'; 63.3, C- 3'; 23.6, C-4'; 60.2, C-5'; 85.7, C-6'; 22.4, C-7'; 27.8, C-8'; 149.9, C-9'; 120.8, C-10'; 168.3, C-11'; 69.2, C-12'; 214.2, C-13'; and 26.6ppm C14'.

Reference

B. B. Jarvis, F. T. Cömezoglu, Y.-W. Lee, J. L. Flippen-Anderson, R. D. Gilardi, and C. F. George; Novel Macrocyclic Trichothecenes from *Myrothecium roridum*; Bull. Soc. Chim. Belg., Vol. 95, pp. 681-697(1986).

20

Baccharinoids

Baccharinoid B1
Baccharinoid B2
Baccharinoid B3
Baccharinoid B4
Baccharinoid B5
Baccharinoid B6
Baccharinoid B7
Baccharinoid B8
Baccharinoid B9
Baccharinoid B10
Baccharinoid B12
Baccharinoid B13
Baccharinoid B14
Baccharinoid B16
Baccharinoid B17
Baccharinoid B20
Baccharinoid B21
Baccharinoid B23
Baccharinoid B24
Baccharinoid B25
Baccharinoid B27

Common/Systematic Name

Baccharinoid B1

Molecular Formula/Molecular Weight

$C_{29}H_{40}O_{10}$; MW = 548.226215

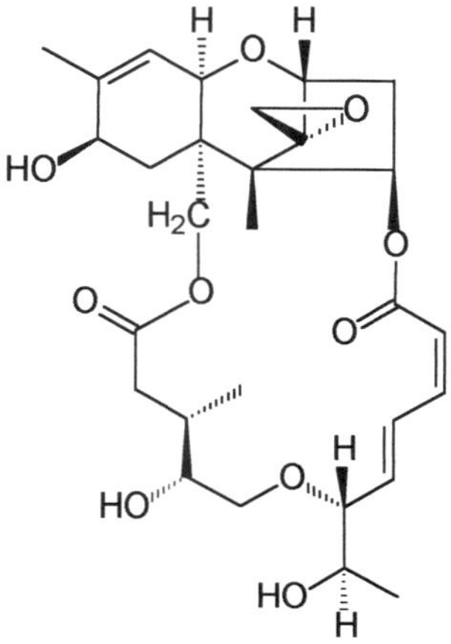

General Characteristics

Melting point, 158-161°C; $[\alpha]_D$ = +100.0° (*c*=1.40, in CH_2Cl_2).

Plant Source

Baccharis megapotamica.

Isolation/Purification

A portion (200mg) of fraction 9D-4 (see isolation of baccharinoid B25) was subjected to semi-preparative HPLC (amino column, 1.5% MeOH-CH_2Cl_2) to give two fractions, the first of which gave 60mg of baccharinoid B1, recrystallized from ethyl acetate-hexane. The second fraction gave 100mg of B2, recrystallized from ethyl acetate-methylene chloride.

Spectral Data

UV:

λ_{max}^{EtOH} 263nm (ε=20,100).

^{1}H NMR:

($CDCl_3$) 0.77(3H, s, H-14); 1.02(3H, d, *J*=6.4Hz, H-12'); 1.20(3H, d, *J*=6.0Hz, H-14'); 1.83(3H, s, H-16); 2.20(5H, m, H-2', H-3, and H-7); 2.44(2H, m, H-3' and H-3); 2.85, 3.13(1H each, AB pattern, *J*=4.0Hz, H-13); 3.6(2H, m, H-5'); 3.63(1H, d, *J*=5.3Hz, H-11); 3.70(2H, m, H-4' and H-13'); 3.86(1H, d, *J*=4.5Hz, H-2); 4.01(1H, m, H-8); 3.76, 4.68(1H each, AB pattern, *J*=12.4Hz, H-15); 4.10(1H, m, H-6'); 5.50(1H, d, J=5.3Hz, H-10); 5.77(1H, m, H-4); 5.78(1H, d, J=11.3Hz, H-10'); 6.05(1H, dd, J=3.1 and 15.5Hz, H-7'); 6.67(1H, dd, $J_{8',9'}$=$J_{9',10'}$=11.3Hz, H-9'); and 7.70ppm (1H, dd, J=11.3 and 15.5Hz, H-8').

^{13}C NMR:

($CDCl_3$) 79.3, C-2; 34.9, C-3; 74.1, C-4; 49.4, C-5; 45.3, C-6; 30.7, C-7; 68.3, C-8; 143.0, C-9; 120.8, C-10; 67.3, C-11; 65.3, C-12; 47.9, C-13; 7.0, C-14; 64.1, C-15; 18.8, C-16; 172.7, C-1'; 38.3, C-2'; 32.4, C-3'; 73.1, C-4'; and 74.1ppm C-5'.

Reference

B. B. Jarvis, S. N. Cömezoglu, H. L. Ammon, C. K. Breedlove, R. F. Bryan, R. W. Miller, M. K. Woode, D. R. Streelman, A. T. Sneden, R. G. Dailey, Jr., and S. M. Kupchan; New Macrocyclic Trichothecenes from *Baccharis megapotamica*; J. Nat. Prod., Vol. 50, pp. 815-828(1987).

Common/Systematic Name
Baccharinoid B2

Molecular Formula/Molecular Weight
$C_{29}H_{40}O_{10}$; MW = 548.226215

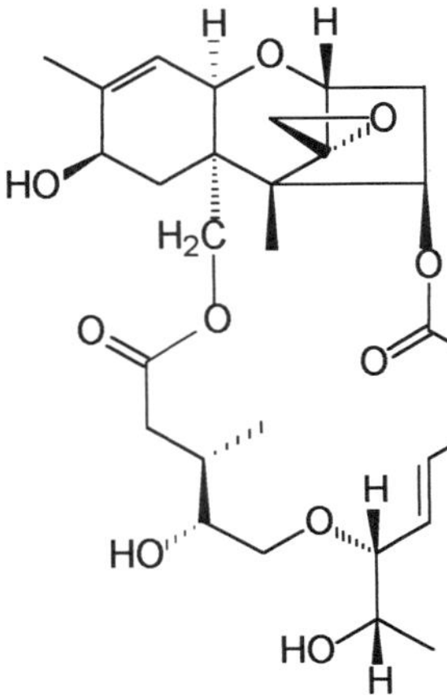

General Characteristics
Crystals; m.p., 177-180°C; $[\alpha]_D$ = +116.0° (*c*=1.0, in CH_2Cl_2).

Plant Source
Baccharis megapotamica.

Isolation/Purification
See isolation of baccharinoid B1

Spectral Data

UV:
λ_{max}^{EtOH} 263nm (ϵ=20,100).

^{1}H NMR:
($CDCl_3$) 0.77(3H, s, H-14); 1.02(3H, d, *J*=6.4Hz, H-12'); 1.20(3H, d, *J*=6.0Hz, H-14'); 1.83(3H, s, H-16); 2.20(5H, m, H-2', H-3, and H-7); 2.44(2H, m, H-3' and H-3); 2.85, 3.13(1H each, AB pattern, *J*=4.0Hz, H-13); 3.6(2H, m, H-5'); 3.63(1H, d, *J*=5.3Hz, H-11); 3.70(2H, m, H-4' and H-13'); 3.86(1H, d, *J*=4.5Hz, H-2); 4.01(1H, m, H-8); 3.76, 4.68(1H each, AB pattern, *J*=12.4Hz, H-15); 4.10(1H, m, H-6'); 5.50(1H, d, *J*=5.3Hz, H-10); 5.77(1H, m, H-4); 5.78(1H, d, *J*=11.3Hz, H-10'); 6.05(1H, dd, *J*=3.1 and 15.5Hz, H-7'); 6.67(1H, dd, $J_{8',9'}=J_{9',10'}$=11.3Hz, H-9'); and 7.70ppm (1H, dd, *J*=11.3 and 15.5Hz, H-8').

^{13}C NMR:

($CDCl_3$) 79.3, C-2; 34.9, C-3; 74.1, C-4; 49.4, C-5; 45.3, C-6; 30.7, C-7; 68.3, C-8; 143.0, C-9; 120.8, C-10; 67.3, C-11; 65.3, C-12; 47.9, C-13; 7.0, C-14; 64.1, C-15; 18.8, C-16; 172.7, C-1'; 38.3, C-2'; 32.4, C-3'; 73.1, C-4'; and 74.1ppm C-5'.

Reference

B. B. Jarvis, S. N. Cömezoglu, H. L. Ammon, C. K. Breedlove, R. F. Bryan, R. W. Miller, M. K. Woode, D. R. Streelman, A. T. Sneden, R. G. Dailey, Jr., and S. M. Kupchan; New Macrocyclic Trichothecenes from *Baccharis megapotamica*; J. Nat. Prod., Vol. 50, pp. 815-828(1987).

Common/Systematic Name
Baccharinoid B3

Molecular Formula/Molecular Weight
$C_{29}H_{40}O_{10}$; MW = 548.26215

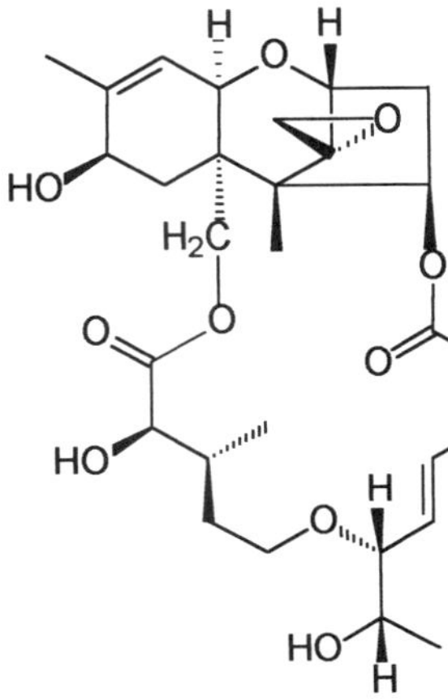

General Characteristics
Melting point, 172-180°C; $[\alpha]_D$ = +164.0° (*c*=0.58, in CH_2Cl_2).

Plant Source
Baccharis megapotamica.

Isolation/Purification
See isolation of baccharinoid B7. The mother liquor from the first crystallization of baccharinoid B7 was subjected to PTLC (10% MeOH-CH_2Cl_2, SiO_2, 2mm plates) to yield baccharinoid B3.

Spectral Data

UV:
λ_{max}^{EtOH} 263nm (ϵ=20,200).

IR:
($CHCl_3$) 3590, 2450, 1720, 1650, and 1605cm^{-1}.

^{1}H NMR:
($CDCl_3$) 0.79(3H, s, H-14); 1.12(3H, d, *J*=6.9Hz, H-12'-H); 1.19(3H, d, *J*=6.0Hz, H-14'); 1.55(2H, m, H-4'); 1.83(3H, s, H-16); 2.10(2H, m, H-7); 2.20(1H, m, H-3β); 2.28(1H, m, H-3'); 2.44(1H, dd, *J*=8.4 and 15.3, H-3α); 2.85, 3.13(1H each, AB

pattern, J=4.0 Hz, H-13); 3.30(1H, s, H-2'); 3.40-3.65(5H, m, H-11, H-5', H-6' and H-13'); 3.87(1H, m, H-2); 4.01(1H, dd, J=5.3 and 10.3Hz, H-8); 3.91, 4.85(1H each, AB pattern, J=12.4Hz, H-15); 4.16(1H, d, J=4.2Hz, H-2'); 5.49(1H, d, J=5.2Hz, H-10); 5.75(1H, dd, J=4.5 and 8.4Hz, H-4); 5.78(1H, d, J=11.6Hz, H-10'); 6.01(1H, dd, J=2.6 and 15.4Hz, H-7'); 6.67(1H, dd, $J_{8',9'}=J_{9',10'}$=11.6Hz, H-9'); and 7.60ppm (1H, dd, J=11.6 and 15.4Hz, H-8').

^{13}C NMR:

($CDCl_3$) 79.3, C-2; 35.0, C-3; 74.3, C-4; 49.4, C-5; 45.7, C-6; 30.8, C-7; 68.2, C-8; 143.3, C-9; 120.6, C-10; 67.2, C-11; 65.1, C-12; 47.8, C-13; 7.1, C-14; 64.7, C-15; 18.8, C-16; 172.6, C-1'; 76.9, C-2'; 35.0, C-3'; 31.0, C-4'; 68.3, C-5'; 82.6, C-6'; 138.8, C-7'; 127.0, C-8'; 143.8, C-9'; 117.3, C-10'; 166.8, C-11'; 16.1, C-12'; 69.7, C-13'; and 18.1ppm C-14'.

Reference

B. B. Jarvis, S. N. Cömezoglu, H. L. Ammon, C. K. Breedlove, R. F. Bryan, R. W. Miller, M. K. Woode, D. R. Streelman, A. T. Sneden, R. G. Dailey, Jr., and S. M. Kupchan; New Macrocyclic Trichothecenes from *Baccharis megapotamica*; J. Nat. Prod., Vol. 50, pp. 815-828(1987).

Common/Systematic Name

Baccharinoid B4

Baccharinol

Molecular formulamolecular Weight

$C_{29}H_{38}O_{11}$; MW = 562.24142

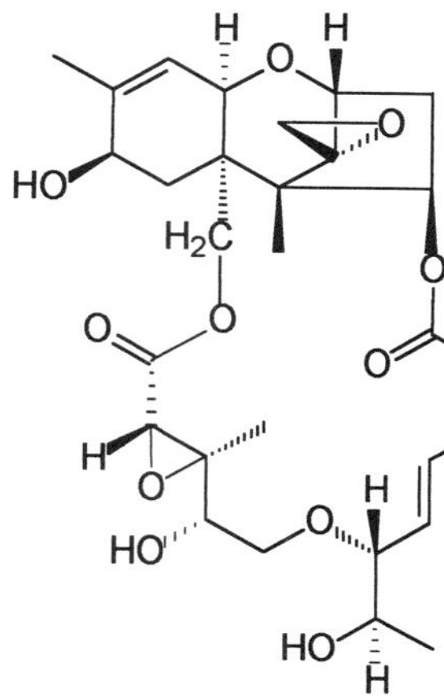

General Characteristics

Melting point, 259-263°C; $[\alpha]_D$ = + 165.0° (*c*=0.50, in MeOH).

Plant Source

Baccharis megapotamica.

Isolation/Purification

See isolation of baccharinoid B5. The 100% methanol fraction from the initial alumina column was subjected to silica gel (MeOH-$CHCl_3$) chromatography and the 10% MeOH fraction crystallized (MeOH-$CHCl_3$) and recrystallized (acetone-hexane) to give 3.5g of baccharinoid B4.

Spectral Data

UV:

λ_{max}^{EtOH} 260nm (ε=20,400).

IR:

($CHCl_3$) 3360, 1750, 1715, 1170, 1640, and 1600cm^{-1}.

^{1}H NMR:

(CDCl$_3$) 0.83(3H, s, H-14); 1.18(3H, d, *J*=6.6Hz, H-14'); 1.59(3H, s, H-12'); 1.83(3H, s, H-16); 2.50(1H, dd, *J*=15 and 8Hz, H-3α); 2.88, 3.13(1H each, AB pattern, *J*=4Hz, H-13); 3.44(1H, s, H-2'); 4.24, 4.44(1H each, AB pattern, *J*=12Hz, H-15); 5.46(1H, d, *J*=5Hz, H-10); 5.8(1H, m, H-4); 5.83(1H, d, *J*=11Hz, H-10'); 6.02(1H, dd, *J*=3 and 15Hz, H-7'); 6.63(1H, dd, $J_{8',9'}$=$J_{9',10'}$=11Hz, H-9'); and 7.42ppm (1H, dd, *J*=11 and 15Hz, H-8').

^{13}C NMR:

(CDCl$_3$) 78.6, C-2; 34.5, C-3; 73.8, C-4; 48.9, C-5; 44.7, C-6; 29.6, C-7; 66.7, C-8; 143.2, C-9; 119.4, C-10; 66.4, C-11; 65.0, C-12; 47.2, C-13; 6.5, C-14; 64.4, C-15; 18.3, C-16; 167.3, C-1'; 55.9, C-2'; 64.8, C-3'; 74.9, C-4'; 72.0, C-5'; 85.7, C-6'; 138.1, C-7'; 125.3, C-8'; 142.2, C-9'; 117.7, C-10'; 166.2, C-11'; 11.8, C-12'; 71.0, C-13'; and 17.8ppm C-14'.

Reference

S. M. Kupchan, D. R. Streelman, B. B. Jarvis, R. G. Dailey, Jr., and A. T. Sneden; Isolation of Potent New Antileukemic Trichothecenes from *Baccharis megapotamica*; J. Org. Chem., Vol. 42, pp. 4221-4225(1977).

Common/Systematic Name

Baccharinoid B5; Baccharin

Molecular Formula/Molecular Weight

$C_{29}H_{38}O_{11}$; MW = 562.24141

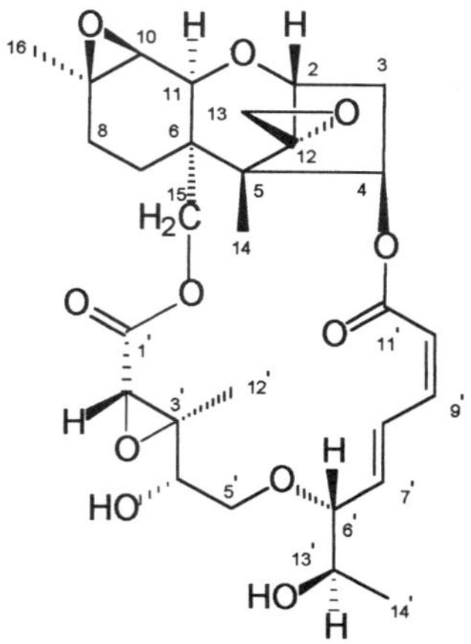

General Characteristics

Melting point, 238-240°C; diacetate, mp., 254-256°C; $[\alpha]_D$ = + 41.5° (*c*=2.2, in $CHCl_3$).

Plant Source

Baccharis megapotamica.

Isolation/Purification

An ethanol extract of 54kg of plant material (leaves and twigs) was concentrated to a black tar and then partitioned between water and ethyl acetate. The ethyl acetate solubles were partitioned between hexane and 10% water in methanol. The methanol solubles were taken up in methanol-ethyl acetate (1:4, v/v) and the mixture filtered through a column of alumina (activity II-III), washing with 6L of 20% methanol in ethyl acetate. The filtrates were combined, concentrated, and subjected to column chromatography over alumina (activity II-III, elution with increasing methanol in ethyl ether). The 10% methanol-ethyl ether (48g) was subjected to column chromatography on silica gel (methanol-chloroform) and an early 2% methanol fraction (3g) upon crystallization from methanol-chloroform gave a solid which upon recrystallization from acetone-hexane gave 1.1g of baccarinoid B5.

Spectral Data

UV:

λ_{max}^{EtOH} 260nm.

IR:

($CHCl_3$) 3580, 2880, 1755, 1720, 1170, and 1100cm^{-1}.

^{1}H NMR:

($CDCl_3$) 0.77(3H, s, H-14); 1.23(3H, d, J=6.5Hz, H-14'); 1.37(3H, s, H-12'); 1.66(3H, s, H-16); 2.19(1H, ddd, $J_{2,3\beta}$=$J_{3\beta,4}$=4.6Hz and J_{gem}=15.3Hz, H-3β); 2.4-2.6(3H, m, H-3 and H- 4'); 2.76, 3.17(1H each, AB pattern, J=3.9 Hz, H-13); 3.09(1H, d, J=5.4Hz, H-10); 3.30(1H, s, H-2'); 3.32-3.38(1H, m, H-5'B); 3.57(1H, d, J=5.4Hz, H-11); 3.84-3.92(1H, m, H-H-5'A); 3.94(1H, d, J=5.0Hz, H-2); 4.20, 4.43(1H each, AB pattern, J=12.6Hz, H-15); 5.76(1H, dd, J=4.6 and 8.2Hz, H-4); 5.80(1H, d, J=11.2Hz, H-10'); 5.97(1H, dd, J=3.0 and 15.6Hz, H-7'); 6.60(1H, dd, $J_{8',9'}$=$J_{9',10'}$=11.2Hz, H-9'); and 7.54ppm (1H, dd, J=11.2 and 15.6Hz, H-8').

^{13}C NMR:

($CDCl_3$) 78.1, C-2; 34.0, C-3; 73.8, C-4; 48.5, C-5; 42.3, C-6; 16.7, C-7; 25.7, C-8; 57.7, C-9; 56.9, C-10; 66.6, C-11; 65.2, C-12; 47.1, C-13; 6.5, C-14; 63.1, C-15; 21.6, C-16; 167.4, C-1'; 56.0, C-2'; 64.4, C-3'; 75.3, C-4'; 72.1, C-5'; 86.8, C-6'; 138.2, C-7'; 125.1, C-8'; 142.6, C-9'; 117.4, C-10'; 166.3, C-11'; 11.6, C-12'; 71.0, C-13'; and 17.7ppm C-14'.

Reference

B. B. Jarvis, S. N. Cömezoglu, M. M. Rao, N. B. Pena, F. E. Boettner, T. M. Williams, G. Forsyth, and B. Epling; Isolation of Macrocyclic Trichothecenes from a Large Scale Extract of *Baccharis megapotamica*; J. Org. Chem., Vol. 52, pp. 45-56(1987).

Common/Systematic Name

Baccharinoid B6; Isobaccharinol

Molecular Formula/Molecular Weight

$C_{29}H_{38}O_{11}$; MW = 562.24141

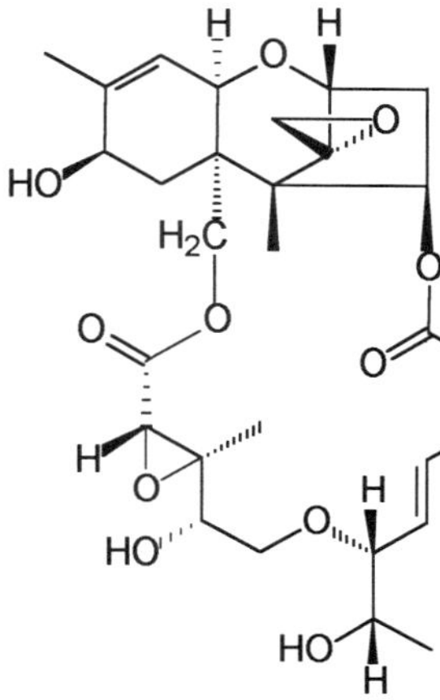

General Characteristics

Melting point, 249-251°C; $[\alpha]_D$ = + 149.0° (*c*=0.66, in MeOH).

Plant Source

Baccharis megapotamica.

Isolation/Purification

See isolation of baccharinoid B4. The 10% methanol fraction from which baccharinoid B4 was isolated was crystallized from methanol-chloroform followed by recrystallization from acetone-hexane to give 0.20g of baccharinoid B6.

Spectral Data

UV:

λ_{max}^{EtOH} 260nm (ϵ=20,400).

IR:

(KBr) 3420, 1750, 1720, 1170, 1650, and 1605cm^{-1}.

^{1}H NMR:

(CDCl$_3$) 0.83(3H, s, H-14); 1.16(3H, d, J=6.6Hz, H-14'); 1.65(3H, s, H-12'); 1.83(3H, s, H-16); 2.84, 3.13(1H each, AB pattern, J=4Hz, H-13); 3.38(1H, s, H-2'); 4.24, 4.46(1H each, AB pattern, J=12Hz, H-15); 5.52(1H, d, J=5Hz, H-10); 5.8(1H, m, H-4); 5.81(1H, d, J=11Hz, H-10'); 5.92(1H, dd, J=3 and 15Hz, H-7'); 6.59(1H, dd, $J_{8',9'}$=$J_{9',10'}$=11Hz, H-9'); and 7.40ppm (1H, dd, J=11 and 15Hz, H-8').

^{13}C NMR:

(CDCl$_3$) 78.8, C-2; 34.5, C-3; 73.9, C-4; 49.1, C-5; 44.8, C-6; 29.7, C-7; 67.0, C-8; 143.3, C-9; 119.6, C-10; 66.7, C-11; 65.4, C-12; 47.5, C-13; 6.7, C-14; 64.6, C-15; 18.5, C-16; 167.4, C-1'; 56.3, C-2'; 65.0, C-3'; 75.5, C-4'; 72.3, C-5'; 85.2, C-6'; 138.4, C-7'; 125.3, C-8'; 142.5, C-9'; 117.5, C-10'; 166.4, C-11'; 11.9, C-12'; 69.0, C-13'; and 15.8ppm C-14'.

Reference

S. M. Kupchan, D. R. Streelman, B. B. Jarvis, R. G. Dailey, Jr., and A. T. Sneden; Isolation of Potent New Antileukemic Trichothecenes from *Baccharis megapotamica*; J. Org. Chem., Vol. 42, pp. 4221-4225(1977).

Common/Systematic Name
Baccharinoid B7

Molecular Formula/Molecular Weight
$C_{29}H_{40}O_{10}$; MW = 548.26215

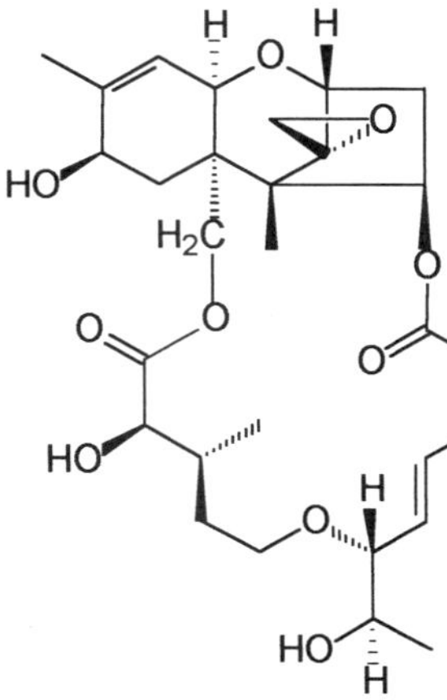

General Characteristics
Melting point, 229-231°C; $[\alpha]_D$ = + 150° (*c*=0.66, in CH_2Cl_2).

Plant Source
Baccharis megapotamica.

Isolation/Purification
See isolation of baccharinoid B17. Fraction F8 from the first silica gel column of the large scale extract was taken up in methylene chloride and the solution carefully washed with 2.5% aqueous NaOH. The methylene chloride soluble material was subjected to filtration chromatography over alumina (activity III, 15 % isopropyl alcohol-hexane, 100 % isopropyl alcohol, and 100 % MeOH). Crystallization of the 100 % isopropyl alcohol fraction from ethyl acetate-hexane and recrystallization from ethanol gave baccharinoid B7.

Spectral Data

UV:
λ_{max}^{EtOH} 263nm (ϵ=20,100).

IR:
(KBr) 3590, 2450, 1720, 1650, and 1605cm^{-1}.

^{1}H NMR:
($CDCl_3$) 0.78(3H, s, H-14); 1.12(3H, d, *J*=6.9Hz, H-12'); 1.19(3H, d, *J*=6.0Hz, H-14'); 1.60(2H, m, H-4'); 1.83(3H, s, H-16); 2.10(2H, m, H-7); 2.22(1H, m, H-3β);

2.28(1H, m, H-3'); 2.44(1H, dd, J=8.1 and 15.2Hz, H-3α); 2.85, 3.13(1H each, AB pattern, J=4.0Hz, H-13); 3.30(1H, s, H-2'); 3.40-3.65(5H, m, H-11, H-5', H-6' and H-13'); 3.87(1H, d, J=4.0Hz, H-2); 4.01(1H, dd, J=4.9 and 9.4Hz, H-8); 3.91, 4.89(1H each, AB pattern, J=12.3Hz, H-15); 4.18(1H, d, J=4.0Hz, H-2'); 5.50(1H, d, J=5.4Hz, H-10); 5.76(1H, dd, J=4.7 and 8.1Hz, H-4); 5.79(1H, d, J=11.5Hz, 10'-H); 6.00(1H, dd, J=2.5 and 15.5Hz, H-7'); 6.66(1H, dd, $J_{8',9'}$=$J_{9',10'}$=11.5Hz, H-9'), and 7.65ppm (1H, dd, J=11.5 and 15.5Hz, H-8').

^{13}C NMR:

($CDCl_3$) 79.2, C-2; 35.0, C-3; 74.3, C-4; 49.4, C-5; 45.7, C-6; 30.9, C-7; 68.2, C-8; 143.3, C-9; 120.9, C-10; 67.2, C-11; 65.1, C-12; 47.8, C-13; 7.1, C-14; 64.8, C-15; 18.8, C-16; 172.5, C-1'; 76.9, C-2'; 34.8, C-3'; 30.8, C-4'; 67.9, C-5'; 83.9ppm, C-6'; 139.1, C-7'; 126.8, C-8'; 143.7, C-9'; 117.6, C-10'; 166.7, C-11'; 16.1, C-12'; 70.7, C-13'; and 18.3ppm, C-14'.

TLC Data

Rf=0.54 (5% MeOH-CH_2Cl_2), 0.29 (EtOAc), and 0.55 (40% isopropyl alcohol-hexane).

Reference

B. B. Jarvis, S. N. Cömezoglu, M. M. Rao, N. B. Pena, F. E. Boettner, T. M. Williams, G. Forsyth, and B. Epling; Isolation of Macrocyclic Trichothecenes from a Large Scale Extract of *Baccharis megapotamica*; J. Org. Chem., Vol. 52, pp. 45-56(1987).

Common/Systematic Name

Baccharinoid B8; Isobaccharin

Molecular Formula/Molecular Weight

$C_{29}H_{38}O_{11}$; MW = 562.24141

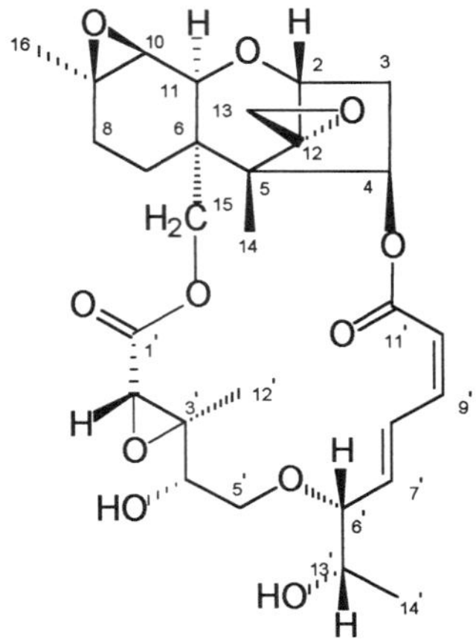

General Characteristics

Melting point, 228-230°C; $[\alpha]_D$ = + 42.0° (*c*=0.36, in $CHCl_3$).

Plant Source

Baccharis megapotamica.

Isolation/Purification

See baccharinoid B5. Continued elution of the silica gel column with 2% MeOH-$CHCl_3$ gave a baccharinoid B8-containing fraction which upon PTLC (25% isopropyl alcohol-benzene) followed by recrystallization from acetone-hexane gave baccharinoid B8.

Spectral Data

UV:

λ_{max}^{EtOH} 260nm (ε=21,300).

IR:

(KBr) 3470, 1755, 1710, 1170, 1650, and 1605cm^{-1}.

^{1}H NMR:

($CDCl_3$) 0.76(3H, s, H-16); 1.17(3H, d, *J*=6.6 Hz, H-14'); 1.34(3H, s, H-16); 1.68(3H, s, H-12'); 2.47(1H, dd, *J*=16 and 8 Hz, H-3α); 2.75, 3.16(1H each, AB pattern, *J*=4 Hz, H-13), 3.09(1H, d, *J*=6 Hz, H-10); 3.35(1H, s, H-2'); 4.22, 4.47(1H each, AB pattern, *J*=12.2 Hz, H-15), 5.8(1H, m, H-4); 5.80(1H, d, *J*=11 Hz, H-10');

each, AB pattern, J=12.2 Hz, H-15), 5.8(1H, m, H-4); 5.80(1H, d, J=11 Hz, H-10'); 5.93(1H, dd, J=3 and 15.5 Hz, H-7'); 6.60(1H, dd, $J_{8',9'}=J_{9',10'}$=11 Hz, H-9'); and 7.44ppm (1H, dd, J=11 and 15.5 Hz, 8'-H).

^{13}C NMR:

($CDCl_3$) 78.2, C-2; 34.0, C-3; 73.9, C-4; 48.5, C-5; 42.4, C-6; 16.7, C-7; 25.8, C-8; 57.7, C-9; 57.0, C-10; 66.7, C-11; 65.4, C-12; 47.2, C-13; 6.6, C-14; 63.1, C-15; 21.6, C-16; 167.4, C-1'; 56.1, C-2'; 64.4, C-3'; 75.6, C-4'; 72.1, C-5'; 85.3, C-6'; 138.7, C-7'; 125.0, C-8'; 142.7, C-9'; 117.1, C-10'; 166.3, C-11'; 11.6, C-12'; 68.8, C-13'; and 15.6ppm, C-14'.

Reference

B. B. Jarvis, S. N. Cömezoglu, M. M. Rao, N. B. Pena, F. E. Boettner, T. M. Williams, G. Forsyth, and B. Epling; Isolation of Macrocyclic Trichothecenes from a Large Scale Extract of *Baccharis megapotamica*; J. Org. Chem., Vol. 52, pp. 45-56(1987).

Common/Systematic Name

Baccharinoid B9

Molecular Formula/Molecular Weight

$C_{29}H_{38}O_{10}$; MW = 546.24650

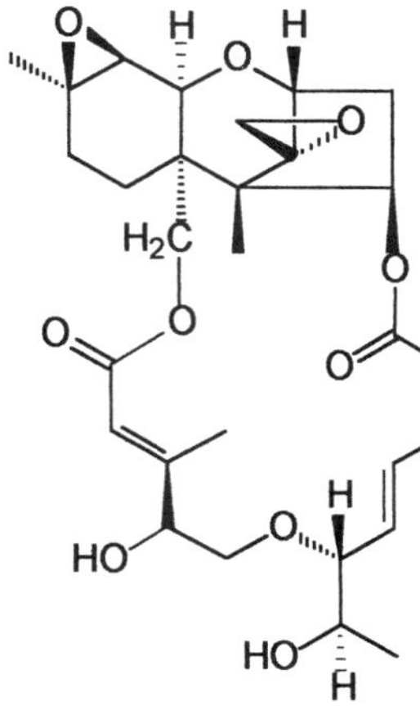

General Characteristics

Crystals; mp., 216-218°C; $[\alpha]_D$ = + 2.4° (*c*= 0.68, in CH_2Cl_2).

Plant Source

Baccharis megapotamica.

Isolation/Purification

See baccharinoid B10 isolation. On the basis of TLC analysis, two of the later chromatography fractions from fractions E1 and E2 were combined and crystallized from ethyl ether-methylene chloride to give baccharinoid B9.

Spectral Data

IR:

($CHCl_3$) 2930, 2870, 1720, 1650, 1610, and 1095cm^{-1}.

UV:

λ_{max} 220 and 262nm.

^{1}H NMR:

(CDCl$_3$) 0.69(3H, s, H-14); 1.18(3H, d, J=6.0Hz, H-14'); 1.33(3H, s, H-16); 2.10-2.25(1H, m, H-3β); 2.31(3H, d, J=1.2Hz, H-12'); 2.45(1H, dd, J=8.5, 15.8Hz, H-3α); 2.74, 3.14(1H each, AB pattern, J=4.0Hz, H-13); 3.07(1H, d, J=5.2Hz, H-10); 3.63-3.73(6H, m, H-4', H5', H-6', H-11, and H-13'); 3.90(1H, d, J=5.0Hz, H-2); 3.76, 4.46(1H each, AB pattern, J=12.7Hz, H-15); 5.71(1H, d, J=11.3Hz, H-10'); 5.87(1H, dd, J=2.5, 16.1Hz, H-7'); 5.98 (2H, m, H-2', H-4); 6.53 (1H, dd, $J_{8',9'}$=$J_{9',10'}$=11.3Hz, H-9'); and 7.38ppm (1H, dd, J=11.3, 16.1Hz, H-8').

^{13}C NMR:

(CDCl$_3$) 78.8, C-2; 35.1, C-3; 74.1, C-4; 47.8, C-5; 42.5, C-6; 18.3, C-7; 26.3, C-8; 57.5, C-9; 57.5, C-10; 67.7, C-11; 65.0, C-12; 48.5, C-13; 6.9, C-14; 63.1, C-15; 22.3, C-16; 166.4, C-1'; 115.0, C-2'; 161.0, C-3'; 74.8, C-4'; 74.7, C-5'; 84.2, C-6'; 138.0, C-7'; 126.6, C-8'; 143.7, C-9'; 117.8, C-10'; 166.0, C-11'; 15.7, C-12'; 70.9, C-13'; and 18.6ppm, C-14'.

TLC Data

R_f= 0.40 (4% methanol-methylene chloride), 0.43 (ethyl acetate), and 0.48 (30% isopropyl alcohol-hexane).

Reference

B. B. Jarvis, S. N. Cömezoglu, M. M. Rao, N. B. Pena, F. E. Boettner, T. M. Williams, G. Forsyth, and B. Epling; Isolation of Macrocyclic Trichothecenes from A Large Scale Extract of *Baccharis megapotamica*; J. Org. Chem., Vol. 52, pp. 45-56(1987).

Common/Systematic Name

Baccharinoid B10

Molecular Formula/Molecular Weight

$C_{29}H_{38}O_{10}$; MW = 546.24650

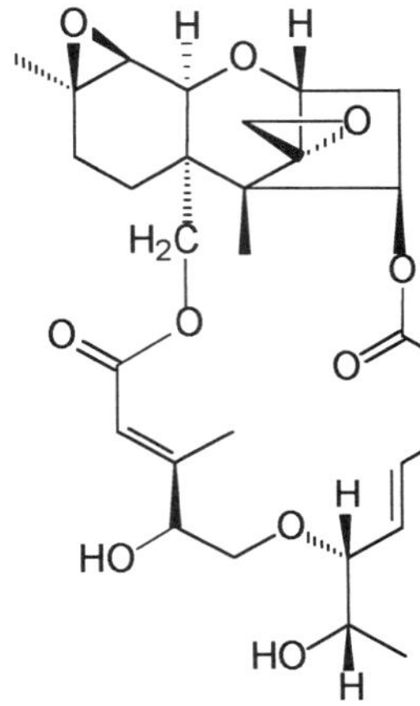

General Characteristics

Crystals; mp., 157-158°C; $[\alpha]_D = +8.1$ (*c*=0.62, $CHCl_3$).

Plant Source

Baccharis megapotamica (original trichothecene nucleus suspected to be of fungal origin).

Isolation/Purification

See baccharinoid B17 for general isolation procedure through the first column. Fraction 7 (1.125kg) from this column was chromatographed over SiO_2 with increasing MeOH in CH_2Cl_2 to give five fractions: F7A-F7E. Fraction F7E (290g) was taken up in CH_2Cl_2 and carefully washed with 2.5% aqueous NaOH to give 121g of CH_2Cl_2 material which was subjected to filtration chromatography over alumina: 20% i-PrOH/hexane (E1), 100 % i-PrOH (E2), and 100% MeOH (E3) fractions. The 20% i-PrOH/hexane fraction (80g) was subjected to filtration chromatography (Al_2O_3) and MPLC (SiO_2) and several PTLC's (Chromatotron) to give baccharinoids B1 - B5 and two additional fractions E1a and E1b that contained additional baccharinoids. Fraction E2 (100% i-PrOH) was subjected to Sephadex chromatography (CH_2Cl_2) to give four fractions. Fraction E2b (5.4g) was subjected to flash chromatography (EtOAc/hexane) and PTLC (Al_2O_3, i-PrOH/CH_2Cl_2, Chromatotron). A fraction from this was combined with E1b and crystallized from $Et_2O/CHCl_3$ to give 65mg of B10.

Spectral Data

IR:
(CHCl$_3$) 3420, 1720, 1650, 1610, and 1170cm^{-1}.

UV:
λ_{max} 220 and 260nm.

^{1}H NMR:
(CDCl$_3$) 0.72(3H, s, 14-H); 1.19(3H, d, J=6.4Hz, 14'-H); 1.33(3H, s, 16-H); 2.10-2.25(1H, m, 3β-H); 2.33(3H, d, J=1.0Hz, 12'-H); 2.43(1H, dd, J=8.0 and 15.5Hz, 3α-H); 2.74, 3.18(1H each, AB pattern, J=4.0Hz, 13-H); 3.08(1H, d, J=5.2Hz,10-H); 3.60(1H, d, J=5.2Hz, 11-H); 3.90(1H, d, J=4.9Hz, 2-H); 3.81, 4.45(1H each, AB pattern, J=12.7Hz, 15-H); 5.71(1H, d, J=11.4Hz, 10'-H); 5.87(1H, dd, J=3.0 and 15.6Hz, 7'-H); 5.97(1H, br s, 2'-H); 5.98(1H, dd, J=4.2 and 8.0Hz, 4-H); 6.53(1H, dd, $J_{8',9'}$=$J_{9',10'}$=11.4Hz, 9'-H); and 7.34ppm (1H, dd, J=11.4 and 15.6Hz, 8'-H).

^{13}C NMR:
(CDCl$_3$) C-2, 78.7; C-3, 34.9; C-4, 74.2; C-5, 48.4; C-6, 42.5; C-7, 18.2; C-8, 25.2; C-9, 57.4; C-10, 57.5; C-11, 67.7; C-12, 65.0; C-13, 47.6; C-14, 6.9; C-15, 62.9; C-16, 22.2; C-1', 166.3; C-2', 115.0; C-3', 161.3; C-4', 75.1; C-5', 74.3; C-6', 83.0; C-7', 137.9; C-8', 126.6; C-9', 143.5; C-10', 117.5; C-11', 166.2; C-12', 15.5; C- 13', 68.9; and C-14', 17.1ppm.

TLC Data
R_f= 0.40 (4% MeOH/CH$_2$Cl$_2$), 0.36 (EtOAc), and 0.43 (30% i-PrOH/hexane).

Reference
B. B. Jarvis, S. N. Cömezoglu, M. M. Rao, N. B. Pena, F. E. Boettner, T. M.Williams, G. Forsyth, and B. Epling; Isolation of Macrocyclic Trichothecenes from a Large Scale Extract of *Baccharis megapotamica*; J. Org. Chem., Vol. 52, pp. 45-56 (1987).

Common/Systematic Name

Baccharinoid B12

Molecular Formula/Molecular Weight

$C_{29}H_{38}O_{11}$; MW = 562.24142

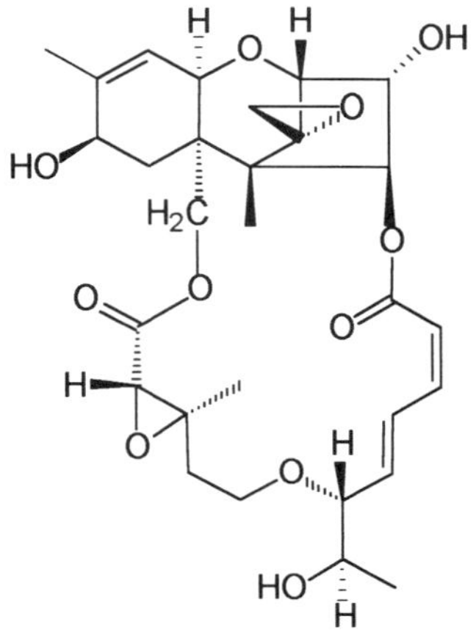

Plant Source

Baccharis megapotamica.

Isolation/Purification

See baccharinoid B17 for general isolation procedure through the first column. Fraction 7 (1.125kg) from this column was chromatographed over silica gel with increasing methanol in methylene chloride to give five fractions: F7A-F7E. Fraction F7B (290g) was taken up in CH_2Cl_2 and carefully washed with 2.5% aqueous NaOH to give 172g of methylene chloride material which was subjected to filtration chromatography over alumina: 15% isopropanol-hexane, 100% isopropanol , and 100% methanol fractions. The 100% isopropanol fraction was triturated with ethyl ether-methylene chloride to give a precipitate which upon recrystallization from acetone-hexane gave 430mg of baccharinoid B12.

Spectral Data

UV:

λ_{max}^{EtOH} 260nm.

IR:

($CHCl_3$) 3500, 2990, 1730, 1715, 1180, and 1100cm^{-1}.

^{1}H NMR:

(CDCl$_3$) 0.85(3H, s, H-14); 1.19(3H, d, J=6.4Hz, H-14'); 1.46(3H, s, H-12'); 1.75(3H, s, H-16); 2.79, 3.08(1H each, AB pattern, J=4.0Hz, H-13); 3.30(1H, s, H-2'); 3.4-3.5 (1H, m, H-5'B); 3.62-3.75 (5H, m, H-5'A, H-6'A, and H-13'); 4.18 (1H, d, J=5.6Hz, H-11); 4.19, 4.43(1H each, AB pattern, J=12.6Hz, H-15); 4.35 (1H, dd, J=2.7 and 5.0Hz, H-3β); 5.76(1H, dd, J=4.6 and 8.2Hz, H-4); 5.80(1H, d, J=11.2Hz, H-10'); 5.57(1H, d, J=5.6Hz, H-10); 6.02(1H, dd, J=2.7 and 15.6Hz, H-7'); 6.63(1H, dd, $J_{8',9'}$=$J_{9',10'}$=11.5Hz, H-9'); and 7.50ppm(1H, dd, J=11.5 and 15.6Hz, H-8').

^{13}C NMR:

(CDCl$_3$) C-2, 79.4; C-3, 75.5; C-4, 83.0; C-5, 49.2; C-6, 44.1; C-7, 20.0; C-8, 25.5; C-9, 139.0; C-10, 119.1; C-11, 67.4; C-12, 64.4; C-13, 46.3; C-14, 6.8; C-15, 63.7; C-16, 23.0; C-1', 167.9; C-2', 57.8; C-3', 63.1; C-4', 39.8; C-5', 67.9; C-6', 84.7; C-7', 140.6; C-8', 125.2; C-9', 143.7; C-10', 116.7; C-11', 166.2; C-12', 17.2; C- 13', 69.1; and C-14', 17.9ppm.

Reference

B. B. Jarvis, S. N. Cömezoglu, M. M. Rao, N. B. Pena, F. E. Boettner, T. M. Williams, G. Forsyth, and B. Epling; Isolation of Macrocyclic Trichothecenes from a Large Scale Extract of *Baccharis megapotamica*; J. Org. Chem., Vol. 52, pp. 45-56(1987).

Common/Systematic Name

Baccharinoid B13

Molecular Formula/Molecular Weight

$C_{29}H_{38}O_{10}$; MW = 546.24650

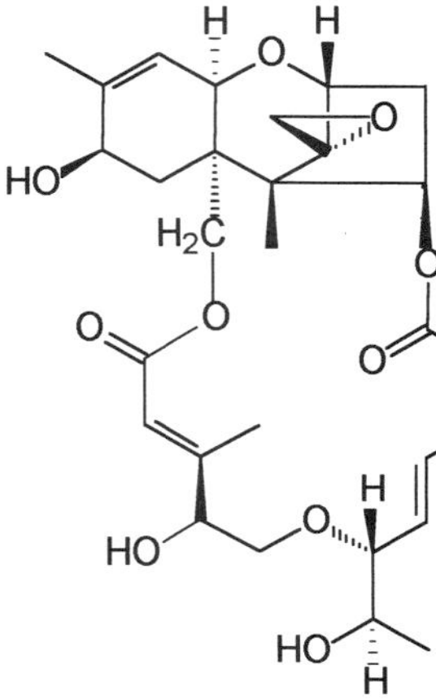

General Characteristics

Crystals, m.p., 218-219°C; $[\alpha]_D$ = + 130° (*c*=0.74, in MeOH).

Plant Source

Baccharis megapotamica.

Isolation/Purification

See baccharinoid B17 for general isolation procedure through the first column. Fraction 9 from this column was chromatographed over silica gel with increasing methanol in methylene chloride to give five fractions 9A-9E. Fraction 9D was dissolved in methylene chloride and hexane was added slowly to give a precipitate. This material was dissolved in methylene chloride and the solution washed with 2.5% aqueous NaOH, concentrated to dryness, and subjected to preparative HPLC using alumina and eluting with isopropyl alcohol-methylene chloride to give six fractions. From these fractions by successive chromatographic procedures baccharinoids B13, B14, B23, B24, B25, and B27 were isolated.

Spectral Data

UV:

λ_{max}^{EtOH} 220 and 262nm.

IR:

($CHCl_3$) 3600, 2880, 1720, and 1180cm^{-1}

^{1}H NMR:

(CDCl$_3$) 0.76(3H, s, H-14); 1.21(3H, d, *J*=6.4Hz, H-14'); 1.81(3H, s, H-16); 2.05-2.15(1H, m, H-3β); 2.22(3H, d, *J*=1.2 Hz, H-12'); 2.51(1H, dd, *J*=8.3, 15.7Hz, H-3α); 2.83, 3.14(1H each, AB pattern, *J* =4.0Hz, H-13); 3.62-3.69 (3H, m, H-13', H-5'B, H-6'); 3.85(1H, d, *J*=5.2Hz, H-2); 3.90-3.96(2H, m, H-11 and H-5'); 3.93, 4.23 (1H each, AB pattern, *J*=12.5Hz, H-15); 4.05(1H, br s, H-8); 4.37(1H, br s, H-4'); 5.54(1H, d, *J*=5.6Hz, H-10); 5.75(1H, d, *J*=11.5Hz, H-10'); 5.85(1H, dd, *J*=3.0, 15.7Hz, H-7'); 6.21(1H, dd, *J*=3.9, 8.1Hz, H-4); 6.24(1H, br s, H-2'); 6.55(1H, dd, $J_{8',9'}$=$J_{9',10'}$=11.5Hz, H-9'); and 7.48ppm (1H, dd, *J*=1.5, 15.7Hz, H-8').

^{13}C NMR:

(CDCl$_3$) 79.3, C-2; 35.6, C-3; 73.9, C-4; 48.7, C-5; 45.2, C-6; 31.7, C-7; 68.1, C-8; 142.4, C-9; 118.0, C-10; 67.1, C-11; 65.5, C-12; 48.0, C-13; 6.8, C-14; 64.2, C-15; 18.6, C-16; 166.3, C-1'; 121.1, C-2'; 160.5, C-3'; 74.3, C-4'; 73.6, C-5'; 84.0, C-6'; 137.6, C-7'; 126.8, C-8'; 143.5, C-9'; 115.0, C-10'; 165.9, C-11'; 18.9, C-12'; 70.8, C-13'; and 16.0ppm, C-14'.

TLC Data

Rf 0.19 (4% methanol-methylene chloride), 0.28 (ethyl acetate), and 0.43 (30% isopropyl alcohol-hexane).

Reference

B. B. Jarvis, S. N. Cömezoglu, M. M. Rao, N. B. Pena, F. E. Boettner, T. M. Williams, G. Forsyth, and B. Epling; Isolation of Macrocyclic Trichothecenes from a Large Scale Extract of *Baccharis megapotamica*; J. Org. Chem., Vol. 52, pp. 45-56(1987).

Common/Systematic Name

Baccharinoid B14

Molecular Formula/Molecular Weight

$C_{29}H_{38}O_{10}$; MW = 546.24650

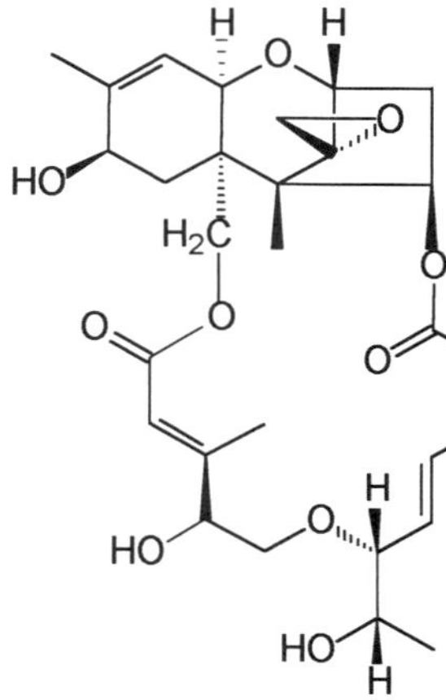

General Characteristics

Crystals from ethyl acetate-hexane; m.p., 149-151°C; $[\alpha]_D = + 72.4°$ (c=0.76, in MeOH).

Plant Source

Baccharis megapotamica.

Isolation/Purification

See baccharinoid B17 for general isolation procedure through the first column. Fraction 9 from this column was chromatographed over silica gel with increasing methanol in methylene chloride to give five fractions 9A-9E. Fraction 9D was dissolved in methylene chloride and hexane was added slowly to give a precipitate. This material was dissolved in methylene chloride and the solution washed with 2.5% aqueous NaOH, concentrated to dryness, and subjected to preparative HPLC using alumina and eluting with isopropyl alcohol-methylene chloride to give six fractions. From these fractions by successive chromatographic procedures baccharinoids B13, B14, B23, B24, B25, and B27 were isolated.

Spectral Data

UV:

λ_{max}^{EtOH} 220 and 260nm.

IR:

($CHCl_3$) 3590, 2870, 1715, and 1180cm^{-1}.

^{1}H NMR:

(CDCl$_3$) 0.79(3H, s, H-14); 1.20(3H, d, J=6.4Hz, H-14'); 1.83(3H, s, H-16); 2.05-2.20(1H, m, H-3β); 2.27(3H, s, H-12'); 2.52(1H, dd, J=8.0, 15.4Hz, H-3α); 2.86, 3.16(1H each, AB pattern, J=3.9Hz, H-13); 3.66, 3.77(1H each, d of AB pattern, J=3.9, $J_{4',5B}$=4.7Hz, J_{gem}=9.8Hz, H-5'); 3.87(1H, d, J=5.0Hz, H-2); 3.86-4.04(4H, m, H-11, H-4', H-6', and H-13'); 3.99, 4.26(1H each, AB pattern, J=12.7Hz, H- 15); 5.57(1H, d, J=6.0Hz, H-10); 5.76(1H, d, J=11.2Hz, H-10'); 5.89(1H, dd, J=3.0, 15.5Hz, H-7'); 6.17-6.18(2H, m, H-2' and H-4' overlapping); 6.57(1H, dd, $J_{8',9'}$=$J_{9',10'}$=11.5Hz, H-9'); and 7.41ppm (1H, dd, J=11.5, 15.4Hz, H-8').

^{13}C NMR:

(CDCl$_3$) 79.3, C-2; 35.6, C-3; 74.0, C-4; 48.6, C-5; 45.2, C-6; 31.5, C-7; 68.1, C-8; 142.4, C-9; 117.7, C-10; 67.1, C-11; 65.5, C-12; 48.0, C-13; 6.8, C-14; 64.1, C-15; 17.1, C-16; 166.3, C-1'; 121.1, C-2'; 161.3, C-3'; 74.8, C-4'; 73.1, C-5'; 82.7, C-6'; 137.3, C-7'; 126.9, C-8'; 143.5, C-9'; 114.9, C-10'; 166.3, C-11'; 19.0, C-12'; 68.5, C-13'; and 15.9ppm, C-14'.

TLC Data

Rf=0.19 (4% methanol-methylene chloride), 0.21 (ethyl acetate), and 0.42 (30% isopropyl alcohol-hexane).

Reference

B. B. Jarvis, S. N. Cömezoglu, M. M. Rao, N. B. Pena, F. E. Boettner, T. M. Williams, G. Forsyth, and B. Epling; Isolation of Macrocyclic Trichothecenes from a Large Scale Extract of *Baccharis megapotamica*; J. Org. Chem., Vol. 52, pp. 45-56(1987).

Common/Systematic Name

Baccharinoid B16

Molecular Formula/Molecular Weight

$C_{29}H_{38}O_{10}$; MW = 546.24650

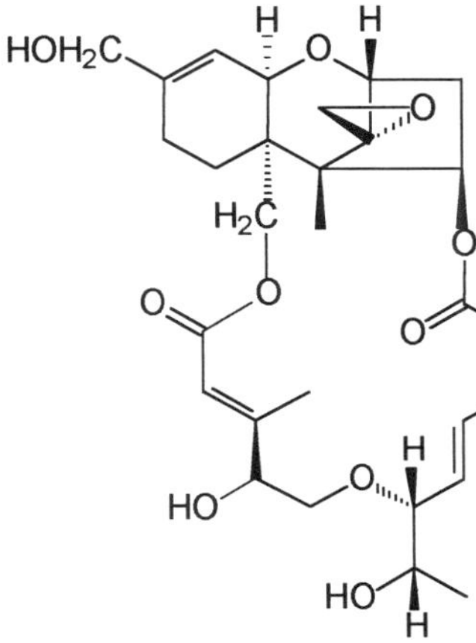

General Characteristics

Crystals from ethanol-hexane, mp., 160-161°C;; $[\alpha]_D$ = + 63.5° (*c*=0.47, in MeOH).

Plant Source

Baccharis megapotamica.

Isolation/Purification

See isolation for baccharinoid B25. Fraction 9E in methylene chloride was washed with 2.5% aqueous NaOH, concentrated, and chromatographed by silica gel MPLC eluting with ethyl acetate-hexane to give two fractions. The second fraction was fractionated using preparative PTLC (60% ethyl acetate-hexane, Chromatotron) which gave baccharinoid B16 which crystallized from methylene chloride-hexane.

Spectral Data

UV:

λ_{max} 220 and 260nm.

IR:

($CHCl_3$) 3600, 2860, 1710, and 1180cm^{-1}.

^{1}H NMR:

(CDCl$_3$) 0.78(3H, s, H-14); 1.16(3H, d, J=6.4Hz, H-14'); 2.15-2.20(1H, m, H-3β); 2.22(3H, d, J=1.0Hz, H-12'); 2.54(1H, dd, J=8.2, 15.5Hz, H-3α); 2.81, 3.12(1H each, AB pattern, J=4.0Hz, H-13); 3.62, 3.76(1H each, d of AB pattern, J=3.7, 9.1Hz, H-5'); 3.63(1H, d overlapping with H-5', H-11); 3.84(1H, d, J=4.9Hz, H-2); 3.96-4.07(1H, m, H-6'); 4.01(2H, br s, H-16); 4.26(1H, br s, H-4'); 4.04, 4.29(1H each, AB pattern, J=12.5Hz, H-15); 5.74(1H, d, J=11.4Hz, H-10'); 5.82(1H, d, J= 5.4Hz, H-10); 5.86(1H, dd, J=2.8, 15.8Hz, H-7'); 6.08(1H, br s, H-2'); 6.55(1H, dd, $J_{8',9'}$=$J_{9',10'}$=11.4Hz, H-9'); and 7.38ppm (1H, dd, J=11.4, 15.8 Hz, H-8').

^{13}C NMR:

(CDCl$_3$) 79.4, C-2; 35.4, C-3; 74.5, C-4; 48.9, C-5; 43.5, C-6; 20.8, C-7; 23.2, C-8; 143.7, C-9; 117.6, C-10; 67.1, C-11; 65.7, C-12; 48.1, C-13; 6.9, C-14; 65.7, C-15; 63.5, C-16; 166.8, C-1'; 118.6, C-2'; 161.4, C-3'; 75.1, C-4'; 74.0, C-5'; 83.2, C-6'; 138.1, C-7'; 126.8, C-8'; 143.5, C-9'; 115.0, C-10'; 165.9, C-11'; 18.9, C-12'; 70.8, C-13'; and 16.0ppm, C-14'.

TLC Data

Rf 0.10 (4% methanol-methylene chloride), 0.17 (ethyl acetate), and 0.29 (30% isopropyl alcohol-hexane).

Reference

B. B. Jarvis, S. N. Cömezoglu, M. M. Rao, N. B. Pena, F. E. Boettner, T. M. Williams, G. Forsyth, and B. Epling; Isolation of Macrocyclic Trichothecenes from a Large Scale Extract of *Baccharis megapotamica*; J. Org. Chem., Vol. 52, pp. 45-56(1987).

Common/Systematic Name

Baccharinoid B17

Molecular Formula/Molecular Weight

$C_{29}H_{38}O_{10}$; MW = 546.24650

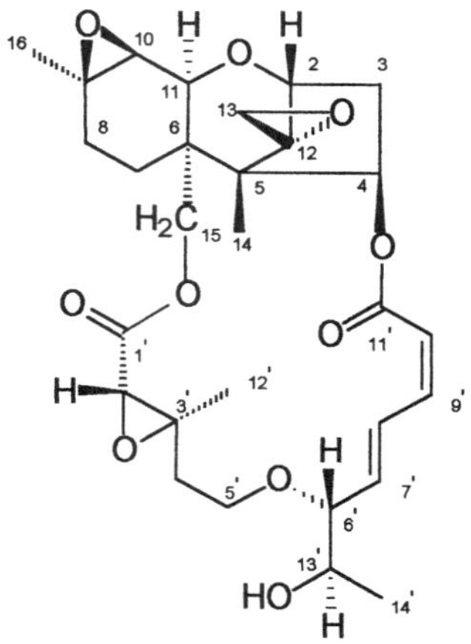

General Characteristics

Crystals from ethyl ether-methylene chloride, m.p., >300°C; $[\alpha]_D$ = + 11.0° (*c*= 0.68, in CH_2Cl_2).

Plant Source

Baccharis megapotamica.

Isolation/Purification

A large scale extract of 1800 kg of plant material was extracted with a total of 6000gal of isopropyl alcohol, which was concentrated to a black tar and partitioned between hexane and 10% water in methanol. The methanol solubles were treated by ferric gel precipitation, filtered, and the "pudding-like" insolubles washed with 50% aqueous methanol. The resulting filtrate was extracted with methylene chloride, and concentrated to give a total of 4.7kg of a dark oil. This material was chromatographed over silica gel, eluted with methylene chloride in hexane, methanol in methylene chloride, and 100% methanol to give 10 fractions (F1 - F10). Fraction F6 was taken up in methylene chloride and the solution carefully washed with a solution of 2.5% aqueous NaOH. The methylene chloride soluble material was subjected to filtration chromatography using alumina eluted with 10% isopropyl alcohol-hexane, 100% isopropyl alcohol, and 10% methanol in isopropyl alcohol). The 100% isopropyl alcohol fraction was chromatographed over Sephadex LH-20 eluted with methylene chloride and then chromatographed by flash chromatography over silica gel eluted with ethyl acetate-hexane). Final purification was by PTLC (Chromatotron) to give baccharinoid B17 after recrystallization from ethyl ether-methylene chloride.

Spectral Data

UV:

λ_{max}^{EtOH} 260nm.

IR:

($CHCl_3$) 3580, 2880, 1755, 1720, 1170, and 1100cm^{-1}.

^{1}H NMR:

($CDCl_3$) 0.77(3H, s, H-14); 1.23(3H, d, J=6.5Hz, H-14'); 1.37(3H, s, H-12'); 1.66 (3H, s, H-16); 2.19(1H, ddd, $J_{2,3\beta}=J_{3\beta,4}$=4.6Hz and J_{gem}=15.3Hz, H-3β); 2.4- 2.6(3H, m, H-3α and H-4'); 2.76, 3.17(1H each, AB pattern, J=3.9Hz, H-13); 3.09 (1H, d, J=5.4Hz, H-10); 3.30(1H, s, H-2'); 3.32-3.38(1H, m, H-5'B); 3.57(1H, d, J= 5.4Hz, H-11); 3.84-3.92(1H, m, H-5'A); 3.94(1H, d, J=5.0Hz, H-2); 4.20, 4.43(1H each, AB pattern, J=12.6Hz, H-15); 5.76(1H, dd, J=4.6, 8.2Hz, H-4); 5.80(1H, d, J=11.2Hz, H-10'); 5.97(1H, dd, J=3.0, 15.6Hz, H-7'); 6.60(1H, dd, $J_{8',9'}=J_{9',10'}$=11.2Hz, H-9'); and 7.54ppm (1H, dd, J=11.2, 15.6Hz, H-8').

^{13}C NMR:

($CDCl_3$) 78.8, C-2; 34.8, C-3; 74.3, C-4; 49.1, C-5; 42.9, C-6; 17.6, C-7; 26.4, C-8; 57.7, C-9; 58.2, C-10; 67.5, C-11; 64.9, C-12; 47.6, C-13; 7.1, C-14; 63.7, C-15; 22.2, C-16; 168.2, C-1'; 57.4, C-2'; 63.7, C-3'; 40.1, C-4'; 67.9, C-5'; 86.0, C-6'; 138.6, C-7'; 126.3, C-8'; 143.5, C-9'; 117.9, C-10'; 166.5, C-11'; 17.4, C-12'; 70.8, C-13'; 18.3, C-14'.

TLC Data

Rf 0.66 (4% methanol-methylene chloride), 0.74 (ethyl acetate), and 0.54 (30% isopropyl alcohol-hexane).

Reference

B. B. Jarvis, S. N. Cömezoglu, M. M. Rao, N. B. Pena, F. E. Boettner, T. M. Williams, G. Forsyth, and B. Epling; Isolation of Macrocyclic Trichothecenes from a Large Scale Extract of *Baccharis megapotamica*; J. Org. Chem., Vol. 52, pp. 45-56(1987).

Common/Systematic Name

Baccharinoid B20

Molecular Formula/Molecular Weight

$C_{29}H_{40}O_{10}$; MW = 548.26213

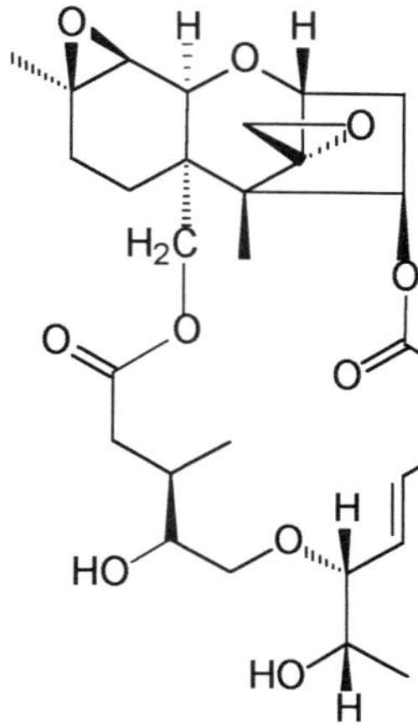

General Characteristics

Melting point, 170-172°C; $[\alpha]_D$ = + 39.9° (*c*=1.44, in $CHCl_3$).

Plant Source

Baccharis megapotamica.

Isolation/Purification

See isolation of baccharinoid B9. Fractions E1 and E2 were combined and crystallized from acetone-hexane to give 210mg baccharinoid B20.

Spectral Data

UV:

λ_{max}^{EtOH} 262nm.

IR:

($CHCl_3$) 940, 1730, and 1370cm^{-1}.

^{1}H NMR:

($CDCl_3$) 0.69(3H, s, H-14); 0.98(3H, d, *J*=6.6Hz, H-12'); 1.16(1H, d, *J*=6.5Hz, H-14'); 1.34(3H, s, H-16); 2.05-2.21(1H, m, H-3β); 2.35-2.50(2H, m, H-3α and H-3'); 2.74, 3.14(1H each, AB pattern, *J*=4.0Hz, H-13); 3.06(1H, d, *J*=5.1Hz, H-10); 3.54(1H, d, *J*=5.1 Hz, H-11); 3.60-3.68(3H, m, H-4' and H-5'); 3.80-4.00(3H, m, H-2,

H-6', and H-13'); 3.78, 4.64(1H each, AB pattern, J=12.3Hz, H-15), 5.74(1H, d, J=11.1Hz, H-10'); 5.74(1H, m, H-4); 6.05(1H, dd, J=3.4 and 16.4Hz, H-7'); 6.71(1H, dd, $J_{8',9'}=J_{9',10'}$=11.1Hz, H-9'); and 7.77ppm (1H, dd, J=11.1 and 16.4Hz, H-8').

^{13}C NMR:

($CDCl_3$) 78.6, C-2; 34.6, C-3; 74.4, C-4; 48.8, C-5; 42.9, C-6; 17.6, C-7; 26.4, C-8; 57.4, C-9; 57.8, C-10; 67.6, C-11; 64.8, C-12; 47.6, C-13; 6.9, C-14; 63.7, C-15; 22.1, C-16; 172.7, C-1'; 38.3, C-2'; 32.5, C-3'; 73.4, C-4'; 74.2, C-5'; 84.4, C-6'; 139.6, C-7'; 126.3, C-8'; 144.1, C-9'; 117.1, C-10'; 166.7, C-11'; 14.9, C-12'; 69.8, C-13'; and 17.9ppm C-14'.

Reference

B. B. Jarvis, S. N. Cömezoglu, M. M. Rao, N. B. Pena, F. E. Boettner, T. M. Williams, G. Forsyth, and B. Epling; Isolation of Macrocyclic Trichothecenes from a Large Scale Extract of *Baccharis megapotamica*; J. Org. Chem., Vol. 52, pp. 45-56(1987).

Common/Systematic Name

Baccharinoid B21

Molecular Formula/Molecular Weight

$C_{29}H_{38}O_{10}$; MW = 546.24650

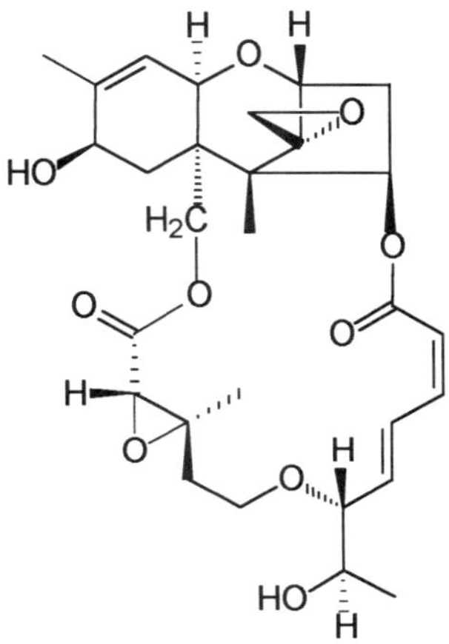

General Characteristics

Melting point, 259-260°C; $[\alpha]_D$ = + 73.5° (*c*=0.68, in CH_2Cl_2).

Plant Source

Baccharis megapotamica.

Isolation/Purification

See baccharinoid B17 for general isolation procedure through the second column. Fraction 7C was subjected to preparative HPLC (3.5% methanol-methylene chloride, Waters Prep. LC/500) to give 10 fractions. The third fraction was sequentially subjected to MPLC (ethyl acetate-hexane) and PTLC (50-100% ethyl acetate-hexane, Chromatotron) to give a fraction which upon crystallization from ethyl ether-methylene chloride gave 140mg of baccharinoid B21.

Spectral Data

UV:

λ_{max}^{EtOH} 260nm.

IR:

($CHCl_3$) 2880, 1750, 1715, 1170, and 1100cm^{-1}.

^{1}H NMR:

(CDCl$_3$) 0.82(3H, s, H-14); 1.18(3H, d, J=6.0Hz, H-14'); 1.55(3H, s, H-12'); 1.81(3H, s, H-16); 2.10-2.22(3H, m, H-3β, and H-7); 2.44(1H, dd, $J_{3\alpha,4}$=8.3Hz and J_{gem}=15.3Hz, H-3α); 2.82, 3.11(1H each, AB pattern, J=4.0Hz, H-13); 3.29(1H, s, H-2'); 3.33-3.37(1H, m, H-5'B), 3.58-3.64(2H, m, H-5'A and H-11); 3.64-3.80(2H, m, H-6' and H-13'); 3.85(1H, d, J=4.9Hz, H-2); 3.82-3.99(1H, m, H-8); 4.19, 4.40(1H each, AB pattern, J=12.3Hz, H-15); 5.48(1H, d, J=5.3Hz, H-10); 5.75(1H, dd, J=4.3 and 8.3Hz, H-4); 5.78(1H, d, J=11.4Hz, H-10'); 5.95(1H, dd, J=2.9 and 15.7Hz, H-7'); 6.58(1H, dd, $J_{8',9'}$=$J_{9',10'}$=11.4Hz, H-9'); and 7.48ppm (1H, dd, J=11.4 and 15.7Hz, H-8').

^{13}C NMR:

(CDCl$_3$) 79.2, C-2; 35.1, C-3; 74.0, C-4; 49.4, C-5; 45.2, C-6; 30.7, C-7; 67.0, C-8; 142.9, C-9; 120.8, C-10; 68.0, C-11; 65.2, C-12; 47.8, C-13; 7.0, C-14; 65.0, C-15; 18.8, C-16; 168.1, C-1'; 58.2, C-2'; 63.4, C-3'; 39.7, C-4'; 67.6, C-5'; 85.8, C-6'; 138.5, C-7'; 126.3, C-8'; 142.8, C-9'; 118.0, C-10'; 166.4, C-11'; 17.4, C-12'; 70.9, C-13'; and 18.3ppm C-14'.

Reference

B. B. Jarvis, S. N. Cömezoglu, M. M. Rao, N. B. Pena, F. E. Boettner, T. M. Williams, G. Forsyth, and B. Epling; Isolation of Macrocyclic Trichothecenes from a Large Scale Extract of *Baccharis megapotamica*; J. Org. Chem., Vol. 52, pp. 45-56(1987).

Common/Systematic Name

Baccharinoid B23

Molecular Formula/Molecular Weight

$C_{29}H_{40}O_{10}$; MW = 548.26215

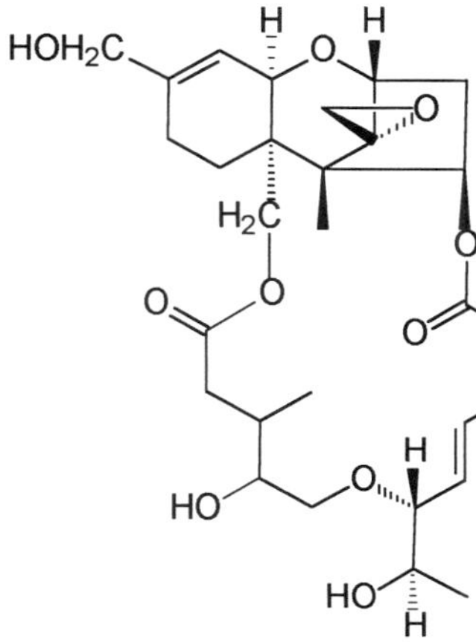

General Characteristics

Colorless glass; $[\alpha]_D$ = + 113.5° (*c*=0.90, in MeOH).

Plant Source

Baccharis megapotamica.

Isolation/Purification

See isolation procedure for baccharinoid B25.

Spectral Data

UV:

λ_{max}^{EtOH} 261nm.

IR:

(CH_2Cl_2) 3600, 2870, 1730, 1715, and 1175cm^{-1}.

^{1}H NMR:

($CDCl_3$) 0.77(3H, s, H-14); 1.00(3H, d, *J*=6.4Hz, H-12'); 1.21(3H, s, H-14'); 2.10-2.25(3H, m, H-3β, and H-2'); 2.40-2.53(2H, m, H-3α and H-3'); 2.82, 3.12(1H each, AB pattern, *J*=4.0Hz, H-13); 3.60-3.75(4H, m, H-4', H-5', and H-13'); 3.73(2H, s, H-16); 3.84(1H, d, *J*=4.8Hz, H-2); 4.06(1H, br s, H-6'); 3.92, 4.67(1H each, AB pattern, *J*=12.5Hz, H-15); 5.77-5.85(2H, m, H-10 and H-4); 5.79(1H, d, *J*=11.3Hz, H-10');

6.06(1H, dd, J=3.3 and 15.7Hz, H-7'); 6.58(1H, dd, $J_{8',9'}$=$J_{9',10'}$=11.3Hz, H-9'); and 7.81ppm (1H, dd, J=11.3 and 15.7Hz, H-8'-H).

^{13}C NMR:

($CDCl_3$) 79.2, C-2; 34.9, C-3; 74.5, C-4; 49.2, C-5; 43.9, C-6; 20.1, C-7; 23.2, C-8; 143.6, C-9; 118.3, C-10; 66.8, C-11; 65.3, C-12; 47.9, C-13; 7.0, C-14; 66.0, C-15; 63.5, C-16; 172.8, C-1'; 38.2, C-2'; 32.4, C-3'; 73.0, C-4'; 74.3, C-5'; 86.0, C-6'; 139.8, C-7'; 126.5, C-8'; 144.0, C-9'; 117.6, C-10'; 166.8, C-11'; 15.0, C-12'; 71.0, C-13'; and 18.6ppm C-14'.

Reference

B. B. Jarvis, S. N. Cömezoglu, M. M. Rao, N. B. Pena, F. E. Boettner, T. M. Williams, G. Forsyth, and B. Epling; Isolation of Macrocyclic Trichothecenes from a Large Scale Extract of *Baccharis megapotamica*; J. Org. Chem., Vol. 52, pp. 45-56(1987).

Common/Systematic Name
Baccharinoid B24

Molecular Formula/Molecular Weight
$C_{29}H_{40}O_{10}$; MW = 548.26215

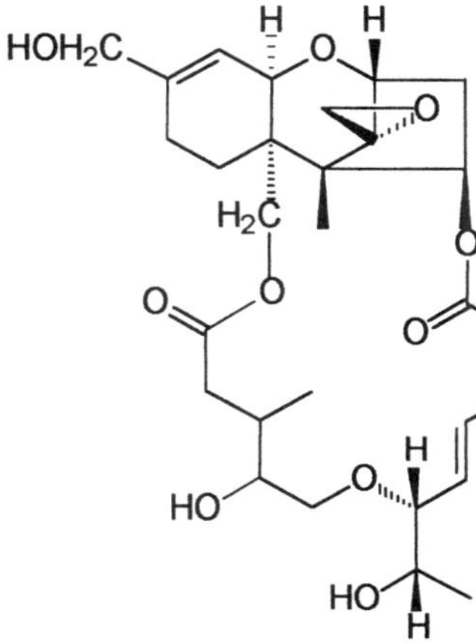

General Characteristics
Colorless glass from methylene chloride-hexane; $[\alpha]_D$ = + 90.8° (*c*=1.36, in MeOH).

Plant Source
Baccharis megapotamica.

Isolation/Purification
See isolation for isolation of baccharinoid B25.

Spectral Data

UV:
λ_{max} 260nm.

IR:
($CHCl_3$) 3600, 2875, 1720, 1715, and 1180cm^{-1}.

^{1}H NMR:
($CDCl_3$) 0.79(3H, s, H-14); 1.01(3H, d, *J*=6.5 Hz, H-12'); 1.17(3H, d, *J*=6.4Hz, H-14'); 2.10-2.50(5H, m, H-3, H-2', and H-3'); 2.82, 3.12(1H each, AB pattern, *J*=4.0 Hz, H-13); 3.62-3.74(4H, m, H-11', H-5', and H-13'); 3.72(2H, s, H-16); 3.84(1H, d, *J*=4.8Hz, H-2); 4.04(1H, br s, H-6'); 3.94, 4.63(1H each, AB pattern, *J*=12.4Hz, H-15); 5.69(1H, d, *J*=5.3Hz, H-10); 5.78(1H, d, *J*=11.3Hz, H-10'); 5.84(1H, dd, *J*=4.5

and 8.2Hz, H-4); 6.06(1H, dd, J=3.0 and 15.6Hz, H-7'); 6.69(1H, dd, $J_{8',9'}=J_{9',10'}$=11.3Hz, H-9'); and 7.79ppm (1H, dd, J=11.3 and 15.6Hz, H-8').

^{13}C NMR:
($CDCl_3$) 79.3, C-2; 35.0, C-3; 74.7, C-4; 49.4, C-5; 44.0, C-6; 20.2, C-7; 23.3, C-8; 143.6, C-9; 118.5, C-10; 66.9, C-11; 65.3, C-12; 47.9, C-13; 7.0, C-14; 66.1, C-15; 63.4, C-16; 172.8, C-1'; 38.4, C-2'; 32.6, C-3'; 73.2, C-4'; 74.7, C-5'; 84.7, C-6'; 139.3, C-7'; 126.8, C-8'; 144.0, C-9'; 117.5, C-10'; 166.8, C-11'; 14.8, C-12'; 70.1, C-13'; and 18.0ppm C-14'.

Reference

B. B. Jarvis, S. N. Cömezoglu, M. M. Rao, N. B. Pena, F. E. Boettner, T. M. Williams, G. Forsyth, and B. Epling; Isolation of Macrocyclic Trichothecenes from a Large Scale Extract of *Baccharis megapotamica*; J. Org. Chem., Vol. 52, pp. 45-56(1987).

Common/Systematic Name
Baccharinoid B25

Molecular Formula/Molecular Weight
$C_{27}H_{32}O_{10}$; MW = 516.19955

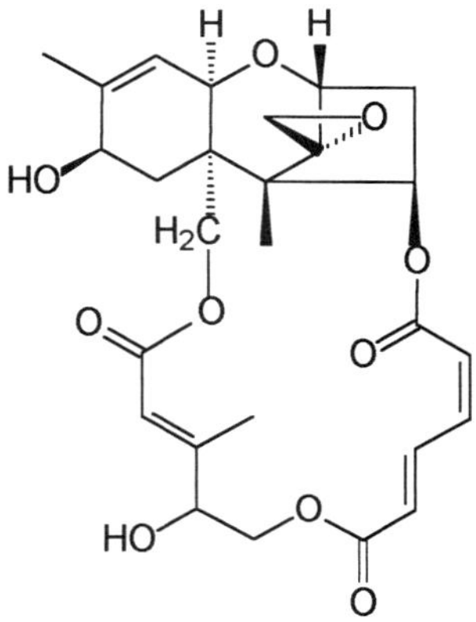

General Characteristics
Melting point, 205°C(dec.); $[\alpha]_D$ = + 214° (*c*=0.70, in MeOH).

Plant Source
Baccharis megapotamica.

Isolation/Purification
See baccharinoid B17 for general isolation procedure through the first column. Fraction 9 from this column was chromatographed over silica gel with increasing methanol in methylene chloride to give five fractions 9A-9E. Fraction 9D was dissolved in methylene chloride and hexane was added slowly to give a precipitate. This material was dissolved in methylene chloride and the solution washed with 2.5% aqueous NaOH, concentrated to dryness, and subjected to preparative HPLC using alumina and eluting with isopropyl alcohol-methylene chloride to give six fractions. From these fractions by successive chromatographic procedures baccharinoids B13, B14, B23, B24, B25, and B27 were isolated.

Spectral Data

UV:
λ_{max}^{EtOH} 220 and 260nm.

IR:
(KBr) 1740, and 1165cm^{-1}.

^{1}H NMR:

(CDCl$_3$) 0.81(3H, s, H-14); 1.83(3H, s, H-16); 2.10-2.30(1H, m, H-3β); 2.53(1H, dd, $J_{3\alpha,4}$=8.1Hz, J_{gem}=15.5Hz, H-3α); 2.86, 3.17(1H each, AB pattern, J=4.0Hz, H-13); 3.88(1H, d, J=5.0Hz, H-2); 3.91(1H, d, J=5.4Hz, H-11); 4.03-4.14(3H, m, H-5'A, H-8-H, and H-15B); 4.40-4.48(2H, m, H-4' and H-5'A); 4.17(1H, AB pattern, J=12.7Hz, H-15A); 5.56(1H, d, J=5.4Hz, H-10); 5.99(1H, dd, J=2.9, 15.7Hz, H-7'); 6.07(1H, br s, H-2'); 6.06-6.11(1H, m, H-4); 6.12(1H, d, J=11.3Hz, H-10'); 6.63(1H, dd, $J_{8',9'}$=$J_{9',10'}$=11.3Hz, H-9'); and 8.11ppm (1H, dd, J=11.3, 15.8 Hz, H-8').

^{13}C NMR:

(CDCl$_3$) 78.3, C-2; 35.4, C-3; 75.1, C-4; 48.7, C-5; 45.4, C-6; 31.6, C-7; 68.3, C-8; 142.4, C-9; 121.2, C-10; 66.9, C-11; 65.4, C-12; 48.1, C-13; 6.8, C-14; 64.2, C-15; 18.9, C-16; 165.8, C-1'; 116.8, C-2'; 158.3, C-3'; 74.3, C-4'; 63.7, C-5'; 165.1, C-6'; 126.5, C-7'; 139.1, C-8'; 139.7, C-9'; 125.9, C-10'; 165.8, C-11'; and 13.9ppm, C-12'.

TLC Data

R_f 0.31 (4% methanol-methylene chloride), 0.64 (ethyl acetate), and 0.58 (30% isopropyl alcohol-hexane).

Reference

B. B. Jarvis, S. N. Cömezoglu, M. M. Rao, N. B. Pena, F. E. Boettner, T. M. Williams, G. Forsyth, and B. Epling; Isolation of Macrocyclic Trichothecenes from a Large Scale Extract of *Baccharis megapotamica*; J. Org. Chem., Vol. 52, pp. 45-56(1987).

Common/Systematic Name
Baccharinoid B27

Molecular Formula/Molecular Weight
$C_{29}H_{36}O_{10}$; MW = 544.23085

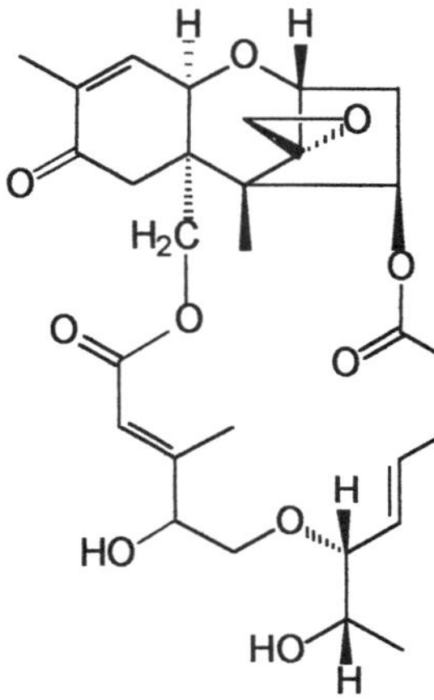

General Characteristics
Melting point, 165°C(dec.); $[\alpha]_D$ = + 5.4° (*c*=0.40, in methanol).

Plant Source
Baccharis megapotamica.

Isolation/Purification
See description for isolation of baccharinoid B25.

Spectral Data

UV:
λ_{max}^{EtOH} 223 and 263nm.

IR:
(KBr) 3600, 2900, 1720, and 1685cm^{-1}.

^{1}H NMR:
($CDCl_3$) 0.76(3H, s, 1H-14); 1.18(3H, d, *J*=6.4Hz, H-14'); 1.83(3H, s, H-16); 2.10(1H, ddd, $J_{2,3\beta}$=4.9Hz, $J_{3\beta,4\alpha}$=3.9Hz, J_{gem}=15.5Hz, H-3β); 2.24(1H, d, *J*=1.1Hz, H-12'); 2.60(1H, dd, *J*=8.1, 15.5Hz, H-3α); 2.42, 2.94(1H each, AB pattern, *J*=16.3Hz, H-7); 2.85, 3.15(1H each, AB pattern, *J*=4.0Hz, 13-H); 3.64, 3.82(1H each, d of AB pattern, *J*=4.0, 9.1Hz, H-5'); 3.93(1H, d, *J*=4.9Hz, H-2); 4.00-4.31(6H, m, H-11, H-15, H-4', H-6', and H-13'); 5.75(1H, d, *J*=11.5Hz, H-10'); 5.91(1H, dd, *J*=2.6, 15.4Hz, H-7'); 6.18(1H, br s, H-2'); 6.20(1H, dd, *J*=3.9, 8.1Hz, H-4); 6.57(1H, d, *J*=5.0Hz, H-

10); 6.58(1H, dd, $J_{8',9'}$=$J_{9',10'}$=11.5Hz, H-9'); and 7.48ppm (1H, dd, J=11.5, 15.4Hz, H-8').

^{13}C NMR:

($CDCl_3$) 79.4, C-2; 36.1, C-3; 73.6, C-4; 48.3, C-5; 46.5, C-6; 38.8, C-7; 197.1, C-8; 136.6, C-9; 138.5, C-10; 66.4, C-11; 65.7, C-12; 47.9, C-13; 6.4, C-14; 64.6, C-15; 17.4, C-16; 166.4, C-1'; 114.6, C-2'; 161.1, C-3'; 74.6, C-4'; 71.8, C-5'; 82.3, C-6'; 137.2, C-7'; 127.3, C-8'; 143.4, C-9'; 117.7, C-10'; 165.8, C-11'; 15.5, C-12'; 68.2, C-13'; and 16.1ppm, C-14'.

TLC Data

Rf=0.44 (4% methanol-methylene chloride), 0.44 (ethyl acetate), and 0.51 (30% isopropyl alcohol-hexane).

Reference

B. B. Jarvis, S. N. Cömezoglu, M. M. Rao, N. B. Pena, F. E. Boettner, T. M. Williams, G. Forsyth, and B. Epling; Isolation of Macrocyclic Trichothecenes from a Large Scale Extract of *Baccharis megapotamica*; J. Org. Chem., Vol. 52, pp. 45-56(1987).

21

Fumonisins, AAL Toxins, and Related Metabolites

Fumonisin B_1
Fumonisin B_2
Fumonisin B_3
Fumonisin B_4
Fumonisin A_1
Fumonisin A_2
Fumonisin C_1
Hydroxylated Fumonisin C_1
Fumonisin C_3
Fumonisin C_4
Fumonisin AK_1
AAL Toxin TA_1
AAL Toxin TA_2
AAL Toxin TB_1
AAL Toxin TB_2
AAL Toxin TC_1
AAL Toxin TC_2
AAL Toxin TD_1
AAL Toxin TD_2
AAL Toxin TE_1
AAL Toxin TE_2
Sphingofungin A
Sphingofungin B
Sphingofungin C
Sphingofungin D
Myriocin

Common/Systematic Name

Fumonisin B_1; Macrofusin

Molecular Formula/Molecular Weight

$C_{34}H_{59}NO_{15}$; MW = 721.38847

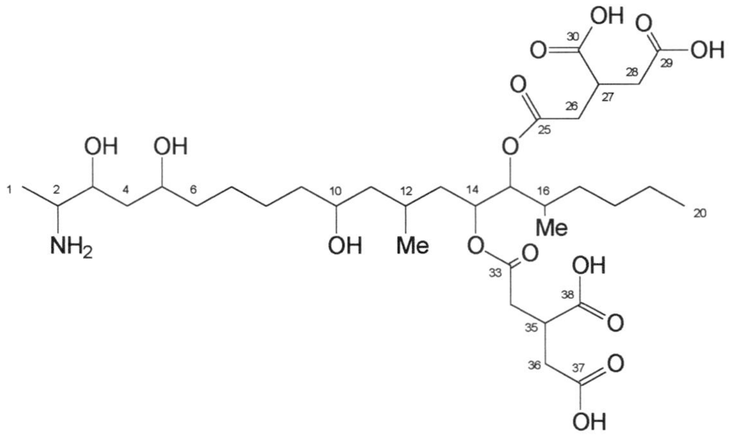

General Characteristics

Fumonisins are highly functionalized hydrocarbon derivatives that are readily soluble in polar solvents and nearly insoluble in nonpolar solvents.

Fungal Source

Fusarium moniliforme Sheldon (M-2326), (MRC-826).

Isolation/Purification

Culture material was extracted twice with ethyl acetate to remove lipid soluble materials. The residue after filtration was extracted with methanol-water (1:3, v/v). The extract was partitioned with chloroform and the aqueous phase was evaporated to dryness under vacuum at 50°C. The dried extract was dissolved in methanol-water (1:3, v/v) and applied to an Amberlite XAD-2 column previously equilibrated with methanol-water (1:3, v/v). The column was eluted successively with methanol-water (1:3, v/v), methanol-water (1:1, v/v), and methanol. The fumonisins were eluted with the methanol fraction. The methanol fraction was chromatographed on a silica gel 60 column (anhydrous sodium sulfate on top of column) eluted with chloroform-methanol-acetic acid (6:3:1, v/v/v). The main fumonisin B_1 fraction was again fractionated on a silica gel 60 column eluted with chloroform-methanol-water-acetic acid (55:36:8:1, v/v/v/v) but without the anhydrous sodium sulfate on top of column. Fractions containing only fumonisin B_1 were combined and finally purified using RP-C_{18} column using methanol-water (1:1,v/v) as eluant. The pH of the sample was adjusted to 3.5 with 1N HCl prior to application to the column. Fractionation was achieved using a linear gradient from methanol-water (1:1,v/v) to methanol-water (4:1, v/v) to produce purified fumonisin B_1.

Biological Activity

The primary animal diseases that have been caused by the fumonisins are leucoencephalomalacia in equine and porcine pulmonary edema. Acute liver and kidney toxicity has also been reported from feeding culture materials containing high levels of the fumonisins. The mode of action of the fumonisins involves disruption of sphingolipid metabolism which, in turn, may lead to disruption of normal cellular regulation. Fumonisins are carcinogenic and also highly phytotoxic.

Spectral Data

^{13}C NMR:

(D_2O) 17.7, C-1; 55.5, C-2; 71.8, C-3; 42.2, C-4; 69.9, C-5; 39.5, C-6; 27.7, C-7; 27.6, C-8; 39.8, C-9; 71.4, C-10; 45.1, C-11; 27.7, C-12; 37.5, C-13; 74.7, C-14; 80.6, C-15; 35.9, C-16; 34.3, C-17; 30.8, C-18; 25.1, C-19; 16.3, C-20; 17.3, C-21; 22.4, C-22; 175.2, C-1'; 37.8, C-2'; 40.0, C-3'; 38.1, C-4'; 179.6, C-5'; 179.1, C-6'; 175.1, C-1''; 37.8, C-2''; 39.9, C-3''; 38.0, C-4''; 178.0, C-5''; and 177.6ppm, C-6''.

(Hydrolysis product) 16.8, C-1; 53.8, C-2; 70.4, C-3; 42.9, C-4; 68.5, C-5; 39.3, C-6; 26.8, C-7; 26.9, C-8; 39.6, C-9; 70.7, C-10; 44.6, C-11; 26.9, C-12; 41.6, C-13; 70.4, C-14; 80.8, C-15; 35.9, C-16; 31.7, C-17; 30.6, C-18; 24.2, C-19; 14.5, C-20; 16.0, C-21; and 21.4ppm, C-22.

Mass Spectrum:

FABMS: $(M+H)^+$ 722*m/e* and $(M+Na)^+$ 744*m/e*.

References

S. C. Bezuuidenhout, W. C. A. Gelderblom, C. P. Gorst-Allman, R. M. Horak, W. F. O. Marasas, G. Spiteller, and R. Vleggaar; Structure Elucidation of the Fumonisins, Mycotoxins from *Fusarium moniliforme*; J. Chem. Soc., Chem. Commun.; pp. 743-745 (1988).

D. Laurent, N. Platzer, F. Kohler, M. P. Sauviat and F. Pellegrin; Macrofusine et Micromoniline: Deux Nouvelles Mycotoxines Isolees De Mais Infeste par *Fusarium moniliforme* Sheld.; Microbiol, Aliments, Nutrition; Vol. 7, pp. 9-16(1989).

R. G. Powell and R.D. Plattner; Fumonisins; In Alkaloids: Chemical and Biological Perspectives; ed. S. W. Pelletier; Pergamon Press; pp. 247-278(1995).

M. E. Cawood, W. C. A. Gelderblom, R. Vleggaar, Y. Behrend, P. G . Thiel, and W. F. O. Marasas; Isolation of the Fumonisins: A Quantitative Approach; J. Agric. Food Chem.;Vol. 39, pp. 1958-1962(1991).

Common/Systematic Name

Fumonisin B_2

Molecular Formula/Molecular Weight

$C_{34}H_{59}NO_{14}$; MW = 705.39356

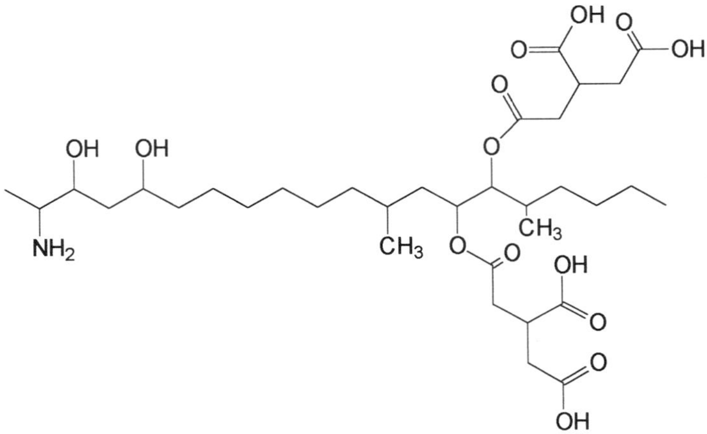

General Characteristics

Fumonisins are highly functionalized hydrocarbon derivatives that are readily soluble in polar solvents and nearly insoluble in nonpolar solvents.

Fungal Source

Fusarium moniliforme Sheldon (M-2326); (MRC-826).

Isolation/Purification

Culture material was extracted twice with ethyl acetate to remove lipid soluble materials. The residue after filtration was extracted with methanol-water (1:3, v/v). The extract was partitioned with chloroform and the aqueous phase was evaporated to dryness under vacuum at 50° C. The dried extract was dissolved in methanol-water (1:3, v/v) and applied to an Amberlite XAD-2 column previously equilibrated with methanol-water (1:3, v/v). The column was eluted successively with methanol-water (1:3, v/v), methanol-water (1:1, v/v), and methanol. The fumonisins were eluted with the methanol fraction. The methanol fraction was chromatographed on a silica gel 60 column (anhydrous sodium sulfate on top of column) eluted with chloroform-methanol-acetic acid (6:3:1, v/v/v). The fumonisin B_2 fraction that coeluted with B_1 and B_3 was again fractionated on a silica gel 60 column eluting with chloroform-methanol-water-acetic acid (55:36:8:1, v/v/v/v) but without the anhydrous sodium sulfate on top of column. Fractions containing only fumonisin B_2 were combined and finally purified using RP-C_{18} column using methanol-water (1:1, v/v) as eluant. The pH of the sample was adjusted to 3.5 with 1N HCl prior to application to the column. Fractionation was achieved using a linear gradient from methanol-water (1:1, v/v) to methanol-water (4:1, v/v) to produce purified fumonisin B_2 (92% purity).

Biological Activity

The primary animal diseases that have been caused by the fumonisins are leucoencephalomalacia in equine and porcine pulmonary edema. Acute liver and kidney toxicity has also been reported from feeding culture materials containing high levels of the fumonisins. The mode of action of the fumonisins involves disruption of sphingolipid metabolism which, in turn, may lead to disruption of normal cellular regulation. Fumonisins are carcinogenic and also highly phytotoxic.

Spectral Data

^{13}C NMR:

(D_2O) 16.0, C-1; 53.8, C-2; 70.4, C-3; 41.8, C-4; 68.7, C-5; 39.3, C-6; 27.7, C-7; 29.7, C-8; 26.7, C-9; 30.7, C-10; 36.1, C-11; 30.2, C-12; 36.2, C-13; 73.1, C-14; 78.9, C-15; 34.9, C-16; 33.2, C-17; 30.8, C-18; 23.9, C-19; 14.4, C-20; 16.0, C-21; 20.9, C-22; 173.0, C-1'; 36.5, C-2'; 38.6, C-3'; 36.1, C-4'; 276.8, C-5'; 175.2, C-6'; 172.9, C-1''; 36.5, C-2''; 38.5, C-3''; 36.1, C-4''; 176.6, C-5''; and 175.0ppm, C-6''.

(Hydrolysis product) 16.8, C-1; 53.8, C-2; 70.9, C-3; 41.9, C-4; 68.6, C-5; 39.3, C-6; 26.8, C-7; 27.9, C-8; 31.2, C-9; 30.8, C-10; 36.9, C-11; 30.5, C-12; 40.7, C-13; 70.4, C-14; 80.9, C-15; 36.0, C-16; 31.9, C-17; 30.6, C-18; 24.2, C-19; 14.5, C-20; 16.0, C-21; and 21.5ppm, C-22.

Mass Spectrum:

FABMS $(M+H)^+$ 706*m/e* and $(M+Na)^+$ 728*m/e*.

References

S. C. Bezuidenhout, W. C. A. Gelderblom, C. P. Gorst-Allman, R. M. Horak, W. F. O. Marasas, G. Spiteller, and R. Vleggaar; Structure Elucidation of the Fumonisins, Mycotoxins from *Fusarium moniliforme*; J. Chem. Soc., Chem. Commun.; pp. 743-745 (1988).

D. Laurent, N. Platzer, F. Kohler, M. P. Sauviat and F. Pellegrin; Macrofusine et Micromoniline: Deux Nouvelles Mycotoxines Isolees De Mais Infeste par *Fusarium moniliforme* Sheld.; Microbiol, Aliments, Nutrition; Vol. 7, pp. 9-16(1989).

R. G. Powell and R.D. Plattner; Fumonisins; In Alkaloids: Chemical and Biological Perspectives; ed. S. W. Pelletier; Pergamon Press; pp. 247-278(1995).

M. E. Cawood, W. C. A. Gelderblom, R. Vleggaar, Y. Behrend, P. G. Thiel, and W. F. O. Marasas; Isolation of the Fumonisins: A Quantitative Approach; J. Agric. Food Chem.;Vol. 39, pp. 1958-1962(1991).

B. E. Branham and R. D. Plattner; Isolation and Characterization of a New Fumonisin from Liquid Cultures of *Fusarium moniliforme*; J. Nat. Products; Vol. 56, pp. 1630-1633 (1993).

Common/Systematic Name
Fumonisin B_3

Molecular Formula/Molecular Weight
$C_{34}H_{59}NO_{14}$; MW = 705.39356

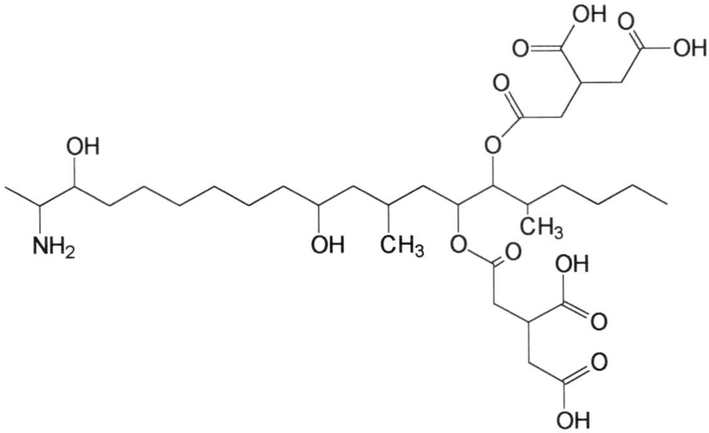

General Characteristics
Fumonisins are highly functionalized hydrocarbon derivatives that are readily soluble in polar solvents and nearly insoluble in nonpolar solvents.

Fungal Source
Fusarium moniliforme Sheldon (M-2326); (MRC-826).

Isolation/Purification
Culture material was extracted twice with ethyl acetate to remove lipid soluble materials. The residue after filtration was extracted with methanol-water (1:3, v/v). The extract was partitioned with chloroform and the aqueous phase was evaporated to dryness under vacuum at 50°C. The dried extract was dissolved in methanol-water (1:3, v/v) and applied to an Amberlite XAD-2 column previously equilibrated with methanol-water (1:3, v/v). The column was eluted successively with methanol-water (1:3, v/v), methanol-water (1:1, v/v), and methanol. The fumonisins were eluted with the methanol fraction. The methanol fraction was chromatographed on a silica gel 60 column (anhydrous sodium sulfate on top of column) eluted with chloroform-methanol-acetic acid (6:3:1, v/v/v). The fumonisin B_2 fraction that coeluted with B_1 and B_3 was fractionated on an Amberlite XAD-2 column equilibrated with methanol-water (1:1, v/v). The pH of the sample was adjusted to 3.5 with 1N HCl prior to application to the column. The column was washed with methanol-water (1:1, v/v). Fractionation was achieved using acetonitrile-methanol (1:1, v/v) to produce purified fumonisin B_3.

Biological Activity

The primary animal diseases that have been caused by the fumonisins are leucoencephalomalacia in equine and porcine pulmonary edema. Acute liver and kidney toxicity has also been reported from feeding culture materials containing high levels of the fumonisins. The mode of action of the fumonisins involves disruption of sphingolipid metabolism which, in turn, may lead to disruption of normal cellular regulation. Fumonisins are carcinogenic and also highly phytotoxic.

Spectral Data

^{13}C NMR:

(D_2O) 15.9, C-1; 53.5, C-2; 73.1, C-3; 34.6, C-4; 26.2, C-5; 26.1, C-6; 26.8, C-7; 29.6, C-8; 39.3, C-9; 69.9, C-10; 44.5, C-11; 26.9, C-12; 36.4, C-13; 73.1, C-14; 78.8, C-15; 34.9, C-16; 33.1, C-17; 30.7, C-18; 23.8, C-19; 14.4, C-20; 16.0, C-21; 20.6, C-22; 173.1, C-1'; 36.6, C-2'; 38.6, C-3'; 36.1, C-4'; 177.0, C-5'; 175.2, C-6'; 173.0, C-1''; 36.6, C-2''; 38.6, C-3''; 36.1, C-4''; 176.6, C-5''; and 175.0ppm, C-6''.

(Hydrolysis product) 16.8, C-1; 53.5, C-2; 73.1, C-3; 34.7, C-4; 26.3, C-5; 30.7, C-6; 30.8, C-7; 26.9, C-8; 39.6, C-9; 70.1, C-10; 44.6, C-11; 27.0, C-12; 41.6, C-13; 70.4, C-14; 80.8, C-15; 35.9, C-16; 31.7, C-17; 30.7, C-18; 24.2, C-19; 14.5, C-20; 16.0, C-21; and 21.4ppm, C-22.

Mass Spectrum:

FABMS: 706*m/e* $(M+H)^+$ and MS/MS of M^+ from FABMS (706m/e).

References

S. C. Bezuidenhout, W. C. A. Gelderblom, C. P. Gorst-Allman, R. M. Horak, W. F. O. Marasas, G. Spiteller, and R. Vleggaar; Structure Elucidation of the Fumonisins, Mycotoxins from *Fusarium moniliforme*; J. Chem. Soc., Chem. Commun.; pp. 743-745 (1988).

D. Laurent, N. Platzer, F. Kohler, M. P. Sauviat and F. Pellegrin; Macrofusine et Micromoniline: Deux Nouvelles Mycotoxines Isolees De Mais Infeste par *Fusarium moniliforme* Sheld.; Microbiol, Aliments, Nutrition; Vol. 7, pp. 9-16(1989).

R. G. Powell and R.D. Plattner; Fumonisins; In Alkaloids: Chemical and Biological Perspectives; ed. S. W. Pelletier; Pergamon Press; pp. 247-278(1995).

M. E. Cawood, W. C. A. Gelderblom, R. Vleggaar, Y. Behrend, P. G. Thiel, and W. F. O. Marasas; Isolation of the Fumonisins: A Quantitative Approach; J. Agric. Food Chem.;Vol. 39, pp. 1958-1962(1991).

B. E. Branham and R. D. Plattner; Isolation and Characterization of a New Fumonisin from Liquid Cultures of *Fusarium moniliforme*; J. Nat. Products; Vol. 56, pp. 1630-1633 (1993).

Common/Systematic Name

Fumonisin B_4

Molecular Formula/Molecular Weight

$C_{34}H_{59}NO_{13}$; MW = 689.39864

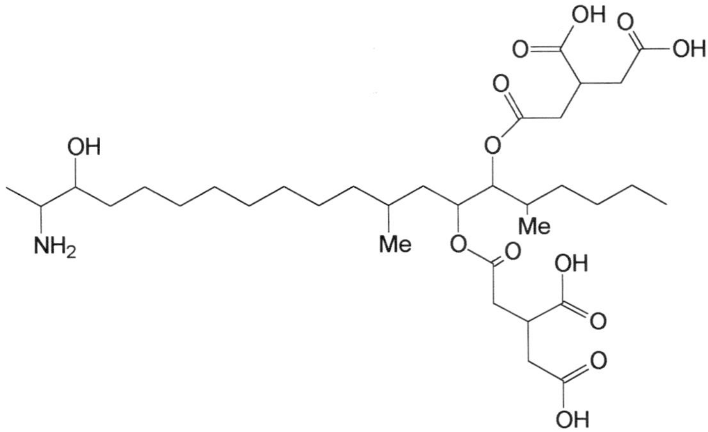

General Characteristics

Fumonisins are highly functionalized hydrocarbon derivatives that are readily soluble in polar solvents and nearly insoluble in nonpolar solvents.

Fungal Source

Fusarium moniliforme Sheldon (M-2326); (MRC-826).

Isolation/Purification

Culture material was extracted twice with ethyl acetate to remove lipid soluble materials. The residue after filtration was extracted with methanol-water (1:3, v/v). The extract was partitioned with chloroform and the aqueous phase was evaporated to dryness under vacuum at 50°C. The dried extract was dissolved in methanol-water (1:1, v/v) and applied to an Amberlite XAD-2 column previously equilibrated with methanol-water (1:1, v/v). The column was eluted with methanol-acetonitrile (1:1, v/v). The fractions containing fumonisin B_4 were further chromatographed on a silica gel 60 column eluted with chloroform-methanol-water-acetic acid (55:36:8:1, v/v/v/v). The fumonisin B_4 was finally fractionated through a Sep-Pak C_{18} cartridge.

Biological Activity

The primary animal diseases that have been caused by the fumonisins are leucoencephalomalacia in equine and porcine pulmonary edema. Acute liver and kidney toxicity has also been reported from feeding culture materials containing high levels of the fumonisins. The mode of action of the fumonisins involves disruption of sphingolipid metabolism which, in turn, may lead to disruption of normal cellular regulation. Fumonisins are carcinogenic and also highly phytotoxic.

References

S. C. Bezuidenhout, W. C. A. Gelderblom, C. P. Gorst-Allman, R. M. Horak, W. F. O. Marasas, G. Spiteller, and R. Vleggaar; Structure Elucidation of the Fumonisins, Mycotoxins from *Fusarium moniliforme*; J. Chem. Soc., Chem. Commun.; pp. 743-745 (1988).

D. Laurent, N. Platzer, F. Kohler, M. P. Sauviat and F. Pellegrin; Macrofusine et Micromoniline: Deux Nouvelles Mycotoxines Isolees De Mais Infeste par *Fusarium moniliforme* Sheld.; Microbiol, Aliments, Nutrition; Vol. 7, pp. 9-16(1989).

R. G. Powell and R.D. Plattner; Fumonisins; In Alkaloids: Chemical and Biological Perspectives; ed. S. W. Pelletier; Pergamon Press; pp. 247-278(1995).

M. E. Cawood, W. C. A. Gelderblom, R. Vleggaar, Y. Behrend, P. G. Thiel, and W. F. O. Marasas; Isolation of the Fumonisins: A Quantitative Approach; J. Agric. Food Chem.;Vol. 39, pp. 1958-1962(1991).

B. E. Branham and R. D. Plattner; Isolation and Characterization of a New Fumonisin from Liquid Cultures of *Fusarium moniliforme*; J. Nat. Products; Vol. 56, pp. 1630-1633 (1993).

Common/Systematic Name

Fumonisin A_1

Molecular Formula/Molecular Weight

$C_{36}H_{61}NO_{16}$; MW = 763.39904

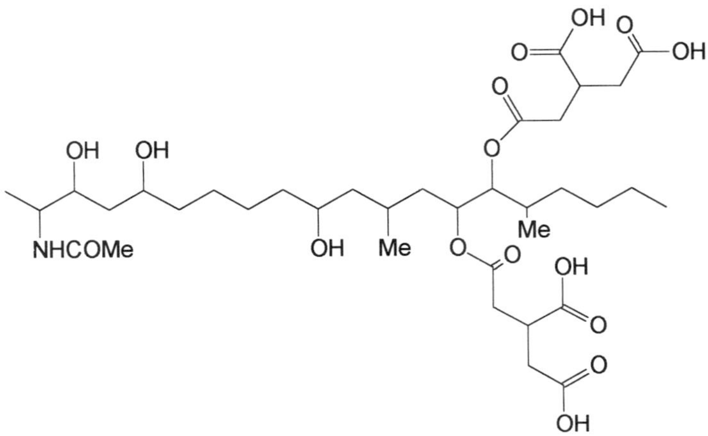

General Characteristics

Fumonisins are highly functionalized hydrocarbon derivatives that are readily soluble in polar solvents and nearly insoluble in nonpolar solvents. Fumonisin A_1 was isolated as the tetramethyl derivative as a colorless oil.

Fungal Source

Fusarium moniliforme Sheldon (M-2326), (MRC-826).

Isolation/Purification

Culture material was extracted twice with ethyl acetate to remove lipid soluble materials. The residue after filtration was extracted with methanol-water (1:3, v/v). The extract was partitioned with chloroform and the aqueous phase was evaporated to dryness under vacuum at 50° C. The dried extract was dissolved in methanol-water (1:3, v/v) and applied to an Amberlite XAD-2 column previously equilibrated with methanol-water (1:3, v/v). The column was eluted successively with methanol-water (1:3, v/v), methanol-water (1:1, v/v), and methanol. The fumonisins were eluted with the methanol fraction. The methanol fraction was chromatographed on a silica gel 60 column (anhydrous sodium sulfate on top of column) eluted with chloroform-methanol-acetic acid (6:3:1, v/v/v). Fractions containing fumonisin A_1 and A_2 were further purified using an Amberlite XAD-2 column. The column was eluted successively with methanol-water (1:3, v/v), methanol-water (1:1, v/v), and methanol. Fumonisins A_1 and A_2 were further purified on a silica gel column eluted with chloroform-methanol-acetic acid-water (65:25:6:4, v/v/v/v) which resulted in separation of fumonisins A_1 and A_2. Final purification was achieved on a RP C_{18} column equilibrated with methanol-water (1:1, v/v) and eluted with methanol-water (3:1, v/v).

Biological Activity

The primary animal diseases that have been caused by the fumonisins are leucoencephalomalacia in equine and porcine pulmonary edema. Acute liver and kidney toxicity has also been reported from feeding culture materials containing high levels of the fumonisins. The mode of action of the fumonisins involves disruption of sphingolipid metabolism which, in turn, may lead to disruption of normal cellular regulation. Fumonisins are carcinogenic and also highly phytotoxic.

Spectral Data

^{13}C NMR:

Tetramethyl derivative; ($CDCl_3$) 18.03, C-1; 49.72, C-2; 71.49; C-3; 40.22, C-4; 68.83, C-5; 38.55, C-6; 25.63, C-7; 25.48, C-8; 37.22, C-9; 68.78, C-10; 43.08, C-11; 25.17, C-12; 35.39, C-13; 71.24, C-14; 77.79, C-15; 33.64, C-16; 31.84, C-17; 28.48, C-18; 22.73, C-19; 13.92, C-20; 15.36, C-21; 20.36, C-22; 175.48, C-23; 2332, C-24; 170.88, C-25; 35.27, C-26; 37.28, C-27; 35.10, C-28; 173.41, C-29; 171.69, C-30; 52.31, C-31; and 51.82ppm, C-32.

Mass Spectrum:

Tetramethyl derivative; FABMS: $(M+H)^+$ 820*m/e* and $(M+Na)^+$ 842*m/e*.

References

S. C. Bezuuidenhout, W. C. A. Gelderblom, C. P. Gorst-Allman, R. M. Horak, W. F. O. Marasas, G. Spiteller, and R. Vleggaar; Structure Elucidation of the Fumonisins, Mycotoxins from *Fusarium moniliforme*; J. Chem. Soc., Chem. Commun.; pp. 743-745 (1988).

R. G. Powell and R.D. Plattner; Fumonisins; In Alkaloids: Chemical and Biological Perspectives; ed. S. W. Pelletier; Pergamon Press; pp. 247-278(1995).

M. E. Cawood, W. C. A. Gelderblom, R. Vleggaar, Y. Behrend, P. G. Thiel, and W. F. O. Marasas; Isolation of the Fumonisins: A Quantitative Approach; J. Agric. Food Chem.;Vol. 39, pp. 1958-1962(1991).

Common/Systematic Name

Fumonisin A_2

Molecular Formula/Molecular Weight

$C_{36}H_{61}NO_{15}$; MW = 747.40412

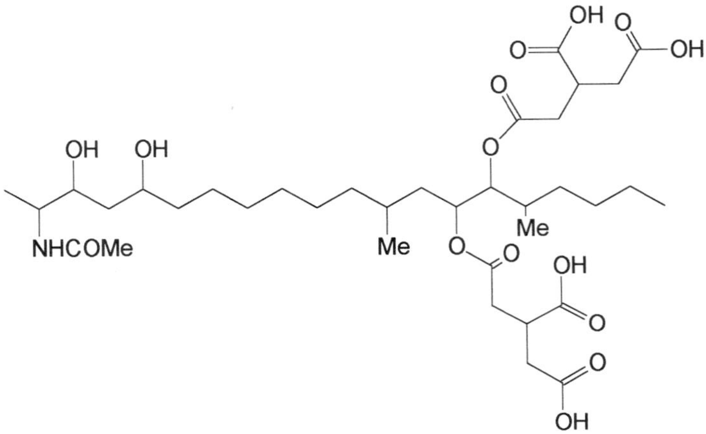

General Characteristics

Fumonisins are highly functionalized hydrocarbon derivatives that are readily soluble in polar solvents and nearly insoluble in nonpolar solvents. Fumonisin A_2 was isolated as the tetramethyl derivative as a colorless oil.

Fungal Source

Fusarium moniliforme Sheldon (M-2326), (MRC-826).

Isolation/Purification

Culture material was extracted twice with ethyl acetate to remove lipid soluble materials. The residue after filtration was extracted with methanol-water (1:3, v/v). The extract was partitioned with chloroform and the aqueous phase was evaporated to dryness under vacuum at 50° C. The dried extract was dissolved in methanol-water (1:3, v/v) and applied to an Amberlite XAD-2 column previously equilibrated with methanol-water (1:3, v/v). The column was eluted successively with methanol-water (1:3, v/v), methanol-water (1:1, v/v), and methanol. The fumonisins were eluted with the methanol fraction. The methanol fraction was chromatographed on a silica gel 60 column (anhydrous sodium sulfate on top of column) eluted with chloroform-methanol-acetic acid (6:3:1, v/v/v). Fractions containing fumonisin A_1 and A_2 were further purified using an Amberlite XAD-2 column. The column was eluted successively with methanol-water (1:3, v/v), methanol-water (1:1, v/v), and methanol. Fumonisins A_1 and A_2 were further purified on a silica gel column eluted with chloroform-methanol-acetic acid-water (65:25:6:4, v/v/v/v) which resulted in separation of fumonisins A_1 and A_2. Final purification was achieved on a RP C_{18} column equilibrated with methanol-water (1:1, v/v) and eluted with methanol-water (3:1, v/v).

Biological Activity

The primary animal diseases that have been caused by the fumonisins are leucoencephalomalacia in equine and porcine pulmonary edema. Acute liver and kidney toxicity has also been reported from feeding culture materials containing high levels of the fumonisins. The mode of action of the fumonisins involves disruption of sphingolipid metabolism which, in turn, may lead to disruption of normal cellular regulation. Fumonisins are carcinogenic and also highly phytotoxic.

Spectral Data

Mass Spectrum:

Tetramethyl derivative; FABMS: $(M+H^+)$ 84*m/e*.

References

S. C. Bezuuidenhout, W. C. A. Gelderblom, C. P. Gorst-Allman, R. M. Horak, W. F. O. Marasas, G. Spiteller, and R. Vleggaar; Structure Elucidation of the Fumonisins, Mycotoxins from *Fusarium moniliforme*; J. Chem. Soc., Chem. Commun.; pp. 743-745 (1988).

R. G. Powell and R.D. Plattner; Fumonisins; In Alkaloids: Chemical and Biological Perspectives; ed. S. W. Pelletier; Pergamon Press; pp. 247-278(1995).

M. E. Cawood, W. C. A. Gelderblom, R. Vleggaar, Y. Behrend, P. G. Thiel, and W. F. O. Marasas; Isolation of the Fumonisins: a quantitative approach; J. Agric. Food Chem.;Vol. 39, pp. 1958-1962(1991).

Common/Systematic Name
Fumonisin C_1

Molecular Formula/Molecular Weight
$C_{33}H_{57}NO_{15}$; MW = 707.37282

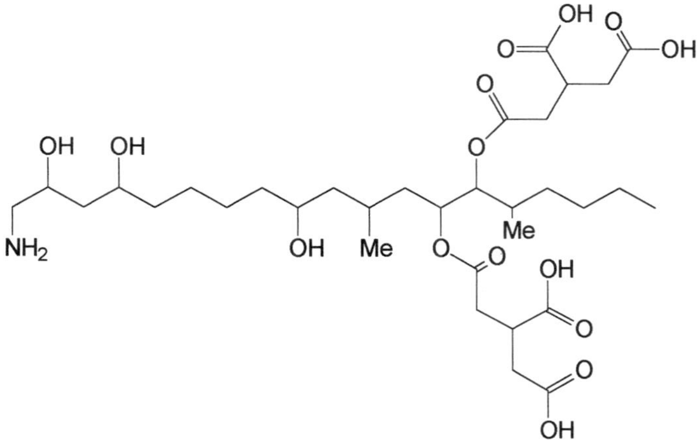

General Characteristics
Obtained as a colorless liquid.

Fungal Source
Fusarium moniliforme Sheldon (M-2326); (MRC-826).

Isolation/Purification
Method 1. The crude culture material was separated on preparative reversed-phase HPLC using a C_{18} column eluted with a gradient from 100% water to 100% methanol. The fraction containing a solvent concentration of approximately methanol-water (60:40) was taken to dryness and chromatographed on a C_{18} column using an isocratic mobile phase of 0.05 M NaH_2PO_4 (adjusted to pH 3.35)-acetonitrile (72:24, v/v). Fractions containing both fumonisins B_1 and C_1 were rechromatographed on a C_{18} column using a mobile phase of 0.05 M NaH_2PO_4 (adjusted to pH 3.35)-acetonitrile (74:26, v/v). Fractions containing fumonisin C_1 were combined, taken to dryness, and desalted on a C_{18} mini-column.

Method 2. Solid culture material was extracted with methanol-water (3:1, v/v), filtered, and concentrated to dryness. The aqueous phase was chromatographed on an Amberlite XAD-2 column eluted successively with methanol-water (1:3, v/v), (1:1, v/v), (3:1, v/v), and finally with methanol. Fumonisin C_1, hydroxylated C_1, C_3, and C_4 were eluted in the methanol-water (3:1) and methanol fractions. These fractions were combined, concentrated to dryness and chromatographed on a silica gel column eluted with chloroform-methanol-acetic acid (6:3:1, v/v). The eluant was reduced to two fractions, F-1 and F-2. The F-1 fraction was chromatographed on a silica gel column eluted with ethyl acetate-acetic acid-hexane-water (6:2:2:1, v/v/v/v). The fractions containing fumonisin C_3 or C_4 were combined separately and concentrated to dryness. Fraction F-2 was separated on a μBondapak C_{18} column eluted with a gradient from methanol-water-acetic acid (20:80:1, v/v/v) to methanol-acetic acid (100:1, v/v). Fractions containing either fumonisin C_1 or hydroxylated C_1 were combined separately and reduced to dryness. Final purification of each of the fumonisins was performed on a strong-anion exchange (SAX) Sep-Pak cartridge successively washed with methanol-water (3:1, v/v) and methanol. The fumonisins were eluted from the column with 1% acetic acid in methanol.

Biological Activity

The primary animal diseases that have been caused by the fumonisins are leucoencephalomalacia in equine and porcine pulmonary edema. Acute liver and kidney toxicity has also been reported from feeding culture materials containing high levels of the fumonisins. The mode of action of the fumonisins involves disruption of sphingolipid metabolism which, in turn, may lead to disruption of normal cellular regulation. Fumonisins are carcinogenic and also highly phytotoxic.

Spectral Data

^{13}C NMR:

(D_2O) 47.5, C-1; 71.2, C-2; 43.6, C-3; 67.4, C-4; 39.7, C-5; 27.6, C-6; 27.5, C-7; 39.7, C-8; 69.8, C-9; 42.5, C-10; 27.9, C-11; 37.6, C-12; 74.7, C-13; 80.5, C-14; 35.8, C-15; 34.0, C-16; 30.5, C-17; 24.9, C-18; 15.9, C-19; 17.4, C-20; 22.2, C-21; 175.4, C-1'; 38.4, C-2'; 41.0, C-3'; 39.0, C-4'; 180.4, C-5'; 180.0, C-6'; 175.4, C-1''; 38.4, C-2''; 41.0, C-3''; 38.9, C-4''; 179.0, C-5''; and 178.6ppm, C-6''. (CD_3OD) 46.6, C-1; 70.0, C-2; 43.1, C-3; 66.3, C-4; 37.9, C-5; 26.7, C-6; 26.6, C-7; 39.0, C-8; 68.6, C-9; 44.6, C-10; 26.9, C-11; 34.9, C-12; 72.8, C-13; 78.8, C-14; 34.9, C-15; 33.0, C-16; 29.7, C-17; 23.9, C-18; 14.4, C-19; 16.0, C-20; 20.8, C-21; 173.5, C-22; 37.0, C-23; 39.7, C-24; 37.6, C-25; 178.7, C-26; 178.0, C-27; 173.3, C-28; 36.8, C-29; 39.6, C-30; 37.2, C-31; 176.7, C-32; and 176.7ppm, C-33.

^{1}H NMR:

(CD_3OH) 5.14(1H, dt, *J*=11.3, 3.7Hz, H-13); 4.93(1H, dd, *J*=8.3, 3.9Hz, H-14); 4.00(1H, m, H-2); 3.79(1H,m, H-4); 3.66(1H, m, H-9); 3.14(2 x 1H, m, H-24 and H-30); 3.03(1H, dd, *J*=13.0, 3.4Hz, H-1_b); 2.80(1H, dd, *J*=12.9, 7.6Hz); 2.76(1H, H-1_a); 2.72(1H, dd, *J*=7.6, 3.0Hz); 2.72(1H, dd, 7.6,3.0Hz); 2.69-2.66(3 x 1H, m); 2.53-2.41(3 x 1H, m); 1.81(1H, m, H-11); 1.67(1H, H-15); 1.58(1H, H-12_b); 1.35-1.54(16H,m); 1.30(1H, m, H-17_a); 1.16(1H, 10_a); 1.11(1H, H-16_a); 0.95(3H, d, *J*= 6.3Hz, H-21); 0.93(3H, d, *J*=6.8Hz, H-20); and 0.88ppm (3H, t, *J*=7.1Hz, H-19).

Mass Spectrum:

FABMS: $(M+H)^+$ 708*m/e* and MS/MS of 708*m/e* from FABMS 708*m/e*. 708(parent ion), 690(25), 532(7), 514(5), 374(5), 356(30), 338(100), and 320*m/e*(55). TFA derivative of hydrolyzed fumonisin C_1 (molecular weight 981), 740(0.1), 626(6),

568(2), 542(3), 541(3), 528(7), 512(6), 414(3), 264(4), 211(20), 180(60), 126(59), 97(100), 55(66), and 43*m/e* (43).

TLC:

R_f = 0.29 on C_{18} reversed phase plates developed in chloroform-methanol-water-acetic acid (55:36:8:1, v/v/v/v). Fumonisins were visualized by spraying with 0.5% *p*-anisaldehyde solution in methanol-sulfuric acid-acetic acid (85:5:10, v/v/v) and heating at 110°C for 10 min.

References

B. E. Branham and R. D. Plattner; Isolation and Characterization of a New Fumonisin from Liquid Cultures of *Fusarium moniliforme*; J. Nat. Products; Vol. 56, pp. 1630-1633 (1993).

J-A Seo, J-C. Kim, and Y-W Lee; Isolation and Characterization of Two New Type C Fumonisins Produced by *Fusarium oxysporum*; J. Nat. Products; Vol. 59, pp. 1003-1005 (1996).

Common/Systematic Name

Hydroxylated Fumonisin C_1

Molecular Formula/Molecular Weight

$C_{33}H_{57}NO_{16}$; MW = 723.36774

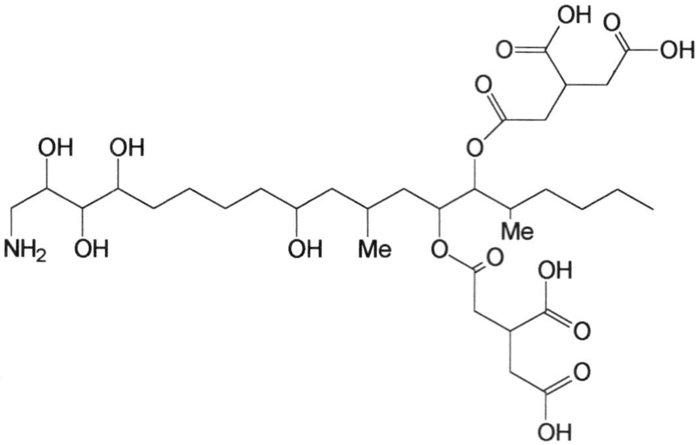

General Characteristics

Obtained as a colorless liquid.

Fungal Source

Fusarium oxysporum.

Isolation/Purification

Solid culture material was extracted with methanol-water (3:1, v/v), filtered, and concentrated to dryness. The aqueous phase was chromatographed on an Amberlite XAD-2 column eluted successively with methanol-water (1:3, v/v), (1:1, v/v), (3:1, v/v), and finally with methanol. Fumonisin C_1, hydroxylated C_1, C_3, and C_4 were eluted in the methanol-water (3:1) and methanol fractions. These fractions were combined, concentrated to dryness and chromatographed on a silica gel column eluted with chloroform-methanol-acetic acid (6:3:1, v/v). The eluant was reduced to two fractions, F-1 and F-2. The F-1 fraction was chromatographed on a silica gel column eluted with ethyl acetate-acetic acid-hexane-water (6:2:2:1, v/v/v/v). The fractions containing fumonisin C_3 or C_4 were combined separately and concentrated to dryness. Fraction F-2 was separated on a μBondapak C_{18} column eluted with a gradient from methanol-water-acetic acid (20:80:1v/v/v) to methanol-acetic acid (100:1, v/v). Fractions containing either fumonisin C_1 or hydroxylated C_1 were combined separately and reduced to dryness. Final purification of each of the fumonisins was performed on a strong-anion exchange (SAX) Sep-Pak cartridge successively washed with methanol-water (3:1, v/v) and methanol. The fumonisins were eluted from the column with 1% acetic acid in methanol.

Biological Activity

The primary animal diseases that have been caused by the fumonisins are leucoencephalomalacia in equine and porcine pulmonary edema. Acute liver and kidney toxicity has also been reported from feeding culture materials containing high levels of the fumonisins. The mode of action of the fumonisins involves disruption of sphingolipid metabolism which, in turn, may lead to disruption of normal cellular regulation. Fumonisins are carcinogenic and also highly phytotoxic.

Spectral Data

^{1}H NMR:

(CD_3OH) 5.14(1H, dt, *J*=11.0, 3.0Hz, H-13); 4.95(1H, dd, *J*=8.3, 3.2Hz, H-14); 3.88(1H, td, *J*=8.0, 3.4Hz, H-2); 3.79(1H, td, *J*=7.8, 3.4Hz, H-4); 3.63(1H, m, H-9); 3.36(1H, m, H-3); 3.28(1H, dd, *J*=13.4, 3.4Hz, H-1_b); 3.15(2 x 1H, m, H-24 and H-30); 3.00(1H, dd, *J*=12.7, 8.3Hz, H-1_a); 2.78(1H, dd, *J*=16.6, 7.1Hz); 2.74(1H, dd, 11.8, 3.9Hz); 2.69(1H, dd, *J*=7.1, 4.3Hz); 2.63(1H, dd, *J*=7.6, 4.9Hz); 2.57 (1H, dd, *J*=13.9, 6.6Hz); 2.56 (1H, dd, *J*=11.2, 5.4Hz); 2.50 (1H, dd, *J*=11.7, 6.1Hz); 2.46 (1H, dd, *J*=10.5, 6.3Hz); 2.46 (1H, dd, *J*=10.5, 6.3Hz); 1.81(1H, m, H-11); 1.698(1H, H-15); 1.64(1H, H-12_b); 1.35- 1.57(14H,m); 1.31(1H, m, H-17_a); 1.16(1H, H-10_a); 1.09(1H, H-16_a); 0.96(3H, d, *J*=6.3Hz, H-21); 0.94(3H, d, *J*=6.8Hz, H-20); and 0.90ppm (3H, t, *J*=7.1Hz, H-19).

^{13}C NMR:

(CD_3OH) 44.5, C-1; 70.9, C-2; 76.0, C-3; 69.0, C-4; 37.6, C-5; 26.9, C-6; 26.8, C-7; 39.2, C-8; 70.0, C-9; 44.0, C-10; 26.9, C-11; 34.8, C-12; 72.9, C-13; 78.7, C-14; 34.6, C-15; 34.6, C-16; 33.0, C-17; 23.9, C-18; 14.4, C-19; 16.0, C-20; 20.7, C-21; 173.4, C-22; 36.8, C-23; 39.5, C-24; 37.3, C-25; 178.6, C-26; 178.0, C-27; 173.2, C-28; 36.7, C-29; 39.5, C-30; 37.1, C-31; 176.9, C-32; and 176.5ppm, C-33.

Mass Spectrum:

FABMS: $(M+H)^+$ 724*m/e* (100%) 706(6), 688(4), 548(9), 372(12), 354(6), and 336*m/e* (4).

TLC:

R_f = 0.26 on C_{18} reversed phase plates developed in chloroform-methanol-water-acetic acid (55:36:8:1, v/v/v/v). Fumonisins were visualized by spraying with 0.5% *p*-anisaldehyde solution in methanol-sulfuric acid-acetic acid (85:5:10, v/v/v) and heating at 110°C for 10 min.

References

B. E. Branham and R. D. Plattner; Isolation and Characterization of a New Fumonisin from Liquid Cultures of *Fusarium moniliforme*; J. Nat. Products; Vol. 56, pp. 1630-1633(1993).

J-A Seo, J-C. Kim, and Y-W Lee; Isolation and Characterization of Two New Type C Fumonisins Produced by *Fusarium oxysporum*; J. Nat. Products; Vol. 59, pp. 1003-1005(1996).

Common/Systematic Name

Fumonisin C_3

Molecular Formula/Molecular Weight

$C_{33}H_{57}NO_{14}$; MW = 691.37791

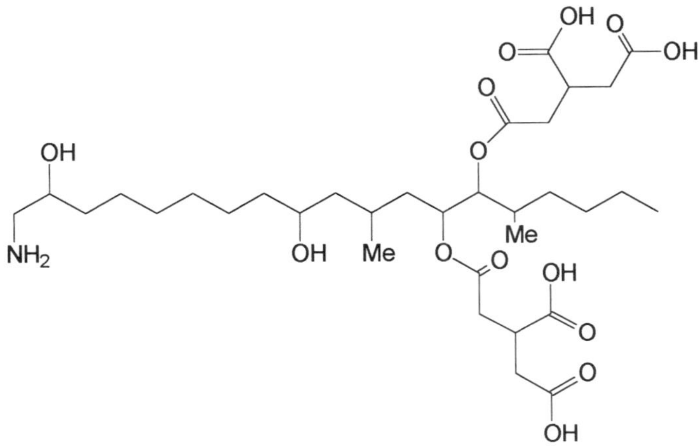

General Characteristics

Obtained as a colorless liquid.

Fungal Source

Fusarium moniliforme Sheldon (M-2326); (MRC-826).

Isolation/Purification

Solid culture material was extracted with methanol-water (3:1, v/v), filtered, and concentrated to dryness. The aqueous phase was chromatographed on an Amberlite XAD-2 column eluted successively with methanol-water (1:3, v/v), (1:1, v/v), (3:1, v/v), and finally with methanol. Fumonisin C_1, hydroxylated C_1, C_3, and C_4 were eluted in the methanol-water (3:1) and methanol fractions. These fractions were combined, concentrated to dryness and chromatographed on a silica gel column eluted with chloroform-methanol-acetic acid (6:3:1, v/v/v). The eluant was reduced to two fractions, F-1 and F-2. The F-1 fraction was chromatographed on a silica gel column eluted with ethyl acetate-acetic acid-hexane-water (6:2:2:1, v/v/v/v). The fractions containing fumonisin C_3 or C_4 were combined separately and concentrated to dryness. Fraction F-2 was separated on a μBondapak C_{18} column eluted with a gradient from methanol-water-acetic acid (20:80:1, v/v/v) to methanol-acetic acid (100:1, v/v). Fractions containing either fumonisin C_1 or hydroxylated C_1 were combined separately and reduced to dryness. Final purification of each of the fumonisins was performed on a strong-anion exchange (SAX) Sep-Pak cartridge successively washed with methanol-water (3:1, v/v) and methanol. The fumonisins were eluted from the column with 1% acetic acid in methanol.

Biological Activity

The primary animal diseases that have been caused by the fumonisins are leucoencephalomalacia in equine and porcine pulmonary edema. Acute liver and kidney toxicity has also been reported from feeding culture materials containing high levels of the fumonisins. The mode of action of the fumonisins involves disruption of sphingolipid metabolism which, in turn, may lead to disruption of normal cellular regulation. Fumonisins are carcinogenic and also highly phytotoxic.

Spectral Data

^{1}H NMR:

(CD_3OD) 5.13(1H, dt, *J*=11.3, 2.9Hz, H-13); 4.95(1H, dd, *J*=8.6, 2.9Hz, H-14); 3.77(1H, m, H-2); 3.61(1H, m, H-9); 3.16(2 x 1H, m, H-24 and H-30); 3.03(1H, dd, *J*=12.7, 2.7Hz, H-1_b); 2.80(1H, dd, *J*=11.7, 7.3Hz); 2.76(1H, H-1_a); 2.74-2.64(3 x 1H, m); 2.61-2.52(3 x 1H, m); 2.48(1H, dd, *J*=16.6, 6.6Hz); 1.79(1H, m, H-11); 1.70(1H, H-15); 1.66(1H, H-12_b); 1.27-1.53(19H,m); 1.17(1H, H-10_a); 1.09(1H, 16_a); 0.95(3H, d, *J*=6.6Hz, H-21); 0.94(3H, d, *J*=6.6Hz, H-20); and 0.88ppm (3H, t, *J*=6.8Hz, H-19).

^{13}C NMR:

(CD_3OD) 46.1, C-1; 69.9, C-2; 39.2, C-3; 30.6, C-4; 30.5, C-5; 26.7, C-6; 26.2, C-7; 39.0, C-8; 68.7, C-9; 44.5, C-10; 26.9, C-11; 35.8, C-12; 73.0, C-13; 78.7, C-14; 34.8, C-15; 33.0, C-16; 29.5, C-17; 23.8, C-18; 14.4, C-19; 15.9, C-20; 20.6, C-21; 173.3, C-22; 36.6, C-23; 39.0, C-24; 36.8, C-25; 177.7, C-26; 177.3, C-27; 173.1, C-28; 36.6, C-29; 39.0, C-30; 36.8, C-31; 176.0, C-32; and 175.7ppm, C-33.

Mass Spectrum:

FABMS: $(M+H)^+$ 692(100), 674(7), 516(8), 340(15), 322(14) and 304(7), 512(6), 414(3), 264(4), 211(20), 180(60), 126(59), 97(100), 55(66), and 43*m/e* (43).

TLC:

R_f = 0.36 on C_{18} reversed phase plates developed in chloroform-methanol-water-acetic acid (55:36:8:1, v/v/v/v). Fumonisins were visualized by spraying with 0.5% *p*-anisaldehyde solution in methanol-sulfuric acid-acetic acid (85:5:10, v/v/v) and heating at 110°C for 10 min.

Reference

J-A. Seo, J-C. Kim, and Y-W. Lee; Isolation and Characterization of Two New Type C Fumonisins Produced by *Fusarium oxysporum*; J. Nat. Products; Vol. 59, pp. 1003-1005 (1996).

Common/Systematic Name

Fumonisin C_4

Molecular Formula/Molecular Weight

$C_{33}H_{57}NO_{13}$; MW = 675.38299

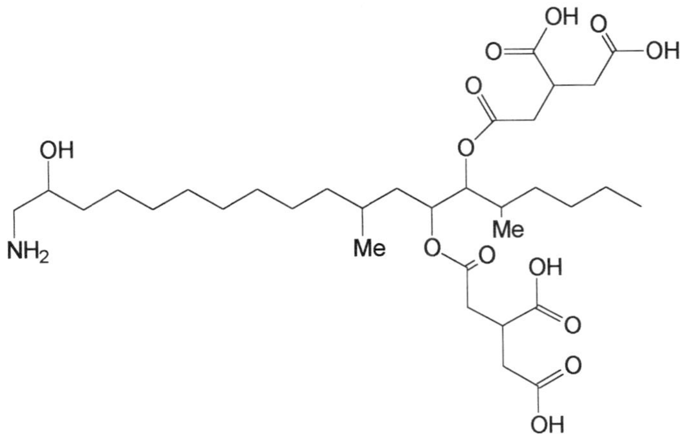

General Characteristics

Obtained as a colorless liquid.

Fungal Source

Fusarium oxysporum (strain CAR isolated from carnation in Korea; *F. moniliforme* Sheldon).

Isolation/Purification

Solid culture material was extracted with methanol-water (3:1, v/v), filtered, and concentrated to dryness. The aqueous phase was chromatographed on an Amberlite XAD-2 column eluted successively with methanol-water (1:3, v/v), (1:1, v/v), (3:1, v/v), and finally with methanol. Fumonisin C_1, hydroxylated C_1, C_3, and C_4 were eluted in the methanol-water (3:1) and methanol fractions. These fractions were combined, concentrated to dryness and chromatographed on a silica gel column eluted with chloroform-methanol-acetic acid (6:3:1, v/v/v). The eluant was reduced to two fractions, F-1 and F-2. The F-1 fraction was chromatographed on a silica gel column eluted with ethyl acetate-acetic acid-hexane-water (6:2:2:1, v/v/v/v). The fractions containing fumonisins C_3 or C_4 were combined separately and concentrated to dryness. Fraction F-2 was separated on a μBondapak C_{18} column eluted with a gradient from methanol-water-acetic acid (20:80:1, v/v/v) to methanol-acetic acid (100:1, v/v). Fractions containing either fumonisin C_1 or hydroxylated C_1 were combined separately and reduced to dryness. Final purification of each of the fumonisins was performed on a strong-anion exchange (SAX) Sep-Pak cartridge successively washed with methanol-water (3:1, v/v) and methanol. The fumonisins were eluted from the column with 1% acetic acid in methanol.

Biological Activity

The primary animal diseases that have been caused by the fumonisins are leucoencephalomalacia in equine and porcine pulmonary edema. Acute liver and kidney toxicity has also been reported from feeding culture materials containing high levels of the fumonisins. The mode of action of the fumonisins involves disruption of sphingolipid metabolism which, in turn, may lead to disruption of normal cellular regulation. Fumonisins are carcinogenic and also highly phytotoxic.

Spectral Data

^{13}C NMR:

(CD_3OD) 46.1, C-1; 68.9, C-2; 39.0, C-3; 30.7, C-4; 30.5, C-5; 27.5, C-6; 26.3, C-7; 30.5, C-8; 30.5, C-9; 30.1, C-10; 20.9, C-11; 35.9, C-12; 73.0, C-13; 78.8, C-14; 34.9, C-15; 33.0, C-16; 29.6, C-17; 23.8, C-18; 14.4, C-19; 16.0, C-20; 20.9, C-21; 173.1, C-22; 36.3, C-23; 38.9, C-24; 36.7, C-25; 177.5, C-26; 177.3, C-27; 173.0, C-28; 36.1, C-29; 38.9, C-30; 36.6, C-31; 175.9, C-32; and 175.6ppm, C-33.

^{1}H NMR:

(CD_3OD) 5.17(1H, dt, *J*=11.1, 3.2Hz, H-13); 4.92(1H, dd, *J*=8.5, 3.4Hz, H-14); 3.76(1H, m, H-2); 3.16(2 x 1H, m, H-24 and H-30); 3.03(1H, dd, *J*=12.7, 2.9Hz, H-1_b); 2.80(1H, dd, *J*=12.7, 7.1Hz); 2.76(1H, H-1_a); 2.74-2.64(3 x 1H, m); 2.59(1H, dd, *J*=10.3, 6.4Hz); 2.56-2.472(3 x 1H, m); 1.71(1H, H-15); 1.62(1H, H-12_b); 1.14-1.54(23H,m); 1.06(1H, 16_a); 0.93(3H, d, *J*=7.1Hz, H-21); 0.91(3H, d, *J*=6.4Hz, H-20); and 0.89ppm (3H, t, *J*=7.1Hz, H-19).

Mass Spectrum:

FABMS: $(M+H)^+$ 676(100), 658 (3), 500 (5), 324 (30), and 306*m/e* (11).

TLC:

R_f = 0.44 on C_{18} reversed phase plates developed in chloroform-methanol-water-acetic acid (55:36:8:1, v/v/v/v). Fumonisins were visualized by spraying with 0.5% *p*-anisaldehyde solution in methanol-sulfuric acid-acetic acid (85:5:10, v/v/v) and heating at 110°C for 10 min.

References

J.-A. Seo, J.-C. Kim, and Y.-W. Lee; Isolation and Characterization of Two New Type C Fumonisins Produced by *Fusarium oxysporum*; J. Nat. Products; Vol. 59, pp. 1003-1005 (1996).

B. E. Branham and R. D. Plattner; Isolation and Characterization of a New Fumonisin from Liquid Cultures of *Fusarium moniliforme*; J. Nat. Products; Vol. 56, pp. 1630-1633 (1993).

Common/Systematic Name

Fumonisin AK_1

Molecular Formula/Molecular Weight

$C_{30}H_{45}NO_{11}$; MW = 604.36969

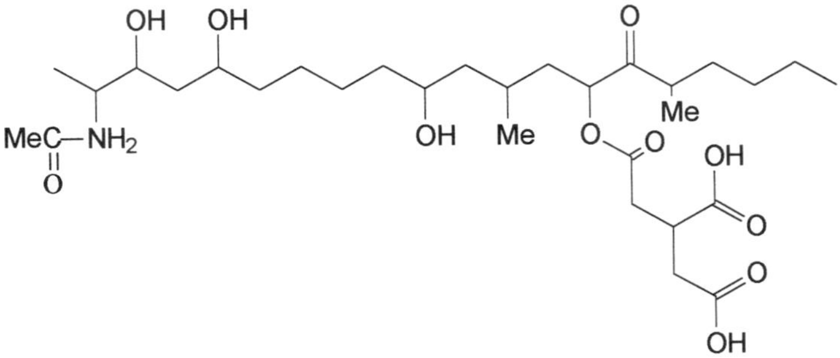

General Characteristics

Fumonisins are highly functionalized hydrocarbon derivatives that are readily soluble in polar solvents and nearly insoluble in non-polar solvents.

Fungal Source

Fusarium proliferatum (M-1597).

Isolation/Purification

Solid culture material was extracted with methanol-water (75:25, v/v) and filtered. The filtrate was diluted with water to a final methanol concentration of 30%. The diluted solution was chromatographed on a Bondapak C_{18} preparative column washed with water, methanol-water (50:50, v/v), and eluted with methanol-water (70:30, v/v). The methanol was removed from this fraction and the aqueous portion was applied to a Dynamax C_{18} column (Rainin Corp.) washed with acetonitrile-water (25:75, v/v). The fumonisin containing fractions were eluted with acetonitrile-water (70:30, v/v). The acetonitrile was removed *in vacuo* and the aqueous fraction was applied to a µBondapak cyano column. The fumonisins were eluted with 1% pyridine in water. Final purification and separation of fumonisin B_1 and fumonisin AK_1 was achieved on a C_8 column using a gradient from acetonitrile containing 0.1% acetic acid-water (20:80, v/v) to acetonitrile-water (45:55, v/v).

Biological Activity

The primary animal diseases that have been caused by the fumonisins are leucoencephalomalacia in equine and porcine pulmonary edema. Acute liver and kidney toxicity has also been reported from feeding culture materials containing high levels of the fumonisins. The mode of action of the fumonisins involves disruption of sphingolipid metabolism which, in turn, may lead to disruption of normal cellular regulation. Fumonisins are carcinogenic and also highly phytotoxic.

Spectral Data

^{13}C NMR:

(D_2O) 18.4, C-1; 52.3, C-2; 72.5, C-3; 42.1, C-4; 70.3, C-5; 39.2, C-6; 27.1, C-7; 27.3, C-8; 27.1, C-9; 71.4, C-10; 44.6, C-11; 28.6, C-12; 39.0, C-13; 79.4, C-14; 219.5, C-15; 44.8, C-16; 33.9, C-17; 31.3, C-18; 24.4, C-19; 15.6, C-20; 21.6, C-21; 19.7, C-22; 181.6, C-23; 38.2, C-24; 41.4, C-25; 39.3, C-26; 179.1, C-27; 176.2, C-28; 175.9, C-33; and 24.5ppm, C-34'.

Mass Spectrum:

Negative-ion ESMS: Showed only a molecular anion at 603 daltons.

References

S. M. Musser, R. M. Eppley, E. P. Mazzola, C. E. Hadden, J. P. Shockcor, and G. E. Martin; Identification of an N-Acetyl Keto Derivative of Fumonisin B1 in Corn Cultures of *Fusarium proliferatum*; J. Natural Prod., Vol. 58, pp. 1392-1397(1995).

Common/Systematic Name

AAL Toxin TA_1

Molecular Formula/Molecular Weight

$C_{25}H_{47}NO_{10}$; MW = 521.32000

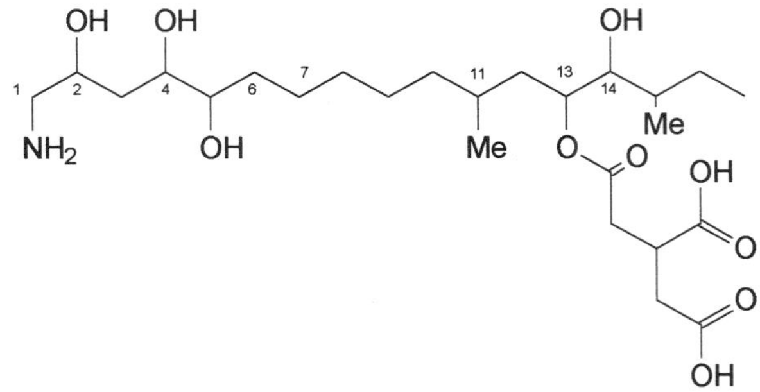

General Characteristics

AAL toxin TA_1 was ninhydrin positive.

Fungal Source

Alternaria alternata f. sp. *lycopersici*.

Isolation/Purification

XAD-2 was added to culture filtrates and stirred for 4-6 hours, the adsorbed XAD beads were washed with water, and the toxins eluted with methanol. The extract was evaporated to dryness *in vacuo*, dissolved in ethyl acetate-acetic acid-hexane-water (6:2:2:1, v/v/v/v), and fractionated on a silica gel column by flash chromatography using the same solvent system. After 20 fractions were collected the solvent system was changed to ethyl acetate-acetic acid-water (6:3:1, v/v/v). Fractions were evaluated by TLC using the solvent system ethyl acetate-acetic acid-water (6:8:1, v/v/v). Toxins were detected by spraying plates with *p*-anisaldehyde. Final purification was performed on a SAX column washed successively with 0.1 N NaOH, water to pH 7.0, and equilibrated with methanol at pH 7.7. The selected fractions were dried, dissolved in methanol at pH 7.7, applied to a SAX column, washed with methanol, and eluted with 1% acetic acid in methanol.

Biological Activity

The AAL toxins are responsible for expression of *Alternaria* stem canker disease of tomato. All five congers were toxic to leaf tissue of the *asc/asc* isoline of tomato in the standard detached leaflet assay.

Spectral Data

^{1}H NMR:
(CD$_3$OD) 3.05(1H, H-1); 2.82(1H, H-1'); 4.01(1H, H-2); 1.72(1H, H-3); 1.51(1H, H-3'); 3.67(1H, H-4); 3.44(1H, H-5); 1.36(1H, H-6); 1.68(1H, H-12); 5.12(1H, dd, *J*=3.5, 3.7Hz, H-13); 3.89(1H, dd, *J*=3.5, 3.7Hz, H-13); and 1.34ppm (1H, H-15).

^{13}C NMR:
(CD$_3$OD) 47.9, C-1; 64.97, C-2; 70.46, C-4; 74.70, C-5; 74.46, C-13; and 76.30ppm C-14.

Mass Spectrum:
FABMS: $(M+H)^+$ 522*m/e*.

References

A.T. Bottini, J. R. Bowen, and D. G. Gilchrist; Phytotoxins. II. Characterization of A Phytotoxic Fraction from *Alternaria alternata* F. sp. *Lycopersici*; Tetrahedron Letters, Vol. 22, pp. 2723-2726(1981).

E. D. Caldas, A. D. Jones, B. Ward, C. K. Winter, and D. G. Gilchrist; Structural Characterization of Three New AAL Toxins Produced by *Alternaria alternata* f. sp. *Lycopersici*; J. Agric. Food Chem., Vol. 42, pp. 327-333(1994).

Common/Systematic Name

AAL Toxin TA_2

Molecular Formula/Molecular Weight

$C_{25}H_{47}NO_{10}$; MW = 521.32000

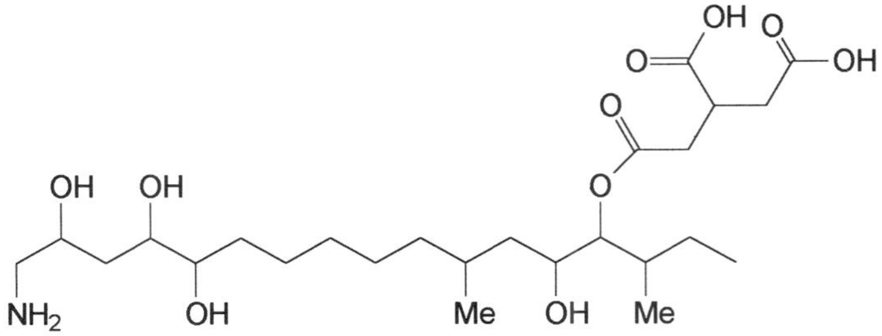

General Characteristics

AAL toxin TA_2 was ninhydrin positive. All AAL toxin pairs are regioisomers at C-13 and C-14.

Fungal Source

Alternaria alternata f. sp. *lycopersici*.

Isolation/Purification

XAD-2 was added to culture filtrates and stirred for 4-6 hours, the adsorbed XAD beads were washed with water, and the toxins eluted with methanol. The extract was evaporated to dryness *in vacuo*, dissolved in ethyl acetate-acetic acid-hexane-water (6:2:2:1, v/v/v/v), and fractionated on a silica gel column by flash chromatography using the same solvent system. After 20 fractions were collected the solvent system was changed to ethyl acetate-acetic acid-water (6:3:1, v/v/v). Fractions were evaluated by TLC using the solvent system ethyl acetate-acetic acid-water (6:8:1, v/v/v). Toxins were detected by spraying plates with *p*-anisaldehyde. Final purification was performed on a SAX column washed successively with 0.1 N NaOH, water to pH 7.0, and equilibrated with methanol at pH 7.7. The selected fractions were dried, dissolved in methanol at pH 7.7, applied to a SAX column, washed with methanol, and eluted with 1% acetic acid in methanol.

Biological Activity

The AAL toxins are responsible for expression of *Alternaria* stem canker disease of tomato. All five congers were toxic to leaf tissue of the *asc/asc* isoline of tomato in the standard detached leaflet assay.

Spectral Data

^{1}H NMR:
(CD$_3$OD) 3.05(1H, H-1); 2.82(1H, H-1'); 4.01(1H, H-2); 1.72(1H, 5.2Hz, H-3); 1.51(1H, H-3'); 3.67(1H, H-4); 3.44(1H, H-5); 1.36(1H, H-6); 1.81(1H, H-12); 3.75,(1H, dd, *J*=3.5, 3.7Hz, H-13); 4.76(1H, dd, *J*=2.9, 8.0Hz, H-14); and 1.77ppm (1H, H-15).

^{13}C NMR:
(CD$_3$OD) 47.9, C-1; 64.97, C-2; 70.46, C-4; 74.70, C-5; 69.16, C-13; and 81.72ppm C-14.

Mass Spectrum:
FABMS: $(M+H)^+$ 522*m/e*.

References

A.T. Bottini, J. R. Bowen, and D. G. Gilchrist; Phytotoxins. II. Characterization of A Phytotoxic Fraction from *Alternaria alternata* F. sp. *Lycopersici*; Tetrahedron Letters, Vol. 22, pp. 2723-2726(1981).

E. D. Caldas, A. D. Jones, B. Ward, C. K. Winter, and D. G. Gilchrist; Structural Characterization of Three New AAL Toxins Produced by *Alternaria alternata* f. sp. *Lycopersici*; J. Agric. Food Chem., Vol. 42, pp. 327-333(1994).

Common/Systematic Name

AAL Toxin TB_1

Molecular Formula/Molecular Weight

$C_{25}H_{47}NO_9$; MW = 505.32508

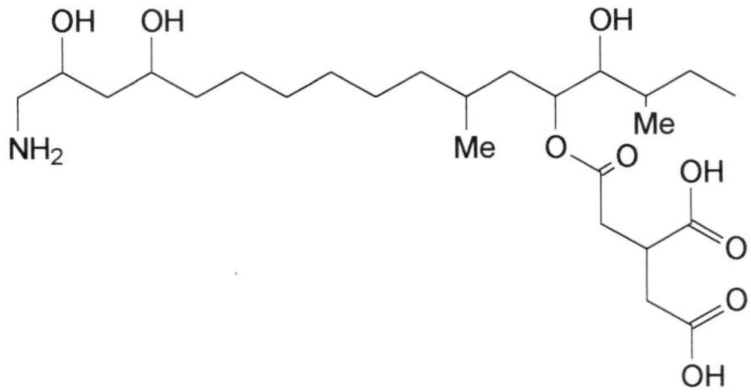

General Characteristics

AAL toxin TB_1 was ninhydrin positive. All five AAL toxin pairs are regioisomers at C-13 and C-14.

Fungal Source

Alternaria alternata f. sp. *lycopersici*.

Isolation/Purification

XAD-2 was added to culture filtrates and stirred for 4-6 hours, the adsorbed XAD beads were washed with water, and the toxins eluted with methanol. The extract was evaporated to dryness *in vacuo*, dissolved in ethyl acetate-acetic acid-hexane-water (6:2:2:1, v/v/v/v), and fractionated on a silica gel column by flash chromatography using the same solvent system. After 20 fractions were collected the solvent system was changed to ethyl acetate-acetic acid-water (6:3:1, v/v/v). Fractions were evaluated by TLC using the solvent system ethyl acetate-acetic acid-water (6:8:1, v/v/v). Toxins were detected by spraying plates with *p*-anisaldehyde. Final purification was performed on a SAX column washed successively with 0.1 N NaOH, water to pH 7.0, and equilibrated with methanol at pH 7.7. The selected fractions were dried, dissolved in methanol at pH 7.7, applied to a SAX column, washed with methanol, and eluted with 1% acetic acid in methanol.

Biological Activity

The AAL toxins are responsible for expression of *Alternaria* stem canker disease of tomato. All five congers were toxic to leaf tissue of the *asc/asc* isoline of tomato in the standard detached leaflet assay.

Spectral Data

^{1}H NMR:
(CD$_3$OD) 3.03(1H, H-1); 2.82(1H, H-1'); 4.02(1H, H-2); 1.57(1H, H-3); 1.44(1H, H-3'); 3.79(1H, H-4); 1.58(1H, H-5); 1.68(1H, H-12); 5.11(1H, dd, *J*=3.5, 3.7Hz, H-13); 3.39(1H, dd, *J*=3.5, 3.7Hz, H-14); and 1.37ppm (1H, H-15).

^{13}C NMR:
(CD$_3$OD) 46.50, C-1; 66.27, C-2; 68.58, C-4; 74.62, C-13; and 77.30ppm C-14.

Mass Spectrum:
FABMS: $(M+H)^+$ 506*m/e*.

References

A.T. Bottini, J. R. Bowen, and D. G. Gilchrist; Phytotoxins. II. Characterization of A Phytotoxic Fraction from *Alternaria alternata* F. sp. *Lycopersici*; Tetrahedron Letters, Vol. 22, pp. 2723-2726(1981).

E. D. Caldas, A. D. Jones, B. Ward, C. K. Winter, and D. G. Gilchrist; Structural Characterization of Three New AALToxins Produced by *Alternaria alternata* f. sp. *Lycopersici*; J. Agric. Food Chem., Vol. 42, pp. 327-333(1994).

Common/Systematic Name

AAL Toxin TB_2

Molecular Formula/Molecular Weight

$C_{25}H_{47}NO_9$; MW = 505.32508

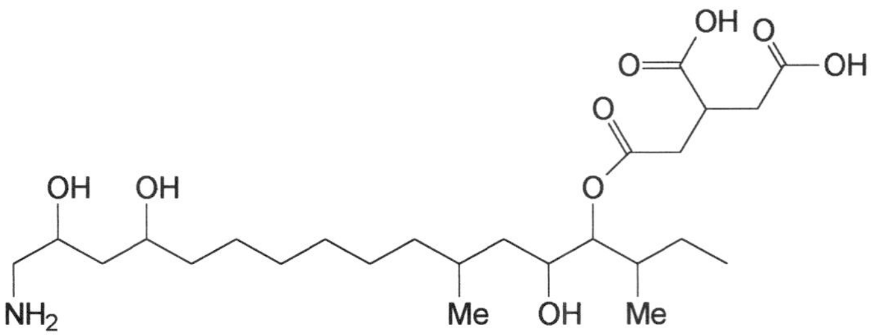

General Characteristics

AAL toxin TB_2 was ninhydrin positive. All AAL toxin pairs are regioisomers at C-13 and C-14.

Fungal Source

Alternaria alternata f. sp. *lycopersici*.

Isolation/Purification

XAD-2 was added to culture filtrates and stirred for 4-6 hours, the adsorbed XAD beads were washed with water, and the toxins eluted with methanol. The extract was evaporated to dryness *in vacuo*, dissolved in ethyl acetate-acetic acid-hexane-water (6:2:2:1, v/v/v/v), and fractionated on a silica gel column by flash chromatography using the same solvent system. After 20 fractions were collected the solvent system was changed to ethyl acetate-acetic acid-water (6:3:1, v/v/v). Fractions were evaluated by TLC using the solvent system ethyl acetate-acetic acid-water (6:8:1, v/v/v). Toxins were detected by spraying plates with *p*-anisaldehyde. Final purification was performed on a SAX column washed successively with 0.1 N NaOH, water to pH 7.0, and equilibrated with methanol at pH 7.7. The selected fractions were dried, dissolved in methanol at pH 7.7, applied to a SAX column, washed with methanol, and eluted with 1% acetic acid in methanol.

Biological Activity

The AAL toxins are responsible for expression of *Alternaria* stem canker disease of tomato. All five congers were toxic to leaf tissue of the *asc/asc* isoline of tomato in the standard detached leaflet assay.

Spectral Data

^{1}H NMR:
(CD_3OD) 3.03(1H, H-1); 2.82(1H, H-1'); 4.02(1H, H-2); 1.57(1H, H-3); 1.44(1H, H-3'); 3.79(1H, H-4); 1.58(1H, H-5); 1.81(1H, H-12); 3.76(1H, dd, *J*=3.5, 3.7Hz, H-13); 4.77(1H, t, *J*=5.7Hz, H-14); and 1.74ppm (1H, H-15).

^{13}C NMR:
(CD_3OD) 46.50, C-1; 66.27, C-2; 68.58, C-4; 69.75, C-13; and 82.12ppm, C-14.

Mass Spectrum:
FABMS: $(M+H)^+$ 506*m/e*.

References

A.T. Bottini, J. R. Bowen, and D. G. Gilchrist; Phytotoxins. II. Characterization of A Phytotoxic Fraction from *Alternaria alternata* F. sp. *Lycopersici*; Tetrahedron Letters, Vol. 22, pp. 2723-2726(1981).

E. D. Caldas, A. D. Jones, B. Ward, C. K. Winter, and D. G. Gilchrist; Structural Characterization of Three New AAL Toxins Produced by *Alternaria alternata* f. sp. *Lycopersici*; J. Agric. Food Chem., Vol. 42, pp. 327-333(1994).

Common/Systematic Name

AAL Toxin TC_1

Molecular Formula/Molecular Weight

$C_{25}H_{47}O_8$; MW = 489.33017

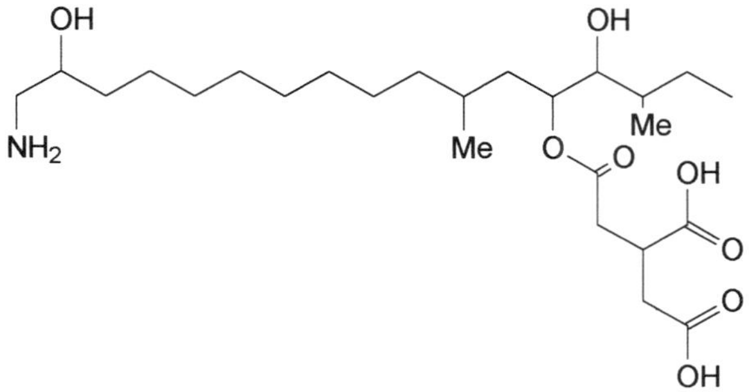

General Characteristics

AAL toxin TC_1 was not ninhydrin positive. All AAL toxin pairs are regioisomers at C-13 and C-14.

Fungal Source

Alternaria alternata f. sp. *lycopersici*.

Isolation/Purification

XAD-2 was added to culture filtrates and stirred for 4-6 hours, the adsorbed XAD beads were washed with water, and the toxins eluted with methanol. The extract was evaporated to dryness *in vacuo*, dissolved in ethyl acetate-acetic acid-hexane-water (6:2:2:1, v/v/v/v), and fractionated on a silica gel column by flash chromatography using the same solvent system. After 20 fractions were collected the solvent system was changed to ethyl acetate-acetic acid-water (6:3:1, v/v/v). Fractions were evaluated by TLC using the solvent system ethyl acetate-acetic acid-water (6:8:1, v/v/v). Toxins were detected by spraying plates with *p*-anisaldehyde. Final purification was performed on a SAX column washed successively with 0.1 N NaOH, water to pH 7.0, and equilibrated with methanol at pH 7.7. The selected fractions were dried, dissolved in methanol at pH 7.7, applied to a SAX column, washed with methanol, and eluted with 1% acetic acid in methanol.

Biological Activity

The AAL toxins are responsible for expression of *Alternaria* stem canker disease of tomato. All five congers were toxic to leaf tissue of the *asc/asc* isoline of tomato in the standard detached leaflet assay.

Spectral Data

^{1}H NMR:
(CD_3OD) 3.01(1H, H-1); 2.75(1H, H-1'); 3.77(1H, H-2); 1.70(1H, H-3); 1.46(1H, H-3'); 1.67(1H, H-12); 3.39(1H, dd, *J*=3.5, 3.7Hz, H-13); 5.02(1H, dd, *J*=3.5Hz, H-14); and 1.37ppm (1H, H-15).

Mass Spectrum:
FABMS: $(M+H)^+$ 490*m/e*.

Reference

E. D. Caldas, A. D. Jones, B. Ward, C. K. Winter, and D. G. Gilchrist; Structural Characterization of Three New AAL Toxins Produced by *Alternaria alternata* f. sp. *Lycopersici*; J. Agric. Food Chem., Vol. 42, pp. 327-333(1994).

Common/Systematic Name

AAL Toxin TC_2

Molecular Formula/Molecular Weight

$C_{25}H_{47}NO_8$; MW = 489.33017

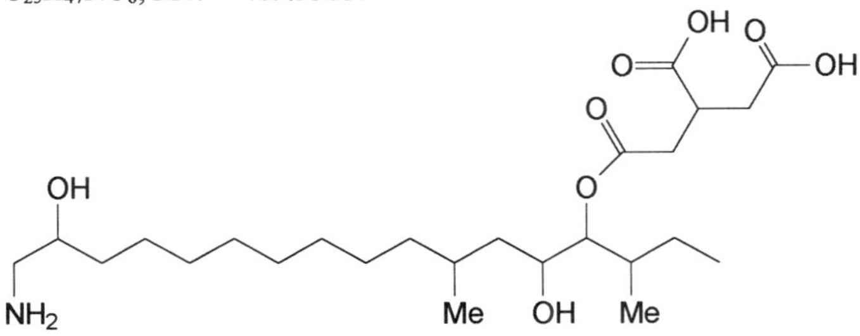

General Characteristics

AAL toxin TC_2 was not ninhydrin positive. All five AAL toxin pairs are regioisomers at C-13 and C-14.

Fungal Source

Alternaria alternata f. sp. *lycopersici*

Isolation/Purification

XAD-2 was added to culture filtrates and stirred for 4-6 hours, the adsorbed XAD beads were washed with water, and the toxins eluted with methanol. The extract was evaporated to dryness *in vacuo*, dissolved in ethyl acetate-acetic acid-hexane-water (6:2:2:1, v/v/v/v), and fractionated on a silica gel column by flash chromatography using the same solvent system. After 20 fractions were collected the solvent system was changed to ethyl acetate-acetic acid-water (6:3:1, v/v/v). Fractions were evaluated by TLC using the solvent system ethyl acetate-acetic acid-water (6:8:1, v/v/v). Toxins were detected by spraying plates with *p*-anisaldehyde. Final purification was performed on a SAX column washed successively with 0.1 N NaOH, water to pH 7.0, and equilibrated with methanol at pH 7.7. The selected fractions were dried, dissolved in methanol at pH 7.7, applied to a SAX column, washed with methanol, and eluted with 1% acetic acid in methanol.

Biological Activity

The AAL toxins are responsible for expression of *Alternaria* stem canker disease of tomato. All five congers were toxic to leaf tissue of the *asc/asc* isoline of tomato in the standard detached leaflet assay.

Spectral Data

^1H NMR:

(CD_3OD) 3.01(1H, H-1); 2.75(1H, H-1'); 3.77(1H, H-2); 1.70(1H, H-3); 1.46(1H, H-3'); 1.81(1H, H-12); 3.74(1H, H-13); 4.75(1H, t, *J*=5.7Hz, H-14); and 1.75ppm (1H, H-15).

Mass Spectrum:
FABMS: $(M+H)^+$ 490*m/e*.

Reference

E. D. Caldas, A. D. Jones, B. Ward, C. K. Winter, and D. G. Gilchrist; Structural Characterization of Three New AAL Toxins Produced by *Alternaria alternata* f. sp. *Lycopersici*; J. Agric. Food Chem., vol. 42, pp. 327-333(1994).

Common/Systematic Name

AAL Toxin TD_1

Molecular Formula/Molecular Weight

$C_{27}H_{49}NO_{10}$; MW = 547.33565

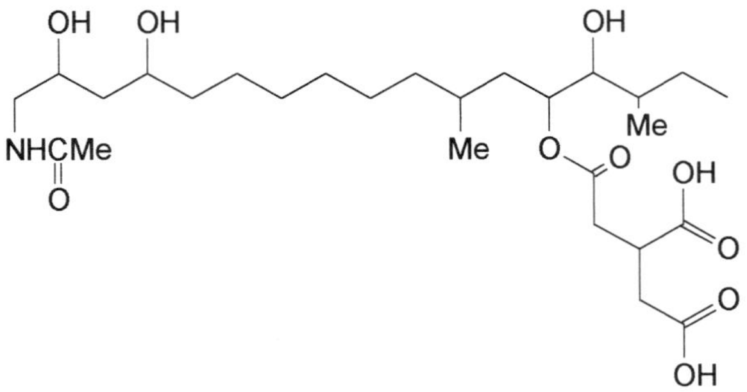

General Characteristics

AAL toxin TD_1 was not ninhydrin positive. All AAL toxin pairs are regioisomers at C-13 and C-14.

Fungal Source

Alternaria alternata f. sp.. *lycopersici*.

Isolation/Purification

XAD-2 was added to culture filtrates and stirred for 4-6 hours, the adsorbed XAD beads were washed with water, and the toxins eluted with methanol. The extract was evaporated to dryness *in vacuo*, dissolved in ethyl acetate-acetic acid-hexane-water (6:2:2:1, v/v/v/v), and fractionated on a silica gel column by flash chromatography using the same solvent system. After 20 fractions were collected the solvent system was changed to ethyl acetate-acetic acid-water (6:3:1, v/v/v). Fractions were evaluated by TLC using the solvent system ethyl acetate-acetic acid-water (6:8:1, v/v/v). Toxins were detected by spraying plates with *p*-anisaldehyde. Final purification was performed on a SAX column washed successively with 0.1 N NaOH, water to pH 7.0, and equilibrated with methanol at pH 7.7. The selected fractions were dried, dissolved in methanol at pH 7.7, applied to a SAX column, washed with methanol, and eluted with 1% acetic acid in methanol.

Biological Activity

The AAL toxins are responsible for expression of *Alternaria* stem canker disease of tomato. All five congers were toxic to leaf tissue of the *asc/asc* isoline of tomato in the standard detached leaflet assay.

Spectral Data

^{1}H NMR:

(CD_3OD) 3.01(1H, H-1); 2.75(1H, H-1'); 3.77(1H, H-2); 1.70(1H, H-3); 1.46(1H, H-3'); 1.67(1H, H-12); 5.02(1H, dd, *J*=3.5, 3.7Hz, H-13); 3.39(1H, dd, *J*=3.5, 3.7Hz, H-14); and 1.37ppm (1H, H-15).

Mass Spectrum:

FABMS: $(M+H)^+$ 548*m/e*.

Reference

E. D. Caldas, A. D. Jones, B. Ward, C. K. Winter, and D. G. Gilchrist; Structural Characterization of Three New AAL Toxins Produced by *Alternaria alternata* f. sp. *Lycopersici*; J. Agric. Food Chem., vol. 42, pp. 327-333(1994).

Common/Systematic Name

AAL Toxin TD_2

Molecular Formula/Molecular Weight

$C_{27}H_{49}NO_{10}$; MW = 547.33565

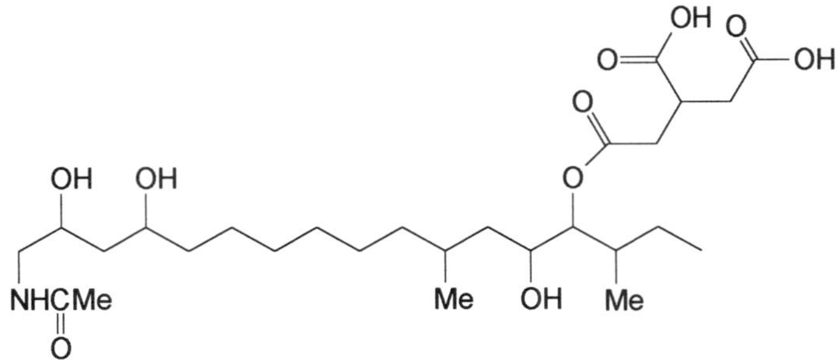

General Characteristics

AAL toxin TD_2 was not ninhydrin positive. All AAL toxin pairs are regioisomers at C-13 and C-14.

Fungal Source

Alternaria alternata f. sp. *Lycopersici.*

Isolation/Purification

XAD-2 was added to culture filtrates and stirred for 4-6 hours, the adsorbed XAD beads were washed with water, and the toxins eluted with methanol. The extract was evaporated to dryness *in vacuo*, dissolved in ethyl acetate-acetic acid-hexane-water (6:2:2:1, v/v/v/v), and fractionated on a silica gel column by flash chromatography using the same solvent system. After 20 fractions were collected the solvent system was changed to ethyl acetate-acetic acid-water (6:3:1, v/v/v). Fractions were evaluated by TLC using the solvent system ethyl acetate-acetic acid-water (6:8:1, v/v/v). Toxins were detected by spraying plates with *p*-anisaldehyde. Final purification was performed on a SAX column washed successively with 0.1 N NaOH, water to pH 7.0, and equilibrated with methanol at pH 7.7. The selected fractions were dried, dissolved in methanol at pH 7.7, applied to a SAX column, washed with methanol, and eluted with 1% acetic acid in methanol.

Biological Activity

The AAL toxins are responsible for expression of *Alternaria* stem canker disease of tomato. All five congers were toxic to leaf tissue of the *asc/asc* isoline of tomato in the standard detached leaflet assay.

Spectral Data

^{1}H NMR:
(CD$_3$OD) 3.25(1H, dd, *J*=4.8, 5.2Hz,H-1); 3.12(1H, H-1'); 3.82(1H, m, *J*=2.2-2.8Hz, H-2); 1.48(1H, H-3); 1.46(1H, H-3'); 3.76(1H, H-4); 1.39(1H, H-5); 1.31(1H, H-12); 8.78(1H, H-13); 4.77(1H, t, *J*=5.7Hz, H-14); and 1.74ppm (1H, H-15).

^{13}C NMR:
(CD$_3$OD) 46.13, C-1; 68.37, C-2; 69.49, C-4; 68.94, C-13; and 82.24ppm C-14.

Mass Spectrum:
FABMS: $(M+H)^+$ 548*m/e*.

Reference

E. D. Caldas, A. D. Jones, B. Ward, C. K. Winter, and D. G. Gilchrist; Structural Characterization of Three New AALToxins Produced by *Alternaria alternata* f. sp. *Lycopersici*; J. Agric. Food Chem., vol. 42, pp. 327-333(1994).

Common/Systematic Name

AAL Toxin TE_1

Molecular Formula/Molecular Weight

$C_{27}H_{49}NO_9$; MW = 531.34073

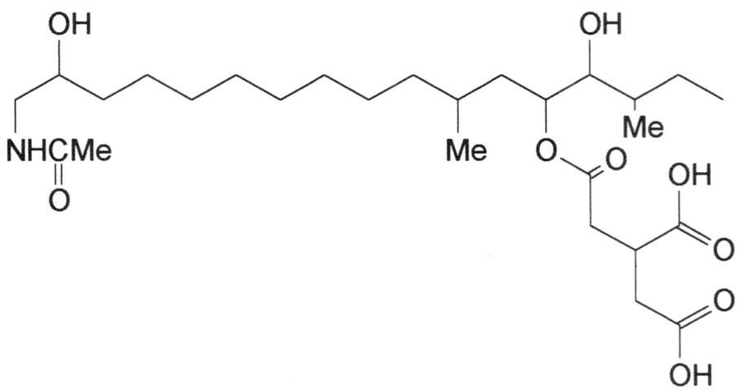

General Characteristics

AAL toxin TE_1 was not ninhydrin positive. All AAL toxin pairs are regioisomers at C-13 and C-14.

Fungal Source

Alternaria alternata f. sp. *lycopersici*.

Isolation/Purification

XAD-2 was added to culture filtrates and stirred for 4-6 hours, the adsorbed XAD beads were washed with water, and the toxins eluted with methanol. The extract was evaporated to dryness *in vacuo*, dissolved in ethyl acetate-acetic acid-hexane-water (6:2:2:1, v/v/v/v), and fractionated on a silica gel column by flash chromatography using the same solvent system. After 20 fractions were collected the solvent system was changed to ethyl acetate-acetic acid-water (6:3:1, v/v/v). Fractions were evaluated by TLC using the solvent system ethyl acetate-acetic acid-water (6:8:1, v/v/v). Toxins were detected by spraying plates with *p*-anisaldehyde. Final purification was performed on a SAX column washed successively with 0.1 N NaOH, water to pH 7.0, and equilibrated with methanol at pH 7.7. The selected fractions were dried, dissolved in methanol at pH 7.7, applied to a SAX column, washed with methanol, and eluted with 1% acetic acid in methanol.

Biological Activity

The AAL toxins are responsible for expression of *Alternaria* stem canker disease of tomato. All five congers were toxic to leaf tissue of the *asc/asc* isoline of tomato in the standard detached leaflet assay.

Spectral Data

^{1}H NMR:

(CD_3OD) 3.26(1H, dd, *J*=4.0, 4.5Hz, H-1); 3.06(1H, H-1'); 3.60(1H, dd, *J*=2.9, 8.0Hz, H-2); 1.36(1H, H-3); 1.38(1H, H-3'); 1.60(1H, H-12); 5.11(1H, H-13); 3.36(1H, dd, *J*=3.5, 3.7Hz, H-14); and 1.36ppm (1H, H-15).

^{13}C NMR:
(CD_3OD) 46.71, C-1; 68.49, C-2; 74.89, C-13; and 77.58ppm C-14.

Mass Spectrum:
FABMS: $(M+H)^+$ 532*m/e*.

Reference

E. D. Caldas, A. D. Jones, B. Ward, C. K. Winter, and D. G. Gilchrist; Structural Characterization of Three New AAL Toxins Produced by *Alternaria alternata* f. sp. *Lycopersici*; J. Agric. Food Chem., Vol. 42, pp. 327-333(1994).

Common/Systematic Name

AAL Toxin TE_2

Molecular Formula/Molecular Weight

$C_{27}H_{49}NO_9$; MW = 531.34073

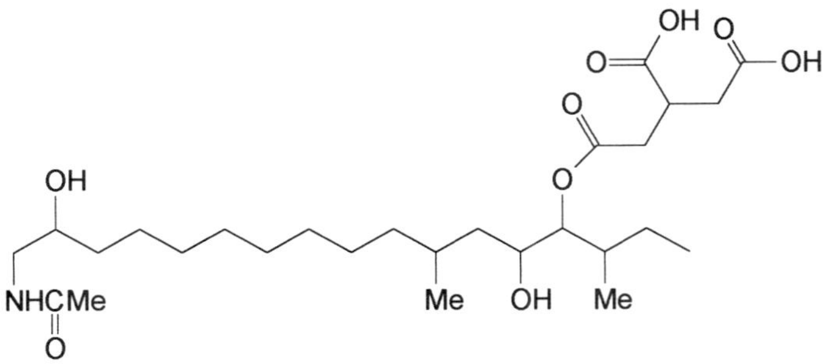

General Characteristics

AAL toxin TE_2 was not ninhydrin positive. All AAL toxin pairs are regioisomers at C-13 and C-14.

Fungal Source

Alternaria alternata f. sp. *lycopersici*.

Isolation/Purification

XAD-2 was added to culture filtrates and stirred for 4-6 hours, the adsorbed XAD beads were washed with water, and the toxins eluted with methanol. The extract was evaporated to dryness *in vacuo*, dissolved in ethyl acetate-acetic acid-hexane-water (6:2:2:1, v/v/v/v), and fractionated on a silica gel column by flash chromatography using the same solvent system. After 20 fractions were collected the solvent system was changed to ethyl acetate-acetic acid-water (6:3:1, v/v/v). Fractions were evaluated by TLC using the solvent system ethyl acetate-acetic acid-water (6:8:1, v/v/v). Toxins were detected by spraying plates with *p*-anisaldehyde. Final purification was performed on a SAX column washed successively with 0.1 N NaOH, water to pH 7.0, and equilibrated with methanol at pH 7.7. The selected fractions were dried, dissolved in methanol at pH 7.7, applied to a SAX column, washed with methanol, and eluted with 1% acetic acid in methanol.

Biological Activity

The AAL toxins are responsible for expression of *Alternaria* stem canker disease of tomato. All five congers were toxic to leaf tissue of the *asc/asc* isoline of tomato in the standard detached leaflet assay.

Spectral Data

^{1}H NMR:

(CD_3OD) 3.26(1H, dd, *J*=4.0, 4.5Hz, H-1); 3.06(1H, H-1'); 3.60(1H, dd, *J*=2.9, 8.0Hz, H-2); 1.36(1H, H-3); 1.38(1H, H-3'); 1.81(1H, H-12); 3.77(1H, H-13); 4.78(1H, dd, *J*=2.9, 3.0Hz, H-14); and 1.74ppm (1H, H-15).

^{13}C NMR:

(CD_3OD) 46.71, C-1; 68.49, C-2; 71.33, C-13; and 82.30ppm C-14.

Mass Spectrum:

FABMS: $(M+H)^+$ 532*m/e*.

Reference

E. D. Caldas, A. D. Jones, B. Ward, C. K. Winter, and D. G. Gilchrist; Structural Characterization of Three New AAL toxins Produced by *Alternaria alternata* f. sp. *Lycopersici*; J. Agric. Food Chem., vol. 42, pp. 327-333(1994).

Common/Systematic Name

Sphingofungin A

Molecular Formula/Molecular Weight

$C_{21}H_{41}N_3O_6$; MW = 431.29954

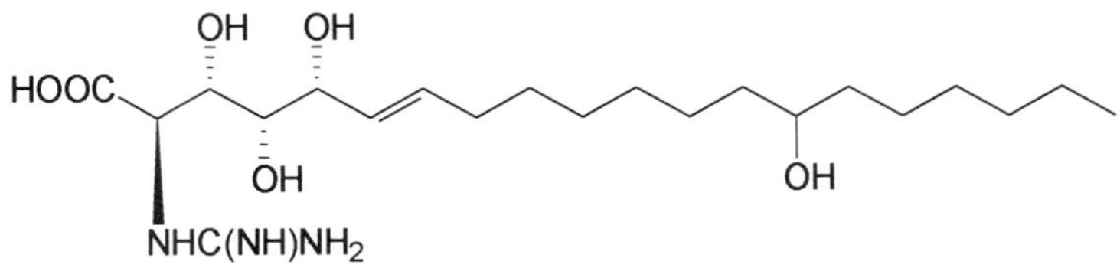

Fungal Source

Aspergillus fumigatus Fres. (ATCC 20857 = MF 5038) was isolated from soil collected from a pasture in Young, Departmento Rio Negro, Uruguay.

Isolation/Purification

The fermentation broth was extracted with methanol, filtered, concentrated, and purified by various chromatographic techniques including Amberlite XAD-2, silica gel, and Sephadex LH-20. Final separation of the four sphingofungins was accomplished with reversed phase C_{18} HPLC chromatography. For larger liquid fermentations a five step isolation procedure was developed. After extraction with methanol and removal of the solids by centrifugation, the aqueous filtrate was adsorbed onto a SP207 column. After elution of sphingofungins B and C with methanol, the eluate was diluted with water, and the pH was adjusted to 6.0. The solution was passed through a column of Dowex 1 (Cl^-) resin. The Dowex 1 eluant, containing sphingofungins B and C was adsorbed onto Diaion HP-20 and eluted with a stepwise gradient of aqueous methanol. Lipophilic contaminants were removed by washing the aqueous methanol solution with hexane-ethyl acetate. The methanol and water were removed to obtain a mixture of sphingofungins B and C, which were separated by HPLC chromatography.

Biological Activity

The sphingofungins A, B, and C are potent antifungal agents especially against *Cryptococcus neoformans*. They also show selective activity against various *Candida* species and are essentially inactive against filamentous fungi and bacteria. In general sphingofungin D is much less potent than the other three sphingofungins.

References

F. VanMiddlesworth, R. A. Giacobbe, M. Lopez, G. Garrity, J. A. Bland, K. Bartizal, R. A. Fromtling, J. Polishook, M Zweerink, A. M. Edison, W. Rozdilsky, K. E. Wilson and R. L. Monaghan; Sphingofungins A, B, C, and D; A New Family of Antifungal Agents. 1. Fermentation, Isolation, and Biological Activity; Journal of Antibiotics, Vol. 45, pp. 861-867(1992).

F. VanMiddlesworth, C. Dufresne, R. T. Moslely, and K. E. Wilson; Determination of the Relative and Absolute Stereochemistry of Sphingofungins A, B, C, and D; Tetrahedron Letters, pp. 297-300(1992).

Common/Systematic Name

Sphingofungin B

Molecular Formula/Molecular Weight

$C_{20}H_{39}NO_6$; MW = 389.27774

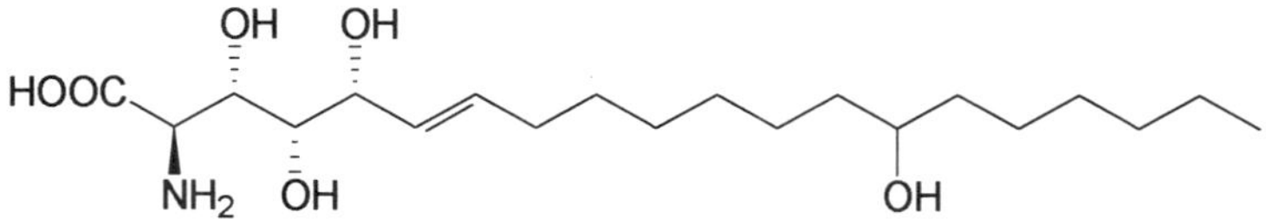

Fungal Source

Aspergillus fumigatus Fres. (ATCC 20857 = MF 5038) was isolated from soil collected from a pasture in Young, Departmento Rio Negro, Uruguay.

Isolation/Purification

The fermentation broth was extracted with methanol, filtered, concentrated, and purified by various chromatographic techniques including Amberlite XAD-2, silica gel, and Sephadex LH-20. Final separation of the four sphingofungins was accomplished with reversed phase C_{18} HPLC chromatography. For larger liquid fermentations a five step isolation procedure was developed. After extraction with methanol and removal of the solids by centrifugation, the aqueous filtrate was adsorbed onto a SP207 column. After elution of sphingofungins B and C with methanol, the eluate was diluted with water, and the pH was adjusted to 6.0. The solution was passed through a column of Dowex 1 (Cl^-) resin. The Dowex 1 eluant, containing sphingofungins B and C was adsorbed onto Diaion HP-20 and eluted with a stepwise gradient of aqueous methanol. Lipophilic contaminants were removed by washing the aqueous methanol solution with hexane-ethyl acetate. The methanol and water were removed to obtain a mixture of sphingofungins B and C, which were separated by HPLC chromatography.

Biological Activity

The sphingofungins A, B, and C are potent antifungal agents especially against *Cryptococcus neoformans*. They also show selective activity against various *Candida* species and are essentially inactive against filamentous fungi and bacteria. In general sphingofungin D is much less potent than the other three sphingofungins.

References

F. VanMiddlesworth, R. A. Giacobbe, M. Lopez, G. Garrity, J. A. Bland, K. Bartizal, R. A. Fromtling, J. Polishook, M Zweerink, A. M. Edison, W. Rozdilsky, K. E. Wilson and R. L. Monaghan; Sphingofungins A, B, C, and D; A New Family of Antifungal Agents. 1. Fermentation, Isolation, and Biological Activity; Journal of Antibiotics, Vol. 45, pp. 861-867(1992).

F. VanMiddlesworth, C. Dufresne, R. T. Moslely, and K. E. Wilson; Determination of the Relative and Absolute Stereochemistry of Sphingofungins A, B, C, and D; Tetrahedron Letters, pp. 297-300(1992).

Common/Systematic Name

Sphingofungin C

Molecular Formula/Molecular Weight

$C_{22}H_{43}NO_5$; MW = 401.31412

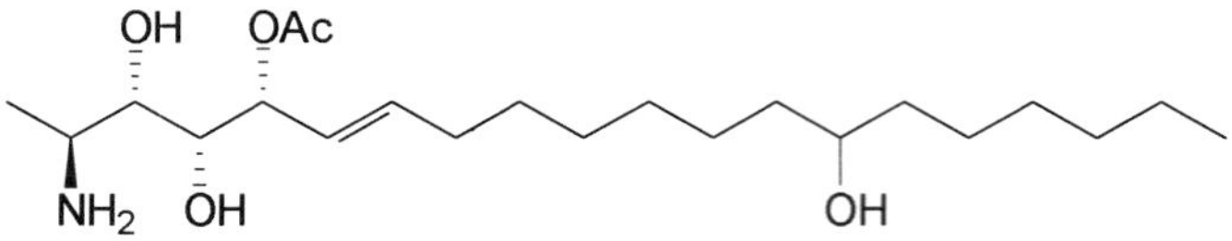

Fungal Source

Aspergillus fumigatus Fres. (ATCC 20857 = MF 5038) was isolated from soil collected from a pasture in Young, Departmento Rio Negro, Uruguay.

Isolation/Purification

The fermentation broth was extracted with methanol, filtered, concentrated, and purified by various chromatographic techniques including Amberlite XAD-2, silica gel, and Sephadex LH-20. Final separation of the four sphingofungins was accomplished with reversed phase C_{18} HPLC chromatography. For larger liquid fermentations a five step isolation procedure was developed. After extraction with methanol and removal of the solids by centrifugation, the aqueous filtrate was adsorbed onto a SP207 column. After elution of sphingofungins B and C with methanol, the eluate was diluted with water, and the pH was adjusted to 6.0. The solution was passed through a column of Dowex 1 (Cl^-) resin. The Dowex 1 eluant, containing sphingofungins B and C, was adsorbed onto Diaion HP-20 and eluted with a stepwise gradient of aqueous methanol. Lipophilic contaminants were removed by washing the aqueous methanol solution with hexane-ethyl acetate. The methanol and water were removed to obtain a mixture of sphingofungins B and C, which were separated by HPLC chromatography.

Biological Activity

The sphingofungins A, B, and C are potent antifungal agents especially against *Cryptococcus neoformans*. They also show selective activity against various *Candida* species and are essentially inactive against filamentous fungi and bacteria. In general, sphingofungin D is much less potent than the other three sphingofungins.

References

F. VanMiddlesworth, R. A. Giacobbe, M. Lopez, G. Garrity, J. A. Bland, K. Bartizal, R. A. Fromtling, J. Polishook, M Zweerink, A. M. Edison, W. Rozdilsky, K. E. Wilson and R. L. Monaghan; Sphingofungins A, B, C, and D; A New Family of Antifungal Agents. 1. Fermentation, Isolation, and Biological Activity; Journal of Antibiotics, Vol. 45, pp. 861-867(1992).

F. VanMiddlesworth, C. Dufresne, R. T. Moslely, and K. E. Wilson; Determination of the Relative and Absolute Stereochemistry of Sphingofungins A, B, C, and D; Tetrahedron Letters, pp. 297-300(1992).

Common/Systematic Name

Sphingofungin D

Molecular Formula/Molecular Weight

$C_{22}H_{41}NO_8$; MW = 447.28322

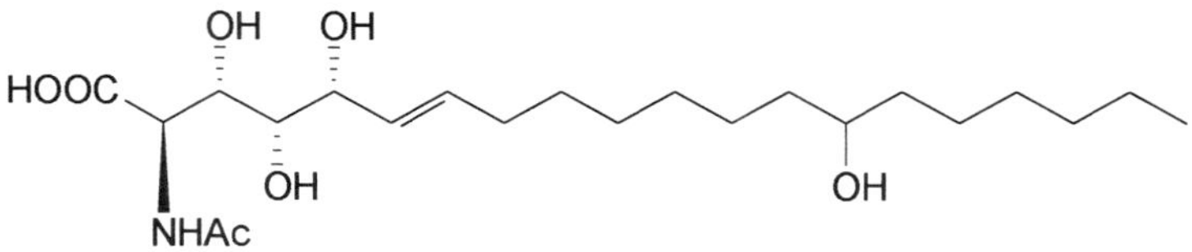

Fungal Source

Aspergillus fumigatus Fres. (ATCC 20857 = MF 5038) was isolated from soil collected from a pasture in Young, Departmento Rio Negro, Uruguay.

Isolation/Purification

The fermentation broth was extracted with methanol, filtered, concentrated, and purified by various chromatographic techniques including Amberlite XAD-2, silica gel, and Sephadex LH-20. Final separation of the four sphingofungins was accomplished with reversed phase C_{18} HPLC chromatography. For larger liquid fermentations a five step isolation procedure was developed. After extraction with methanol and removal of the solids by centrifugation, the aqueous filtrate was adsorbed onto a SP207 column. After elution of sphingofungins B and C with methanol, the eluate was diluted with water, and the pH was adjusted to 6.0. The solution was passed through a column of Dowex 1 (Cl^-) resin. The Dowex 1 eluant, containing sphingofungins B and C,was adsorbed onto Diaion HP-20 and eluted with a stepwise gradient of aqueous methanol. Lipophilic contaminants were removed by washing the aqueous methanol solution with hexane-ethyl acetate. The methanol and water were removed to obtain a mixture of sphingofungins B and C, which were separated by HPLC chromatography.

Biological Activity

The sphingofungins A, B, and C are potent antifungal agents especially against *Cryptococcus neoformans*. They also show selective activity against various *Candida* species and are essentially inactive against filamentous fungi and bacteria. In general, sphingofungin D is much less potent than the other three sphingofungins.

References

F. VanMiddlesworth, R. A. Giacobbe, M. Lopez, G. Garrity, J. A. Bland, K. Bartizal, R. A. Fromtling, J. Polishook, M Zweerink, A. M. Edison, W. Rozdilsky, K. E. Wilson and R. L. Monaghan; Sphingofungins A, B, C, and D; A New Family of Antifungal Agents. 1. Fermentation, Isolation, and Biological Activity; Journal of Antibiotics, Vol. 45, pp. 861-867(1992).

F. VanMiddlesworth, C. Dufresne, R. T. Moslely, and K. E. Wilson; Determination of the Relative and Absolute Stereochemistry of Sphingofungins A, B, C, and D; Tetrahedron Letters, pp. 297-300(1992).

Common/Systematic Name
Myriocin

Molecular Formula/Molecular Weight
$C_{21}H_{39}NO_6$; MW = 401.27774

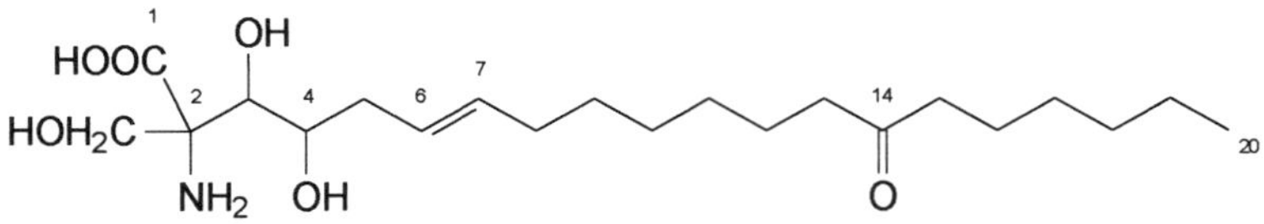

General Characteristics
Crystals from methanol; mp., 180-181°C; $[\alpha]_D^{24}$ + 10.3° (*c*=0.386, in MeOH). Positive ninhydrin test.

Fungal Source
Myriococcum albomyces.

Isolation/Purification
See D. Kluepfel *et. al.*, Journal of Antibiotics, Vol. 25, p. 109 (1972).

Biological Activity
Antifungal activity.

Spectral Data

IR:
(Nujol) Broad band in OH region, 1702, 1665, and 962cm^{-1}.

^{1}H NMR:
($CDCl_3$) (Tetraacetate derivative) 6.30(1H, NH); 4.51(s); 5.79(d); 4.74(m); 5.5(q) and 0.88ppm.

Mass Spectrum:
LREIMS: 383(M^+ - 18) and 256*m/e* (base peak, M^+ - [127 + 18]).

Reference
J. F. Bagli, D. Kluepfel, and M. St-Jacques; Elucidation of Structure and Stereochemistry of Myriocin. A Novel Antifungal Antibiotic; J. Organ. Chem., Vol. 38, pp. 1253-1260 (1973).

22

Ochratoxins and Related Metabolites

Ochratoxin A
Ochratoxin B
4-Hydroxyochratoxin A
Ochratoxin C
Mellein
4-Hydroxymellein

Common/Systematic Name

Ochratoxin A

7-Carboxy-5-chloro-8-hydroxy-3,4-dihydro-3*R*-methylisocoumarin-7-L-β-phenylalanine

Molecular Formula/Molecular Weight

$C_{20}H_{18}O_6NCl$; MW = 403.0822

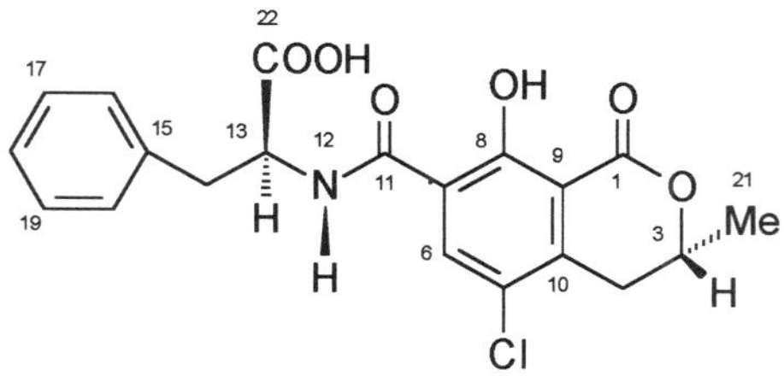

General Characteristics

Crystals from benzene; mp., 94-96°C; Crystals from xylene; mp., 169°C; $[\alpha]_D^{25}$ -118° (*c*=1.1, in chloroform).

Fungal Source

Aspergillus ochraceus (NRRL 3174); *A. sulphureus* (NRRL 4077); *A. melleus* (NRRL 3519; 3520); *Penicillium viridicatum* (ATCC 18411).

Biological Activity

LD_{50} in weanling rats dosed orally was 22mg/kg, in trout IP, 3.0mg/kg.

Spectral Data

UV:

λ_{max}^{EtOH} 215 (36,800) and 333nm (6,400).

^{1}H NMR:

($CDCl_3$) 4.76 (1H, H-3); 2.97 (2H, H-4); 8.07 (1H, H-6); 8.58 (1H, d, *J*= 7.3Hz, NH-12); 4.76 (1H, H-13); 3.18 (2H, H-14); 7.25 (5H, H-16-H-20); and 1.46ppm (3H, d, *J*= 6.1Hz, H-21).

^{13}C NMR:

($CDCl_3$) 169.1, s, C-1; 76.2, d, C-3; 32.4, t, C-4; 122.3, s, C-5; 136.8, d, C-6; 120.9, s, C-7; 163.5, s, C-8; 112.1, s, C-9; 142.6, s, C-10; 159.1, s, C-11; 54.3, d, C-13; 37.4, t, C-14; 137.7, s, C-15; 129.1, d, C-16, C-20; 130.0, d, C-17, C-19; 127.4, d, C-18; 20.8, q, C-21; and 173.1ppm, s, C-22.

Mass Spectrum:

LREIMS: 256m/e $(M)^+$.

TLC Data

Silica gel; benzene-acetic acid(3:1, v/v), R_f = 0.50; detected as a green fluorescent spot under UV light.

References

P. S. Steyn; Ochratoxin and Other Dihydroisocoumarins; In Microbial Toxins; A. Ciegler, S. Kadis and S. J. Ajil, eds. Academic Press, New York, N.Y., Vol. VI, pp. 179-203 (1971).

R. J. Cole and R. H. Cox; Ochratoxins; In Handbook of Toxic Fungal Metabolites; Academic Press, Inc., New York, N.Y., pp. 137-140 (1981).

Common/Systematic Name

Ochratoxin B

7-Carboxy-8-hydroxy-3,4-dihydro-3*R*-methylisocoumarin-7-L-β-phenylalanine

Molecular Formula/Molecular Weight

$C_{20}H_{19}O_6N$; MW = 369.12124

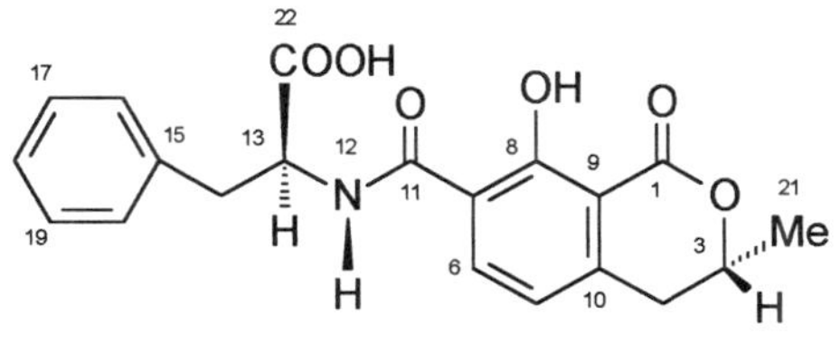

General Characteristics

Crystals from acidic methanol; mp., 221°C; $[\alpha]_D^{25}$ -35° (*c*=0.15, in EtOH); $[\alpha]_D^{25}$ -56° (*c*=0.29, in MeOH).

Fungal Source

Aspergillus ochraceus.

Biological Activity

Ochratoxin B is considerably less toxic than ochratoxins A or C. The LD_{50} in day-old chicks was dosed orally was 54mg/kg while ochratoxin A was 3.3-3.9mg/kg in the same assay.

Spectral Data

UV:

λ_{max}^{EtOH} 218(37,200) and 318nm (6,900).

^{1}H NMR:

($CDCl_3$) 4.90(1H, H-3); 3.10(2H, H-4); 8.21(d, *J*=6.8Hz, H-5); 7.02(1H, d, *J*=6.0Hz, H-6); 8.64(1H, d, *J*=6.1Hz, NH-12); 4.90(1H, H-13); 3.10(2H, H-14); 7.28(5H, H-16-H-20); and 1.45ppm (3H, d, *J*=5.4Hz, H-21).

^{13}C NMR:

($CDCl_3$) 168.7, s, C-1; 75.1, d, C-3; 33.1, t, C-4; 117.3, d, C-5; 135.5, d, C-6; 117.9, s, C-7; 162.0, s, C-8; 107.7, s, C-9; 142.7, s, C-10; 158.9, s, C-11; 52.8, d, C-13; 36.3, t, C-14; 137.0, s, C-15; 128.2, d, C-16, C-20; 127.0, d, C-17, C-19; 125.5, d, C-18; 19.3, q, C-21; and 171.6ppm, s, C-22.

Mass Spectrum:

LREIMS: 369*m/e* $(M)^+$.

TLC Data

Silica gel; benzene-acetic acid (4:1, v/v), $R_f = 0.35$; detected as a blue fluorescent spot under UV light.

References

P. S. Steyn; Ochratoxin and Other Dihydroisocoumarins; In Microbial Toxins; A. Ciegler, Kadis and S. J. Ajil, eds. Academic Press, New York, N.Y., Vol. VI, pp. 179-203 (1971).

R. J. Cole and R. H. Cox; Ochratoxins; In Handbook of Toxic Fungal Metabolites; Press, Inc., New York, N.Y., pp. 137-140 (1981).

Common/Systematic Name

4-Hydroxyochratoxin A

7-Carboxy-5-chloro-4,8-dihydroxy-3,4-dihydro-3*R*-methylisocoumarin-7-L-β-phenylalanine

Molecular Formula/Molecular Weight

$C_{20}H_{18}O_7NCl$; MW = 419.07718

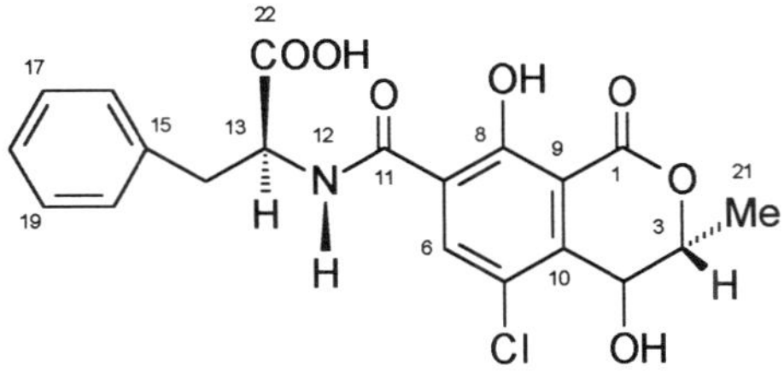

General Characteristics

Colorless crystals from benzene; mp., 216-218°C.

Fungal Source

Penicillium viridicatum (ATCC 18411).

Biological Activity

4-Hydroxyochratoxin A was excreted in urine of male Wister rats dosed with ochratoxin A (IP). 4-Hydroxyochratoxin A had no effect when dosed to rats at a level of 40mg/kg; ochratoxin A at this level caused 100% mortality. Therefore, 4-hydroxyochratoxin A may be a detoxification product in animals dosed with ochratoxin A

Spectral Data

UV:

λ_{max}^{EtOH} 213 (32,500) and 334nm (6,400).

IR:

(CH_3Cl) 3380, 3000, 2500, 1723, 1678, 1655, and 1535cm^{-1}.

^1H NMR:

($CDCl_3$) 4.80(1H, d, *J*=7.2Hz, H-3); 5.11(1H, d, *J*=2.0Hz, H-4); and 8.70ppm (1H, H-6).

Mass Spectrum:

LREIMS: 419*m/e* $(M)^+$.

TLC Data

Silica gel; benzene-acetic acid (3:1, v/v), R_f = 0.25; detected as a green fluorescent spot under UV light.

References

P. S. Steyn; Ochratoxin and Other Dihydroisocoumarins; In Microbial Toxins; A. Ciegler, Kadis and S. J. Ajil, eds. Academic Press, New York, N.Y., Vol. VI, pp. 179-203 (1971).

R. J. Cole and R. H. Cox; Ochratoxins; In Handbook of Toxic Fungal Metabolites; Press, Inc., New York, N.Y., pp. 137-140 (1981).

Common/Systematic Name
Ochratoxin C

Molecular Formula/Molecular Weight
$C_{22}H_{22}O_6NCl$; MW = 431.11357

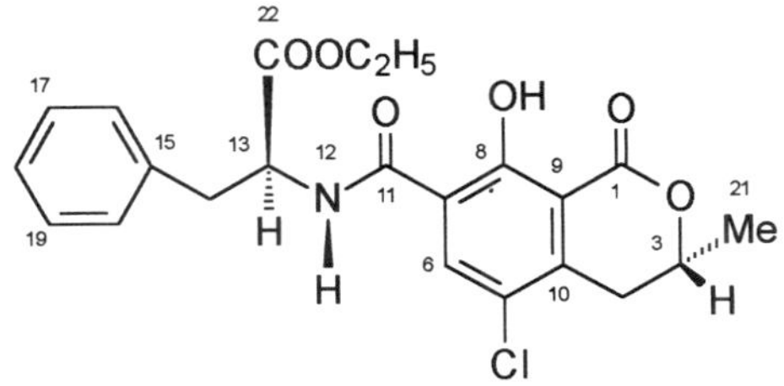

General Characteristics
Amorphous compound.

Fungal Source
Aspergillus ochraceus.

Biological Activity
Originally thought to be relatively nontoxic; however, it was later reported to be comparable to ochratoxin A.

Spectral Data
UV:
λ_{max}^{EtOH} 214 (30,000), 333 (7,000) and 378nm (2,050).

IR:
(CH_3Cl) 1730 and 1680cm^{-1}.

Mass Spectrum:
LREIMS: 431*m/e* $(M)^+$.

TLC Data
Silica gel; benzene-acetic acid (25:1, v/v), R_f = 0.55; detected as a light green fluorescent spot under UV light.

References
P. S. Steyn; Ochratoxin and Other Dihydroisocoumarins; In Microbial Toxins; A. Ciegler, Kadis and S. J. Ajil, eds. Academic Press, New York, N.Y., Vol. VI, pp. 179-203 (1971).

R. J. Cole and R. H. Cox; Ochratoxins; In Handbook of Toxic Fungal Metabolites; Press, Inc., New York, N.Y., pp. 137-140 (1981).

Common/Systematic Name

Mellein; Ochracin

(-)3,4-Dihydro-8-hydroxy-3-methylisocoumarin

Molecular Formula/Molecular Weight

$C_{10}H_{10}O_3$; MW = 178.06299

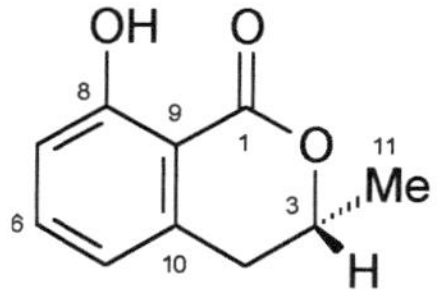

General Characteristics

Crystals (subl.); mp., 54-55°C.

Fungal Source

Aspergillus melleus; *A. ochraceus*.

Biological Activity

Biological activity unknown.

Spectral Data

UV:

λ_{max}^{EtOH} 212 (20,000), 246 (6,500) and 314nm (4,100).

^{1}H NMR:

($CDCl_3$) 4.76(1H, dd, *J*=7.0, 7.0Hz, H-3); 2.95 (2H, d, *J*=7.0Hz, H-4); 6.72 (1H, d, *J*=7.5Hz, H-5). 7.44 (1H, dd, *J*=7.5, 8.0Hz, H-6); 6.91 (1H, d, *J*=8.0Hz, H-7); 1.55 (d, *J*=7.0Hz, H-11); and 11.07ppm (1H, OH-8).

^{13}C NMR:

($CDCl_3$) 169.8, C-1; 76.1, C-3; 34.7, C-4; 117.8, C-5; 136.0, C-6; 116.2, C-7; 162.1, C-8; 108.2, C-9; 139.2, C-10; and 20.8ppm, C-11.

Mass Spectrum:

LREIMS: 178(M)$^+$ (100%), 161, 149, and 134*m/e*.

TLC Data

Silica gel G-HR; toluene-ethyl acetate-formic acid (5:4:1, v/v/v), R_f = 0.82; detected as a blue fluorescent spot under UV light.

References

P. S. Steyn; Ochratoxin and Other Dihydroisocoumarins; In Microbial Toxins; A. Ciegler, Kadis and S. J. Ajil, eds. Academic Press, New York, N.Y., Vol. VI, pp. 179-203 (1971).

R. J. Cole and R. H. Cox; Ochratoxins; In Handbook of Toxic Fungal Metabolites; Press, Inc., New York, N.Y., pp. 137-140 (1981).

Common/Systematic Name
4-Hydroxymellein
(-)3,4-Dihydro-4,8-dihydroxy-3-methylisocoumarin

Molecular Formula/Molecular Weight
$C_{10}H_{10}O_4$; MW = 194.05791

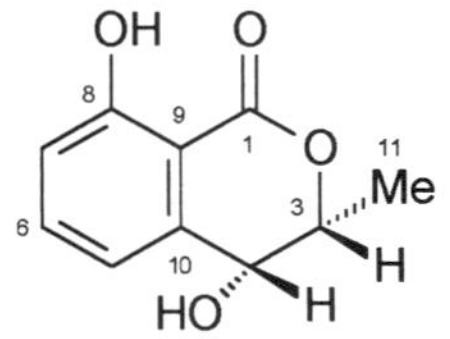

General Characteristics
Crystals from chloroform-methanol; mp., 131-132°C; $[\alpha]_D^{25}$ - 40° (*c*=1.0, in $CHCl_3$).

Fungal Source
Aspergillus melleus; *A. ochraceus*; *A. oniki*; *Lasiodiplodia theobromae (cis*-4-hydroxymellein); *Apiospora camptospora*.

Biological Activity
Biological activity unknown.

Spectral Data
UV:
λ_{max}^{EtOH} 247(5,300) and 315nm (4,200).

^{1}H NMR:
($CDCl_3$) 4.63(1H, H-3); 4.63(1H, H-4); 7.04(1H, d, *J*=7.5Hz, H-5); 7.57(1H, H-6); 7.02(1H, d, *J*=8.2Hz, H-7); 1.52(d, *J*=6.5Hz, H-11); 2.16(1H, H-4OH); and 11.01ppm (1H, H-8OH).

^{13}C NMR:
($CDCl_3$) 168.1, C-1; 79.7, C-3; 69.1, C-4; 117.7, C-5; 136.4, C-6; 115.9, C-7; 161.7, C-8; 106.5, C-9; 140.9, C-10; and 29.6ppm, C-11.

Mass Spectrum:
LREIMS: 194(M)$^+$ (100%), 161, 149, and 134*m/e*.

TLC Data
Silica gel G-HR; toluene-ethyl acetate-formic acid (5:4:1, v/v/v), R_f = 0.74; detected as a blue fluorescent spot under UV light.

References

P. S. Steyn; Ochratoxin and Other Dihydroisocoumarins; In Microbial Toxins; A. Ciegler, Kadis and S. J. Ajil, eds. Academic Press, New York, N.Y., Vol. VI, pp. 179-203 (1971).

R. J. Cole and R. H. Cox; Ochratoxins; In Handbook of Toxic Fungal Metabolites; Press, Inc., New York, N.Y., pp. 137-140 (1981).

23

Miscellaneous Metabolites

4,5,10,11-Tetrahydroxybisboline
24-Ethyllanosta-8,24(24')-diene-3β,22ξ-diol
25-Methylpisolactone
24-Methyllanosta-8,24'-diene-3β,22ξ-diol
24-Methyllanosta-8,24(24')-diene-3β,22ξ-diol
3α-Acetoxylanosta-8,24-dien-21-oic acid
21-Hydroxylanosta-8,24-dien-3-one
3α-(4-Carboxymethyl-3-hydroxy-3-methylbutanoyloxy)lanosta-8,24-dien-21-oic acid
Isofunicone
Xylobovatin
Deacetyl-19,20-epoxycytochalasin Q
19,20-Epoxycytochalasin Q
Deacetyl-19,20-epoxycytochalasin C
19,20-Epoxycytochalasin C
Fusaproliferin
Retigeranic Acid
Moniliformin
Cyclopiazonic Acid

Common/Systematic Name

4,5,10,11-Tetrahydroxybisboline

Molecular Formula/Molecular Weight

$C_{15}H_{28}O_4$; MW = 272.19876

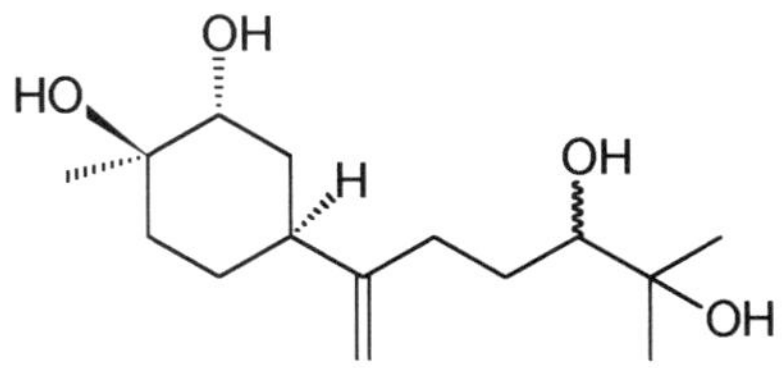

General Characteristics

Colorless glass.

Isolation/Purification

Fungal cultures were extracted with chloroform-acetone (85:15, v/v), allowed to sit overnight, filtered, and the solid residue re-extracted with acetone. The acetone extract was combined with the chloroform-acetone extract, concentrated under vacuum, and the non-polar materials removed by hexane drip. The solvent was decanted, concentrated, and chromatographed by flash chromatography with toluene, toluene-acetone 4:1, 2:1, 1:1 (v/v), acetone, and acetone-methanol, 1:1 (v/v). The toluene-acetone (1:1, v/v) fraction was further purified by reversed-phase TLC using methanol-water, 7:3 (v/v), which resulted in purified 4,5,10,11-tetrahydroxybisboline.

Fungal Source

Fusarium sambucinum.

Spectral Data

UV:

$\lambda_{max}^{Acetonitrile}$ 195nm (ϵ=5,000, π to π^* transition).

IR:

(film) 3376(OH), 1370, 1158, 1124, 1048, and 1050cm^{-1} (-C-O-C-).

^{1}H NMR:

($CDCl_3$) 1.17(3H, s, H-12); 1.22(3H, s, H-13); 1.27(3H, s H-14); 1.47(1H, m, H-9a); 1.57(1H, m, H-3a); 1.59(1H, m, 2a); 1.64(1H, m, H-9b); 1.69(1H, m, H-6a); 1.74(1H, m, H-2b); 1.78(1H, m, H-3b); 1.92(1H, m, H-6b); 2.10(1H, m, H-8a); 2.30(1H, m, H-1); 2.36(1H, m, H-8b); 3.38(1H, dd, *J*=1.7, 10.4Hz, H-10); 3.64(1H, b t, *J*=3.0Hz, H-5); 4.79(1H, b m, H-15a); and 4.84ppm (1H, m, H-15b).

^{13}C NMR:
(acetone-d_6) 25.1 (q, C-12); 25.9(q, C-13); 27.7(t, C-2); 28.1(q, C-14); 31.0(t, C-6); (t, C-8); 34.6(t, C-3); 35.8(t, C-9); 37.1(t, C-1); 70.8(s, C-4); 72.8(s, C-11); 74.1(d, C-10); 78.7(d, C-5); 107.2(t, C-15); and 156.1ppm (s, C-7).

Mass Data:
LREIMS: 254(M^+ - H_2O, 1%), 239(2), 236(3), 218(2), 125(21), 108(64), 81(89), and 43*m/e* (100); exact mass for $C_{15}H_{26}O_3$ (M^+ - H_2O); calcd 254.188; found 254.190*m/e*.

Reference

D. R. Sanson, D. G. Corley, C. L. Barnes, S. Searles, E. O. Schlemper, M. S. Tempesta, and G. E. Rottinghaus; New Mycotoxins from *Fusarium sambucinum*; J. Org. Chem., Vol. 54, pp. 4313-4318(1989).

Common/Systematic Name

24-Ethyllanosta-8,24(24')-diene-3β,22ξ-diol

Molecular Formula/Molecular Weight

$C_{32}H_{54}O_2$; MW = 470.41238

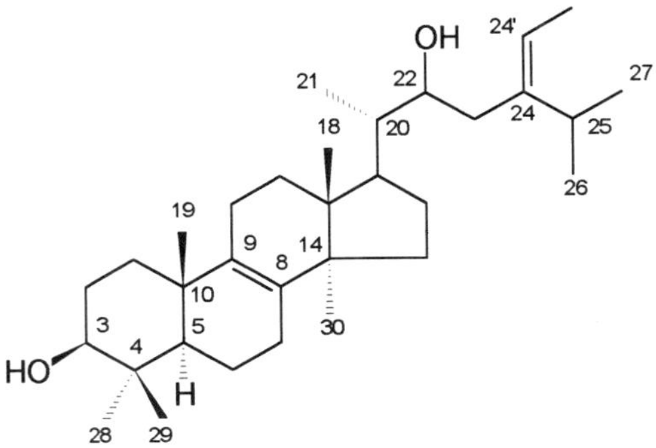

General Characteristics

Crystals; mp., 170-180°C; $[\alpha]_D^{24}$ +39.27° (*c*=0.45, in $CHCl_3$).

Fungal Source

Pisolithus tinctorius, a commercially important ectomycorrhizal fungus that is considered to have a broad host range.

Isolation/Purification

Freeze-dried *P. tinctorius* mycelia from submerged cultures were powdered in liquid N_2 and extracted three times with ethyl ether. The combined extracts were evaporated to dryness yielding a pale yellow solid containing mainly a mixture of triterpenoids. The solid was redissolved in 2-propanol and centrifuged. Separation and purification of the triterpenoids was carried out by repeated chromatography on a reversed-phase (C_8) HPLC column (PrepPack Bondapak 25 x 200 mm) using 80% aqueous methanol (adjusted to pH 3 with formic acid) as eluting solvent at a flow rate of 10ml/minute and detection at 210nm.

Spectral Data

UV:

End absorption.

^{1}H NMR:

(CDCl$_3$) 1.72, 1.23(2H, H-1); 1.67, 1.58(2H, H-2); 3.24(1H, dd, *J*=11.6, 4.6Hz, H-3); 1.05(1H, H-5); 1.68, 1.50(2H, H-6); 2.04, 2.04(2H, H-7); 2.01, 2.01(2H, H-11); 1.78, 1.67(2H, H-12); 1.61, 1.20(2H, H-15); 2.00, 1.35(2H, H-16); 1.92(1H, H-17); 0.70(3H, s, H-18); 0.99(3H, s, H-19); 1.42(1H, H-20); 0.91(3H, d, *J*=6.6Hz, H-21); 3.77(1H, ddd, *J*=8.6, 4.6, 1.5Hz, H-22); 2.05, 2.05(2H, H-23); 2.85(1H, septet, *J*=7.0Hz, H-25); 1.06(3H, d, *J*=7.0Hz, H26*); 1.00(3H, d, *J*=6.9Hz, H-27*); 5.25(1H, q, *J*=6.8Hz, H-24'); 1.00(3H, s, H-28); 0.81(3H, s, H-29); 0.91(3H, s, H-30); and 1.65ppm (3H, d, *J*=6.8Hz).

* Assignments may be reversed.

^{13}C NMR:

(CDCl$_3$) 35.6, C-1; 27.9, C-2; 79.0, C-3; 38.9, C-4; 50.4, C-5; 18.3, C-6; 26.5, C-7; 134.4, C-8; 134.5, C-9; 37.0, C-10; 21.0, C-11; 21.0, C-12; 44.5, C-13; 49.9, C-14; 30.8, C-15; 27.7, C-16; 47.2, C-17; 15.6, C-18; 19.1, C-19; 41.3, C-20; 12.0, C-21; 71.0, C-22; 38.7, C-23; 142.4, C-24; 28.6, C-25; 21.2, C-26; 21.0, C-27; 120.6, C-24'; 28.0, C-28; 15.4, C-29; 24.4, C-30; and 12.9ppm C-31.

Mass Spectrum:

HREIMS: 470.4096(M$^+$, calcd for $C_{32}H_{54}O_2$, 470.4124, 16%), 455[M - Me]$^+$ (6%), 437[M - Me - H_2O]$^+$ (8), 419(3), 372.3037[calcd for $C_{25}H_{40}O_2$, 372.3029] (36), 357.2782[calcd for $C_{24}H_{37}O_2$, 357.2794] (100), 344(8), 339.2664[calc for $C_{24}H_{35}O$, 339.2688] (32), 329(5), 321(6), 314(9), 311(11), 299(12), 281(9), 215(6), 187(8), 161(7), and 109*m/e* (9).

Reference

A. Baumbert, B. Schumann, A. Porzel, J. Schmidt, and D. Strack; Triterpenoids from *Pisolithus tinctorium* Isolates and Ectomycorrhizas; Phytochemistry, Vol. 45, pp. 499-504(1997).

Common/Systematic Name
25-Methylpisolactone
(22*S*)-24-Methyllanosta-8-ene-22,24'-epoxy-3β-ol-24'-one

Molecular Formula/Molecular Weight
$C_{32}H_{52}O_3$; MW = 484.39165

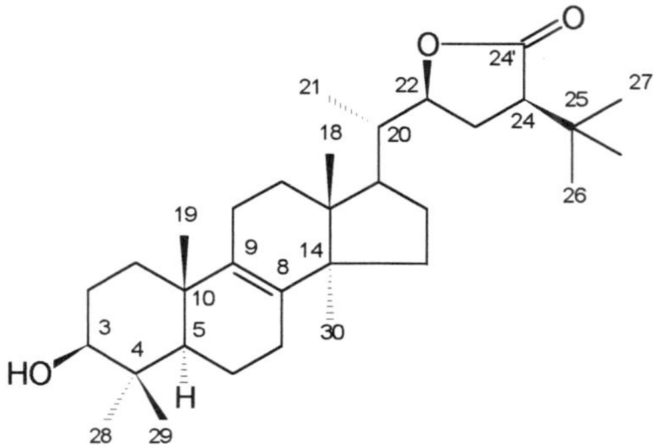

General Characteristics
Colorless needles; mp., 313-316°C; $[\alpha]_D^{24}$ +38.7° (*c*=0.23, in $CHCl_3$).

Fungal Source
Pisolithus tinctorius, a commercially important ectomycorrhizal fungus that is considered to have a broad host range.

Isolation/Purification
Freeze-dried *P. tinctorius* mycelia from submerged cultures were powdered in liquid N_2 and extracted three times with ethyl ether. The combined extracts were evaporated to dryness yielding a pale yellow solid containing mainly a mixture of triterpenoids. The solid was redissolved in 2-propanol and centrifuged. Separation and purification of the triterpenoids was carried out by repeated chromatography on a reversed-phase (C_8) HPLC column PrepPack Bondapak (25 x 200 mm) using 80% aqueous methanol (adjusted to pH 3 with formic acid) as eluting solvent at a flow rate of 10ml/minute and detection at 210nm.

Spectral Data

UV:
End absorption.

^{1}H NMR:

(CDCl$_3$) 1.72, 1.23(2H, H-1); 1.68, 1.58(2H, H-2); 3.24(1H, dd , J=11.4, 4.6Hz, H-3); 1.05(1H, H-5); 1.68, 1.50(2H, H-6); 2.03, 2.03(2H, H-7); 2.03, 2.02(2H, H-11); 1.77, 1.65(2H, H-12); 1.61, 1.23(2H, H-15); 2.01, 1.34(2H, H-16); 1.96(1H, H-17); 0.70(3H, s, H-18); 0.98(3H, s, H-19); 1.58(1H, H-20); 0.94(3H, d, J=6.7Hz, H-21); 4.39(1H, ddd, J=10.7, 6.1, 1.5Hz, H-22); 2.01, 1.92(2H, H-23); 2.46(1H, dd, J=12.6, 8.9Hz, H-24); 1.07(3H, s, H-26*); 1.07(3H, s, H-27*); 1.00(3H, s, H-28); 0.81(3H, s, H-29); 0.89(3H, s, H-30); and 1.07ppm (3H, s, H-31).

* Assignments may be reversed.

^{13}C NMR:

(CDCl$_3$) 35.6, C-1; 27.9, C-2; 78.9, C-3; 38.9, C-4; 50.4, C-5; 18.2, C-6; 26.5, C-7; 134.2, C-8; 134.7, C-9; 37.0, C-10; 21.0, C-11; 30.9, C-12; 44.6, C-13; 49.8, C-14; 30.8, C-15; 27.9, C-16; 47.4, C-17; 15.6, C-18; 19.1, C-19; 39.8, C-20; 12.2, C-21; 79.4, C-22; 28.5, C-23; 50.6, C-24; 31.8, C-25; 29.6, C-26; 29.6, C-27; 177.2, C-24'; 28.0, C-28; 15.4, C-29; 24.2, C-30; and 29.6ppm, C-31.

Mass Spectrum:

HREIMS: 484.3905[calcd for $C_{32}H_{52}O_3$, 484.3917] (28), 469[M - Me]$^+$ (80), 451.3542[M -Me - H_2O]$^+$ [calcd for $C_{31}H_{47}O_2$, 451.3576] (100), 329(7), 299(9), 281(14), 227(9), 215(8), 213(8), 187(10), 161(10), 159(9), 147(6), 135(17), 121(10), 95(15), and 57*m/e* (18).

Reference

A. Baumbert, B. Schumann, A. Porzel, J. Schmidt, and D. Strack; Triterpenoids from *Pisolithus tinctorium* Isolates and Ectomycorrhizas; Phytochemistry, Vol. 45, pp. 499-504(1997).

Common/Systematic Name

24-Methyllanosta-8,24(24')-diene-3β,22ξ-diol

Molecular Formula/Molecular Weight

$C_{31}H_{52}O_2$; MW = 456.39673

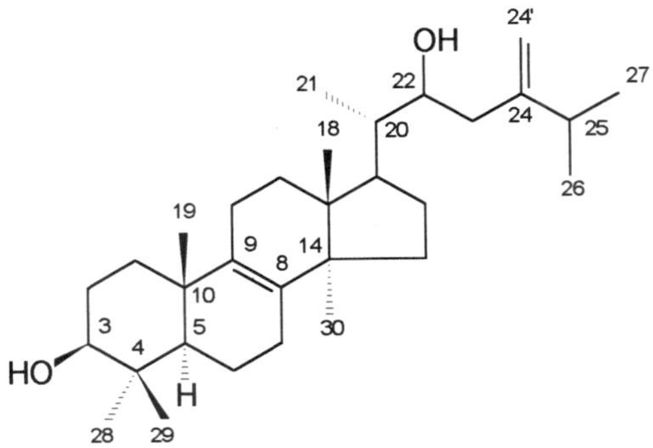

General Characteristics

Crystals from isopropanol, mp. 177-179°C; $[\alpha]_D^{24}$ +49.7° (*c*=0.20, in $CHCl_3$).

Fungal Source

Pisolithus tinctorius, a commercially important ectomycorrhizal fungus that is considered to have a broad host range.

Isolation/Purification

Freeze-dried *P. tinctorius* mycelia from submerged cultures were powdered in liquid N_2 and extracted three times with ethyl ether. The combined extracts were evaporated to dryness yielding a pale yellow solid containing mainly a mixture of triterpenoids. The solid was redissolved in 2-propanol and centrifuged. Separation and purification of the triterpenoids was carried out by repeated chromatography on a reversed-phase (C_8) HPLC PrepPack Bondapak column (25 x 200 mm) using 80% aqueous methanol (adjusted to pH 3 with formic acid) as eluting solvent at a flow rate of 10ml/minute and detection at 210nm.

Spectral Data

UV:

End absorption.

^{1}H NMR:

(CDCl$_3$) 1.72, 1.23(2H, H-1); 1.66, 1.58(2H, H-2); 3.239(1H, dd, *J*=11.7, 4.5Hz, H-3); 1.04(1H, H-5); 1.68, 1.49(2H, H-6); 2.03, 2.03(2H, H-7); 2.03, 2.01(2H, H-11); 1.79, 1.68(2H, H-12); 1.61, 1.21(2H, H-15); 2.00, 1.36(2H, H-16); 1.91(1H, H-17); 0.70(3H, s, H-18); 0.99(3H, s, H-19); 1.43(1H, H-20); 0.92(3H, d, *J*=6.6Hz, H-21); 3.81(1H, ddd, *J*=9.4, 3.9, 1.4Hz, H-22); 2.26(1H, dd, *J*=14.3, 9.4Hz, H-23); 2.10(1H, dd, *J*=14.3, 3.9Hz, H-23); 2.24(1H, septet, *J*=6.8Hz, H-25); 1.06(3H, d, *J*=6.8Hz, H26*); 1.04(3H, d, *J*=6.9Hz, H-27*); 4.89(1H, dd, *J*=1.3, 1.3Hz, H-24'); 4.79(1H, dd, *J*=2.4, 1.3Hz, H-24'); 1.00(3H; s, H-28); 0.81(3H, s, H-29); and 0.92ppm (3H, s, H-30).

* Assignments may be reversed.

^{13}C NMR:

(CDCl$_3$) 35.6, C-1; 27.9, C-2; 79.0, C-3; 38.9, C-4; 50.4, C-5; 18.3, C-6; 26.5, C-7; 134.4, C-8; 134.6, C-9; 37.0, C-10; 21.0, C-11; 31.0, C-12; 44.5, C-13; 49.9, C-14; 30.8, C-15; 27.7, C-16; 47.1, C-17; 15.6, C-18; 19.1, C-19; 41.1, C-20; 12.0, C-21; 70.8, C-22; 41.2, C-23; 153.4, C-24; 33.5, C-25; 21.7, C-26; 22.0, C-27; 109.2, C-24'; 28.0, C-28; 15.4, C-29; and 24.3ppm C-30.

Mass Spectrum:

LREIMS: 456$[M]^+$ (32%), 441$[M-Me]^+$ (5), 423$[M-Me-H_2O]^+$ (9), 405(4), 372(8), 357(100), 344(6), 339(35), 329(5), 321(9), 314(6), 311(13), 299(11), 281(10), 215(6), 187(7), 161(6), 135(6), and 95*m/e* (8).

Reference

A. Baumbert, B. Schumann, A. Porzel, J. Schmidt, and D. Strack; Triterpenoids from *Pisolithus tinctorium* Isolates and Ectomycorrhizas; Phytochemistry, Vol. 45, pp. 499-504(1997).

Common/Systematic Name

3α-Acetoxylanosta-8,24-dien-21-oic acid

Molecular Formula/Molecular Weight

$C_{32}H_{50}O_4$; MW = 498.37091

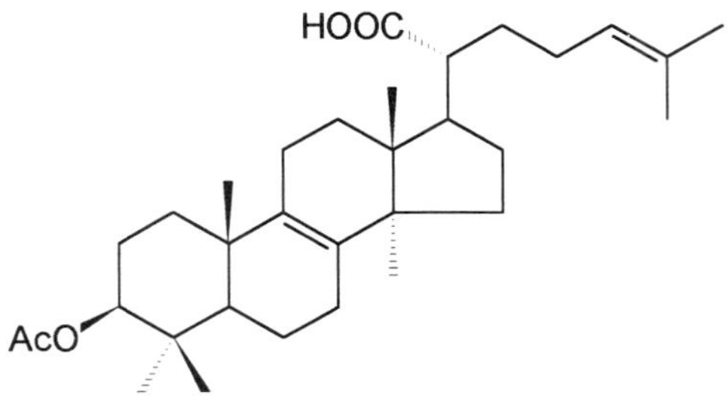

General Characteristics

White powder; mp., 192-194°C; $[\alpha]_D^{21}$ +14° (*c*=1.0, in $CHCl_3$).

Fungal Source

Fomitopsis pinicola, a wood-rotting fungus growing on coniferous and broad-leafed trees in Europe.

Isolation/Purification

Lyophilized fruiting bodies of *F. pinicola* were extracted successively with methylene chloride and methanol (3x). The methylene chloride extract was separated on a silica gel column Si 60 with a step-gradient of petrol-ethyl acetate (95:5-9:1-7:1-5:1-3:1-1:1, v/v), ethyl acetate and finally methanol to give 19 fractions (A-S). Fraction I was submitted to low pressure liquid chromatography (LPLC) on silica gel with chloroform-isopropanol (98:2, v/v) giving two fractions (I1 and I2). Fraction I1 was further purified on a Sephadex LH_{20} column with chloroform-methanol (1:1, v/v) to yield the non-UV absorbing metabolite 3α-acetoxylanosta-8,24-dien-21-oic acid. Fraction H was submitted to LPLC with petrol-ethyl acetate (5:1, v/v) which gave five fractions (H1-H5). Further separation of fraction H4 on a Sephadex LH_{20} column with chloroform-methanol (1:1, v/v) afforded 21-hydroxylanosta-8,24-dien-3-one. Fraction N was submitted to medium pressure liquid chromatography on DIOL with a stepwise gradient of *n*-hexane-chloroform (2:1-1:1, v/v) affording 3 fractions (N1-N3). A further purification of fraction N3 on a Sephadex LH_{20} column with chloroform-methanol (1:1, v/v) yielded 3α-(4-carboxymethyl-3-hydroxy-3-methylbutanoyloxy)lanosta-8,24-dien-21-oic acid as a white non-UV absorbing powder.

Biological Activity

Antimicrobial activity against *Bacillus subtilis* in a TLC bioassay.

Spectral Data

IR:
3600-2750, 2920, 1715, and 1680cm^{-1}.

^{1}H NMR:
($CDCl_3$) 0.74(3H, s, H-18); 0.83(3H, s, H-29); 0.88(3H, s, H-28); 0.92(3H, s, H-30); 0.95(3H, s, H-19); 1.56, 1.65(each 3H, s, H-26, H-27); 2.04(3H, s, acetoxy); 4.65(1H, br s, H-3); and 5.07ppm (1H, t, H-24).

^{13}C NMR:
($CDCl_3$) 30.3, C-1; 23.4, C-2; 77.9, C-3; 36.8, C-4; 45.2, C-5; 17.9, C-6; 26.9, C-7; 134.4, C-8; 133.8, C-9; 36.9, C-10; 20.8, C-11; 28.9, C-12; 44.2, C-13; 49.5, C-14; 30.8, C-15; 27.0, C-16; 47.1, C-17; 16.0, C-18; 18.8, C-19; 47.7, C-20; 183.3, C-21; 32.4, C-22; 25.9, C-23; 123.6, C-24; 132.2, C-25; 17.6, C-26; 25.7, C-27; 21.8, C-28; 27.5, C-29; 24.3, C-30; 171.0, $CH_3\underline{C}$=O; and 21.3ppm, $\underline{C}H_3C$=O.

Mass Spectrum:
LREIMS: 498(M)$^+$ (45%), 483(18), 437(17), 423(100), 281(27), 187(23), and 69*m/e* (23). D/CI-MS: 516[M + NH_4]$^+$ (100%), 499[M + H]$^+$ (6), and 472*m/e* (21).

TLC Data
Ethyl acetate-petrol (1:1, v/v), R_f = 0.54; ethyl acetate-petrol (1:3, v/v), R_f = 0.24.

Reference
A. C. Keller, M. P. Maillard, and K. Hostettmann; Antimicrobial Steroids from the Fungus *Fomitopsis pinicola*; Phytochemistry, Vol. 41, pp. 1041-1046(1996).

Common/Systematic Name

21-Hydroxylanosta-8,24-dien-3-one

Molecular Formula/Molecular Weight

$C_{30}H_{48}O_2$; MW = 440.36543

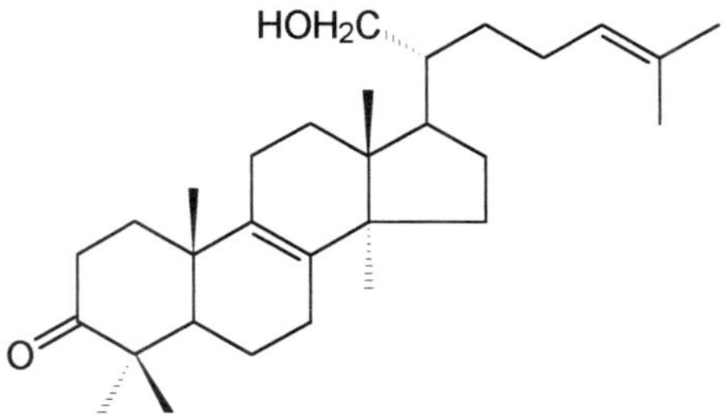

General Characteristics

White powder; mp., 92-96°C; $[\alpha]_D^{21}$ +59° (*c*=1.0, in $CHCl_3$).

Fungal Source

Fomitopsis pinicola, a wood-rotting fungus growing on coniferous and broad-leafed trees in Europe.

Isolation/Purification

Lyophilized fruiting bodies of *F. pinicola* were extracted successively with methylene chloride and methanol (3x). The methylene chloride extract was separated on a silica gel column Si 60 with a step-gradient of petrol-ethyl acetate (95:5-9:1-7:1-5:1-3:1-1:1, v/v), ethyl acetate and finally methanol to give 19 fractions (A-S). Fraction I was submitted to low pressure liquid chromatography (LPLC) on silica gel with chloroform-isopropanol (98:2, v/v) giving two fractions (I1 and I2). Fraction I1 was further purified on a Sephadex LH_{20} column with chloroform-methanol (1:1, v/v) to yield the non-UV absorbing metabolite 3α-acetoxylanosta-8,24-dien-21-oic acid. Fraction H was submitted to LPLC with petrol-ethyl acetate (5:1,v/v),which gave five fractions (H1-H5). Further separation of fraction H4 on a Sephadex LH_{20} column with chloroform-methanol (1:1, v/v) afforded 21-hydroxylanosta-8,24-dien-3-one. Fraction N was submitted to medium pressure liquid chromatography on DIOL with a stepwise gradient of *n*-hexane-chloroform (2:1-1:1, v/v) affording 3 fractions (N1-N3). A further purification of fraction N3 on a Sephadex LH_{20} column with chloroform-methanol (1:1, v/v) yielded 3α-(4-carboxymethyl-3-hydroxy-3-methylbutanoyloxy)lanosta-8,24-dien-21-oic acid as a white non-UV absorbing powder.

Biological Activity

Antimicrobial activity against *Bacillus subtilis* in a TLC bioassay.

Spectral Data

IR:
3250, 2905, and 1685cm^{-1}.

^{1}H NMR:
($CDCl_3$) 0.69(3H, s, H-18); 0.86(3H, s, H-30); 1.01(3H, s, H-28); 1.04(3H, s, H-29); 1.07(3H, s, H-19); 1.56, 1.63(each 3H, s, H-26, H-27); 3.65(2H, *m*,H-21); and 5.07ppm (1H, t, H-24).

^{13}C NMR:
($CDCl_3$) 35.9, C-1; 34.4, C-2; 217.0, C-3; 47.2, C-4; 51.0, C-5; 19.3, C-6; 26.2, C-7; 133.0, C-8; 135.1, C-9; 36.8, C-10; 20.9, C-11; 29.6, C-12; 44.1, C-13; 49.8, C-14; 30.7, C-15; 27.5, C-16; 44.2, C-17; 16.0, C-18; 18.6, C-19; 42.7, C-20; 62.3, C-21; 30.3, C-22; 24.8, C-23; 124.8, C-24; 132.2, C-25; 17.6, C-26; 25.6, C-27; 21.2, C-28; 26.0, C-29; and 24.3ppm, C-30.

Mass Spectrum:
LREIMS: 440$[M]^+$ (100%), 425(61), 407(54), 271(16), 257(19), 245(25), 109(63), and 69*m/e* (23). D/CI-MS: 458$[M + NH_4]^+$ (100).

TLC Data
Ethyl acetate-petrol (1:3, v/v), R_f= 0.25.

Reference
A. C. Keller, M. P. Maillard, and K. Hostettmann; Antimicrobial Steroids from the Fungus *Fomitopsis pinicola*; Phytochemistry, Vol. 41, pp. 1041-1046(1996).

Common/Systematic Name

3α-(4-Carboxymethyl-3-hydroxy-3-methylbutanoyloxy)lanosta-8,24-dien-21-oic acid

Molecular Formula/Molecular Weight

$C_{37}H_{58}O_7$; MW = 614.41825

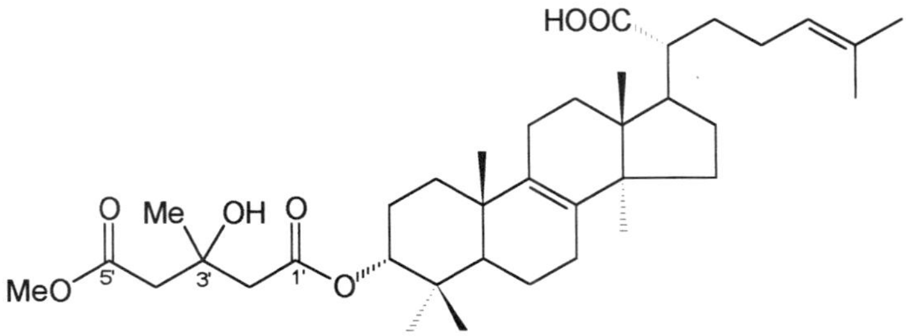

General Characteristics

White powder; mp., 147°C; $[\alpha]_D^{21}$ +5° (*c*=1.0, in $CHCl_3$).

Fungal Source

Fomitopsis pinicola, a wood-rotting fungus growing on coniferous and broad-leafed trees in Europe.

Isolation/Purification

Lyophilized fruiting bodies of *F. pinicola* were extracted successively with methylene chloride and methanol (3x). The methylene chloride extract was separated on a silica gel column Si 60 with a step-gradient of petrol-ethyl acetate (95:5-9:1-7:1-5:1-3:1-1:1, v/v), ethyl acetate and finally methanol to give 19 fractions (A-S). Fraction I was submitted to low pressure liquid chromatography (LPLC) on silica gel with chloroform-isopropanol (98:2, v/v) giving two fractions (I1 and I2). Fraction I1was further purified on a Sephadex LH_{20} column with chloroform-methanol (1:1, v/v) to yield the non-UV absorbing metabolite 3α-acetoxylanosta-8,24-dien-21-oic acid. Fraction H was submitted to LPLC with petrol-ethyl acetate (5:1, v/v) which gave five fractions (H1-H5). Further separation of fraction H4 on a Sephadex LH_{20} column with chloroform-methanol (1:1, v/v) afforded 21-hydroxylanosta-8,24-dien-3-one. Fraction N was submitted to medium pressure liquid chromatography on DIOL with a stepwise gradient of *n*-hexane-chloroform (2:1-1:1 v/v) affording 3 fractions (N1-N3). A further purification of fraction N3 on a Sephadex LH_{20} column with chloroform-methanol (1:1, v/v) yielded 3α-(4-carboxymethyl-3-hydroxy-3-methylbutanoyloxy)lanosta-8,24-dien-21-oic acid as a white non-UV absorbing powder.

Biological Activity

Antimicrobial activity against *Bacillus subtilis* in a TLC bioassay.

Spectral Data

^{1}H NMR:

(pyridine-d_5) 0.86(3H, s, H-18); 0.91(3H, s, H-29); 0.95(3H, s, H-28); 0.99(3H, s, H-30); 1.05(3H, s, H-19); 1.62, 1.66(each 3H, s, H-26, H-27); 1.66(3H, s, 3'-methyl); 2.97(2H, s); 3.01(d, J=13.9Hz); 3.61(3H, s, 5'-methoxy); 4.93(1H, s, H-3); and 5.32ppm (1H, t, H-24).

^{13}C NMR:

(pyridine-d_5) 30.7, C-1; 23.5, C-2; 78.1, C-3; 36.8, C-4; 45.8, C-5; 18.2, C-6; 26.7, C-7; 134.2, C-8; 134.1, C-9;-37.1, C-10; 21.1, C-11; 29.2, C-12; 44.8, C-13; 49.8, C-14; 30.9, C-15; 27.4, C-16; 47.6, C-17; 16.3, C-18; 19.0, C-19; 49.0, C-20; 178.6, C-21; 33.2, C-22; 26.2, C-23; 124.8, C-24; 131.7, C- 25; 17.6, C-26; 25.7, C-27; 21.8, C-28; 27.5, C-29; 24.2, C-30; 171.8, C-1'; 45.9, C-2'; 69.8, C-3'; 28.4, C-3' methyl; 46.3, C-5'; 171.2, C-6'; and 51.2ppm C-5'-O-methyl.

Mass Spectrum:

LREIMS: 614$[M]^+$ (0.4%), 540(1.6), 438(56), 423(100), 296(32), 281(24), 187(29), 177(60), 159(39), 117(30), and 69*m/e* (17). D/CI-MS: 632$[M + NH_4]^+$ (50%), 615$[M + H]^+$ (16), 474$[M\text{-side chain} + NH_4]^+$ (17), 458(22), 439$[M\text{-side chain} + H]^+$ (68), 194$[\text{side chain} + NH_4]^+$ (100).

TLC Data

Chloroform-isopropanol (9:1 v/v), $R_f = 0.60$.

Reference

A. C. Keller, M. P. Maillard, and K. Hostettmann; Antimicrobial Steroids from the Fungus *Fomitopsis pinicola*; Phytochemistry, Vol. 41, pp. 1041-1046(1996).

Common/Systematic Name
Isofunicone
(*E*)-3-Methoxy-2-propenyl-5-(2'-carbomethoxy-4'-hydroxy-6'-methoxybenzoyl)-4-pyrone

Molecular Formula/Molecular Weight
$C_{19}H_{18}O_8$; MW = 374.10017

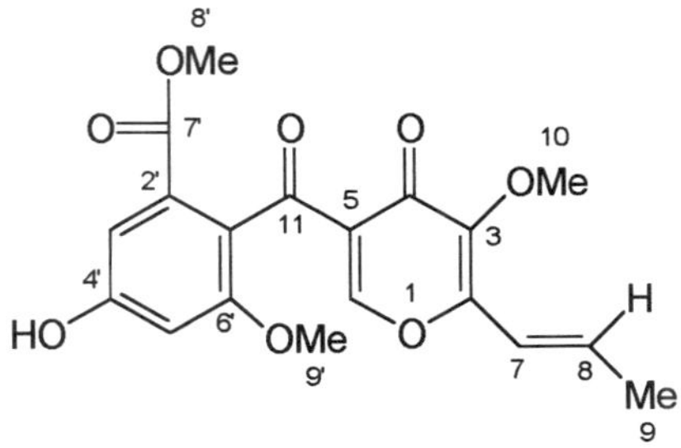

General Characteristics
Recrystallized from methanol to give plates; mp., 215-218°C.

Isolation/Purification
The culture broth was grown at 24°C without shaking for 21 days and then filtered to separate the mycelium from the broth. The filtrate was adjusted to pH 2.0 with dilute HCl solution, and successively extracted with ethyl acetate. After evaporating the solvent, the residue was fractionated by silica gel column chromatography with hexane-ethyl acetate mixtures. Fractions containing 50% ethyl acetate were bulked and further purified by silica gel column chromatography with benzene-ethyl acetate mixtures. The active fraction (inhibited tea pollen growth) was evaporated to dryness and recrystallized from methanol, to give plates of isofunicone

Fungal Source
Unidentified *Penicillium* sp.

Biological Activity
Inhibited tea pollen (*Camellia sinensis*) growth by 84% at a concentration of 3mg/ml and 100% at 10mg/ml.

Spectral Data

UV:
λ_{max}^{EtOH} 293, 285, and 249nm.

IR:
(KBr) 3228, 2950, 2852, 1715, 1681, 1653, 1611, and 1443cm^{-1}.

^{1}H NMR:

(DMSO) 1.94(3H, s, H-9); 3.64(3H, s, H-10); 3.66(3H, s, H-8'); 3.71(3H, s, H-9'); 6.54(1H, br, d, *J*=15Hz, H-7); 6.62(1H, m, H-8); 6.64(1H, d, *J*=2Hz, H-5'); 6.81(IH, d, *J*=2Hz, H-3'); 8.51(1H, s, H-6); and 10.21ppm (1H, br s, H-4').

^{13}C NMR:

(DMSO) 18.4(q, C-9); 52.0(q, C-8'); 55.9(q, C- 10); 60.0(q, C-9'); 102.9(d, C-5'); 107.7(d, C-3'); 118.1(d, C-8); 122.6(s, C-1'); 126.8(s, C-5); 130.6(s, C-2'); 135.1(d, C-7); 143.2(s, C-6'); 153.7(s, C-2); 157.9(s, C-3); 159.0(d, C-6); 159.3(s, C-4'); 166.3(s, C-7'); 171.1(s, C-4); and 189.7ppm (s, C-11).

Mass Spectrum:

374(M)$^+$ (82%), 343(M - OMe)$^+$ (39), 315(M-COOMe)$^+$ (42), 209(M-165)$^+$ (40), 192(M-182)$^+$ (100); found: C, 60.99%; H, 4.75, $C_{19}H_{18}O_8$ requires: C, 60.96; H, 4.85%

Reference

Y. Kimura, T. Yoshinari, A. Shimada and T. Hamasaki; Isofunicone, A Pollen Growth Inhibitor Produced by the Fungus *Penicillium sp.*; Phytochemistry, Vol. 40, pp. 629-631(1995).

Common/Systematic Name

Xylobovatin

18-Deoxy-19,20-epoxycytochalasin Q

Molecular Formula/Molecular Weight

$C_{30}H_{37}NO_6$; MW = 507.26209

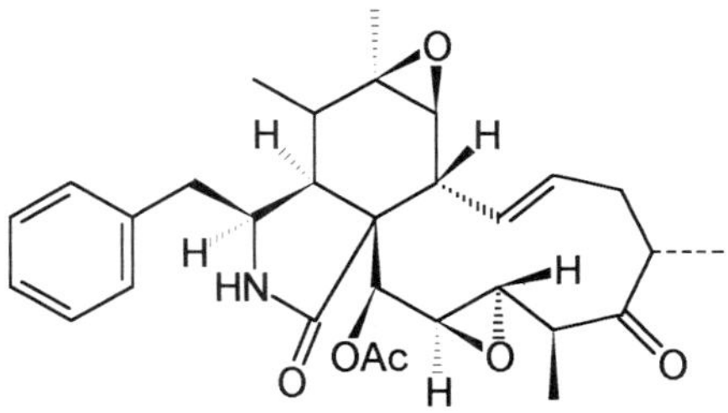

Fungal Source

Xylaria obovata (ADA-228), a wood-inhabiting tropical fungus collected from the Munesa Forest in southern Ethiopia.

Isolation/Purification

Cultured on a rice medium; after 20-40 days the moldy rice was extracted with chloroform, dried over Na_2SO_4, filtered and evaporated to dryness. The crude extract was separated on a Si-60 column eluted with a gradient from *n*-hexane-ethyl acetate (19:1, v/v) to ethyl acetate. When necessary, the collected fractions were further purified by preparative TLC [*n*-hexane-ethyl acetate (1:2 v/v); R_f 0.71].

Biological Activity

Cytotoxic.

Spectral Data

IR:

(KBr) 3430, 1745, 1710, and 1685cm^{-1}.

CD:

$[\alpha]^{27}$ 589nm, + 44.5°; 578nm, + 45.4°; 546nm, + 49.6°; 436nm, + 79.6°; 365nm, + 139.6° (*c*=1.3, in MeOH).

^{1}H NMR:

($CDCl_3$) 3.60(1H, ddd, *J*=7.0, 7.0, 2.5Hz, H-3); 2.12(1H, dd, *J*=5.7, 2.5Hz, H-4); 1.61(1H, qd, *J*=7.2, 5.7Hz, H-6); 2.74(1H, *J*=5.5Hz, H-7); 2.38(1H, *J*=10.0, 5.5Hz, H-8); 2.83(2H, m, H-10); 0.79(3H, d, *J*=7.2Hz, H-11); 1.20(3H, s, H-12); 6.27(1H, dd, *J*=15.0, 10.0, 1.0Hz, H-13); 5.57(1H, ddd, *J*=15.0, 10.5, 5.0Hz, H-14); 2.50(1H, td, *J*=13.0, 10.5Hz, H-15); 2.17(1H, dddd, *J*=13.0, 5.0, 3.5, 1.0Hz, H-15); 2.97(1H, dqd, *J*=13.0, 6.7, 3.5Hz, H-16); 2.26(3H, dq, *J*=9.0, 7.0, H-18); 2.94(1H, dd, *J*=9.0,

2.0Hz, H-19); 3.55(1H, dd, *J*=2.0, 1.0Hz, H-20); 5.55(1H, s, H-21); 1.14(3H, d, *J*=6.7Hz, H-22); 1.30(3H, d, *J*=7.0Hz, H-23); 7.20(1H, m, H-25); 7.33(1H, m, H-26); 7.25(1H, m, H-27); and 2.12ppm (3H, s, acetate).

^{13}C NMR:
(CDCl$_3$) 170.0, C-1; 54.5, C-3; 50.9, C-4; 36.7, C-5; 57.2, C-6; 62.5, C-7; 44.5, C-8; 54.1, C-9; 45.8, C-10; 12.7, C-11; 19.7, C-12; 131.4, C-13; 130.8, C-14; 37.5, C-15; 43.6, C-16; 215.9, C-17, 50.6, C-18; 58.6, C-19; 57.4, C-20; 72.8, C-21; 18.6, C-22; 14.8, C-23; 136.9, C-24; 129.2, C-25; 129.0, C-26; 127.2, C-27; 174.7, <u>CO</u>Me; and 20.6ppm CO<u>Me</u>.

Mass Spectrum:
HREIMS: 507.2586, calc. for $C_{30}H_{37}NO_6$, 507.2621 (17%), 489.2557, calc. for $C_{30}H_{35}NO_5$, 489.2515[M - H$_2$O]$^+$ (7), 448.2484, calc. for $C_{28}H_{34}NO4$, 448.2488[M - Ac]$^+$ (6), 416.2032, calc. for $C_{23}H_{30}NO_6$, 416.2073[M - benzyl]$^+$ (100), 356.1854, calc. for $C_{21}H_{26}NO_4$, 356.1862[416-HOAc]$^+$ (59), 338.1779, calc. for $C_{21}H_{24}NO_3$, 338.1756[356-H$_2$O]$^+$ (60), 328.1923, calc. for $C_{20}H_{26}NO_3$, 328.1913[356-CO]$^+$ (13), 320.1672, calc. for $C_{21}H_{22}NO_2$ 320.1651[338-H$_2$O]$^+$ (9), 310.1770, calc. for $C_{20}H_{24}NO_2$, 310.1807[338-CO]$^+$ (18), 296.1651, calc. for $C_{19}H_{22}NO_2$, 296.1626[310-CH$_2$]$^+$ (9), 91 (21), and 43*m/e* (12).

<u>Reference</u>

D. Abate, W-R. Abraham, and H. Meyer; Cytochalasins and Phytotoxins from the Fungus *Xylaria obovata*; Phytochemistry, Vol. 44, pp. 1443-1448(1997).

Common/Systematic Name

Deacetyl-19,20-epoxycytochalasin Q

Molecular Formula/Molecular Weight

$C_{28}H_{35}NO_6$; MW = 481.24644

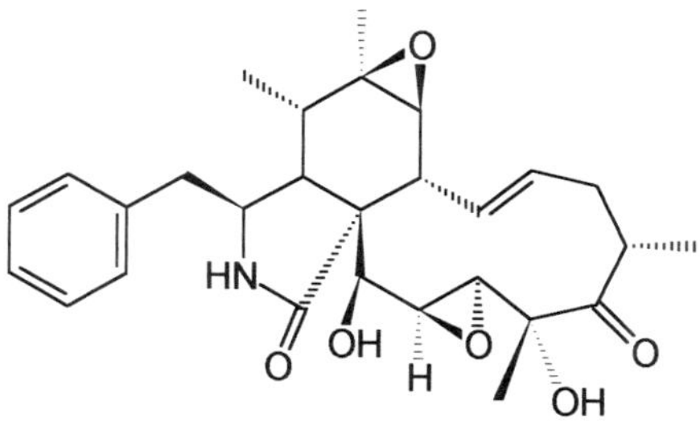

General Characteristics

Crystals; mp., 119-121°C.

Fungal Source

Xylaria obovata (ADA-228), a wood-inhabiting tropical fungus collected from the Munesa Forest in southern Ethiopia.

Isolation/Purification

Rice was allowed to soak for 3 hr. in sterile distilled water, and then sterilized and inoculated with *X. obovata*. When all the seeds were invaded and the mycelial mat had turned black (18 days after inoculation), the moldy rice was ground with a mortar and pestle. The ground moldy rice was soaked overnight in a total volume of 2L of MeOH-water (55:45, v/v). It was then filtered and the filtrate extracted with chloroform. The crude chloroform extract was partitioned between aqueous methanol and hexane and the aqueous portion extracted with chloroform. Removal of the chloroform yielded an extract, which was applied to a silica gel column eluted with a hexane-acetone gradient system. Ten 300ml fractions were collected, and fractions 4-5 were further purified by preparative TLC [hexane-isopropyl alcohol (8:2, v/v)] which yielded pure 19,20-epoxycytochalasin Q (R_f 0.68) and deacetyl-19,20-epoxycytochalasin Q (R_f 0.74).

Biological Activity

Cytotoxic.

Spectral Data

IR:

(KBr) 1370, 1450, 1685, 1740, 2970, and 3400cm^{-1}.

^{1}H NMR:

(pyridine-d_5) 3.91(1H, br t, J=7.0Hz, H-3); 2.10(1H, m, H-4); 1.96(1H, m, H-5); 3.09(1H, d, J=5.6Hz, H-7); 2.75(1H, m, H-8); 2.85(1H, dd, J=13.2, 7.0Hz, H-10); 3.06(1H, dd, J=13.2, 5.8Hz, H-10); 0.82(3H, d, J=7.2Hz, H-11); 1.20(3H, s, H-12); 6.66(1H, dd, J=15.4, 9.6Hz, H-13); 5.85(1H, sept, J=15.6, 10.0, 4.0Hz, H-14); 1.97(2H, m, H-15); 3.21(1H, m, H-16); 3.98(1H, d, J=2.0Hz); 4.27(1H, t, J=1.6Hz, H-20); 4.97(1H, br s, H-21); 1.06(3H, d, J=6.4Hz, H-22); 1.67(3H, s, H-23); 9.25(1H, s, NH); and 7.20ppm (2H, m, H-3', -5').

^{13}C NMR:

(pyridine-d_5) C-1, 177.2 s; C-3, 54.6 d; C-4, 52.8 d; C-5, 37.5 d; C-6, 57.6 s; C-7, 63.6 d; C-8, 44.7 d; C-9, 55.7 s; C-10, 46.2 t; C-11, 12.7 q; C-12, 19.8 q; C-13, 132.9 d; C-14, 131.1 d; C-15, 38.1 t; C-16, 42.2 d; C-17, 216.8 s; C-18, 77.7 s; C-19, 60.8 d; C-20, 56.1 d; C-21, 73.3 d; C-22, 19.2 q; C23, 22.8 q; C-1', 138.3 s; C-2', -6', 130.1 d; C-3', -5', 128.9 d; and C-4', 126.1ppm d.

Mass Spectrum:

HREIMS: 481.2464$[M]^+$ (5%) calc. for $C_{28}H_{35}NO_6$; 481.2467; 390$[M - 91]^+$ (100), and 338*m/e* $[M - H_2O\text{-}C_7H_7]^+$ (96).

Reference

E. Dagne, A. A. L. Gunatilaka, S. Asmellash, D. Abate, D. G. I. Kingston, G. A. Hofmann, and R. K. Johnson; Two Toxic Cytochalasins from *Xylaria obovata*; Tetrahedron, Vol. 50, pp. 5615-5620(1994).

Common/Systematic Name

19,20-Epoxycytochalasin Q

Molecular Formula/Molecular Weight

$C_{30}H_{37}NO_7$; MW = 523.25700

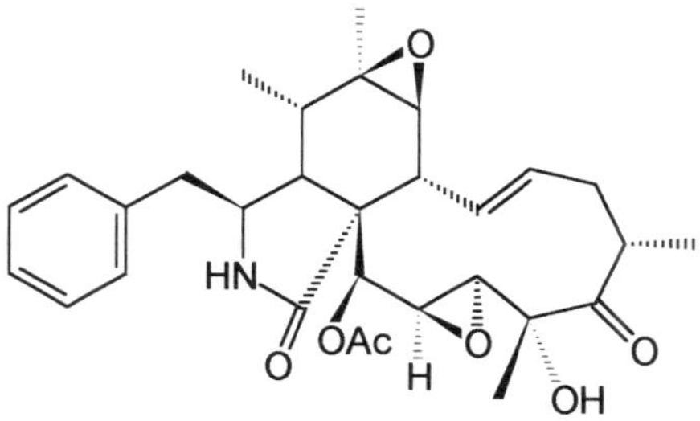

General Characteristics

Crystals; mp., 266-268°C; $[\alpha]_D$ - 73° (*c*=1.1, in $CHCl_3$).

Fungal Source

Xylaria obovata (ADA-228) a wood-inhabiting tropical fungus collected from the Munesa Forest in southern Ethiopia.

Isolation/Purification

Rice was allowed to soak for 3 hr. in sterile distilled water, and then sterilized and inoculated with *X. obovata*. When all the seeds were invaded and the mycelial mat had turned black, 18 days after inoculation, the moldy rice was ground with a mortar and pestle. The ground moldy rice was soaked overnight in a total volume of 2L of MeOH-water (55:45, v/v). It was then filtered and the filtrate extracted with chloroform. The crude chloroform extract was partitioned between aqueous methanol and hexane and the aqueous portion extracted with chloroform. Removal of the chloroform yielded an extract, which was applied to a silica gel column eluted with a hexane-acetone gradient system. Ten 300ml fractions were collected, and fractions 4-5 were further purified by preparative TLC, which yielded pure 19,20-epoxycytochalasin Q and deacetyl-19,20-epoxycytochalasin Q.

Biological Activity

Cytotoxic.

Spectral Data

IR:

(KBr) 1220, 1370, 1450, 1690, 1740, 2970, and 3440cm^{-1}.

^{1}H NMR:

(pyridine-d_5) 3.92(1H, br t, J=7.0Hz, H-3); 2.52(1H, dd, J=5.8, 2.0Hz, H-4); 1.89(1H, dq, J=7.2, 5.8Hz, H-5); 3.02(1H, d, J=5.6Hz, H-7); 2.75(1H, m, H-8); 2.87(1H, dd, J=13.2, 8.0Hz, H-10); 3.08(1H, dd, J=13.2, 6.0Hz, H-10); 0.63(3H, d, J=7.2Hz, H-11); 1.17(3H, s, H-12); 6.64(1H, dd, J=15.2, 10.0Hz, H-13); 5.83(1H, sept, J=15.6, 10.0, 6.0Hz, H-14); 2.00(2H, m, H-15); 3.24(1H, m, H-16); 3.72(1H, d, J=2.0Hz); 4.30(1H, dd, J=2.0, 8.0Hz, H-20); 6.18(1H, br s, H-21); 1.07(3H, d, J=6.8Hz, H-22); 1.64(3H, s, H-23); 9.58(1H, s, NH); 2.18(3H, s, OAc); 7.40(2H, d, J=6.7Hz, H-2', -6'); 7.34(2H, t, J=7.8Hz, H-3', -5'); and 7.23ppm (1H, d, J=6.7Hz, H-4'). ($CDCl_3$) 3.60(1H, br t, J=6.0, 8.0Hz, H-3); 2.21(1H, m, H-4); 1.60(1H, m, H-5); 2.71(1H, d, J=5.6Hz, H-7); 2.32(1H, dd, H-8); 2.80(2H, d, J=7.2Hz, H-8); 0.80(3H, d, J=7.2Hz, H-11); 1.18(3H, s, H-12); 6.08(1H, dd, J=15.2, 10.0Hz, H-13); 5.65(1H, m, H-14); 2.61(2H, dd, J=12.0, 11.4Hz, H-15); 3.20(1H, m, H-16); 3.15(1H, br s, H-19); 3.52(1H, d, J=1.2Hz, H-20); 5.65(1H, m, H-21); 1.19(3H, d, J=6.4Hz, H-22); 1.52(3H, s, H-23); 5.80(1H, br s, NH); 2.10(3H, s, OAc); and 7.20ppm (2H, m, H-3', -5').

^{13}C NMR:

(pyridine-d_5) C-1, 175.4 s; C-3, 54.9 d; C-4, 52.2 d; C-5, 37.3 d; C-6, 57.4 s; C-7, 63.1 d; C-8, 45.7 d; C-9, 55.6 s; C-10, 46.1 t; C-11, 12.4 q; C-12, 19.6 q; C-13, 132.5 d; C-14, 131.6 d; C-15, 37.9 t; C-16, 42.2 d; C-17, 216.3 s; C-18, 77.4 s; C-19, 60.8 d; C-20, 53.9 d; C-21, 73.7 d; C-22, 19.2 q; C-23, 22.7 q; C-1', 138.2 s; C-2', -6', 130.2 d; C-3', -5', 128.9 d; C-4', 127.1 d; $\underline{C}H_3CO$, 40.4 q; and $CH_3\underline{C}O$, 170.8ppm s.

Mass Spectrum:

HREIMS: 523.2648$[M]^+$(8%) calc. for $C_{30}H_{37}NO_7$ 323.2569, 495$[M - CO]^+$ (17), 480$[M - CH_3CO]^+$ (62), 464$[M - OAc]^+$ (90), 432$[M - C_7H_7]^+$ (37), 338$[M - HOAc - C_7H_7]^+$ (77), 91*m/e* $[C_7H_7]^+$ (100).

Reference

E. Dagne, A. A. L. Gunatilaka, S. Asmellash, D. Abate, D. G. I. Kingston, G. A. Hofmann, and R. K. Johnson; Two Toxic Cytochalasins from *Xylaria obovata*; Tetrahedron, Vol. 50, pp. 5615-5620(1994).

Common/Systematic Name

Deacetyl-19,20-epoxycytochalasin C

Molecular Formula/Molecular Weight

$C_{28}H_{35}NO_6$; MW = 481.24644

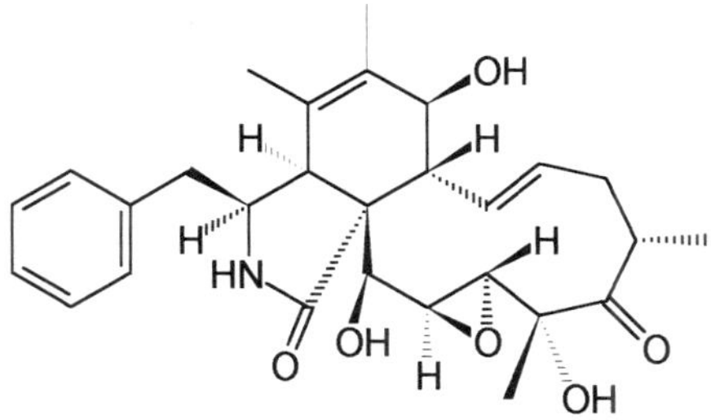

Fungal Source

Xylaria obovata (ADA-228) a wood-inhabiting tropical fungus collected from the Munesa Forest in southern Ethiopia.

Isolation/Purification

Cultured on a rice medium; after 20-40 days the moldy rice was extracted with chloroform, dried over Na_2SO_4, filtered and evaporated to dryness. The crude extract was separated on a Si-60 column eluted with a gradient from *n*-hexane-ethyl acetate (19:1, v/v) to ethyl acetate. The collected fractions were further purified by preparative TLC [*n*-hexane-isopropanol (7:3, v/v); R_f 0.46].

Biological Activity

Cytotoxic.

Spectral Data

IR:

(KBr) 3423, 3347, 1708, and 1684cm^{-1}.

CD:

$[\alpha]^{27}$ 589nm, +11.6° and 578nm, +14.8°(*c*=0.25, in MeOH).

^{1}H NMR:

($CDCl_3$) 3.35(1H, m, H-3); 2.84(1H, s, H-4); 3.75(1H, d, *J*=10Hz, H-7); 2.40(1H, t, *J*=10.0Hz, H-8); 2.96(1H, dd, *J*=13.0, 6.0Hz, H-10); 2.88(1H, dd, *J*=1.0,8.0Hz, H-10); 1.42(3H, s); 1.43(3H, s, H-11); 1.66(3H, s); 1.67(3H, s, H-12); 5.98(1H, dd, *J*=15.5, 10.0Hz); 5.65(1H, ddd, *J*=15.5, 10.0, 6.0Hz, H-14); 2.09(1H, dddd, *J*=12.0, 6.0, 2.0, 1.0Hz, H-15); 2.60(1H, td, *J*=12.0, 10.0Hz, H-15); 3.21(1H, dqd, *J*=12.0, 7.0, 2.0Hz, H-16); 3.47(1H, d, *J*=2.0Hz, H-19); 3.31(1H, m, H-20); 4.13(1H, s, H-21); 1.19(3H, d, *J*=7.0Hz, H-22); 1.56(3H, s, H-23); 7.20(1H, m, H-25); 7.32(1H, m, H-26); and 7.26ppm (1H, m, H-27).

Mass Spectrum:
HREIMS: 481.2450 calc. for $C_{28}H_{35}NO_6$, 481.2464(10%), 463(6), 453(9), 435(28), 321(48), and 91*m/e* (100).

Reference

D. Abate, W.-R. Abraham, and H. Meyer; Cytochalasins and Phytotoxins from the Fungus *Xylaria obovata*; Phytochemistry, Vol. 44, pp. 1443-1448(1997).

Common/Systematic Name

19,20-Epoxycytochalasin C

Molecular Formula/Molecular Weight

$C_{30}H_{37}NO_7$; MW = 523.25700

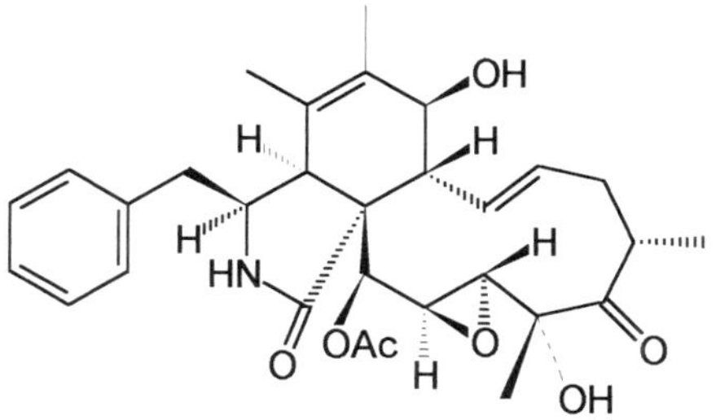

General Characteristics

$[\alpha]_D$ - 6.8° (c=0.25, in $CHCl_3$).

Fungal Source

Xylaria obovata (ADA-228), a wood-inhabiting tropical fungus collected from the Munesa Forest in southern Ethiopia.

Isolation/Purification

Cultured on a rice medium; after 20-40 days the moldy rice was extracted with chloroform, dried over Na_2SO_4, filtered and evaporated to dryness. The crude extract was separated on a Si-60 column eluted with a gradient from *n*-hexane-ethyl acetate (19:1, v/v) to ethyl acetate. The collected fractions were further purified by preparative TLC [*n*-hexane-isopropanol (7:3, v/v), R_f 0.52].

Biological Activity

Cytotoxic.

Spectral Data

IR:

(KBr) 3438, 1745, 1708, and 1685cm^{-1}.

^{1}H NMR:

($CDCl_3$) 3.35(1H, dd, *J*=8.0, 6.0, 1.0Hz, H-3); 2.54(1H, s, H-4); 4.01(1H, dd, *J*=7.0, 2.0Hz, H-5); 3.81(1H, d, *J*=10.0Hz, H-7); 2.26(1H, t, *J*=10.0Hz, H-8); 3.08(1H, dd, *J*=13.0, 6.0Hz, H-10); 3.01(1H, dd, *J*=13.0, 8.0Hz, H-10); 6.16(1H, dd, *J*=16.0, 10.0Hz, H-13); 5.72(1H, ddd, *J*=16.0, 10.0, 6.0Hz, H-14); 2.12(1H, dddd, *J*=12.0, 6.0, 2.0, 1.0Hz, H-15); 2.68(1H, td, *J*=12.0, 10.0Hz, H-15); 3.24(1H, dqd, *J*=12.0, 7.0, 2.0Hz, H-16); 3.21(1H, d, *J*=2.0Hz, H-19); 3.47(1H, dd, *J*=2.0, 1.0Hz, H-20); and 1.22ppm (3H, d, *J*=7.0Hz, H-22).

Mass Spectrum:

HREIMS: 523.2560, calc. for $C_{30}H_{37}NO_7$, 523.2570(15%), 480(10), 477(13), 463(10), 435(14), 432(13), 420(22), 405(20), 372(34), 362(31), 334(13), 316(9), 312(15), 252(40), 238(22), 187(16), 185(17), 174(24), 169(16), 163(9), 162(16), 161(19), 160(20), 133(18),120(43), 98(9), 91(61), and 43*m/e* (100). FABMS: 524.2$[M + H]^+$ and 546.2$[M + Na]^+$.

Reference

D. Abate, W.-R. Abraham, and H. Meyer; Cytochalasins and Phytotoxins from the Fungus *Xylaria obovata*; Phytochemistry, Vol. 44, pp. 1443-1448(1997).

Common/Systematic Name

Fusaproliferin; Proliferin

18-[1-(Acetoxymethyl)-2-methylethyl]-10,17-dihydroxy-3,7,11,15- tetramethylbicyclo-[13.3.0]octadeca-*trans,trans,trans,cis*-2,6,11,17-tetraen-16-one

Molecular Formula/Molecular Weight

$C_{27}H_{40}O_5$; MW = 444.28757

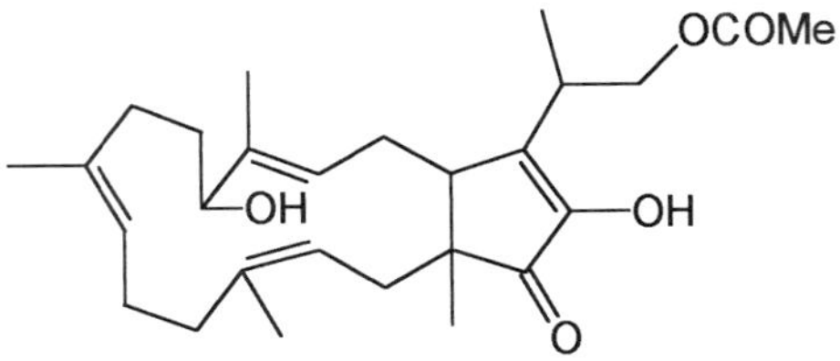

General Characteristics

Crystals from methanol; melting point not reported; $[\alpha]_D^{25}$ -35° (*c*=0.7, in $CHCl_3$).

Fungal Source

Fusarium proliferatum isolated from earrot-infected corn in northern Italy and the strain no. 1494 deposited at the collection of the IstitutoTossine Micotossine da parassiti vegetali (ITEM), Bari, Italy.

Isolation/Purification

Fusaproliferin was obtained by inoculation of autoclaved yellow corn kernels with *F. proliferatum*. Purification was performed as follows: 300g of lyophilized culture filtrate was resuspended in 1.3L of MeOH-1% aqueous NaC1 solution (55:45, v/v). Fusaproliferin was extracted from the aqueous residue with 3.250L of *n*-hexane and concentrated under reduced pressure. Successive steps of the purification were carried out as previously reported (A. Ritieni *et al.*, 1995).

Spectral Data

^{1}H NMR:

($CDCl_3$) 1.71(1H, s, *J*=6.6, 13.6Hz, H-l'); 2.38(1H, m, *J*=10.6, 13.6Hz, H-l"); 5.24(1H, m, H-2); 2.30(1H, m, H-4'); 2.01(1H, m, H-4"); 2.30(lH, m, *J*= 8.8Hz, H-5'); 2.13(1H, m, *J*= 4.5 Hz, H-5"); 5.12(1H, m, H-6); 2.11(lH, m, H-8'); 1.78(1H, m, H-8"); 1.77(1H, m, *J*= 4Hz, H-9'); 1.68(lH, m, *J*=10Hz, H-9"); 4.05(1H, dd, H-10); 5.38(lH, m, H-12); 2.40(lH, m, *J*=3, 17, 2.5Hz, H-13'); 1.92(lH, m, *J*=6-7, 17, 11.1Hz, H-13"); 2.67(1H, dd, *J*=11.1Hz, H-14); 2.78(lH, m, H-19); 1.64(3H, s, H-20); 1.64(3H, s, H-21); 1.56(3H, s, H-22); 0.99(3H, s, H-23); 4.28(2x1H, m, *J*=7.6, 10.6Hz, H-24'); 4.25(1H, m, *J*=6.9Hz, H-24"); 1.31(3H, d, *J*=2Hz, H-25); 2.02(3H, s, H-27); and 5.56ppm (lH, s, OH-17).

^{13}C NMR:

($CDCl_3$) 207.86, C-16; 170.91, C-26; 147.27, C-17; 146.71, C-18; 138.20, C-3; 136.54, C-11; 132.93, C-7; 128.89, C-12; 124.31, C-6; 121.38, C-2; 76.51, C-10; 66.43, C-24; 49.56, C-14; 49.01, C-15; 40.33, C-4; 39.14, C-1; 34.93, C-8; 33.71, C-19; 29.72, C-9; 28.72, C-13; 23.83, C-5; 16.19, C-23; 15.55, C-20; 15.32, C-21; 14.52, C-25; and 10.38ppm, C-22.

References

A. Ritieni, V. Fogliano, G. Randazzo, A. Scarallo, A. Logrieco, A. Moretti, L. Mannina, and A. Bottalico; Structure and Absolute Stereochemistry of Fusaproliferin, A Toxic Metabolite from *Fusarium proliferatum*; Natural Toxins; Vol. 3, pp.17-19(1995).

A. Santini, A. Ritieni, V. Fogliano, G. Randazzo, L. Mannina, A. Logrieco, and E. Benedetti; Structure and Absolute Stereochemistry of Fusaproliferin, a Toxic Metabolite from *Fusarium proliferatum*; J. of Nat. Prod.; Vol. 59, pp. 109-112(1996).

Common/Systematic Name

Retigeranic Acid

Molecular Formula/Molecular Weight

$C_{25}H_{38}O_2$; MW = 370.28718

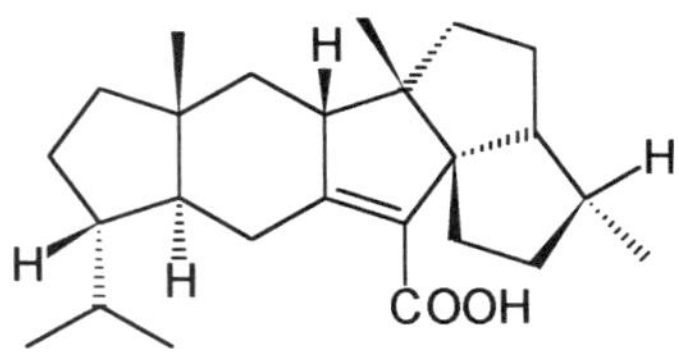

General Characteristics

Crystals; mp. 218-221°C; $[\alpha]_D^{23}$ - 59° ($CHCl_3$).

Fungal Source

Lobaria isidiosa (a lichen) collected in the eastern Himalayas, Bhutan.

Isolation/Purification

Retigeranic acid was obtained from the chloroform-soluble fraction of the ethereal extracts of *Lobaria isidiosa*.

Spectral Data

UV:

λ max 242nm (log ϵ = 3.91).

IR:

(KBr) 1662 and 1608cm^{-1}.

Mass Spectrum:

HREIMS: 370.286*m/e*; calcd. for $C_{25}H_{38}O_2$, 370.287; LREIMS: 370(M^+) and 325*m/e* (M^+ - COOH).

Reference

M. Kaneda, R. Takahashi, Y. Iitaka, and S. Shibata; Retigeranic Acid, a Novel Sesterterpene Isolated from the Lichens of *Lobaria retigera* Group; Tetrahedron Letters; No. 45, pp. 4609-4611(1972).

Common/Systematic Name

Moniliformin

3-Hydroxycyclobut-3-ene-1,2-dione

Molecular Formula/Molecular Weight

C_4HO_3Na 119.9823 (sodium salt)

C_4HO_3K 136.0945 (potasium salt)

$C_4H_2O_3$ 98.0081 (free acid); MW = 98.00039

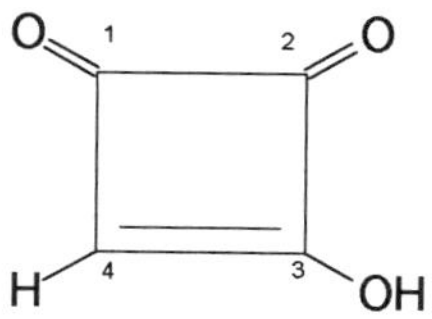

General Characteristics

Crystals from aqueous methanol, decomposes without melting at temperatures up to 350°C (Na or K salts). Crystalline acid, mp., 158°C (dec.). pK_a 1.70.

Fungal Source

Gibberella fujikuroi (ATTC 12763, original isolation), *Fusarium moniliforme* (= *F. subglutinans*), *F. proliferatum*, *F. nygamai*, *F. oxysporum*, *F. anthophilum*, *F. graminearum*, *F. avenaceum*, *F. acuminatum*, *F. concolor*, *F. equiseti*, *F. semitectum*, *F. fusarioides* (*F. chlamydosporum*), *F. sporotrichioides*, *F. culmorum*, and *F. reticulatum*.

Isolation/Purification

Original isolation involved extraction with aqueous methanol followed by column chromatography using Sephadex LH-20 and elution with increasing amounts of methanol in water. Subsequent isolations involved ion-exchange chromatography.

Biological Activity

Moniliformin had an LD_{50} of 4.0 mg/kg in day-old cockerels(160μg/40g cockerel). Gross and histologic lesions in cockerels were ascites with edema of the mesenteries and small hemorrhages in the proventriculus, gizzard, small and large intestine, and skin. The LD_{50} in mice was 20.9mg/kg (females) and 29.1 mg/kg (males). Exceeding low concentrations of moniliformin (less than 5μm) selectively inhibited mitochondrial pyruvate and α-ketoglutarate oxidations by 50%. Moniliformin produced plant-growth regulating and phytotoxic effects in plant systems. It affected mitosis in *Allium* root assays.

Spectral Data

UV:

λ_{max}^{MeOH} 229 (ϵ = 19,100) and 260nm(5,600).

^{1}H NMR:

(D_2O) 8.23ppm (1H, s, H-4) (nonexchangeable with D_2O).

^{13}C NMR:
(D_2O) 202.9, C-1; 207.4, C-2; 202.9, C-3, and 168.8ppm, C-4.

References

J.P. Springer, J.Clardy, R.J. Cole, J.W. Kirksey, R.K. Hill, R.M.Carlson, J.L. Isidor; J. Am. Chem. Soc.; Structure and Synthesis of Moniliformin, A Novel Cyclobutane Microbial Toxin; Vol.96, pp. 2267-2268(1974).

H. G. Cutler, R. J.Cole, B. R. Blankenship, J. W. Kirksey, B. Doupnik,Jr.;Growth Regulating and Phytotoxic Effects of A Metabolite Produced by *Fusarium moniliforme*; Phytopathology; Vol.62, pp.752-754(1972).

Common/Systematic Name

Cyclopiazonic Acid

Molecular Formula/Molecular Weight

$C_{20}H_{20}N_2O_3$; MW = 336.14739

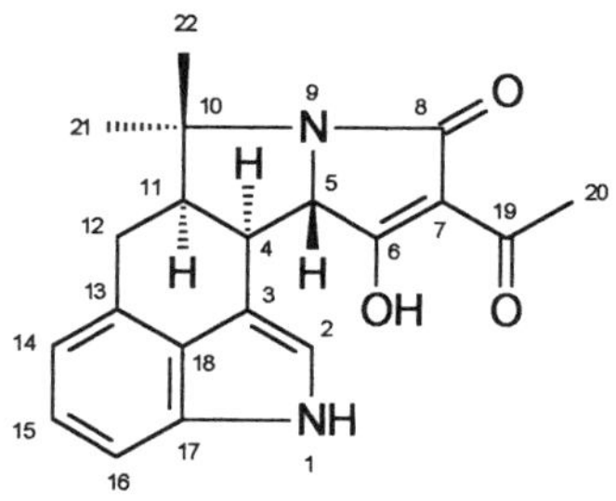

General Characteristics

Crystals from methanol; mp., 245-246°C; $[\alpha]_D^{20}$ - 36.1° (*c*=0.36 in pyridine).

Fungal Source

Penicilliun cyclopium; *P. viridicatum*; *P. camemberti*; *P. grieseofulvum*; *P. urticae*; *P. patulum*; *P. biforme*; *P. puberulum*; *P. chrysogenum*; *P. commune*; *P. hirsutum*; *P. nalgiovense*; *Aspergillus flavus*; *A. tamarii*; *A. oryzae*; and *A. versicolor*.

Isolation/Purification

The original isolation/purification of cyclopiazonic acid was accomplished using chloroform-methanol extraction partitioned between chloroform-water. The dried chloroform extract was distributed between 95% methanol and hexane. The methanol residue was chromatographed on cellulose powder impregnated with 50:3, $HCONH_2$-$(COOH)_2$. Lipids were eluted with hexane and the column further eluted with mixtures of hexane-benzene. The biologically active fraction in ethyl ether was extracted with 0.5M aqueous sodium bicarbonate followed by extraction of the acidified aqueous phase with chloroform. The active fraction was chromatographed on Dowex 1 X 8 using aqueous methanol (1:1, v/v). Final purification was crystallization from methanol. More recently advanced analytical procedures for cyclopiazonic acid include thin-layer chromatography, HPLC, enzyme-linked immunosorbent assay, capillary electrophoresis, and immunoaffinity column chromatography (see Dorner, 2002).

Biological Activity

Cyclopiazonic acid is a potent, specific, and reversible inhibitor of the sarcoplasmic and endoplasmic reticulum Ca^{2+} activated ATPase. It has been demonstrated to efficiently partition into various tissues including eggs and milk. See Burdock and Flamm, 2000 for detailed discussions on the biological effects of cyclopiazonic acid.

Spectral Data

UV:
λ_{max}^{MeOH} 225 (ε = 39,810), 253 (16,595), 275 (sh)(19,054), 284 (20,417), and 292nm(sh)(17,378).

IR:
($CHCl_3$) 3478, 3200-2600, 1708, and 1618cm^{-1}.

^1H NMR:
(See Holzapfel, 1968 for detailed discussion of proton NMR).

Mass Spectra:
HREMS: 336.1463*m/e* (M^+) $C_{20}H_{20}N_2O_3$ requires 336.1474.

References
C. W. Holzapfel; The Isolation and Structure of Cyclopiazonic Acid, A Toxic Metabolite of *Penicillium cyclopium* Westling; Tetrahedron, Vol. 24, pp. 2101-2119(1968).

G. A. Burdock and W. G. Flamm; Review Article: Safety Assessment of the Mycotoxin Cyclopiazonic Acid; International Journal of Toxicology, Vol. 19, pp. 195-218(2000).

J. W. Dorner; Recent Advances in Analytical Methodology for Cyclopiazonic Acid; in Mycotoxins and Food Safety; L. S. Jackson, M. W. Trucksess, and J. W. DeVries (eds.); Kluwer Academic/Plenum Publishers, New York, N.Y.(2002).

Secondary Metabolite Index

Molecular Formula Index

Molecular Weight Index

Fungal/Plant Source Index